COLD SPRING HARBOR SYMPOSIA
ON QUANTITATIVE BIOLOGY

VOLUME XXI

COLD SPRING HARBOR SYMPOSIA
ON QUANTITATIVE BIOLOGY

Founded in 1933
by
REGINALD G. HARRIS
Director of the Biological Laboratory
1924 to 1936

The Symposia were organized and managed by Dr. Harris until his death. Their continued usefulness is a tribute to the soundness of his vision.

The Symposium volumes
are published by the Long Island Biological Association
as a part of the work of the Biological Laboratory
Cold Spring Harbor, L. I., New York

COLD SPRING HARBOR SYMPOSIA ON QUANTITATIVE BIOLOGY

VOLUME XXI

Genetic Mechanisms: Structure and Function

THE BIOLOGICAL LABORATORY

COLD SPRING HARBOR, L. I., NEW YORK

1956

PRINTED BY
WAVERLY PRESS INC., BALTIMORE, MARYLAND, U.S.A.

Foreword

There is very little doubt that genetic mechanisms play a cardinal role in development in higher organisms—development from a single, undifferentiated cell into the aggregate of billions of highly diversified cells that make up an individual. But we are still far from understanding the processes through which this differentiation is accomplished. Our knowledge about the structure of genetic components is considerable, and is being rapidly advanced by the utilization of new research methods. We also know a good deal about the primary function of genes, and have reason to believe that each individual gene controls a specific chemical process in a living cell. Furthermore, there is reliable evidence to indicate a complex interaction between these processes, and to suggest an intricate system of interrelationships among the units that constitute the genome of a cell. But our information is still very meager regarding the function of that system which extends to a group of cells and is responsible for their differentiation.

Recent developments, however, indicate that we may be on the verge of bridging the gap that now separates genetics and experimental embryology. One of the primary objectives of this year's Symposium was to further that trend, by bringing together geneticists engaged in various phases of research into the structure and function of genetic mechanisms, and experimental embryologists interested in the study of cell differentiation.

The meetings were held from June 4 to 12, 1956, and were attended by more than 300 scientists. About 50 of the participants were from overseas, and many of these were specially invited guests. We were able to arrange this meeting because our long-term grant from the Carnegie Corporation of New York for Symposium expenses was supplemented by special grants made by the National Science Foundation, the Association for the Aid of Crippled Children, the U. S. Public Health Service, and the Alfred P. Sloan Foundation. I wish to acknowledge this support and express our gratitude to the organizations that provided it. I wish also to record our appreciation and thanks to the committee who planned the program, consisting of E. W. Caspari, B. P. Kaufmann, A. E. Mirsky, and Jack Schultz.

M. Demerec

Executive Editor: Katherine Brehme Warren, Associate Professor of Biology, Hofstra College, Hempstead, New York

v

LIST OF PREVIOUS VOLUMES

SOME SYMPOSIUM PARTICIPANTS

Top row: G. Stent, A. D. Hershey, C. Levinthal; C. P. Haskins, M. Demerec; C. C. Lindegren, A. Weinstein, G. T. Rudkin (background, N. Zinder).

Second row: R. Osborne, F. B. Hutt; J. Schultz, C. C. Lindegren, T. Caspersson; M. Demerec, J. W. Boyes.

Third row: L. Szilard, S. Spiegelman; C. O. Warren, G. H. Beale, D. G. Catcheside; B. McClintock, F. Schrader.

Bottom row: B. Spassky, A. Sokoloff; M. H. Adams, F. Igalsohn; E. Hadorn, B. H. Willier.

SOME SYMPOSIUM PARTICIPANTS

Top row: N. and G. Braver; B. McClintock, H. B. Creighton; C. Stern, R. P. Levine.

Second row: H. Roman, G. Pontecorvo; M. H. F. Wilkins, D. G. Catcheside; J. W. Boyes, M. Errera.

Third row: W. Hayes, L. C. Dunn, K. B. Warren, W. Szybalski; M. Rizki, E. Caspari, H. C. Dalton, D. F. Poulson.

Bottom row: M. Zalokar, S. Emerson; C. Pavan, G. Pontecorvo; A. Mirsky, B. Glass.

(The photographs were taken by Drs. G. Braver, K. Maramorosch and K. B. Warren.
The art work was done by Mr. Harry Jones.)

List of Those Attending the Symposium

AARONSON, SHELDON, Haskins Laboratories, New York.

ADAMS, MARK H., New York University College of Medicine, New York

ALFERT, MAX, University of California, Berkeley, California

ALLEN, SALLY LYMAN, University of Michigan, Ann Arbor, Michigan

ALPER, TIKVAH, Hammersmith Hospital, London, England

ALTENBURG, EDGAR, The Rice Institute, Houston, Texas

ALTENBURG, LUOLIN, The Rice Institute, Houston, Texas

AMBELLAN, ELISABETH, Columbia University, New York

ANDERSON, LULU F., Brookhaven National Laboratory, Upton, New York

APPLEYARD, RAYMOND K., United Nations, New York

ARONSON, JOHN, University of Rochester, Rochester, New York

AR-RUSHDI, A. H., Scripps Institution of Oceanography, La Jolla, California

ATWOOD, KIMBALL C., Oak Ridge National Laboratory, Oak Ridge, Tennessee

BACON, DONALD F., Yale University Medical School, New Haven, Connecticut

BADER, S., Columbia University, New York

BALINSKY, B. I., University of the Witwatersrand, Johannesburgh, South Africa

BARBOUR, EVELYN, Yale University, New Haven, Connecticut

BARCLAY, RALPH K., Sloan-Kettering Institute, New York

BARKSDALE, LANE, New York University College of Medicine, New York

BARRICELLI, NELS AALL, University of Rochester, Rochester, New York

BAYLOR, MARTHA BARNES, University of Michigan, Ann Arbor, Michigan

BEADLE, G. W., California Institute of Technology, Pasadena, California

BEALE, G. H., Institute of Animal Genetics, Edinburgh, Scotland

BEERMANN, W., Zoologisches Institut der Universitat, Marburg/Lahn, Germany

BELJANSKI, M., Bellevue Medical Center, New York (Institut Pasteur, Paris, France)

BENDICH, A., Sloan-Kettering Institute, New York

BERNHARD, MICHAEL, Scripps Institute of Oceanography, La Jolla, California

BIANCHI, ANGELO, Harvard University, Cambridge, Massachusetts

BLOCH, DAVID P., Columbia University, New York

BLOMSTRAND, INGBRITT, Wesleyan University, Middletown, Connecticut

BONNER, D. M., Yale University, New Haven, Connecticut

BOWSER, HELEN R., Harvard Medical School, Boston, Massachusetts

BOYES, J. WALLACE, McGill University, Montreal, Canada

BRAUN, WERNER, Rutgers University, New Brunswick, New Jersey

BRAVER, GERALD, University of California, Berkeley, California

BRAVER, NORMA, University of California, Berkeley, California

BREUNINGER, EVELYN, Institute for Cancer Research, Philadelphia, Pennsylvania

BRIGGS, R., Institute for Cancer Research, Philadelphia, Pennsylvania

BROCK, DAVID, Columbia University, New York

BROCK, R. D., Commonwealth Scientific and Industrial Research Organization, Canberra, Australia

BRYSON, VERNON, National Science Foundation, Washington, D. C.

BUCH, FLORENCE G., Brookhaven National Laboratory, Upton, New York

BUCHERT, JANSON G., Connecticut Agricultural Experiment Station, New Haven, Connecticut

BURGI, E., Carnegie Institution of Washington, Cold Spring Harbor, New York

BUTLER, L., University of Toronto, Toronto, Canada

CASE, MARY, Yale University, New Haven, Connecticut

CASPARI, E., Wesleyan University, Middletown, Connecticut
CASPERSSON, T., Karolinska Institutet, Stockholm, Sweden
CATCHESIDE, D. G., The University, Birmingham, England
CHANTRENNE, H., Université Libre de Bruxelles, Brussels, Belgium
CHASE, MARTHA, University of Rochester, Rochester, New York
CHOVNICK, A., University of Connecticut, Storrs, Connecticut
CHU, ERNEST H. Y., Yale University, New Haven, Connecticut
CLOWES, ROY C., Carnegie Institution of Washington, Cold Spring Harbor, New York (Wright-Fleming Institute, London, England)
CLUM, FLOYD M., Falls Church, Virginia
COHN, JOSEPH, Massachusetts Institute of Technology, Cambridge, Massachusetts
CORLETTE, SALLY L., Institute for Cancer Research, Philadelphia, Pennsylvania
CREIGHTON, HARRIET, Wellesley College, Wellesley, Massachusetts
DALTON, H. CLARK, New York University, New York
DAVIDSON, HARRIET, Biological Laboratory, Cold Spring Harbor, New York
DE, DEEPESH, Carnegie Institution of Washington, Cold Spring Harbor, New York (Calcutta University, Calcutta, India)
DE GIOVANNI, ROSALIE, Columbia University, New York
DEITCH, A. D., Columbia University, New York
DEMEREC, M., Carnegie Institution of Washington, and Biological Laboratory, Cold Spring Harbor, New York
DE SERRES, F. J., Oak Ridge National Laboratory, Oak Ridge, Tennessee
DI BERARDINO, MARIE, Institute for Cancer Research, Philadelphia, Pennsylvania
DISSOSWAY, CAROLYN, Rutgers University, Newark, New Jersey
DJORDJEVIC, B., Carnegie Institution of Washington, Cold Spring Harbor, New York (Boris Kidrich Institute for Nuclear Science, Belgrade, Yugoslavia)
DOERMANN, AUGUST H., University of Rochester, Rochester, New York
DUNN, L. C., Columbia University, New York
EDGAR, R. S., University of Rochester, Rochester, New York
EMERSON, STERLING, U. S. Atomic Energy Commission, Washington, D. C.
ENGLESBERG, ELLIS, Biological Laboratory, Cold Spring Harbor, New York
EPHRUSSI, BORIS, Université de Paris, Paris, France
EPSTEIN, RICHARD H., University of Rochester, Rochester, New York
ERK, FRANK C., Washington College, Chestertown, Maryland
ERRERA, MAURICE, Université Libre de Bruxelles, Brussels, Belgium
EVERSOLE, RUSSELL A., Eye and Ear Hospital, Pittsburgh, Pennsylvania
FITZGERALD, PATRICK J., State University of New York, Brooklyn, New York
FLEISCHER, MARILYN L., Brookhaven National Laboratory, Upton, New York
FLUKE, DONALD J., Brookhaven National Laboratory, Upton, New York
FOOTHILLS, J. C., Tennessee Intermountain College, Nazareth, Tennessee
FORRO, FREDERICK, JR., Yale University, New Haven, Connecticut
FOSTER, MORRIS, Yale University, New Haven, Connecticut
FREED, JEROME J., Institute for Cancer Research, Philadelphia, Pennsylvania
FUSCALDO, KATHRYN, Carnegie Institution of Washington, Cold Spring Harbor, New York
GALINSKY, IRVING, Biochemical Research Foundation, Newark, Delaware
GARTLER, STANLEY, Columbia University, New York
GAY, HELEN, Carnegie Institution of Washington, Cold Spring Harbor, New York
GENNARO, JOSEPH F., State University of New York, Brooklyn, New York
GILES, NORMAN H., Yale University, New Haven, Connecticut
GLASS, BENTLEY, Johns Hopkins University, Baltimore, Maryland
GODMAN, GABRIEL C., Columbia University, New York

GOLDSCHMIDT, LEONTINE, Creedmoor Institute, Queens Village, New York
GRANOFF, ALLAN, Public Health Research Institute, New York
GRANT, PHILIP, Institute for Cancer Research, Philadelphia, Pennsylvania
GREEN, DONALD MacD., University of Rochester, Rochester, New York
GREEN, MARGARET C., Ohio State University, Columbus, Ohio
GREER, SHELDON, Columbia University, New York
GROSS, SAMSON R., Stanford University, Stanford, California
GÜTTES, EDMUND, University of Wisconsin, Madison, Wisconsin
HACKEL, EMANUEL, Michigan State University, East Lansing, Michigan
HADDEN, JOANNA, Biological Laboratory, Cold Spring Harbor, New York
HADORN, E., University, Zurich, Switzerland
HAMILTON, L. D., Sloan-Kettering Institute, New York
HANSEN, P. ARNE, University of Maryland, College Park, Maryland
HARTMAN, PHILIP E., Harvard Medical School, Boston, Massachusetts
HARTMAN, ZLATA, Harvard Medical School, Boston, Massachusetts
HASKINS, CARYL P., Carnegie Institution of Washington, Washington, D. C.
HASKINS, EDNA F., Carnegie Institution of Washington, Washington, D. C.
HAUROWITZ, FELIX, Indiana University, Bloomington, Indiana
HAYES, WILLIAM, Postgraduate Medical School, London, England
HERRIOTT, ROGER M., Johns Hopkins University, Baltimore, Maryland
HERSHEY, A. D., Carnegie Institution of Washington, Cold Spring Harbor, New
    York
HEXTER, WILLIAM M., Amherst College, Amherst, Massachusetts
HILLMAN, RALPH, Yale University, New Haven, Connecticut
HOECKER, GUSTAVO, Universidad de Chile, Santiago, Chile
HOFFER, J. L., Fordham University, New York
HOLLAENDER, A., Oak Ridge National Laboratory, Oak Ridge, Tennessee
HOTCHKISS, ROLLIN D., Rockefeller Institute, New York
HOWARTH, SHEILA, Carnegie Institution of Washington, Cold Spring Harbor, New
    York (Chester Beatty Research Institute, London, England)
HOYME, LUCILE, U. S. National Museum, Washington, D. C.
HUDIS, JUNE, Brookhaven National Laboratory, Upton, New York
HUGHES, INGE M., Yale University, New Haven, Connecticut
HUNGERFORD, DAVID A., Institute for Cancer Research, Philadelphia, Pennsylvania
HUTT, F. B., Cornell University, Ithaca, New York
IGALSOHN, FRED F., New York University College of Medicine, New York
JACOB, F., Institut Pasteur, Paris, France
JONES, D. F., Agricultural Experiment Station, New Haven, Connecticut
JUDD, BURKE H., University of Texas, Austin, Texas
KACSER, HENRIK, Institute of Animal Genetics, Edinburgh, Scotland
KÄFER, ETTA, The University, Glasgow, Scotland
KAPLAN, A. S., University of Illinois, Urbana, Illinois
KARNOFSKY, DAVID A., Sloan-Kettering Institute, New York
KATAJA, EVA, University of Rochester, Rochester, New York
KAUFMANN, B. P., Carnegie Institution of Washington, Cold Spring Harbor, New
    York
KAYE, JEROME S., Columbia University, New York
KELNER, ALBERT, Brandeis University, Waltham, Massachusetts
KIHLMAN, BENGT, Johns Hopkins University, Baltimore, Maryland (University of
    Uppsala, Uppsala, Sweden)
KINDLER, S. H., New York University, New York
KING, JAMES C., Biological Laboratory, Cold Spring Harbor, New York

King, Thomas J., Institute for Cancer Research, Philadelphia, Pennsylvania

Klein, Deana T., Columbia University, New York

Klein, Richard, New York Botanical Garden, New York

Konzak, Calvin F., Brookhaven National Laboratory, Upton, New York

Krieg, David R., University of Rochester, Rochester, New York

Krivshenko, J., University of Rochester, Rochester, New York

Lacy, Ann M., Yale University, New Haven, Connecticut

Lahr, Ernest L., Carnegie Institution of Washington, Cold Spring Harbor, New York

Lerman, Leonard S., University of Colorado, Denver, Colorado

Levine, R. P., Harvard University, Cambridge, Massachusetts

Levinthal, C., University of Michigan, Ann Arbor, Michigan

Lewin, Ralph, Marine Biological Laboratory, Woods Hole, Massachusetts

Lewis, Daniel, John Innes Horticultural Institution, Bayfordbury, England

Lewis, E. B., California Institute of Technology, Pasadena, California

Lewis, Herman W., Massachusetts Institute of Technology, Cambridge, Massachusetts

Lieb, Margaret, Brandeis University, Waltham, Massachusetts

Lindegren, Carl C., Southern Illinois University, Carbondale, Illinois

Litman, Rose M., University of California, Berkeley, California

Lynch, Clara J., Rockefeller Institute, New York

Maaløe, O., State Serum Institute, Copenhagen, Denmark

Maas, Werner K., New York University, New York

MacDowell, E. C., Cold Spring Harbor, New York

Madden, Carol, Long Island Biological Laboratory, Cold Spring Harbor, New York

Mandel, Benjamin, Public Health Research Institute, New York

Mandell, Joseph, Carnegie Institution of Washington, Cold Spring Harbor, New York

Maramorosch, Karl, Rockefeller Institute, New York

Markert, Clement L., University of Michigan, Ann Arbor, Michigan

Marmur, Julius, Rutgers University, New Brunswick, New Jersey

Mather, Wharton B., University of Queensland, Brisbane, Australia

McClintock, Barbara, Carnegie Institution of Washington, Cold Spring Harbor, New York

McDonald, Margaret, Carnegie Institution of Washington, Cold Spring Harbor, New York

McMasten-Kaye, Rachel, Columbia University, New York

Medill-Brown, Mary, University of Pennsylvania, Philadelphia, Pennsylvania

Melechen, Norman, Carnegie Institution of Washington, Cold Spring Harbor, New York

Metrakos, Julius, McGill University, Montreal, Canada

Metz, C. W., University of Pennsylvania, Philadelphia, Pennsylvania

Metzger-Freed, Liselotte, Institute for Cancer Research, Philadelphia, Pennsylvania

Milkman, Roger, Harvard University, Cambridge, Massachusetts

Miller, Stanley Q., Columbia University, New York

Mirsky, Alfred, Rockefeller Institute, New York

Mitchell, Donald F., Pennsylvania State University, University Park, Pennsylvania

Moore, Lloyd, Hofstra College, Hempstead, New York

MOSER, HERMANN, Carnegie Institution of Washington, Cold Spring Harbor, New York

MOSES, MONTROSE J., Rockefeller Institute, New York

MURPHY, JAMES S., Rockefeller Institute, New York

NATHAN, HELENE A., Haskins Laboratories, New York

NEBEL, B. R., Argonne National Laboratory, Lemont, Illinois

NELSON, NORMA J., Yale University, New Haven, Connecticut

NEMETH, ANDREW, Columbia University Medical School, New York

NOVIKOFF, ALEX B., Albert Einstein College of Medicine, New York

OSAWA, SYOZO, Rockefeller Institute, New York

OSBORN, RICHARD H., Columbia University, New York

OZEKI, HARUO, Carnegie Institution of Washington, Cold Spring Harbor, New York (Kyoto University, Kyoto, Japan)

PALADE, GEORGE E., Rockefeller Institute, New York

PAPAZIAN, HAIG P., Yale University, New Haven, Connecticut

PARTRIDGE, CHESTER, Yale University, New Haven, Connecticut

PATTERSON, ELIZABETH K., Institute for Cancer Research, Philadelphia, Pennsylvania

PAVAN, C., Department of Biologia Geral, São Paulo, Brazil

PAVLOVSKY, OLGA, Columbia University, New York

PITTINGER, T. H., Oak Ridge National Laboratory, Oak Ridge, Tennessee

PLAINE, HENRY L., Ohio State University, Columbus, Ohio

PLOUGH, HAROLD H., Amherst College, Amherst, Massachusetts

PONTECORVO, G., The University, Glasgow, Scotland

PORAT, TAMAR BEN, University of Illinois, Urbana, Illinois

PORTER, KEITH R., Rockefeller Institute, New York

POST, R., Columbia University, New York

POULSON, DONALD F., Yale University, New Haven, Connecticut

PRINCE, A. M., Yale University, New Haven, Connecticut

PRITCHARD, R. H., The University, Glasgow, Scotland

RANADE, SHRIKRISHNAS, Yale University, New Haven, Connecticut (Poona, India)

REITER, HARVARD, New York University, New York

REVEL, JEAN PAUL, Harvard Medical School, Boston, Massachusetts

RICH, KENNETH, Columbia University, New York

RICHTER, ALAN, University of Wisconsin, Madison, Wisconsin

RICK, CHARLES M., Reading, Pennsylvania

RIZKI, M. T. M., Yale University, New Haven, Connecticut

ROGER, MURIEL, Rockefeller Institute, New York

ROMAN, HERSCHEL L., University of Washington, Seattle, Washington

RUDKIN, GEORGE T., Institute for Cancer Research, Philadelphia, Pennsylvania

SACKLER, MURIEL L., Columbia University, New York

SAGAWA, YONEO, Brookhaven National Laboratory, Upton, New York

SAGER, RUTH, Columbia University, New York

SAND, SEAWARD A., Connecticut Agricultural Experiment Station, New Haven, Connecticut

SANG, J. H., Poultry Research Center, Edinburgh, Scotland

SANTER, MELVIN, Yale University, New Haven, Connecticut

SANTER, URSULA, Yale University, New Haven, Connecticut

SCHAECHTER, M., Walter Reed Army Medical Center, Washington, D. C.

SCHRADER, FRANZ, Columbia University, New York

SCHULTZ, JACK, Institute for Cancer Research, Philadelphia, Pennsylvania

SCHWARTZ, DREW, Oak Ridge National Laboratory, Oak Ridge, Tennessee

SCHWINCK, ILSE, Albert Einstein College of Medicine, New York (Hamburg-Berge-dorf, Germany)

SEGAL, WILLIAM, Public Health Research Institute, New York

SHEPARD, PAULINE B., University of Texas, Austin, Texas

SINZBURG, YAEL, Public Health Research Institute, New York

SMITH, DEREK A., Carnegie Institution of Washington, Cold Spring Harbor, New York (Microbiological Research Establishment, Wiltshire, England)

SMITH, LOIS JEAN, Roscoe B. Jackson Laboratory, Bar Harbor, Maine

SOKOLOFF, ALEXANDER, Hofstra College, Hempstead, New York

SPENCER, W. P., College of Wooster, Wooster, Ohio

SPIEGELMAN, S., University of Illinois, Urbana, Illinois

SPOFFORD, JANICE B., University of Chicago, Chicago, Illinois

STADLER, DAVID R., University of Washington, Seattle, Washington

STEFFENSEN, DALE, Brookhaven National Laboratory, Upton, New York

STEIN, OTTO L., Brookhaven National Laboratory, Upton, New York

STENT, GUNTHER S., University of California, Berkeley, California

STERN, CURT, University of California, Berkeley, California

ST. LAWRENCE, PATRICIA, Yale University, New Haven, Connecticut

STONE, WILSON S., University of Texas, Austin, Texas

STREISINGER, G., Carnegie Institution of Washington, Cold Spring Harbor, New York

SUBTELNY, S., Institute for Cancer Research, Philadelphia, Pennsylvania

SZILARD, LEO, University of Chicago, Chicago, Illinois

SZYBALSKI, WACLAW, Rutgers University, New Brunswick, New Jersey

TESSMAN, IRWIN, Cornell University, Ithaca, New York

TESSMAN, MRS. IRWIN, Cornell University, Ithaca, New York

TOBIAS, P. V., University of the Witwatersrand, Johannesburg, South Africa

TRAVAGLINI, ELIZABETH C., Institute for Cancer Research, Philadelphia, Pennsylvania

VETUKHIV, MICHAEL O., Columbia University, New York

VISHNIAC, WOLF, Yale University, New Haven, Connecticut

WAGENAAR, SIBERGINA, Carnegie Institution of Washington, Cold Spring Harbor, New York (Wageningen, Holland)

WAGNER, ROBERT P., University of Texas, Austin, Texas

WALLACE, BRUCE, Biological Laboratory, Cold Spring Harbor, New York

WARREN, CHARLES O., Commonwealth Fund, New York

WARREN, KATHERINE BREHME, Hofstra College, Hempstead, New York; Editor, Cold Spring Harbor Symposia

WASSERMANN, FELIX E., New York University, New York

WEBBER, BROOKE B., Yale University, New Haven, Connecticut

WEINSTEIN, ALEXANDER, Harvard University, Cambridge, Massachusetts

WELSHONS, W. J., Oak Ridge National Laboratory, Oak Ridge, Tennessee

WHITING, P. W., University of Pennsylvania, Philadelphia, Pennsylvania

WILKINS, M. H. F., University of London, London, England

WILLIER, B. H., Johns Hopkins University, Baltimore, Maryland

WITKIN, EVELYN, State University of New York, Brooklyn, New York

WOLLMAN, E.-L., Institut Pasteur, Paris, France

WOLSK, D. I., Massachusetts Institute of Technology, Brookline, Massachusetts

WOLSKY, ALEXANDER, Fordham University, New York

WRIGHT, THEODORE, Yale University, New Haven, Connecticut

YONEDA, MASAHIKO, New York University College of Medicine, New York
YURA, TAKASHI, Yale University, New Haven, Connecticut
ZALOKAR, MARKO, Yale University, New Haven, Connecticut
ZAMENHOF, STEPHEN, Columbia University, New York
ZINDER, NORTON D., Rockefeller Institute, New York
ZWILLING, EDGAR, University of Connecticut, Storrs, Connecticut

work which was a prerequisite to meet simultaneously the four conditions outlined in the beginning of this lecture. Today I may say that the work required to develop and apply procedures for large scale biological use turned out to be even more complicated than we realized in the beginning. The present institute for cell research in Stockholm was built some years ago and more or less specifically equipped for such lines of work, which was a great help but in spite of which it took the main part of the efforts of our entire staff for a period of several years.

Early Microspectrographical Work on Protein Synthesis Connected with Gene Function

The main prerequisites for the early work (cf. Caspersson, 1950a) on protein metabolism in the cell nucleus were two. The first was an ultramicrospectrograph working with high apertures in the ultraviolet region for spot measurements. The size of the spot was limited only by the optical resolving power of the optics. From the technical point of view this spectrograph had in 1940 already been pushed so near the theoretical limit of resolution that no major improvement has later been made. The second prerequisite was particular preparation methods which could be applied to a considerable number of different biological objects. The measuring conditions in the ultramicrospectrograph differ in very important respects from those in the usual macroscale spectrographs. The thickness of the object to be measured corresponds only to a small number of light wavelengths and the measuring aperture is very large. Both these factors diminish to a very great extent the influence of such sources of error as refraction and defraction in the object. These factors in combination with the special preparation methods (see Caspersson, 1950a) made it possible in many types of objects to work on biological objects undisturbed by the factors mentioned. In objects available to microspectrography it was possible to determine the quantity of polynucleotides to a rather satisfactory extent. Less good determinations were made of the tyrosine and tryptophane components of proteins and a semiquantitative judgment of the total amount of proteins could be made using the absorption around 2300 Å. Most work was planned and carried out as comparisons between different cells or cell-elements. Thus it was often possible to plan the experiments so as to get almost equivalent sources of errors in the two cases compared, which made it possible for many problems to use biological material which would else not be accessible for work. It may be noted that the order of size of the nucleotide and protein changes occurring in connection with cell function and cell growth may be enormous and thus in quite a few cases methods with rather low accuracy can be useful, which can simplify the work considerably. Ribose nucleotide changes

with a factor 100 and protein changes with a factor 10 to 50 are often met with. Since 1940 the central instrumentation has also been supplied with equipment for the determination of ultraviolet dichroism. Theoretically this might supply valuable information as to the orientation in the nucleotide material but could also cause disturbances in the absorption measurements. In recent publications these disturbances have sometimes been regrettably exaggerated by misleading calculations. Far from being an important source of error for most biological materials, especially sensitive equipment has to be developed even to detect effects and thus in practical work, with the exception of a few types of materials, this factor is of no importance for absorption measurements owing to the small size of the effects and above all the ease of controlling it (Caspersson, 1940, 1941, 1950a).

The main part of the biological work has dealt with the universal distribution of the polynucleotide group in biological material as well as its importance in connection with protein synthetic processes of various kinds and the process of gene reproduction. I shall not touch upon this work here but shall rather concentrate on the cytochemical observations which demonstrate *intense protein synthetic processes in connection with gene function* and which provoked the previously mentioned efforts to improve the technique.

The protein metabolic data referred to originated mainly from three lines of work:

1) Comparison between functioning interphase nuclei and nuclei in metabolic inactivity, mainly metaphase chromosomes (and sperm). The difference in protein content of the nuclear material is large between these two cases. During metaphase chromosome development (and the development of sperm) large amounts of proteins disappear from the nuclear material (Fig. 2). In favourable cases, as in meiotic prophase in some insects, where morphologically the chromosomes appeared to carry by far the dominating part of the nuclear substances it could be demonstrated how the ratio of nuclei acid to proteins was changed very significantly. Comparison of early prophase to pachytene gave a shift in the ratio between these two classes of substances of the order of magnitude of about 10 times. From the cyto-

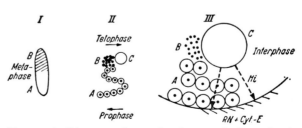

FIGURE 2. Diagram of protein changes during mitosis (from Caspersson, 1941), illustrating the appearance of protein masses around gene loci at the beginning of the functional phase of the cell nucleus.

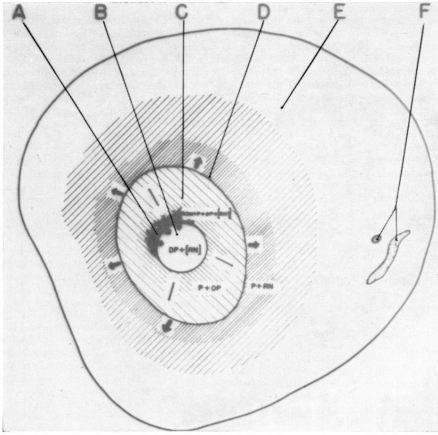

FIGURE 3. Diagram of the system for cytoplasmic protein formation (from Caspersson, 1950a). A, nucleolus-associated chromatin, B, main nucleolus, C, nucleus, D, nuclear membrane, at rapid protein synthesis surrounded by a ring of high concentrations of RNA, E, outer cytoplasm, F, RNA-containing protein producing systems in cytoplasm (mitochondria, ergastoplasmlike structures).

chemical viewpoint these great changes in the protein component of the nuclear material is in fact the most striking phenomenon during mitosis.

The ultraviolet methods give the sum of the DNA and RNA absorption. No hitherto investigated metaphase chromosome material has brought about higher nucleic acid concentrations than, seen from the order of size, half the dry substance, which should be of some interest for the problem of the basic gene structure.

The early work in this field was directly blocked by two factors. First, the need for methods for the determination of total quantities in the most inhomogeneous optical systems formed by the nucleus in its different mitotic or meiotic phases. Second, it was necessary to develop methods for the determination of the optical constants, in the first place for proteins and polynucleotides in very high concentrations as they occur in the chromosome material and which might be expected to diverge considerably from the values in the dilute solutions studied with usual biophysical or biochemical methods.

2) Comparing nuclei in different functional stages, especially with regard to the rate of new formation of cell body protein upon growth or secretion. The diagram, Figure 3, illustrates these observations. Extensive observational material both from plants and animals is available for this mechanism, especially from the work of the last few years. In connection with the rapid cytoplasmic protein synthesis the following changes in the cell take place: In the nucleus there appear protein masses in and around nucleotide-containing chromatin elements—nucleolus-associated chromatin, (A) which are more and more pushed aside, resulting in the formation of a big nucleolus, (B) (Fig. 4). This nucleolus contains proteins in great concentrations and considerable although relatively small and changing amounts of RNA. RNA appears outside the nuclear membrane (D) often in very great amounts, and the cytoplasmic protein mass increases. To simplify matters this special system of cell organelles has been called its system for cytoplasmic protein formation (Caspersson 1941, 1950a, 1954; Moberger, 1954). The degree of development of the organelles of this system follows on the whole the rate of the protein increase.

This system for cytoplasmic protein formation has been observed in all hitherto studied materials of higher organized cells and seems to be a fundamental cell mechanism. Upon slow growth the main nucleolus may be quite small and the RNA ring around the nuclear membrane insignificant. In intense growth or secretion, however, the same cell type may show giant nucleoli and extremely high RNA concentrations around the nuclear membrane, up to several percent of the wet weight. Cells which are not growing, on the other hand, for example, early cleavage cells or spermatocytes, do not show any conspicuous organelles of this kind nor evident signs that this system functions. Cells ready for rapid growth as for instance in the dormant plant embryo or the insect imaginal plates have the organelles of the system well developed and they rapidly start intense new formation of cytoplasmic proteins upon proper stimulus.

From the point of view of gene function the interpretation of this picture seems to imply that part of the chromatin has a special function in the production of the main mass of the proteins in the cell body, and that the chromatin-carried genes rapidly produce large amounts of proteins when in function. These proteins then—entirely or partly—accumulate in the big nucleolus for a time at least during some period. Thereafter they give rise to the process of synthesis in the cytoplasm, where the nuclear membrane (which in some forms is intimately connected with certain nuclear elements with heterochromatic character) very likely plays an important role. The working hypothesis was proposed that the protein masses thus rapidly formed should constitute a kind of basic protein mass which might, by means of adaptation or analogous processes, be transferred to specific enzyme proteins required by the cell for different functions.

The nucleolus associated chromatin therefore seems to offer an excellent opportunity for more thorough studies of certain phases of gene activity.

These observations of cytoplasmic protein formation have given the background for a considerable number of investigations of different kinds. Deeper penetration into the detailed mechanism has, however, as yet been blocked by the difficulty of making determinations of total amounts of nucleotides and proteins in the very heterogeneous and (optically very dense) system afforded by the nucleolus associated chromatin and the nucleolus.

3) The salivary gland type of nuclei offered the possibility of investigating the extent to which proteins occur in or around other gene carrying elements in connection with cell function (Caspersson, 1941). By the unique combination of somatic pairing and endomitosis the chromosome structure may be followed inside the actual functional cell nucleus. Early ultraviolet data revealed that the nucleic acid component was mainly local-

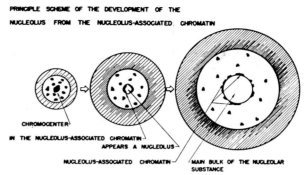

PRINCIPLE SCHEME OF THE DEVELOPMENT OF THE NUCLEOLUS FROM THE NUCLEOLUS-ASSOCIATED CHROMATIN

CHROMOCENTER

IN THE NUCLEOLUS-ASSOCIATED CHROMATIN

APPEARS A NUCLEOLUS

NUCLEOLUS-ASSOCIATED CHROMATIN

MAIN BULK OF THE NUCLEOLAR SUBSTANCE

FIGURE 4.

ized in the stainable sections and the protein components in the interband spaces. The Feulgen reaction shows that certainly the main part of the polynucleotides in the stainable section must be DNA. During the development of the salivary gland the interband spaces of the chromosome increase absolutely and relatively, a sign of increasing protein amount. Detailed studies could, however, not be carried out earlier because of the insufficiently developed technique for protein determination in such heterogeneous objects. The observations strongly indicate a synthesis of proteins around gene carrying loci during cell function, as postulated above. Special interest was focused on some groups of genes with particularly intense function. I refer here to the previously mentioned observations on nucleolus associated chromatin in other cytological material. The correlation between some chromatin parts, the heterochromatin, and the main nucleolus, was already well known for Drosophila. In work carried out in collaboration with J. Schultz it was shown that in various Drosophila strains considerable similarity appeared in the absorption spectra of nucleoli and corresponding heterochromatic chromocenters. This lends further support to the idea of relationship between these regions, similar to that presented earlier for nucleolus associated chromatin and the main nucleolus.

Since the Drosophila material, for various reasons, was not very suitable for cytochemical studies the development of better biological material for such studies became a technical problem as important as that of better biophysical measuring procedures. Shortly after the war this problem was studied in collaboration with Hans Bauer, at that time in Stockholm. Bauer had shown much earlier that apart from the nucleolus and Balbiani rings one could observe bodies, most likely of protein nature occurring outside the chromosomes in certain chromosome sections of Chironomus thummi. Spectrographic work in Stockholm had among other things demonstrated that the absorption curves of the nucleoli and the big Balbiani ring and of corresponding chromosome parts showed characteristic similarities (Figs. 5 and 6). In larvae of various ages the volume of the big

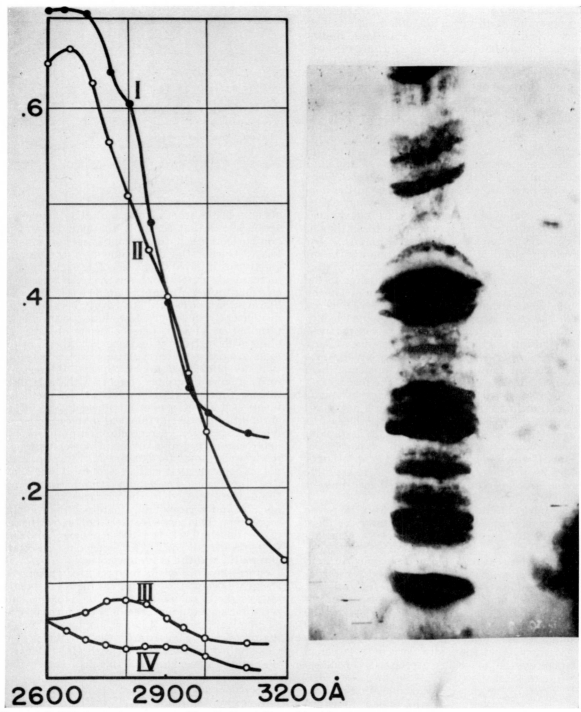

FIGURE 5. UV-absorption spectra of bands (I and II) and interband spaces (III and IV) in *Chironomus thummi*.

Balbiani ring was larger, both absolutely and relatively, in later stages, indicating a parallel of volume with function. Studies carried through by Bauer gave good evidence that in the Balbiani ring sector of the chromosome the strand structure was split up into finer and finer bundles by masses cytochemically found mainly to consist of proteins (Fig. 7). All these observations strongly supported the assumption that protein masses occur in connection with the primary gene function around

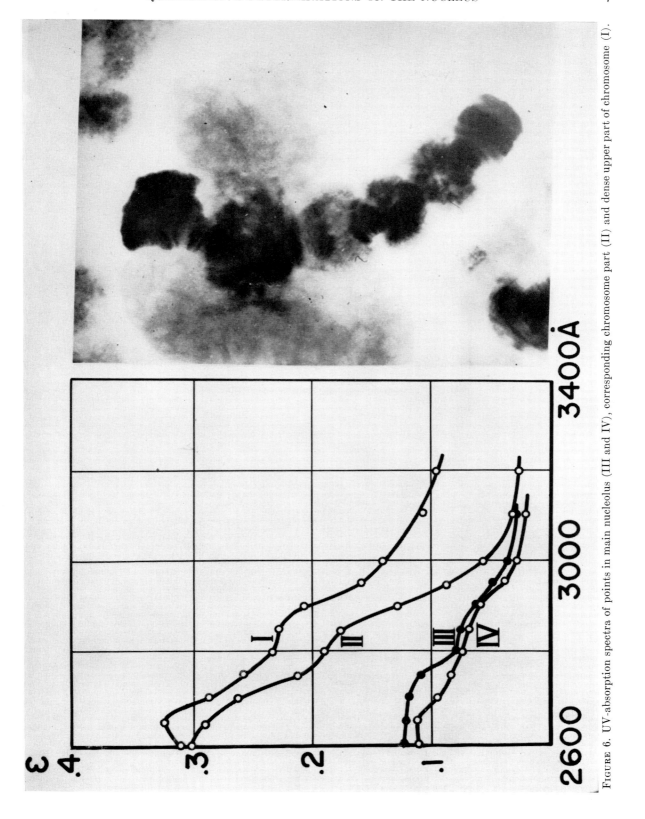

FIGURE 6. UV-absorption spectra of points in main nucleolus (III and IV), corresponding chromosome part (II) and dense upper part of chromosome (I).

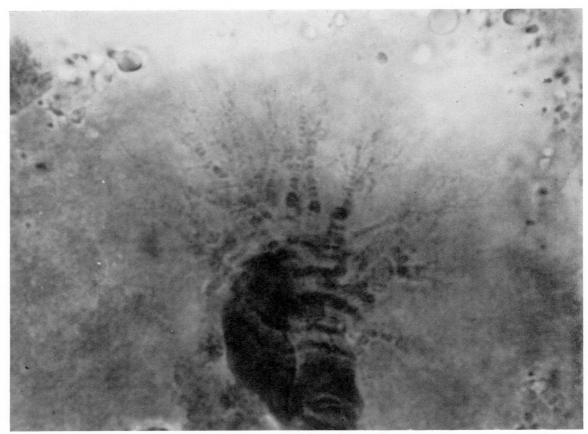

FIGURE 7. Balbiani ring from *Chironomus*. Courtesy of Dr. Hans Bauer. The picture demonstrates how the strands spread apart in the active region.

gene loci, and that some loci or groups of loci may have a highly intense function resulting in the appearance of great protein masses, containing RNA also, either splitting the very chromosome structure or, like the main nucleolus and the small nucleoli, gathering in the neighbourhood of definite chromosome parts. The early work with cytochemical methods had already revealed that the concentrations in various parts of the *Chironomus* chromosomes show great dissimilarities. Judgment of sizes of nuclear structures can in this material be misleading. The variations in concentration between, for instance, different parts of Balbiani rings and main nucleoli and different chromosome sections may amount to a factor of 10 and thus good methods for quantitative determination of total amounts of protein are needed, such as have not been developed until recently.

The very promising results on *Chironomus* were encouraging but the work difficult because of the lack of culture techniques for reasonably constant genetic strains. Because of this Bauer developed culture methods for *Chironomus tentans* and recently very good methods for *Chironomus thummi*, which is still better for cytochemical work. In addition, he has recently developed corresponding methods for *Tipula* species which offer rare

opportunities for cytochemical studies of mitosis meiosis and the spindle mechanism, and are thus an excellent complement to *Chironomus* in the cytochemical work on the gene metabolism. At the end of my lecture I will give some examples from this joint working project. From Bauer's group in Wilhelmshaven has also come strong morphological support for correlations between primary gene products and function. I expect that Dr. Beermann will describe the beautiful work of the Wilhelmshaven group in these fields.

To summarize briefly: Ultramicrospectrography has hitherto demonstrated protein metabolic processes in the primary stages of gene function as follows. The metaphase chromosome contains polynucleotides and proteins. The interphase nucleus contains great amounts of proteins and polynucleotides, RNA as well as DNA. During prophase the main part of the protein in the chromosome material disappears upon contraction. During the meiotic prophase it is possible to follow the disappearance of protein masses from the prophasic chromosomes inside the still unbroken nuclear membrane. During telophase proteins appear again, probably as *primary gene products* around gene loci. In particularly suitable material like the salivary gland type of nuclei these proteins to a considerable extent remain between the gene carrying elements and can be directly observed. The nucleolar material consists of primary gene products which gather in such great quantities that they can be observed clearly with morphological methods. In some material nucleolar organizers play a role in these formations. An excellent opportunity to study these primary protein production processes during gene activity is offered by certain differentiations in the chromatin. Particular chromatin parts are especially active in the formation of the great cytoplasmic protein masses which occur, for example, in rapid cell growth. This nucleolus associated chromatin produces (Fig. 3) very great quantities of proteins and also some RNA, which results in great amounts of nucleolar substances. Simultaneously great RNA masses appear outside the nuclear membrane and the proteins in the cytoplasm increase. This mechanism is universally seen in the animal and plant kingdoms and represents a fundamental mechanism in the function of the cell nucleus. The analogy between nucleolus associated chromatin and the heterochromatic chromocenter is striking in the salivary glands of *Drosophila*, for example. Whether heterochromatin may be identified in a more general way with nucleolus associated chromatin cannot be settled owing to the difficulty of finding an exact and general definition of the concept of heterochromatin from the morphogenetic viewpoint.

INSTRUMENTATION FOR MORE GENERAL QUANTITATIVE WORK ON CELL STRUCTURES

The main working possibilities for direct microspectrography, that is, work on the cell structures in their sites in the cell, are illustrated in Figure 1. In the optical range, substances with selective absorptions can be studied within the whole range where optics with sufficiently high resolving power can be used. In this part of the spectrum the technique was already so advanced in early years that no important improvement with regard to resolution etc. has been possible. Within the X-ray field the possibilities offered are those of mass determination, according to Engström and Lindström (1950) and element determination, according to Engström (1946). Recently Lindström (1954, 1955) developed these procedures to a resolution and a sensitivity which makes it possible to work on endonuclear structures. Suitable photometric procedures for the analysis of microradiograms have been developed by Carlson and Zech (in press) especially adapted for routine work on nuclear structures in larger series. For work with a scanning optical interference method developed by Svensson (Caspersson, 1955a and b), interference optics according to Barer have been used.

In the presentation I have just given of the biological material, I have pointed out how on

numerous occasions the progress was blocked by insufficient technique. Analyzing the situation in these biological projects in some detail one finds that for more penetrating work on protein metabolism in the nucleus the following requirement must be fulfilled:

1) All previously mentioned methods must give a better resolution than 1 μ for spot measurement.

2) It must be possible to work on one and the same biological object with different cytochemical techniques one after another. Special work on preparation techniques for biological objects will also be needed for this purpose.

3) It must be possible to make total determinations of material in very heterogenous systems in large numbers.

4) Time necessary for measurements must be brief and the exposure of the preparation to radiation must be low.

5) Methods suitable for routine work must be developed for determination of the optical constants of the substances to be determined under the conditions prevailing in the biological preparation which is being measured.

6) The cytochemical methods should be worked out so as to render it possible to control one with the other under suitable conditions. In addition, the cytochemical methods should, at least in some critical cases, be directly calibrated with macrochemical determinations.

An inevitable condition for efficient work in the field is that these six fundamental conditions are *simultaneously* fulfilled by the equipment. Little would be gained if only one or two of these requirements were met. That is why we have attempted to carry through a more general program for developing instruments at the institute for cell research in Stockholm during the last few years. We believe now that a point in the program has been reached where the essential ones of the above mentioned requirements are met.[1]

Before going on to describe the technical procedures it is for practical reasons appropriate to treat separately three of the different problems met with: The way of overcoming the heterogeneity of the objects; the procedures for determining the physical constants of the substances to be studied; and finally, certain control procedures. These problems correspond to points 2, 3 and 4 of the basic requirements mentioned in the introduction to this paper.

[1] In this program, the results of which are in the process of publication, a number of people have collaborated in different combinations in the separate working projects. The core of this group has been: Aquilonius, Bahr, Carlson, Kudynowski, Lindström, Lomakka, Issler, Jacobsson, Ruch, Svensson, and Säfström. In the development of biological preparation methods Moberger, Vogt Köhne and Zech have also participated. The work was mainly supported by Swedish government grants, the Wallenberg Foundation and the Swedish Anticancer Society. Parts of the project have been supported by the Rockefeller Foundation.

The Problem of Heterogeneity

One of the most comprehensive of the problems was the development of methods for the mastering of the influence of the inhomogeneity, suitable for biological routine work on large series of material (Caspersson, 1950–1955; Caspersson *et al.*, 1951, 1953, 1955). In principle the technical problem is the same whether it concerns optical absorption measurements, X-ray absorption measurements or measurements of optical path differences. The only precise way to work on an heterogeneous object of the degree of heterogeneity concerned (*e.g.* a *Drosophila* chromocenter or a mammalian nucleus) is to carry out so great a number of separate measurements on the object that together they give a representative value for the total amount of the absorbing substance in question, and to do that with measuring spots so minute that the influence of heterogeneity in each separate spot can be neglected. For the objects mentioned, which are generally representative of the material concerned,

this involves work within the region of the dimension 0.5 μ. In practice this implies two points:

1) Measuring a very great number of separate spots.

2) Conversion of each separate measuring value according to a special function, which is different for optical absorption work, for the X-ray field and for the optical path difference measurements. This is followed by a second calculation, as a rule consisting of additions of these converted measurement values under careful control so that no individual measurements from regions outside the selected region to be measured are involved (*cf.* Fig. 8, part 2a). Practical experience from a considerable number of different lines of biological work has dictated that the number of measuring spots to be managed in this way per day should be of the magnitude 10,000–100,000. Such measurement series could of course not possibly be made by aid of the original spectrographs for spot measurements and in fact this tediousness of the work has been the main factor checking the rapid

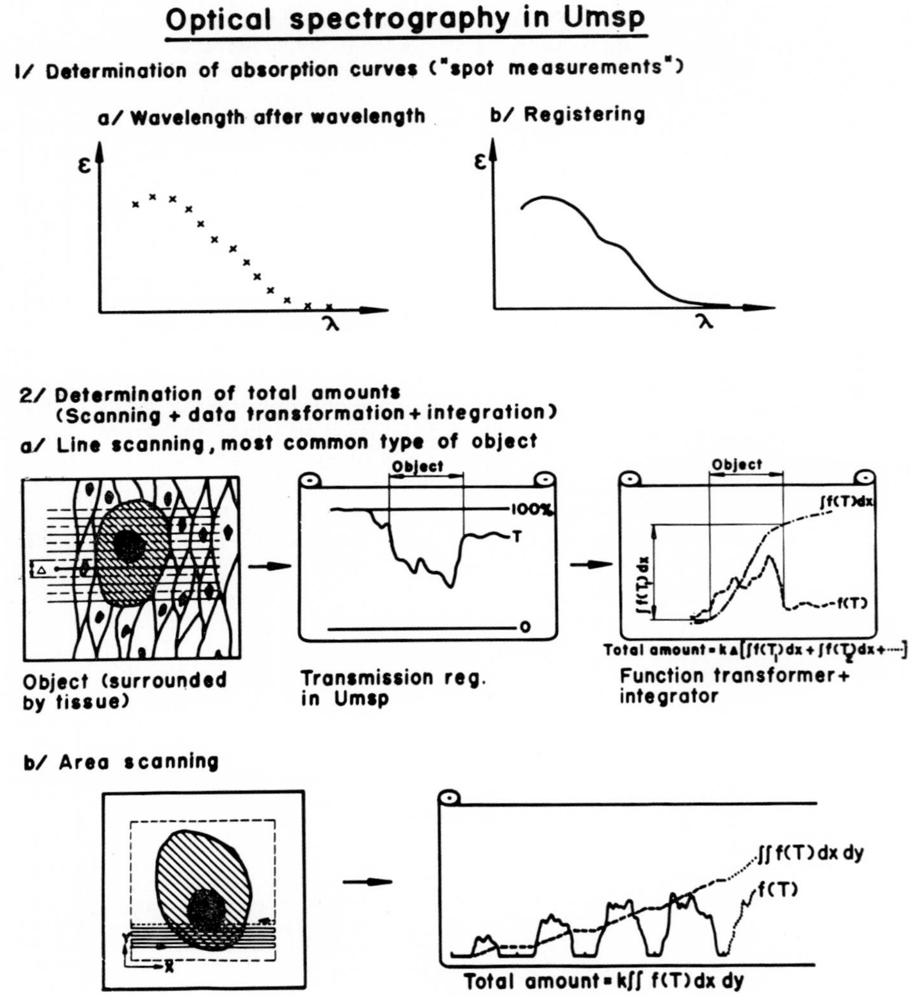

FIGURE 8.

widening of the field of application of microspectrographic techniques to more general biological problems during the last decade. The way to overcome these difficulties has been to automatize the measuring procedure by developing special scanning high resolution spectrographs which can be used as well for direct absorption measurements of the object in visible and ultraviolet light as for analysis of photographic plates from the X-ray spectrograph, for measurements with interference optics, etc. Automatization of this part of the work gives a considerable saving of time, but, however, not enough when dealing with heterogeneous populations of heterogeneous cells and sensitive biological materials. A further very considerable increase in speed of the work has been attained by the development of electronic data handling systems (Lomakka, 1954, 1955 and in press), electronic analogue computers, which convert the measured values and integrate them, either directly during the measurements in the spectrograph or as a later step in the work. One may ask why not develop television-like systems for measurings with direct electronic data transformation, which might permit a further increase of the rate without introducing any serious new instrumental complications. There are two reasons for this choice. Unfortunately the most frequent biological objects by far have the character given in Figure 8, part 2a; the object is of irregular shape and is surrounded by tissues which must not be included in the measurements. This causes obvious difficulties for too greatly automatized systems— inclusion of even a small part of the surrounding cells, which have often quite another absorption, may cause great errors. The second reason is the practical experience that it is most desirable to have a *record of each individual measuring spot*, particularly in the optical microspectrographic work. The object may change during the course of a series of measurements, which are as a rule done at a number of wavelengths one after the other. Furthermore it should be possible later on to control the main course of the absorption spectrum in different parts of the object, which can only be done if permanent records are made. Here I may also mention our practical experience that again

in material which seems ideal for work according to 2b in Figure 8 with more highly automatized scanning systems, such as blood cells, ascitic tumor cells etc. one frequently finds that the "free area" surrounding the object often contains substances which cannot be directly observed with the eye or on the photographic plates in a convenient way, whereas they clearly show up in the recorded curves. Thus the continuous recording as a rule gives much more precise values for the incident radiation than can ever be obtained with unrecording systems in the most common types of biological preparations.

The main functions of the central data-handling spectrograph for optical work are indicated in Figure 8; parts 2a and b give the two main types of biological material. As indicated in the figure every scanning line is continuously recorded and the conversion of the transmission values and the integration of the converted data, which is made in a special computer, is also continuously recorded.

It is not surprising perhaps that the working out of a model of this relatively complex machine, which was well suited for biological routine work on a large scale, proved to be a fairly complex undertaking. Special emphasis has always been put on this practical side of the problem and we believe now that at last the present construction satisfies reasonable demands in this respect. It has been used in continuous large scale work for a couple of years and has become so stabilized that it has now been given over for marketing by Carl Zeiss (Western Germany) as the instrument is decidedly not suitable for construction with the usual university laboratory facilities.

Figure 9 gives the main lines of the computor arrangement. Two types of data-handling units are used in the first place. Both may be classified as electric analogy machines. One of them makes the function transformation by aid of a tapped potentiometer which can be adjusted to give any arbitrary function, integrates the result and records the current integral on the curve. The other type uses systems of diode chains for the function transformation, different for extinction measurements, X-ray measurements and interference

Computer arrangement

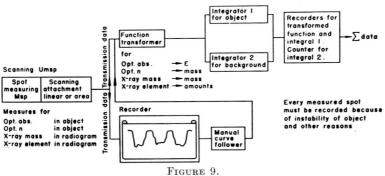

FIGURE 9.

measurements. It also has two integrating systems, one for the object and one for the background. Both types of machines continuously record the results graphically.

The development of this scanning data-handling spectrograph has resulted in some further results, which were originally hardly expected. By suitable arrangement of the biological study—mainly by use of whole cells—it is often possible to get entirely around the difficulties conditioned by a fixation shrinkage of the material and also microtome sectioning, which otherwise often give very unreliable results. Also the scanning procedures give good opportunities to use very low light energies in the study of transient processes in living cells. Finally it has also been possible, by means of this spectrograph, to develop different devices for work on model substances which I shall now deal with.

Measurements on Model Substances

Figure 10 demonstrates the general course of the optical measurements. It goes without saying that there is no use in carrying out measurements with any exactitude of the absorption in the preparation if data on the optical constants of the substances to be analyzed are not available and *valid for exactly the conditions which prevail in the biological preparation to be studied.* The difficulties involved in the determination of these constants lie in the vast distance between the cytochemical working field, 10^{-9} to 10^{-12} g, and most general chemical and physical micromethods which as a rule work near the mg or gamma range. Svensson (1954, 1955, 1956 and in press) has developed procedures for determination of extinction and index of refraction suitable for routine work on such material as, for instance, proteins in concentrations up to more than 40 per cent. The central difficulties are to be found in the handling of such solutions at the time of the measurements, which must be carried through in thicknesses of layers only a few micra thick, the thickness of which has to be known with an accuracy of a few per cent.

Optical ultramicrospectrography

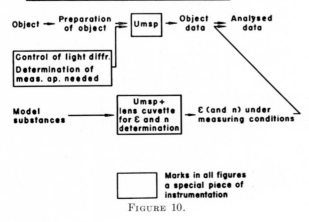

FIGURE 10.

With regard to the extinction, the most important point is the determination of its dependence of concentration. The value of the index of refraction has to be known because of the possible light losses due to refraction and diffraction, and the possibility of anomalous dispersion. The possibility that dichroism may appear has also to be taken into consideration. In general, however, dichroism gives no particular difficulties in the biological work. Since the very start of microspectrography it has as a matter of routine been controlled by very simple instruments (see Caspersson, 1950a; Ruch, 1951) and is of very little practical importance in spite of some regrettably misleading claims in the literature from the last decade.

Recently methods have also been developed (in press) by which the optical constants of solid model systems can be determined. Small drops of solutions were treated by common fixation methods like freeze drying or formalin fixation etc. in the same way as biological objects and after that extinction and refractive increment were determined.

In these ways one can in model substances very closely imitate the conditions in the complex biological objects for measurement and make the proper determinations of the optical constants needed for the data analysis. The kinds of apparatus are rather simple and are constructed as complements to the scanning spectrograph in the form to be described later, the universal ultramicrospectrograph.

Calibration of Methods with each other and with Microchemical Procedures

The first part of this subject needs no special argumentation. With regard to the second point, it is evidently most advantageous if so complex a biophysical procedure could be directly compared with macrochemical determinations in spite of the very great difference in working range—10^6 to 10^9. There is, however, another special reason for making these efforts. The optical conditions at, for instance, polynucleotide determinations in a nucleus with chromatin granules of the magnitude of the light wavelength, irregularly packed, are so complicated that it is not theoretically possible to foresee whether an exceedingly accurate measurement, made in the way described above of a great number of measuring spots, will actually give a correct expression for the total amount of absorbing substances. In this case a comparison with macrochemical determinations on the same object will be decisive. This comparison is, however, difficult since it is not possible to produce entirely homogeneous cell populations of higher organized cells in such quantities as are necessary in order to get macrochemical data. The comparison using the usual more or less heterogeneous cell populations presupposes that one is able to carry out the cytochemical measurements on such a very great number of individual cells that together they are representative of the entire population. With the automatized scanning spectrograph the working rate has now become so high that such determinations can be carried out. Especially regarding the ultraviolet work during the last six months such studies have been made on a rather large scale using ascitic tumor material for determinations of the total nucleotide and protein content in cells and isolated nuclei. In most cases material consisting of 200 cells and on an average corresponding to 100,000 measuring points yield constant results and are thus representative of the population. The macrochemical determinations were on an average made on a 1000 million cells. With the present equipment such series of measurements and data conversions can be made within a few days. The agreement has been satisfactory, in all cases better than ±10 per cent.

GENERAL ARRANGEMENT OF THE INSTRUMENTATION

In our efforts to develop a system of instruments for more general cytochemical work on a quantitative basis the following ten separate lines of work have been the central ones:

1) Development of arrangements for preparation (possibly fixation) of objects and for the measurement of their geometrical dimensions.

2) Development of arrangements for spot measurements (wavelength after wavelength or recording) in the optical region (ultraviolet and visible).

3) Microradiograms for mass determinations suitable for analytical work and working in the range of dimensions of the cell nuclear structures.

4) The same for determination of elements.

5) Instrumentation for scanning interference microphotometry.

6) Instrumentation for the control of light scattering and refraction in objects and determination of the minimal measuring aperture necessary in the microspectrograph.

7) Automatized scanning arrangement for work in optical region.

8) Data-handling units for function transformation and integrations of transformed data.

9) Instrumentation for the determination of optical constants of model substances in highly concentrated solutions and especially in the neighbourhood of the absorption peaks.

10) Instrumentation for the determination of extinction and refractive increment in dried or fixed model substances.

In order to avoid boring you with a number of photographs of different pieces of machinery, I have tried to present the mode of working of the complete instrumentation in series of diagrams. In these diagrams a rectangle marks a special instrument, as a rule a result of one of the lines of work just listed. The abbreviation Umsp denotes the "universal ultramicrospectrograph" described below, a central piece of instrumentation which contains the main scanning and computing units.

X-ray mass determination

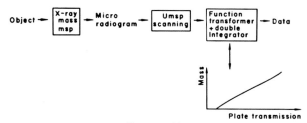

FIGURE 11.

Figure 10 illustrates the main procedure for work with optical absorption measurements. The object, after suitable preparation and after control of light refraction and diffraction in a special instrument, is worked at in the Umsp. The optical constants of suitable model substances are also determined and these data, together with the data from the object, give the background for the final analysis. Figure 8 gives the main different modes of work in the optical region in the Umsp: Spot measurements and scanning measurements, either line scanning or area scanning. The conversion of the scanning data and integration of the converted data occurs in the computers.

Figure 11 shows the course of the X-ray mass determination. Radiograms are taken in the high resolution X-ray microspectrograph for mass-determination according to Lindström. After development the microradiograms are analyzed in the Umsp scanning units. The transmission data are fed into the function transformer and converted according to the density curve of the plate. A very great advantage of the X-ray technique, which outweights its relative complexity, lies in the fact that the X-ray absorptions are largely independent of the physical state of the object and thus model substance determinations in the way in which they are needed for optical work are as a rule not necessary.

X-ray element determinations are made in fundamentally the same way after exposure in the proper X-ray spectrograph, a vacuum X-ray spectrograph developed by Lindström, using curved crystals as monochromators.

The interference mass determination is made with a scanning high resolution procedure using interference microscope optics but otherwise in principle fairly similar to the scanning work for absorption measurements. The Umsp can be equipped with interference optics and the measurements can be made directly in the Umsp. The function transformation is made according to a sinusoidal function indicated in Figure 12. In this case determinations are needed on model substances of the specific refractive increment under the proper conditions, for which a technique has also been developed, as indicated in the figure.

It is evident that the function of the computer is fundamentally quite similar for the different procedures. We have tried specifically to make

Interference mass determination

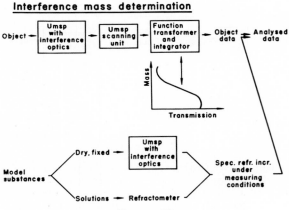

FIGURE 12.

this part as simple and reliable as possible in order to suit the urgent demands of large scale biological work for convenient instrumentation. Figure 9 shows the general arrangements. The computer arrangement can be directly connected with the scanning Umsp in which optical absorptions or optical refractive increment can be measured in an object, or X-ray mass and X-ray element determinations can be made in microradiograms. The transmission data are fed into the function transformer which transforms according to the proper function, as indicated in the diagram. The converted data are accumulated in an integrator, and for some specific types of material, in the first line microradiograms because of their granularity, a second integrator for the background is also provided. All data coming out of the computers

are recorded with exception of the background data, which accumulate in a usual conventional counter. It has proved to be practical in a laboratory where several people work with the equipment to provide also for the possibility of making the curve analysis as a separate step after the original transmission measurements have been made. Experience has shown that in this way the relatively expensive equipment can sometimes be used more efficiently. Thus the computer has been arranged so that transmission recordings from the Umsp can be put into them and analyzed by aid of a manual curve following system.

Time will not allow me to enter into the control systems, and the arrangements for measurements on model systems.

Leaving out details and certain smaller pieces of instrumentation, one can present the whole set as one unit, as in Figure 13. This shows clearly, I hope, the four central lines of work in the optical and X-ray regions, the central place of the scanning arrangements and the computer units and also the fact that it has been feasible to concentrate the more expensive parts, mainly concerned with the scanning work, into one unit, which can be used for all four lines simultaneously and also for the work on model substances. The work on model substances is carried through by aid of special instrumentation for ϵ and n determinations and a considerable part of the work is made by aid of the scanning units. A central thing in the whole system of instrumentation is the fact that it has been possible to concentrate so many different functions in the instrument which is called the Umsp. In that way the amount of instrumentation necessary for practical routine biological

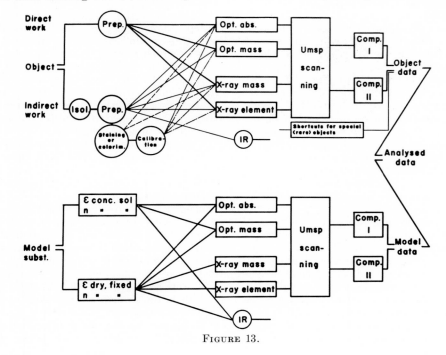

FIGURE 13.

TABLE 1. FUNCTIONS OF THE UNIVERSAL
ULTRAMICROSPECTROGRAPH
(UMSP)

A. Optical msp of biological objects
 1. Absorption curves
   a. Wavelength after wavelength
   b. Recording
 2. Determination of total amounts
   a. Line scanning, data computing
   b. Area scanning, data computing
B. Interference microphotometry, scanning, data computing
C. Analysis of X-ray microradiograms from high resolution X-ray msp for determination of mass or elements, scanning, data computing
 With supplements:
D. Determination of ϵ in highly concentrated solutions
E. Determination of n in highly concentrated solutions
F. Determination of ϵ in fixed or dehydrated models
G. Determination of n in fixed or dehydrated models
H. Determination of dichroism in object
 1. Presence or absence
 2. Measurement thereof

work has been kept down to a minimum. Table 1 summarizes the tasks and function of the Umsp.

Again turning to Figure 13 I would like to point out two things. In particular cases it is possible to take considerable shortcuts in the work. I am sorry to say that the range of work of such methods is extremely limited but they can be of use in preliminary work. For optical absorption work one can exploit the phenomenon that within the straight part of the density curve the transmission of a developed photographic plate is a logarithmic function of the originally incident light energy. Within the fairly long straight part of the density curve of the microradiograms and in the regrettably short straight part of the corresponding curve for interference work, one can also use simpler techniques in suitable material. The second point is the following: As yet only *direct* ultramicrospectrography has been discussed, that is measurements of absorption data directly in the cell structure in its place in the cell. Of course it is possible to use the same procedure on cell structures or cells, with suitable procedures isolated from the tissue and collected in sufficient quantities. In that case the main advantage of the high resolution of the procedures is lost, but on the other hand the field of application is much wider. The group of procedures as presented in the figures present as a whole a good background for the development of ultramicrochemical procedures working in the range between the usual microchemistry and the range of the direct microspectroscopy. Using the scanning procedures it is, for example, easy to determine, in a very small dried droplet the total amount of, say, proteins, nucleic acids, total mass, phosphorus, sulphur and so on. Infrared procedures are also being used in this line

of development which is at present under way in our laboratory. Another interesting and promising mode of application of these procedures is the exploitation of staining or colorimetric techniques. Ultramicrocolorimetric techniques using ultramicrospectrographs of types mentioned has been described earlier (Norberg, 1942). Staining procedures in general are extremely bad for quantitative work, as is well known. The main reason for that is to be found in the fact it has been impossible to introduce the proper model systems in the objects to be measured. With the techniques described above it is often easy, however, to build up a model system, for instance for SH staining

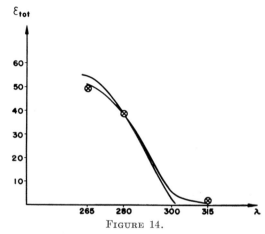

FIGURE 14.

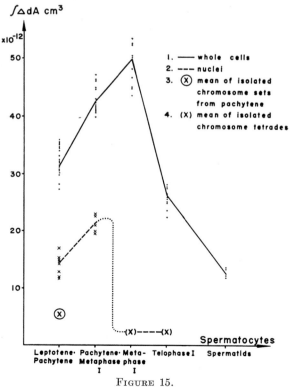

FIGURE 15.

procedures, by introducing a small droplet of protein of known weight and composition in the object to be stained. Then the color reaction in the preparation can be judged on the basis of this simultaneously stained model system. It is possible that this field is one of the most important applications in the future of the general techniques I have described today.

In this presentation I have tried to show how the efforts to develop more general quantitative cytochemical procedures were directly provoked by the early ultraviolet microspectrographic work on gene function and nuclear structure and also that these methods have now on the whole developed so far that the essential ones of the primary conditions mentioned in the beginning have now largely been fulfilled. During the last few months we have taken up the basic biological

line again, but the results are so incomplete that I will not try to give any presentation of the data of a more general kind. I would like to give just a few examples to show that the structures in question are accessible. The ultraviolet procedures need no special presentation. In this respect of course the data I cited earlier about the good agreement in the comparison with macrochemical data, which was made possible by the data-computing spectrograph, shows that these data are solid. Figure 14 gives another example, In an ascitic tumor cell population the macrochemical protein and nucleotide determination gave data corresponding to an absorption spectrum as the curves in the figure for a homogenate of one cell. Cytochemical measurements of 250 cells corresponding to about 150,000 measuring spots, gave the three points marked, when expressed in the same units. The

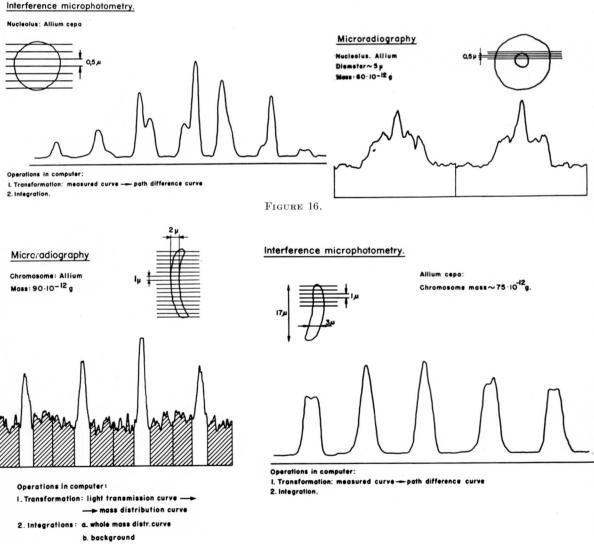

FIGURE 16.

FIGURE 17.

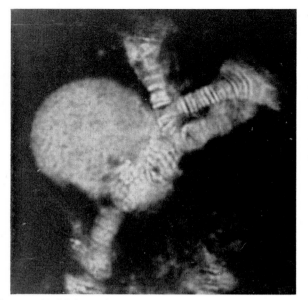
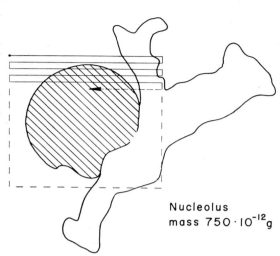

Nucleolus
mass $750 \cdot 10^{-12}$ g

FIGURE 18. Main nucleolus in a fullgrown larva of *Chironomus thummi* (interference micr. photograph), mode of mass measurement and result. Chromosome breadth 7–8 μ. Similar measurement in small young larva from same batch, (with chromosome breadth 60% of the fullgrown ones) gave 25.10^{-12} grams *i.e.* 30 times lower value showing the absolutely and relatively very great increase of these nucleolar masses during salivary gland development.

agreement is good qualitatively as well as quantitatively. Calibration of the X-ray procedures in similar ways also gave very good agreement.

Figure 15 gives, as an example of X-ray and interference methods, measurements during meiosis of *Tipula* of the total mass of individual cells and nuclei. A considerable increase in total cell mass and a parallel increase in the total mass of the nucleus is evident until approximately diakinesis. Then the total mass (of the daughter cells taken together) remains constant. The mass of the tetrads and of metaphase plates has also been measured and marked (+) in the figure. The very great difference between the total mass of the early prophase nucleus and that of the sum of the metaphase chromosomes, indicated in the beginning of my lecture, is very clear (Vogt-Köhne, Zech, Carlson, Svensson, in press.)

Figures 16 and 17 show examples of the procedures used for work on small chromosomes and nucleoli—those of the order of magnitude of two micra are readily accessible for measurement. Lastly, Figure 18 shows measurements on the main nucleolus in a fullgrown larva of *Chironomus thummi*. In the early larval stages studied the mass of the nucleolus was more than ten times lower.

These examples were given only to illustrate that it seems to be possible to go further in the field of the cytochemical study of genetic mechanisms with these procedures.

REFERENCES

BAHR, G. F., 1955, Die Beurteilen der Schnittqualität von Paraffinschnitten. Mikroskopie *10:* 13–18.
BARER, R., 1953, Determination of dry mass, thickness, solid and water concentration in living cells. Nature, Lond. *172:* 1097–1098.
CASPERSSON, T., 1936, Über den Chemischen Aufbau der Strukturen des Zellkernes. Skand. Arch. Physiol. *73:* Suppl. 8.
— 1940, Die Eiweissverteilung in den Strukturen des Zellkerns. Chromosoma *1:* 562–604.
— 1941, Studien über den Eiweissumsatz der Zelle. Naturwiss. *29:* 33–43.
— 1950a, Cell Growth and Cell Function. New York, Norton and Co.
— 1950b, Some recent developments in ultramicrospectrography. Genetica-Iberica *2:* 277–286.
— 1950c, A universal ultramicrospectrograph for the optical range. Exp. Cell Res. *1:* 595–598.
— 1954a, A set of instrumentation for general quantitative cytochemical work by high resolution microspectrography. Exp. Cell Res. *7:* 598–600.
— 1954b, The quantitative cytochemical approach to problems of tumor growth and diagnosis. La prophylaxie en gynécologie et obstétrique, Conférences et rapports du Congrès international de gynécologie et d'obstétrique, Genève *1:* 1–15.
— 1954c, Optische Mikrospektrographie mit quantitativen Zielen in der histochemischen Praxis. Verh. Anat. Ges., Münster 2–25.
— 1954d, Ultra-microspectrophotometry as a basis of quantitative cytochemical work. Anais da Ac. Bras. *26:* 199–214.
— 1955a, Quantitative cytochemical methods for the study of cell metabolism. Experientia *11:* 45–60.
— 1955b, Quantitative ultramikrospektrographische Verfahren. Mikrochim. Acta (Wien) 1–26.
CASPERSSON, T., CARLSON, L., and SVENSSON, G., 1954, A scanning interference microscope arrangement. Exp. Cell Res. *7:* 601–602.
CASPERSSON, T., FREDRIKSSON, T., and THORSSON, K. G., 1953, A microplanimeter for measurement of endonuclear structure. Hereditas, Lund *49:* 201–208.
CASPERSSON, T., JACOBSSON, F., and LOMAKKA, G., 1951, An automatic scanning device for ultramicrospectrography. Exp. Cell Res. *2:* 301–303.
CASPERSSON, T., JACOBSSON, F., LOMAKKA, G., SVENSSON, G., and SÄFSTRÖM, R., 1953, A high resolu-

tion ultra-microspectrophotometer for large scale biological work. Exp. Cell Res. *5:* 560–563.

CASPERSSON, T., LOMAKKA, G., SVENSSON, G., and SÄFSTRÖM, R., 1955, A versatile ultramicrospectrograph for multiple-line and area scanning high resolution measurements employing automatized data analysis. Exp. Cell Res. Suppl. *3:* 40–51.

DAVIES, H. G., WILKINS, M. H. F., CHAYEN, J., and LACOUR, L. F., 1954, The use of the interference microscope to determine dry weight in living cells and as a quantitative cytochemical method. Quart. J. Micr. Sci. *95:* 271–304.

ENGSTRÖM, A., 1946, Quantitative micro- and histochemical elementary analysis. Acta Radiol., Suppl. 63.

ENGSTRÖM, A., and LINDSTRÖM, B., 1950, A method for the determination of the mass of extremely small biological objects. Biochim. Biophys. Acta *4:* 351–373.

LINDSTRÖM, B., 1954, Absorption spectrophotometry with extremely soft X rays for the quantitative determination of the dry weight of cytochemical structures. Exp. Cell Res. *6:* 537–539.

1955, Roentgen absorption spectrophotometry in quantitative cytochemistry. Acta Radiol., Suppl. 125.

LINDSTRÖM, B., and MOBERGER, G., 1954, Studies on the quantitative distribution of the dry weight in squamous epithelium during carcinogenesis. Exp. Cell Res. *6:* 540–542.

LOMAKKA, G., 1954, A general function-transformer for microspectrographic use. Exp. Cell Res. *7:* 603–605.

1955, A recording function transformer and integrator for microspectrographic use. Exp. Cell Res. *9:* 434–445.

MOBERGER, G., 1954, Malignant transformation of squamous epithelium. A cytochemical study, with special reference to cytoplasmic nucleic acids and proteins. Acta Radiol., Suppl. 112.

MOBERGER, G., LINDSTRÖM, B., and ANDERSSON, L., 1954, Freeze-drying with a modified Glick-Malmström apparatus. Exp. Cell Res. *6:* 228–237.

NORBERG, B., 1942, On the histo- and cytochemical determination of phosphorus. Acta Physiol. Scand. *5:* Suppl. 14.

RUCH, F., 1951, Eine Apparatus zur Messung des Ultraviolett-Dichroismus von Zellstrukturen, Exp. Cell Res. *2:* 680–683.

SVENSSON, G., 1954, An apparatus for the measurement of the light distribution around microscopical objects. Exp. Cell Res. *6:* 529–531.

1955, A method for measurement of the absorption in extremely high-absorbing solutions. Exp. Cell Res. *9:* 428–433.

1956, Bestimmung von Absorption und Brechungsindex extrem hochabsorbierender Lösungen immikromasstab. Mikrochimica Acta (Wien) 645–650.

Alterations of Intracellular Deoxyribonucleic Acid and Their Biological Consequence

D. Kanazir[1] and M. Errera

Laboratoire de Morphologie animale, Faculté des Sciences, Université libre de Bruxelles[2]

The study of the early biochemical and biological consequences of the inhibition of the metabolism of deoxyribonucleic acid (DNA) becomes possible if one can find a system in which it can be specifically interfered with. This has been done in the case of *E. coli* with ultra-violet (U.V.) dosages which have only minor immediate effects on the synthesis of ribose nucleic acid (RNA) or proteins, but which are however lethal for 80 per cent of the bacteria. In the present work, we have attempted to find some evidence for possible pathways of DNA synthesis by looking for low molecular weight precursors of this compound and by studying the metabolism of high energy phosphate during DNA synthesis and during its inhibition. We will furthermore give a brief account of attempts which have been made to discover immediate structural effects on DNA or on macromolecular material containing DNA. The method chosen, which consists of disrupting the cells by enzymatic lysis, is not applicable to *E. coli* and was applied to *Micrococcus lysodeikticus*.

Experimental Conditions

Most experiments were carried out on *E. coli* B or B/r, grown on simple aerated media containing glucose as the sole source of carbon (Errera, 1954).

The bacteria were irradiated either in the logarithmic growth phase or during the resting stage, the suspension having been diluted to a constant optical density of 0.2 (read in the Coleman Universal spectrophotometer, mod. 14, at 700 mμ, filter PL 5 and in tubes of 18 mm diameter). A Mineralight lamp with an output of 19.10^2 ergs/mm²/min. placed at 30 cm was used. Bacterial colony counts showed that under these conditions 20 seconds of irradiation of *E. coli* B in the logarithmic phase left 20 per cent survivors. All the incubations were done in the dark.

The determinations of the acid soluble fraction were done on cold ($\pm 4°C$) trichloracetic (5 %) or perchloric (1 %) extracts of delipidated cells. Ribose (acid soluble or RNA) was determined according to Schneider (1945) and deoxyribose (acid soluble or DNA) according to Ceriotti (1952).

[1] Institut des Sciences nucléaire "Boris Kidric," Belgrade.
[2] Part of this work was made possible by a grant from the Centre de Recherches pour la Protection des Populations civiles.

Chromatographic analysis of the acid soluble fraction was conducted in two steps: nitrogen bases and their nucleosides were separated in N butanol-NH₃ (solvent I; Marshak, 1951). The nucleotides which remain at the starting point are eluted and chromatographed in tert. butanol-HCl (solvent II; Markham and Smith, 1951).

High energy phosphate (ATP) determinations were performed with Strehler's modification of McElroy's firefly luciferase technique (Strehler and Totter, 1952; McElroy, 1951).

Experimental Results

a) *Growth of irradiated bacteria*

If, after irradiation, the bacteria are aerated at 37°C, in a synthetic medium, one sees that they continue to grow with no interruption. The optical density and dry weight increases at a slightly reduced rate after $9.5 \cdot 10^2$ ergs/mm² (Fig. 1).

From cytological observations it is apparent that the bacteria are abnormal and grow into long multinucleated filaments which become visible after the time necessary for one normal division to take place. Cells which at the time of irradiation are binucleated have four, then eight nuclei, etc. But, with the dosages used, after two or three hours, although many filaments can still be observed, small bacteria of normal appearance begin to multiply. This probably means that some cytoplasmic division is beginning to take place anew.

E. coli B/r, which are known to be a radioresistant strain derived from *E. coli* B, (Witkin, 1946) do undergo cytoplasmic division, but they appear to develop small abnormal colonies when seeded on agar plates (Wyss, 1950).

If, after irradiation under the usual conditions, the bacteria are not aerated but cultured in anaerobic conditions (Thunberg tubes), they continue to grow at identically the same speed as the controls (Fig. 2).

b) *Nucleic acid synthesis*

1) Ribose nucleic acid. RNA synthesis follows a pattern similar to that of the dry weight, and continues without any lag but at a slightly slower rate than the controls (Fig. 3); even if the dosage has been such that growth is completely inhibited for one hour, RNA is still synthesized to some extent during this time. Kelner (1953) found quite similar results for *E. coli* B/r.

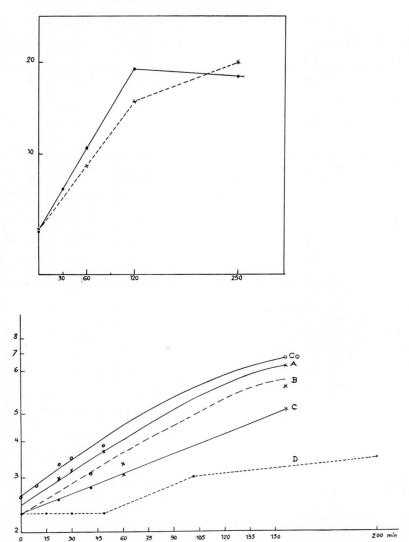

FIGURE 1. Growth of *E. coli* B after irradiation in the logarithmic phase. *Abscissae:* time of culture after irradiation, in minutes. *Ordinates:* top: dry weight of 40 ml bacterial suspension $(9.5.10^2 ergs/mm^2)$; bottom: optical density. A. $6.33.10^2 ergs/mm^2$. B. $9.5.10^2 ergs/mm^2$. C. $12.6.10^2 ergs/mm^2$. D. $19.10^2 ergs/mm^2$. Co. control.

2) Deoxyribonucleic acid. Kelner (1953) has shown that the synthesis of DNA is completely inhibited after U.V. irradiation. In fact, this inhibition only lasts for various periods of time (roughly proportional to dosage), after which DNA is synthesized again. This is in line with the formation of multinucleate filaments (Fig. 4).

Under anaerobic conditions a similar behavior is observed (Fig. 5).

3) Nucleic acid metabolism of radioactive bacteria. If radiocative cells (incubated for 30 minutes with glycine-1-C[14], 1.5 10³ counts/min/cc of medium) are irradiated and cultured afterwards in a non-radioactive medium, the specific activities of RNA and of RNA purines decrease in the same way as the controls; on the contrary, the specific activity of the DNA and DNA purines remains constant during the time when no net synthesis has taken place. This can be taken as evidence for a complete inhibition of DNA synthesis and rules out the possibility of a simultaneous synthesis and breakdown (Table I).

c) Accumulation of deoxyribonucleosides and deoxyribonucleotides

1) Identification. If growing *E. coli* are irradiated ($9.5\ 10^2\ ergs/mm^2$) and analysed after 30 to 40 minutes, one immediately sees that, although growth is slightly inhibited, there is a higher concentration of acid soluble material. This is found a) to absorb in the U.V. with a maximum at 260 mμ, b) to contain both organic and inorganic phosphate, and c) to contain both ribose and deoxyribose (Fig. 6) (Kanazir and Errera,

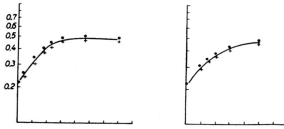

FIGURE 2. Growth of irradiated bacteria in anaerobic conditions ($9.5.10^2$ ergs/mm²). *Left:* E. coli B, *right:* E. coli B/r. *Abscissae:* each division equal to 60 minutes culture after irradiation. *Ordinates:* optical density. Dots: controls; crosses: irradiated.

1954). When the synthesis of DNA is resumed, these differences become smaller and smaller (Fig. 6). One of us (Kanazir) analysed these extracts chromatographically.

The experimental results are grouped in Table 2. The identification of each compound was based on: a) its absorption spectrum in acid and alkali and its Rf value compared to known samples; b) the identification of the sugar by colorimetric methods and of the nitrogen bases obtained by hydrolysis in formic acid at 175°C (Wyatt, 1951) for 30 minutes for purines and for two hours for pyrimidines.

·It is seen that the irradiated bacteria contain from 150 to 300 per cent more deoxyribosides and deoxyribotides than the control bacteria.

A certain number of ribose nucleotides are also formed but in equal amounts in the controls and irradiated bacteria.

2) Specific activity of acid soluble purines. Using glycine-1-C^{14}, as in section b, 3, we confirmed the identity of metabolism of the growing irradiated bacteria with their controls (Table 3).

d) Accumulation of high energy phosphate

As can be seen from Table 2, adenosine triphosphate (ATP) and uridine diphosphate (UDP) are formed in higher concentrations in the irradiated cells. The synthesis of ATP in irradiated cells has been studied in more detail with the luciferase technique. Although the light emission which is measured by this method is standardized against known solutions of ATP, and is referred to as ATP, it is not certain that ATP is the only high energy phosphate source which can catalyse the bioluminescent reaction. In our experiments we used cell homogenates, because these were found to be more active than the supernatant. High energy phosphate bound to insoluble material thus appears to be active; according to Strehler (1952) RNA alone is capable of producing light emission, but as we shall see, changes in ATP do not parallel those found for RNA.

1) ATP in aerobic bacteria. Figures 7 and 8 show the metabolism of ATP during the lag phase and during the logarithmic phase. In the first case, although the irradiation may have been more important than in the previous experiment and growth considerably inhibited, the ATP follows

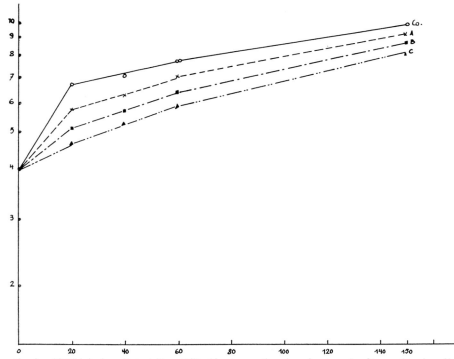

FIGURE 3. Synthesis of RNA in irradiated E. coli B. *Abscissae:* time in minutes of culture after irradiation. *Ordinates:* γ RNA in 40 ml culture. A. $6.3.10^2$ ergs/mm². B. $9.5.10^2$ ergs/mm². C. 19.10^2 ergs/mm². Co. control.

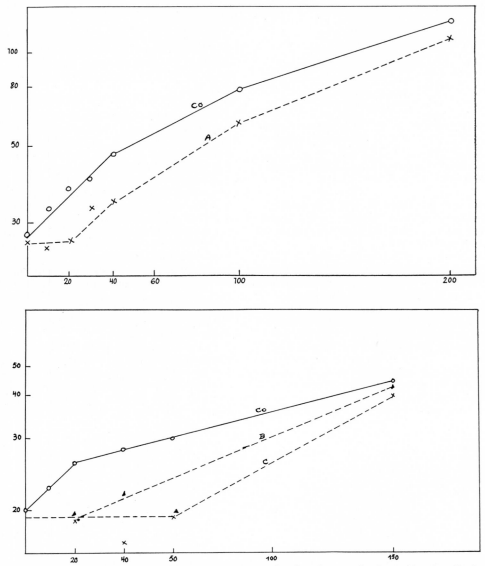

FIGURE 4. Synthesis of DNA in irradiated *E. coli* B. *Abscissae:* time in minutes of culture after irradiation. *Ordinates:* γ DNA in 20 ml bacterial suspension (top); γ DNA in 40 ml bacterial suspension (bottom). Co. control. A. $6.33.10^2$ ergs/mm². B. $9.5.10^2$ ergs/mm². C. $12.6.10^2$ ergs/mm².

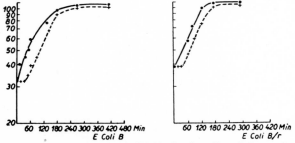

FIGURE 5. Synthesis of DNA in irradiated bacteria grown in anaerobic conditions ($9.5.10^2$ ergs/mm²). *Abscissae:* time in minutes. *Ordinates:* γ DNA in 20 ml bacterial suspension. Solid line: control; dotted line: irradiated.

identically the same evolution as in the control bacteria.

When irradiated in the lag phase, as we have already seen, the amount of ATP remains *higher* during the time DNA is not synthesized although growth, protein and RNA synthesis continue. This means, and the radioactivity measurements confirm it (Table 3), that ATP is synthesized as in the controls, but is not used up as fast, as long as DNA metabolism is blocked.

2) ATP in anaerobic bacteria. When the bacteria are irradiated in air during aerobic growth and then incubated in *anaerobiosis* for the rest of the experiment, one sees that in the controls, the *total amount* of ATP in the culture increases gradu-

TABLE I. SPECIFIC ACTIVITY (COUNTS/MIN/γ) OF RNA AND DNA IN *E. coli* B

	Dry weight/ mg	RNA			DNA		
		Total		Ade- nine	Gua- nine	Total		Ade- nine	Gua- nine
T_0	62.5	29.5	26.7	162	160	23.6	23	200	142.5
T	106	15.4	14.8	93	69	12.8	16	89	78
I	91	14.9	15.8	89	67	23.7	29.5	198	144

T_0: before irradiation.

T: non irradiated control, 30 minutes after T_0.

I: irradiated in log phase ($9.5.10^2$ ergs/mm²); 30 minutes after T_0.

RNA was extracted in cold ClO_4H for 24 hours; DNA was extracted from the first residue in hot trichloracetic acid (5%). Guanine and adenine, when necessary, were hydrolyzed in N. HCl/100°/ for 1 hour and chromatographed in solvent I.

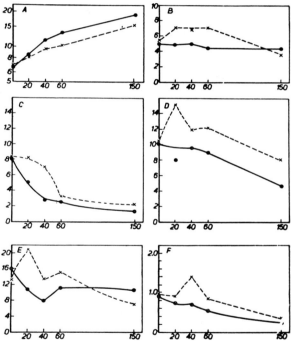

FIGURE 6. Acid soluble constituents of irradiated *E. coli* B. Dotted line: $9.5.10^2$ ergs/mm²; solid line: control. *Abscissae:* time in minutes of culture after irradiation. *Ordinates:* A. mgr. of bacteria in 40 ml culture (growth curve). B. $\mu M.10^3$ p. mgr of bacteria of constituents absorbing at 260 mμ calculated as ribosenucleotides. C. $\mu M.10^3$ inorganic phosphate per mgr of bacteria. D. $\mu M.10^3$ organic phosphate per mgr of bacteria. E. $\mu M.10^3$ acid soluble ribose per mgr of bacteria. F. $\mu M.10^3$ acid soluble deoxyribose per mgr bacteria.

ally. On the contrary in the irradiated lot, although growth of the bacteria is not even slowed down in these conditions, the values for the total ATP increase during the first hour. They begin to *decrease* at the time DNA synthesis is resumed;

TABLE 2. ACID SOLUBLE FRACTION OF *E. coli* B AFTER U. V. IRRADIATION

Ratio of μmoles in the irradiated fractions compared to the controls

	Spectro- photo- metry (N Bases)	Pentoses		Phos- phate
		Deoxy- ribose	Ribose	
Desoxyguanosine........	150	142	—	—
Deoxyadenosine.........	170	168	—	—
Deoxycytidylic acid.....	250	210	—	250
Uridine diphosphate*....	205	230*	(150)	220
Deoxyuridine...........	105	158	—	163
Thymidylic acid........	300	240	—	—

* This compound was contaminated by 20–30% of some unidentified deoxyribose-containing substance.

TABLE 3. SPECIFIC ACTIVITY OF ACID SOLUBLE PURINES

Specific activity (counts/min/μM) of acid soluble purines of growing *E. coli* B

Constituents	T_0	T	I
Adenine....................	13.2	8.0	8.2
Deoxyguanosine............	14	10.9	10.6
Deoxyadenosine............	19	12	12.7
1) non identified*........	17.2	5.5	5.0
2) guanylic acid deoxy- guanylic acid.........	24.0	11.0	10.0
3) ATP or ADP deoxy- adenylic acid.........	31.5	9.5	9.0

T_0 : before irradiation.

T: non irradiated control, 30 minutes after T_0.

I: irradiated in log phase ($9.5.10^2$ ergs/mm²); 30 minutes after T_0.

* The hydrolysis of this compound gives adenine and guanine as well as an unidentified compound whose Rf corresponds to that of the ribosides and deoxyribosides of adenine and guanine.

after a time ATP increases again, when DNA synthesis and growth both stop.

This experiment was also done with *E. coli* B/r. In this case, the effect was much less pronounced (Figs. 9 and 10; Table 4).

3) Uridine diphosphate. This is the only other phosphorylated nucleotide besides ATP which has been found in the irradiated bacteria. It is quite possible that, although the acid soluble extraction took place at low temperature and extracts were rapidly neutralized afterwards, high energy phosphate bonds of other nucleotides underwent hydrolysis at their energy-rich linkage.

e) Accumulation of other components

1) The possibility of the presence of *abnormal* acid soluble material has not been critically studied so far. However, if such compounds do occur, they must be in extremely low quantities

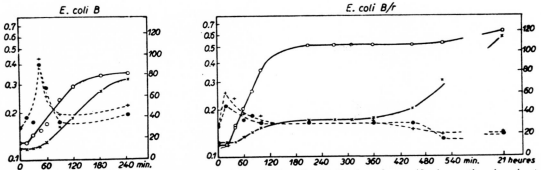

FIGURE 7. Metabolism of ATP after irradiation of *E. coli* B or B/r in the log phase. *Abscissae:* time in minutes. *Ordinates:* optical density and ATP in arbitrary units/mgr dry weight. Left: *E. coli* B 9.5.10² ergs/mm²; right: *E. coli* B/r 38.10² ergs/mm². Solid line: growth curves; dotted line: ATP. Circles: control; crosses: irradiated.

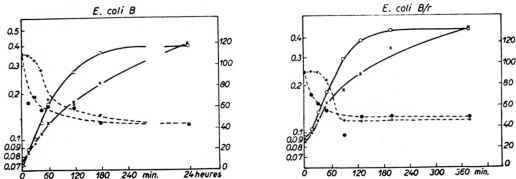

FIGURE 8. Metabolism of ATP after irradiation of *E. coli* B or B/r in the log phase (9.5.10² ergs/mm²). Key: same as Figure 7.

TABLE 4. EFFECT OF U.V. LIGHT ON THE METABOLISM OF ATP DURING ANAEROBIC GROWTH

| Hours After Irradiation | *E. coli* B | | | | *E. coli* B/r | | | | | |
| | Exp. II | | Exp. III | | Exp. I | | Exp. II | | Exp. III | |
	T	I	T	I	T	I	T	I	T	I
0	1.24	1.24	1.17	1.16	1.0	1.34	0.65	0.57	1.24	1.45
1	1.8	1.8	—	—	1.84	1.7	1.13	1.13	1.65	1.7
1.5	—	—	1.46	1.04	—	—	1.35	1.2	2.0	1.76
2	1.98	0.73	—	—	2.55	1.45	1.58	1.44	1.78	1.74
3	2.75	0.82	2.8	1.1	3.55	2.2	2.2	1.52	2.6	1.8
4	—	—	—	—	3.7	2.0	—	—	2.2	1.8
4.5a	3.5	1.39	2.8	2.0	—	—	—	—	—	—
7	—	—	2.3	2.0	—	—	—	—	—	—

γ ATP for 20 ml bacterial suspension.
T: controls; I: irradiated (9.5.10² ergs/mm²).

because no abnormal U.V. absorbing spots were ever found after irradiation; they may have escaped detection on account of identical physical and chemical properties to those of the controls.

2) A certain number of unidentified spots were invariably found on the chromatograms. *Compound X_1*: This compound has an Rf value (Solvent I) of 0.25–0.29. It is fluorescent at 253.7 mµ and 366 mµ and has a ninhydrin reaction (Moore and Stein, 1948) about four times higher in the

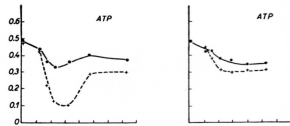

FIGURE 9. Metabolism of ATP in irradiated bacteria grown in anaerobiosis (9.5.10² ergs/mm²). Left: *E. coli* B, right: *E. coli* B/r. *Abscissae:* time in minutes. *Ordinates:* µgr ATP per mgr dry weight.

irradiated material than in the controls. Hydrolysis in 6N HCl liberated three compounds having Rf values comparable to glutamic acid, alanine and glycine and a fourth unidentified spot. *Compound X_3*: the Rf value (Solvent I) is 0.76–0.78; there is no specific absorption in the U.V. but a fluorescence at 263.7 and 366 mµ. There is no pentose nor phosphate but the Moore and Stein reaction (ninhydrin) is positive and 3.5 times higher in the irradiated bacteria. This compound has not been further analysed.

f) Effects of U.V. on lysates of *Micrococcus lysodeikticus*

When *Micrococcus lysodeikticus* are collected from the surface a Roux flask and suspended in a hypotonic acetate buffer (.04 to .05 mgr DNA/cc) and submitted to the action of lysozyme at 37°C (0.3 mgr/cc) the bacteria are completely lysed within a few minutes during which the viscosity of the lysate increases sharply; after having passed by a maximum value after eight or ten minutes the viscosity decreases slowly.

The high viscosity of the lysates was attributed by Frisch Niggemeyer (1953) to the presence of DNA; if deoxyribonuclease is added, the viscosity immediately drops to very low values. Although we have confirmed this point, the interpretation of the high viscosity is somewhat more complex because we observed that, whereas trypsin or ribonuclease were without action, hyaluronidase, on the contrary, also decreased this viscosity. It is thus probable that besides DNA the macromolecular structure responsible for the high viscosity contains other substances, the exact significance of which would need further study.

If the whole bacteria are irradiated and lysed immediately afterwards, viscosity can be measured within ten minutes with the following results: After 1.000 ergs/mm² the viscosity has dropped to 50 per cent of its original value (the same effect can also be obtained after 25 10³ r X rays; Table 5). Dosage of X rays which reduce the viscosity by 50 per cent also strongly inhibit DNA synthesis if the bacteria are cultured in liquid broth (Table 6).

TABLE 5. EFFECTS OF U.V. OR X RAYS ON THE SPECIFIC VISCOSITY OF LYSATES FROM *Micrococcus lysodeikticus*

U.V. Ergs mm²..	165	330	990	1980
% remaining specif. visc..	57 (±15)	66 (±6.5)	41 (±4.1)	18 (±2.6)
X rays (r.10³)	12.2	24.4	48.8	162
% remaining specif. visc..	59 (±6.3)	48 (±3.1)	46 (±5)	±8

TABLE 6. GROWTH AND DNA SYNTHESIS IN *Micrococcus lysodeiktikus* AFTER X IRRADIATION

	Exp. 1: 50.10³ r				Exp. II 75.10³ r			
Incubation time (min.)	Optical density of culture		DNA μgr. in 10 cc culture		Incubation time (min.)	Optical density of culture		DNA μgr. in 10 cc culture	
	Contr.	Irrad.	Contr.	Irrad.		Contr.	Irrad.	Contr.	Irrad.
0	0.325	0.325	13.	14.	0	.380	.380	7.4	8.8
100	0.440	0.395	25.	14.5	80	0.400	0.390	11.6	7.9
200	0.730	.520	34.5	17.0	130	0.480	.450	13.6	6.7

DISCUSSION

The following facts have been established:

a) U.V. irradiation leaving only 20 per cent survivors does not immediately inhibit growth, ribonucleic acid or protein synthesis.

b) On the contrary, the synthesis of DNA is blocked immediately, but not definitively, and nucleotides closely related to DNA precursors accumulate during this period.

c) Energy-rich phosphate compounds (ATP, UDP) also accumulate during this time.

d) Dosages which inhibit DNA synthesis also determine structural abnormalities in high molecular compounds of some bacterial species, which may be observed within a few minutes from the time of irradiation.

1) Effect of irradiation on macromolecular structures containing DNA

The very rapid effect of radiations on a cellular structure probably containing DNA strongly suggests that this compound, or one closely related to it, is involved in early radiation damage. Experiments by Herriott (1951) on the effects of nitrogen or S mustards on *E. coli*, where very similar metabolic alteration to the ones presented in this paper were observed, could also be interpreted as an effect of the mustard on deoxyribonucleic acid. Cytological observations with the electron microscope (Kellenberger, 1952; Hartman, Payne and Mudd, 1955) show that already 15 minutes after U.V. irradiation of *E. coli*, nuclei show clumping, which appears to be reversible if the bacteria survive, but which is followed by fragmentation of the chromatin in those which do not. Ultracentrifugation of homogenates of *E. coli* B/r show that 90 minutes after X irradiation, there does appear to be a fragmentation of the DNA molecule (Billen and Volkin, 1954) as evidenced by ultracentrifugation.

Although these arguments cannot be considered absolutely conclusive, a certain number of other facts point towards similar conclusions.

DNA metabolism can be specifically inhibited in thymineless mutants of *E. coli*: using the strain 15 T⁻, Cohen and Barner, (1954) observed that death in the absence of thymine was identical to death by U. V. irradiation of the same bacteria, grown in the presence of thymine and was, in both cases, caused by the specific inhibition of the synthesis of DNA; thymine deficiency also produces elongated bacteria.

Work with bacteriophage has shown that everything remains in the irradiated bacteria (at least for the first few hours) which is necessary for the synthesis of bacteriophage (Labaw, Mosley and Wyckoff, 1953). On the contrary, irradiated bacteriophage will generally not multiply in normal cells. As the DNA is almost the only part of the phage which penetrates into the bacteria, one cannot escape the conclusion that DNA itself has been altered and that it is for this reason that its autocatalytic synthesis has been inhibited.

Cohen has furthermore shown (1948) that infection of normal bacteria with irradiated bacteriophage leads to an accumulation of purine and pyrimidine compounds which is not followed by DNA synthesis, whereas RNA synthesis remains normal.

Photochemical action on some DNA containing structure is perhaps not the only way abnormal DNA could be induced to appear in a cell. It cannot, on the basis of the present findings, be excluded that some abnormal precursor for DNA synthesis arises as a consequence of irradiation; such a precursor could become incorporated in DNA and form a DNA analogue incapable of autocatalytic synthesis.

Minute amounts of certain analogues like hydroxyuridine are capable of inhibiting the growth of certain mutants of *E. coli* (Slotnik, Visser and Rothenberg, 1953; Beltz and Visser, 1955); however, such a mechanism would not be expected to inhibit DNA synthesis immediately.

2) The nature of DNA synthesis in irradiated bacteria

A second problem which arises is that of the apparent reversibility of the effect of irradiation on DNA synthesis. Something, which might be analogous to what happens in multiplicity reactivation of irradiated bacteriophage appears to take place. After a lag period, during which the U.V. absorption of the bacteria infected with more than one abnormal phage increases faster than when the phage are normal (probable accumulation of precursors), the synthesis of phage DNA is resumed; even if some normal infecting particles remain among abnormal ones, they cannot reproduce before the damaged ones have been reactivated. This seems to indicate that *all* the DNA particles have to duplicate at the same time, and such a mechanism might explain the complete and immediate inhibition of DNA synthesis in noninfected irradiated bacteria. If this interpretation is correct, very few abnormal particles (perhaps only one in the case of bacteriophage) would suffice to inhibit the synthesis of the remaining normal molecules (Cohen and Arbogast, 1950). In multiplicity reactivation the phage irradiated *in vitro* seems to give rise to a normal progeny and mutants can only be obtained from phage irradiated inside the bacterial cell (Latarjet, 1949). When bacteria are irradiated, it still remains to be established whether the DNA which is synthesized after the inhibition period is normal DNA. A direct answer to this question could be given by the study of a transforming principle extracted from irradiated bacteria. The formation of abnormal DNA might be the cause of mutations.

If the DNA molecule is altered through the irradiation (deamination, rupture of the bonds followed by abnormal restitution or otherwise), the reduplication of the complementary chains to this DNA (if it is still possible) could only lead to the formation of some complementary and abnormal DNA. This might be the origin of some late hereditary alteration of some metabolic step, that is, a mutation. We do not believe that the mechanism of gene mutation is such a simple one. If so, the irradiation of a bacteriophage or a virus *in vitro* would be susceptible to determine such alteration. On the contrary, to induce mutations in such simple systems the irradiation has to take place inside the host cell; this has been shown for bacteriophage (Latarjet, 1949) and plant viruses (Kausch and Stubbe, 1939). It is possible that to develop a mutation the altered DNA molecule has to go through its reduplication process which only occurs inside the cell. Actually it has been shown that several cell divisions are necessary for all the mutations to become apparent (zero and end point mutation) in irradiated bacterial cells (Demerec and Latarjet, 1948).

3) Accumulation of DNA precursors

The interpretation of the accumulation of deoxyribonucleotides and nucleosides during the period of inhibition of DNA synthesis is obvious: these acid soluble compounds are related very closely or even constitute a reserve of building blocks for the formation of new DNA. This is not for lack of precursors that the DNA synthesis has stopped in irradiated bacteria. The mechanism through which these building blocks are put together is not known, but one can tentatively accept the hypothesis of Watson and Crick to explain the reduplication of the DNA molecule and imagine that this is done through a biochemical mechanism which is analogous to the one found by Grunberg-Manago, Ortiz and Ochoa (1956) for RNA: diphosphorylated nucleotides would be the necessary precursor. Kornberg and his coworkers (1956) have found evidence for the synthesis of polydesoxyribosenucleotides from triphosphonucleotides.

We have found no di- or tri-phosphorylated deoxyribonucleotides but, as we have suggested, the conditions of extraction may not have been favorable. The only diphosphonucleotide which we did find is uridinediphosphate.

The occurrence of UDP in the normal and irradiated extract may mean that this substance is a precursor of thymine. Cohen and Barner (1954) have shown that uracil derivatives are capable of sustaining growth of the thymineless mutant *E. coli* (15 T$^-$). Friedkin and De Wayne Roberts (1955) have also arrived at the conclusion that UDP serves as a precursor for thymidine in bone marrow and chick embryo.

The relatively high concentration of thymidilic acid found may mean that the other precursors of DNA which accumulates to a somewhat lesser extent and which have a common nitrogen base with RNA may be used for RNA synthesis or may be related to RNA precursors. No free bases have been found in the chromatograms; this suggests that they are not direct precursors of DNA; neither have we found any 4-amino-5-imidazolcarboxamide.

The accumulation of amino acids or of some unidentified constituents (X_1 and X_3) resembling peptides was consistently noted (sometimes 3 to 4 times more abundant in the irradiated bacteria). This might be explained by an inhibition of the synthesis of some specific nucleoprotein. As the amino acids found to accumulate (glycine, alanine and glutamic acid) can be considered as precursors of purines or pyrimidines, their accumulation might just as well be a direct consequence of the inhibition of DNA synthesis and indicate perhaps that these compounds are directly involved in DNA metabolism.

4) Metabolism of ATP

We have shown a definite correlation between the utilization of ATP and the synthesis of DNA.

In *aerobiosis*, the *accumulation* of ATP during growth of irradiated bacteria must mean that the utilisation of this compound is equal to its synthesis during the period in which DNA synthesis is blocked; the isotope measurements indicate that ATP metabolism remains normal. This accumulation of ATP ceases as soon as DNA starts to be synthesized again.

If, in *anaerobic* conditions, ATP concentration begins to be identical in normal and irradiated bacteria, although these do not synthesize DNA, it must mean that irradiation has some effect either on ATP synthesis or on its maintenance in the absence of oxygen; when DNA synthesis starts again, ATP diminishes in the irradiated bacteria.

It is striking that this effect is much more pronounced in *E. coli* B than in *E. coli* B/r. The chief difference between these two strains is that *E. coli* B/r is a radioresistant mutant selected from the B strain (Witkin, 1946) and that it contains more DNA per bacterium (Morse and Carter 1946). Two experiments of Brachet, concerning the role of the cell nucleus or of DNA on anaerobic phosphorylations, are very suggestive; one of the earliest disfunctions which occur in an enucleated amoeba is the increased loss of ATP in anaerobic conditions (Brachet, 1954). When frog embryos develop as a consequence of the fertilization of normal eggs with spermatozoa treated by a nitrogen mustard (methyl-bis-β-chlorethylamine) one observes that the fusion of both nuclei is often incomplete and that the DNA synthesis in the newly formed cells is strikingly abnormal. Development stops at the blastula stage; when the embryos are kept in *aerobic* conditions they accumulate ATP. In anaerobiosis, these lethal embryos lose their ATP much more rapidly than the controls.

Thus the absence of a nucleus or some nuclear abnormality related to DNA metabolism affects anaerobic phosphorylation. The factor which is lacking in nonnucleated, nitrogen mustard treated or irradiated cells may be a common one and one hypothesis put forward by Brachet, at least in the first two instances, is that the anaerobic deficiency in ATP metabolism is caused by a lack of coenzyme probably resulting from the nuclear disturbance.

5) Survival

The relationship between DNA metabolism and survival of the cells is a difficult one to estimate in the cell population we have been working with: U.V. may affect other vital cell mechanisms besides DNA metabolism. But if this function is interfered with specifically by depriving a cell population of a specific precursor for DNA which it cannot synthesize, the cells die and, in the case of *Thermobacterium acidophilus*, they die after having developed into long filaments containing very few nuclei. If such filaments are given thymidine, the nuclei divide and cytoplasmic fission gives rise to normal cells (Jeener and Jeener, 1955). Cohen and Barner (1954), had similar results with *E. coli* 15 T⁻: the state of *unbalanced growth* which develops in the cells whose DNA metabolism is specifically blocked, seems to determine some irreversible alterations from which the cell cannot recover; after a certain time, even when thymine is restituted and DNA synthesis is resumed, the cell cannot survive.

Although an effect of U.V. light on the structure of DNA is a probable cause for the inhibition of its autocatalytic synthesis, one should mot exclude the possibility that there may be other causes of death. Filamentous bacteria do occur as a consequence of a great number of various treatments and the mechanism of their induction has but very rarely been studied critically.

REFERENCES

BELTZ, R. E., and VISSER, D. W., 1955, Growth inhibition of *E. coli* by new thymidine analogs. J. Amer. Chem. Soc. 77: 736–738.

BILLEN, D., and VOLKIN, E., 1954, The effect of X rays on the macromolecular organisation of *E. coli*. J. Bact. 67: 191–197.

BRACHET, J., 1954, Constitution anormale du noyau et métabolisme de l'embryon chez les Batraciens. Arch. Biol. 65: 1–72.

1956, Recherches sur les interactions biochimiques entre le noyau et le cytoplasme chez les organismes unicellulaires. I. *Amoeba proteus*. Biochim. biophys. Acta 18: 247–268.

CERIOTTI, G., 1952, A microchemical determination of desoxyribonucleic acid. J. Biol. Chem. 198: 297–303.

COHEN, S. S., 1948, The synthesis of bacterial viruses. I. The synthesis of nucleic acid and proteins in *E. coli* B infected with T 2r⁺ bacteriophage. J. Biol. Chem. 174: 281–293.

COHEN, S. S. and ARBOGAST, R., 1950, Chemical studies of host virus interactions. VII. The mutual reactivation of T 2r⁺ virus inactivated by U.V. light and the synthesis of desoxyribose nucleic acid. J. Exp. Med. 91: 637–650.

COHEN, S. S. and BARNER, H. D., 1955, Enzymatic adaptation in a thymine requiring strain of *E. coli.* J. Bact. *69:* 59–66.

DEMEREC, M. and LATARJET, R., 1949, Mutations in bacteria induced by radiations. Cold Spr. Harb. Symp. Quant. Biol. *9:* 38–56.

ERRERA, M., 1954, Induction of filamentous forms in U.V. irradiated *E. coli* B. Brit. J. Radiol. *27:* 76–80.

FRIEDKIN, M. and DE WAYNE ROBERTS, 1955, In vitro formation of thymidine from uracil deoxyriboside, an amino pterin sensitive reaction. Federation Proc. *11:* 215.

FRISCH NIGGEMEYER, W., 1953. Freisetzung hochviskoser Desoxyribonucleinsaüre aus Bakterien unter der Einfluss von Lysozym. Enzymol. *16:* 72–79.

GRUENBERG-MANAGO, M., ORTIZ, P. J. and OCHOA, S., 1956, I. Polynucleotide phosphorylase of *Azotobacter vinelandi*. Biochim. biophys. Acta *20:* 269–285.

HARTMAN, P. E., PAYNE, J. I. and MUDD, S., 1955, Cytological analysis of U.V. irradiated *E. coli* I. Cytology of *E. coli* K 12 a nonlysogenic derivative. J. Bact. *70:* 531–539.

HERRIOTT, R. M., 1951, Nucleic acid synthesis in mustard gas treated *E. coli.* J. Gen. Physiol. *34:* 761–764.

JEENER, R., and JEENER, H., 1952, Cytological study of *Thermobacterium acidophilus* R 26 cultured in absence of deoxyribosides or uracil. Exp. Cell Res. *3:* 675–680.

KANAZIR, D., 1954, Accumulation d'acide thymidilique chez *E. coli* après irradiation U.V. Biochim biophys. Acta *13:* 589–590.

——1954, Accumulation de déxoyguanosine chez *E. coli* B après irradiation ultraviolette. Biochim. biophys. Acta *15:* 592–593.

——1955, Contribution à l'étude des effets de l'irradiation U.V. sur le métabolisme d'*E. coli*. Thése de Doctorat spécial. Université de Bruxelles, 106 pp.

KANAZIR, D., and ERRERA, M., 1953, Teneur en adénosine triphosphate de *E. coli* après irradiation U.V. Biochim. biophys. Acta 11: 451–452.

——1954, Métabolisme des acides nucléiques chez *E. coli* B après irradiation. Biochim. biophys. Acta *14:* 62–66.

KAUSCH, G. A., and STUBBE, H., 1940, Frage der Entstehung Röntgenstrahlen induzierte Mutationen beim Tabak mosaik Virus Protein. Naturwiss. *28:* 824.

KELLENBERGER, E., 1952, Aspects cytologiques d'*E. coli* irradiés. Experientia *8:* 99–101.

KELNER, A., 1953, Growth, respiration and nucleic acid synthesis in U.V. irradiated and photoreactivated *E. coli* J. Bact. *65:* 252–262.

KORNBERG, A., LEHMAN, I. R., and SIMMS, E. S., 1956, Polydesoxynucleotide synthesis by enzymes of *E. coli*. Federation Proc. *15:* 291.

LABAW, L. W., MOSLEY, V. M., and WYCKOFF, R. R., 1953, Development of phage in X-ray inactivated bacteria. J. Bact. *65:* 330–336.

LATARJET, R., 1949, Mutation induite chez un virus par irradiation U.V. de cellules infectées. C.R. Acad. Sci. Paris *227:* 1354–1357.

MARKHAM, R., and SMITH, J. D., 1951, Chromatographic studies on nucleic acids. 4. The nucleic acid of the turnip yellow mosaic virus including a note on the nucleic acid of the tomato bushy stunt virus. Biochem. J. *49:* 401–406.

MARSHAK, A., and VOGEL, M. J., 1951, Microdeterminations of purines and pyrimidines in biological material. J. Biol. Chem. *189:* 597–605.

MCELROY, W. D., 1951, Phosphate bond energy and bioluminescence. Phosphorus Metabolism *1:* 585–601.

MOORE, S., and STEIN, W. H., 1948, Photometric ninhydrin method for use in the chromatography of amino acid. J. Biol. Chem. *176:* 367–388.

MORSE, M. L., and CARTER, C. E., 1946, The synthesis of nucleic acids in cultures of *E. coli* strain B and B/r. J. Bact. *58:* 317–326.

SCHNEIDER, W. C., 1945, Phosphorus compounds in animal tissues. I. Extraction and estimation of desoxypentose nucleic acid and of pentose nucleic acid. J. Biol. Chem. *161:* 293–303.

SLOTNIK, I. J., VISSER, D. W., ROTHENBERG, S. C., 1953, Growth inhibition of purine requiring mutants of *E. coli* by 5- hydroxyuridine. J. Biol. Chem. *203:* 647–652.

STREHLER, B. L., and TOTTER, J. R., 1952, Firefly luminescence in the study of energy transfer mechanism. I. Substrate and enzyme determination. Arch. Biochem. Biophys. *40:* 28–41.

WITKIN, E. M., 1946, Inherited differences in sensitivity to radiations in *E. coli* strain B. Proc. Nat. Acad. Sci. Wash. *32:* 59.

WYATT, G. R., 1951, Purine and pyrimidine composition of deoxypentose nucleic acids. Biochem. J. *48:* 584–590.

WYSS, O., HAAS, F., CLARK, J. B., and STONE, W. S., 1950, Some effects of ultraviolet irradiations on microorganisms. J. Cell. Comp. Physiol. *35* (suppl.): 133–144.

DISCUSSION

KELNER: In recent experiments we have extended previous observations on the growth of *E. coli* B/r after ultraviolet irradiation. The findings may have a bearing on the mechanisms controlling rates of cell growth.

As it has been shown, if cells in the exponential growth phase are irradiated, they continue to grow exponentially, that is, synthesize protein and RNA, but at a rate lower than that of the unirradiated control. This immediate inhibition of growth rate is proportional to the dose. This first period of post-U.V. growth, which can be called post-U.V. phase 1, continues under the conditions of our experiment for 60 ± 2 or 3 minutes, at which point the growth suddenly shifts to a lower rate but is still exponential. This post-U.V. phase 2 continues, as far as we know, until growth of dark survivors ends the experiment.

The time when the growth rate shifts is almost dose independent, and the shift is so sudden that one thinks of some trigger reaction. The inhibition in growth in post-U.V. phase 2 is proportional to the dose. At sufficiently high doses, inhibition is almost complete.

It should be pointed out that these phenomena show that in addition to the immediate inhibition of DNA synthesis, there is a lesser but also immediate, as well as a delayed inhibition of RNA and protein synthesis. All these inhibitions are photoreversible.

ERRERA: We are quite well aware that growth of irradiated bacteria, especially with high dosages, shows a complex response; and the cause of the secondary inhibition (after 60 minutes) should certainly be looked into. I do not know of any studies on DNA or RNA metabolism at this post-irradiation time with dosages following which this break occurs in the growth curve. However, some respiration measurements from Dr. Hollaender's laboratory could suggest that the slowing down of growth might be the response to an inhibition of respiratory activity which only becomes apparent after a certain time following irradiation (in this case, X rays were used). On the other hand, this secondary inhibition of growth could also be an indication that the irradiated bacteria begin to die after having undergone their first division, and such an effect would become apparent approximately at the time when Dr. Kelner observes the break in his curves. These two hypotheses should be checked experimentally.

SZYBALSKI: The biochemical studies of Dr. G. Falcone and myself on the effect of chilling on the induction of synchronized cell division in *Bacillus megaterium* were performed along similar lines and with analogous inconclusive results. Cell division was completely arrested by the transfer of the actively multiplying culture from 34° to 15°C. This effect, however, could not be accounted for on the basis of the measured effects of cold on the syntheses of the major cell components and their intermediates, all of which were affected to a considerably lesser extent. Protein synthesis seemed to be the most affected with RNA, DNA and dry weight increasing at comparatively higher rates. Neither a particular reaction responsible for the almost complete arrest of cellular and nuclear division nor an elucidation of the causative relationship between the two was found.

ERRERA: Ultraviolet and cold treatment obviously have different mechanisms in arresting the growth of bacteria. It would be reasonable to suppose that low temperature depresses the respiratory activity. In these conditions one would expect, as is the case in starvation, that the available high energy phosphates would be used preferentially for nucleoprotein synthesis rather than for the synthesis of less essential protein constituents.

HAUROWITZ: It would be interesting to know whether the turnover of proteins is inhibited by X-irradiation like that of DNA. Experiments of Steinberg (Bethesda) have shown that protein breakdown is not simple autolysis, but that it is just as specific as protein synthesis, since it can be inhibited by amino acid analogues.

ERRERA: Studies on protein metabolism after ultraviolet and X-irradiation have been concerned mostly with amino acid incorporation. It is hardly possible to generalize from these findings, but on the whole in microorganisms there usually is a slight inhibition of protein synthesis, which, as our dry weight curve shows and as Kelner has pointed out, starts immediately after irradiation. Induced enzyme synthesis is more specifically inhibited by ultraviolet light.

As for the protein breakdown, I do not know of any work where it has been systematically studied, but it is possible that one could explain certain cases of increased protein synthesis (that is, of globin synthesis in X-irradiated spleen) by an inhibition of the breakdown of this substance.

BRAUN: In connection with this discussion it may be of interest to mention some recent data on the effects of thymine deprivation which were obtained almost independently by Dr. Roger Weinberg, of my former group at Camp Detrick, and Drs. C. A. Coughlin and E. A. Adelberg of the University of California. They employed Seymour Cohen's thymine-requiring strain of *E. coli* which permits control of the rate of DNA turnover by adjustment of thymine concentration in the medium. With this material they observed increased mutation rates from streptomycin sensitivity to streptomycin resistance (Weinberg) and from histidine requirement to non-requirement (Coughlin and Adelberg) following temporary exposure to suboptimal amounts of thymine. It appears possible that such mutagenic effects may be due partly to a dissynchronization of the rates of DNA synthesis in relation to protein synthesis.

Chromatographic Fractionation of Deoxyribonucleic Acids with Special Emphasis on the Transforming Factor of Pneumococcus[1]

AARON BENDICH,[2] HERBERT B. PAHL[3] AND SAM M. BEISER[4]

The Sloan-Kettering Division of Cornell University Medical College and the College of Physicians and Surgeons, Columbia University, New York

In the 85 years which have elapsed since Miescher first reported the isolation of the acidic substance "nuclein" from the nuclei of pus cells, several independent approaches have clearly indicated that deoxyribonucleic acid (DNA), in combination with protein, is the primary chemical material of which chromosomes and genes are constituted. Hotchkiss (1955) has recently summarized in an admirable fashion the chemical, cytological and genetic evidence for the role of DNA as an hereditary determinant. The evidence which is most impressive to the biochemist has come from the findings that the DNA isolated from one strain of a microorganism can transmit heritable properties to another strain of the same microorganism (Avery *et al.*, 1944; Ephrussi-Taylor, 1955a, 1955b; Hotchkiss, 1954; Hotchkiss and Marmur, 1954). This phenomenon has been termed bacterial transformation. It would appear that DNA may not be the only substance capable of carrying genetic information (Fraenkel-Conrat, 1956; Gierer and Schramm, 1956; Lippincott and Commoner, 1956), since it has been reported that plant viruses (Cohen, 1955; Markham, 1953), and certain animal viruses (Ada and Perry, 1955a, b; Schwerdt, 1954) do not contain detectable DNA. However, the absence of DNA in biological systems is relatively infrequent, and when present it is believed to be responsible for the genetic function.

A necessary attribute of hereditary determinants is that they control numerous biological characteristics. For chemical substances to serve in this capacity they must, *a priori*, possess a high degree of complexity or multiplicity. The deoxy-ribonucleic acids appear to satisfy this requirement because, despite the fact that they usually contain only four types of nucleotides, they are often found to possess molecular weights of several millions.

The size of these molecules makes it possible for them to possess a great many different nucleotide sequences within a given molecule, thus giving rise to different regions or combinations of regions which may be endowed with structural (or biological) specificity. Nearly every possible combination of dinucleotides has been identified in enzymatic digests of DNA (Sinsheimer, 1954; 1955). In addition, the various molecules of DNA in a given cell may differ among themselves, not only in composition or sequence, but in shape and size as well. The findings that several independent activities are associated with the bacterial transforming factor may be considered as evidence for intermolecular differences among DNA molecules, whereas the occurrence of linkage in transformation (Hotchkiss and Marmur, 1954) might indicate intramolecular heterogeneity.

The present account deals with an analysis of the heterogeneity of transforming and other DNA as revealed by ion exchange chromatography, and includes a discussion of the significance of the findings in terms of genetic mechanisms.

HETEROGENEITY OF DNA

The evidence for the heterogeneity of DNA has recently been reviewed (Bendich *et al.*, 1956; Chargaff, 1955). The techniques which have been employed to demonstrate this inhomogeneity have included differential centrifugation (Bendich, 1952; Shooter and Butler, 1955), dissociation of nucleoproteins (Chargaff, *et al.*, 1953; Lucy and Butler, 1956) chromatography on columns of histone (Brown and Martin, 1955; Brown and Watson, 1953; Ephrussi-Taylor, 1955b), substituted cellulose (Bendich, *et al.*, 1955) and methylated globin (Lerman, 1955) and differential solubility in alkali (Sherratt and Thomas, 1953). In general the procedures have been based on differential solubility and differences, presumably, in the strengths of the salt linkages which bind the component DNA to the protein or column matrix.

[1] This investigation was supported by funds from the American Cancer Society, National Cancer Institute, National Institutes of Health, Public Health Service (Grant #C-471), and from the Atomic Energy Commission (Contract #AT,(30-1),910). The investigation was also aided by a contract Nonr 266(40) between the Office of Naval Research and Columbia University.

[2] Sloan-Kettering Division of Cornell University Medical College.

[3] Fellow of the National Cancer Institute of the Public Health Service; Sloan-Kettering Division of Cornell University Medical College.

[4] Department of Microbiology, College of Physicians and Surgeons, Columbia University.

Fractions of DNA obtained by the application of these procedures have been shown to differ with respect to such properties as sedimentability in a centrifugal field (Shooter and Butler, 1955), base composition (Bendich, 1952; 1956; Brown and Martin, 1955; Brown and Watson, 1953; Chargaff, et al., 1953; Chargaff, 1955; Lucy and Butler, 1954), metabolic activity and chromatographic behavior (Bendich, 1952; Bendich et al., 1953; 1955). Taken together, these results lead to the conclusion that the DNA as originally isolated is a mixture of differently constituted molecules. In view of the fact that evidence of heterogeneity is obtained regardless of the method of isolation or fractionation employed, it may be inferred that DNA as it exists within the typical cell probably consists of a whole spectrum of different types of molecules.

The DNA of T2r (Brown and Martin, 1955) and T6r and T6r+ bacteriophage (present communication) have also been found to be heterogeneous. In these cases the phage particles are not only obtained free of enzymes which might possibly lead to the degradation of DNA, but the nucleic acids themselves are highly resistant to the action of nucleodepolymerases (Cohen, 1956).

CHROMATOGRAPHY ON SUBSTITUTED CELLULOSE COLUMNS

The polyanionic character of DNA at neutral and alkaline pH values makes it suitable for fractionation on anion exchangers. A very promising anionic column matrix found (Bendich, et al., 1955) has been the base-substituted cellulose derivative ECTEOLA. This was prepared (Peterson and Sober, 1956) from sodium cellulose and a mixture of epichlorohydrin and triethanolamine (see Fig. 1 for the preparation involved). By varying the quantity of triethanolamine used in proportion to the other constituents, preparations of ECTEOLA may be made which have from about one to four nitrogen atoms per 100 glucose residues in the cellulose fiber, and which, accordingly,

PREPARATION OF ECTEOLA-CELLULOSE

EPICHLOROHYDRIN TRIETHANOLAMINE
(Peterson and Sober)

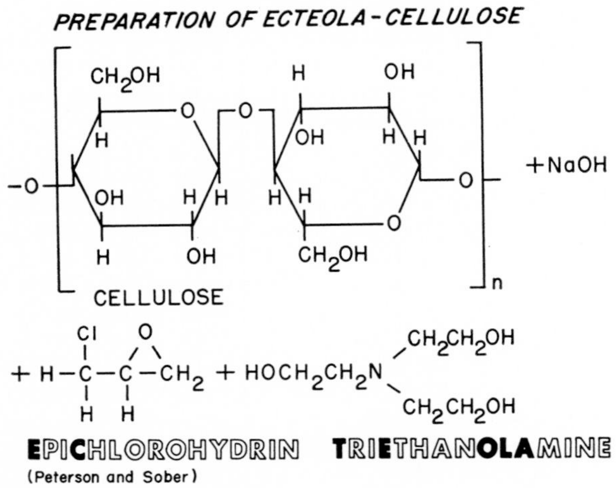

FIGURE 1. Preparation of ECTEOLA from cellulose.

exhibit varying affinities for DNA. Depending on which preparation of ECTEOLA is used, from one to ten mg of DNA can be adsorbed by one gm of exchanger. The elution profile which is subsequently obtained depends upon both the capacity of the ECTEOLA as well as on the source of the DNA. Conversely, cellulose and cation exchange cellulose derivatives lack affinity for DNA.

For chromatography on ECTEOLA, as customarily carried out, a solution of DNA in 0.01 M phosphate buffer (pH 7) is allowed to percolate slowly through a column of the exchanger; unless the capacity is exceeded, all the DNA is removed from solution. The column is then routinely washed with excess 0.01 M phosphate (pH 7). Neutral solutions of NaCl of continuously increasing concentration (gradient elution) are passed through slowly, followed by a solution of ammonia of increasing concentration in either 0.5 or 2.0 M NaCl. The eluates are collected in test tubes and the amount of nucleic acid in each tube is determined by quantitative ultra-violet spectrophotometry and by a sensitive colorimetric test, the Ceriotti (1955) reaction. This test, which measures as little as one to two μg of DNA, gives a color which is proportional to the amount of purine-bound deoxyribose present. The chromatographic profiles are drawn by plotting the optical density value (optical density at 260 mμ multiplied by the volume of the fraction in ml) for each tube against the tube number or against the concentration of eluting solute or both.

A typical chromatogram obtained with a standard preparation of calf thymus DNA prepared by the method of Schwander and Signer (1950) is shown in Figure 2. Duplicate chromatograms obtained with DNA's from the same source are reproducible (see Fig. 3). It can be seen that DNA obtained from the same source (leukocytes from a patient with granulocytic leukemia) by two different procedures (Kay, et al., 1952, on the one hand, and NaCl extraction followed by chloroform-octanol deproteinization on the other hand) give essentially identical patterns. As shown in Figure 4, DNA prepared from leukocytes obtained at different times from a patient with chronic lymphatic leukemia give quite reproducible patterns.

The chromatograms of DNA from different sources vary, and each of the following can be distinguished by its profile: calf thymus, human leukemic leukocytes, E. coli, B. cereus, pneumococcus, T6r phage, T6r+ phage, and spleen, intestine, kidney and brain of the rat. The patterns obtained with DNA from rat brain and kidney and from T6r and T6r+ bacteriophage are given in Figure 5. The elution schedule was the same for all of these materials. Alterations in the DNA from calf thymus following treatment with mutagenic agents (nitrogen mustard and electron irradiation) are reflected in the chromatographic profiles as shown in Figure 6 (compare Fig. 6 with

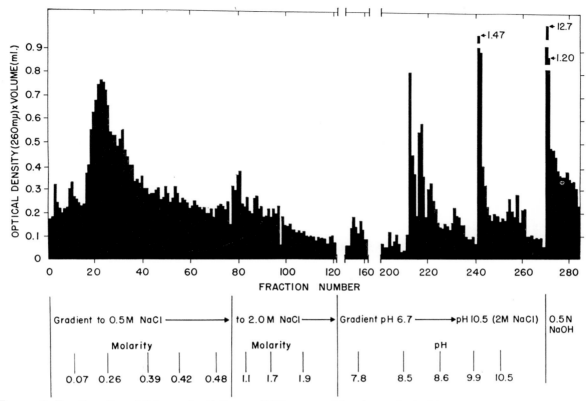

FIGURE 2. Fractionation of 2.1 mg of calf thymus DNA prepared by the method of Schwander-Signer (1950) on 0.5 gm column of ECTEOLA (0.8 × 5.5 cm). The DNA and eluting solutions were made up in 0.01 M phosphate buffer, pH 7 (from Bendich, et al., 1955).

Fig. 2). *E. coli* DNA containing the unnatural base 5-bromouracil gives a pattern different from that of the normal (Bendich, et al., 1956). These findings lead to the conclusion that the differences in the chromatographic patterns reflect differences in the DNA molecules themselves, and are not primarily due to either chromatographic manipulations or to variations in preparative procedures.

This chromatographic procedure is adaptable[5] and flexible, and possesses a considerable degree of resolution. It was therefore applied to studies with biologically active DNA obtained from pneumococcus, the transforming factor. These studies are discussed in detail in a later section.

BASIS OF THE ION-EXCHANGE FRACTIONATION OF DNA ON ECTEOLA

Although the exact basis for the fractionation of DNA by ECTEOLA is not known, one facet of the selection process appears to be the molecular sizes of the DNA molecules. An experiment was carried out in which a mixture of thymidylic, deoxyadenylic, deoxyguanylic and deoxycytidylic acids was added to a column of ECTEOLA. Upon washing the column with 0.01 M phosphate buffer, pH 7, the mixture of mononucleotides was

[5] The procedure has also been applied to ribonucleic acids and enzymatically synthesized polyribonucleotides (unpublished experiments).

quantitatively removed. In another experiment, a deoxyribonuclease digest of calf thymus DNA was added to the column. Such digests have been found to contain about 17 per cent of mono- and dinucleotides, and appreciable amounts of oligonucleotides of the order of hepta- or octanucleotides (Sinsheimer, 1954). The chromatographic pattern which was obtained is shown in Figure 7. Ninety-seven per cent of the digest was eluted before a NaCl concentration of 0.19–0.20 M was reached. It may therefore be concluded that DNA fractions which are eluted at higher NaCl concentrations would be larger than octanucleotides. From these and similar experiments, it appears that the chromatography depends, at least in part, on the molecular size or state of aggregation of the DNA. Preliminary light scattering studies of fractions obtained from calf thymus DNA have shown increases in molecular weight as the tube number of the fraction increases (M. Rosoff, unpub.). On the other hand, sedimentation studies on fractions of DNA from pneumococcus do not show this correlation (D. F. Bradley, unpub.). However, sedimentation studies on the material which is eluted in the first large peak have shown that the early portion of this peak consists largely of low molecular weight material. The significance of this observation will be discussed in connection with the experiments carried out with pneumo-

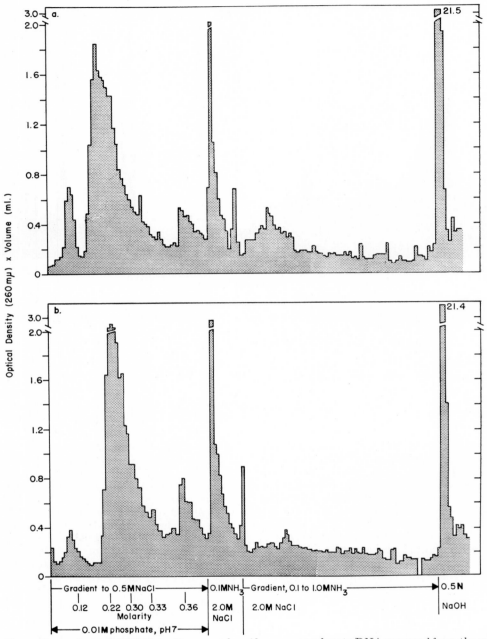

FIGURE 3. Chromatography on ECTEOLA of two samples of human granulocyte DNA prepared from the same starting material by two different procedures: a) (upper chart) 3.0 mg, prepared by the general method of Kay, Simmons and Dounce (1952); b) (lower chart) 3.0 mg, prepared by saline estraction and deproteinization by the Sevag procedure (1938). The dimensions of the columns and the gradient elution schedules were the same in each experiment. We are indebted to Dr. E. Polli (University of Milan) for providing us with these samples of DNA.

coccal transforming factor. Further studies on the molecular sizes of the DNA's in the different column fractions are in progress.

Analysis of the base compositions of fractions from calf thymus DNA has revealed another possible basis for the fractionation. Fractions obtained in different regions show significant variations in base composition (Table 1). The

exchanger therefore shows the additional property of distinguishing among fractions of different composition and, possibly, structural arrangement. Other fractionation methods appear to have a different basis since successive fractions obtained with increasing salt concentration show progressively decreasing guanine contents (Brown and Martin, 1955; Brown and Watson, 1953;

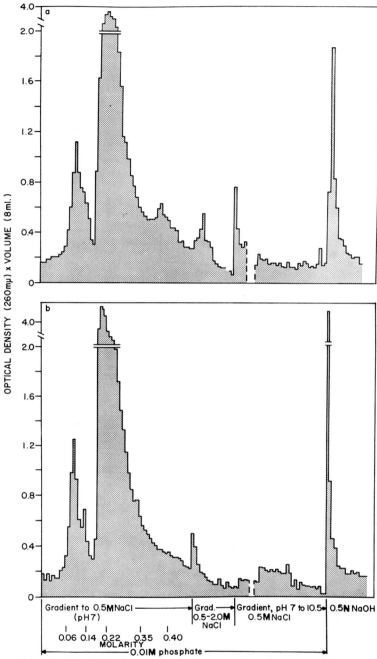

FIGURE 4. Chromatography on ECTEOLA of two samples of human lymphocyte DNA prepared from blood collected from the same patient at two different times: (a) first preparation (upper chart) 2.8 mg; (b) second preparation (lower chart) obtained from blood collected 10 days later, 2.8 mg. Both experiments were carried out under similar conditions. The samples were generously provided by Dr. L. D. Hamilton (Sloan-Kettering Institute).

Chargaff, 1955; Chargaff, *et al.*, 1953; *cf.*, Lucy and Butler, 1954, 1956).

A striking feature of the analytical data is the failure in many cases to obtain unity ratios for the adenine/thymine and guanine/cytosine pairs. Even greater deviation from unity ratios have been reported (Bendich, 1956). These results are in contrast to many other published data, and raise some question concerning the adequacy of the specific-pairing hypothesis (Watson and Crick, 1953a, b) as a complete explanation for DNA reduplication in chromosomes.

For the present discussion, the following observations might be considered. In the prepara-

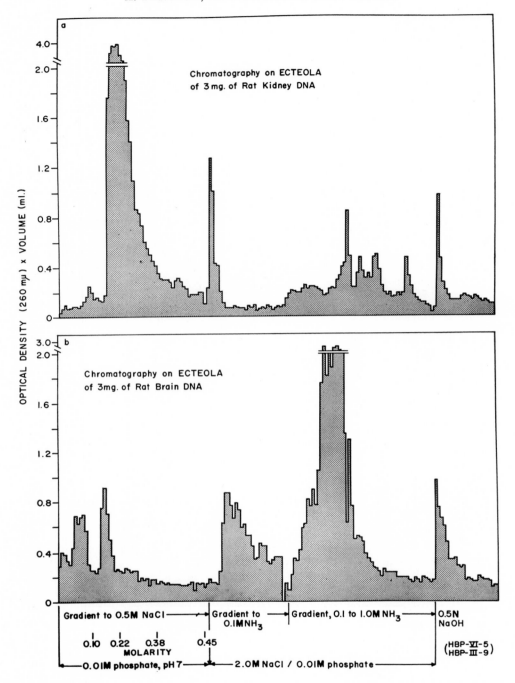

tion of DNA either for base analysis or for crystallographic examination, it is almost a universal practice to clarify solutions of DNA at one or more stages by centrifugation, often at quite high speeds. It has been reported (Bendich, 1952; Bendich, et al., 1953) and confirmed by two other laboratories (Diermeier, et al., 1955; Harbers and Backmann, 1956) that the DNA of mammalian tissues when prepared by either cold or hot salt extraction yields a sedimentable fraction (the so-called DNA_1 fraction) when dilute salt solutions

are centrifuged in fields as low as 20,000 $\times$ g. Such sediments[6] have traditionally been discarded in the quest for "clear" DNA solutions prior to the precipitation of the DNA (an exception to this is the analysis of whole virus particles; Smith and Wyatt, 1951; Wyatt and Cohen, 1953). Therefore, the DNA which is precipitated from solutions clarified in this manner is only a

[6] Often, as in the DNA from rat intestine, the sediment contains from two to four times as much DNA as the supernatant (Bendich, et al., 1953).

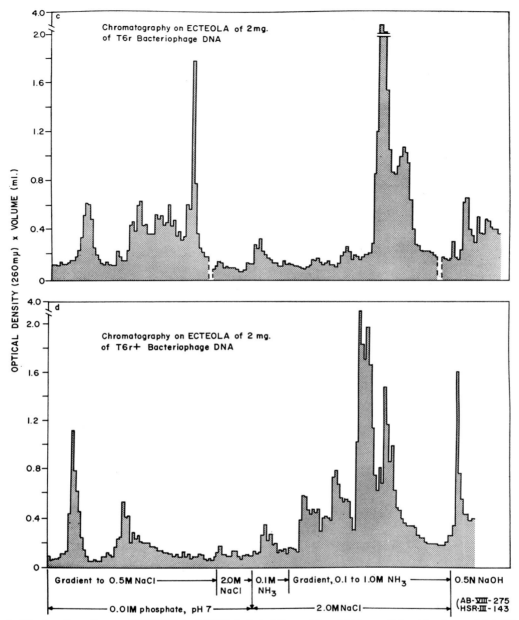

FIGURE 5. The fractionation on ECTEOLA of DNA isolated from (a) rat kidney, (b) rat brain, and (c) T6r and (d) T6r+ bacteriophage. Approximately 2 mg of bacteriophage DNA samples and 3 mg of the rat DNA preparations were used. In all four experiments the gradient elution schedule was the same, with the flow rate about 3 ml/hr. The T6r and T6r+ samples were generously provided by Dr. Seymour S. Cohen (University of Pennsylvania).

part of the total DNA, and is a selected fraction which possesses those properties which have permitted its isolation. Such DNA is, furthermore, heterogeneous. The other fractionation procedures which have yielded fractions showing close (but not perfect) unity ratios do not seem to have the resolution that the present method offers. The greater deviations from unit ratios (Table 1) would thus seem to reflect the higher resolving power of the substituted-cellulose exchanger ECTEOLA.

Of interest in connection with the discussion concerning the possible basis for the fractionation of DNA by ECTEOLA are some experiments on rechromatography of column fractions. It has been found that if a particular column fraction is dialyzed and put back upon the column, the major portion of the material is again eluted at precisely that concentration of solute which initially caused the fraction to be removed from the column. In addition, however, small amounts of material are found both at lower and higher concentrations of

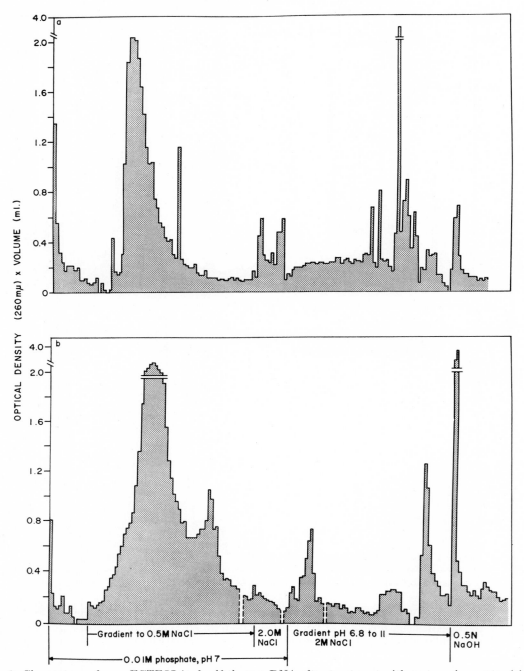

FIGURE 6. Chromatography on ECTEOLA of calf thymus DNA after treatment with mutagenic agents: (a) 2.1 mg of DNA after irradiation (upper chart) with 10⁸ roentgens (electrons); (b) 3 mg of DNA treated with 0.009 M nitrogen mustard (lower chart) in phosphate buffer for 1 week at 25°C. Compare profiles (a) and (b) with that of Figure 2. The irradiation was kindly carried out by Dr. H. Rozendaal (General Electric Co.).

solute, as is shown in Figure 8. If the main peak from the first rechromatography experiment is again dialyzed and placed back on the column, the same behavior is observed (Fig. 8c). The optical density ratios at selected wavelengths (240/260, 250/260, 280/260, 290/260 in mμ) for the main peaks in all three chromatograms are very similar to those of

the starting, unfractionated DNA. These findings are consistent with the interpretation that each peak in the original chromatogram is itself heterogeneous, and that subsequent rechromatography of such a peak tends to sort out again the DNA molecules on the same basis as the starting material was first fractionated, thus per-

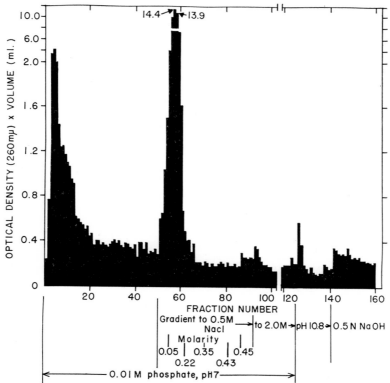

FIGURE 7. Fractionation on ECTEOLA of an oligonucleotide mixture obtained from a deoxyribonuclease digest of 3.6 mg of calf thymus DNA. Flow rate about 4 ml/hr. Size of column, 0.8 × 4.5 cm.

haps effecting a purification with respect to those parameters which determine the basis for this fractionation. The possibility that the column matrix is also heterogeneous (Bradley, *et al.*, 1956) and that a single passage of the DNA solution through the column may not most effectively utilize the binding sites would offer a reasonable explanation as to why a peak is heterogeneous. Similar behavior on rechromatography of ribonucleic acid (RNA) on ECTEOLA has been reported and interpreted on the basis of the heterogeneity of the exchanger (Bradley, *et al.*, 1956). When it is recalled that the molecular weight of many preparations of DNA is at least six times greater than that of RNA, the complexity of the interactions between nucleic acid and exchanger binding sites will easily be appreciated. The extent of purification possibly being effected by rechromatography is not known at the present time. However, measurement of the specific biological activity of pneumococcal transforming DNA or the use of labeled DNA may be of value in determining the effectiveness of rechromatography in purification.

The question concerning the authenticity or "nativeness" of the DNA fractions obtained with ECTEOLA is also of considerable importance. The findings presented above with respect to base analyses and rechromatography might be interpreted to mean that the chromatographic manipulations and column environment were degrading the DNA, and that the fractions represent procedural artefacts. That this is not occurring extensively is made clear from column fractionation experiments with transforming factor. Inasmuch as the biological activity of pneumococcal DNA is a very sensitive index of biological (and presumably chemical) "nativeness" or integrity, it may suffice to state that there appears to be little loss of transforming activity upon chromatography on ECTEOLA (see below). In contrast, such apparently mild treatments as freeze drying or solution in salt-free water brings about an irreversible inactivation of transforming principles (Avery, *et al.*, 1944; Zamenhof, *et al.*, 1954).

SPECIFIC-PAIRING HYPOTHESIS

According to the specific-pairing hypothesis of Watson and Crick (1953a, b), the base composition of one chain in the double helix of DNA is fixed by the sequence of nucleotides present in the adjacent chain. A requirement of this hypothesis is that each of the ratios adenine/thymine and guanine/cytosine must be one, though no restriction is placed upon the absolute amount of any one base. Some difficulty has already been experienced in attempting to fit some of the more recently discovered minor components of DNA into this model of the DNA molecule. As a specific example, Dunn and Smith (1955) found that

TABLE 1. BASE COMPOSITION OF COLUMN FRACTIONS OF CALF THYMUS DNA

Fraction Number	Composition of Eluent		Molar Base Composition (Adenine = 1.00)*			$\dfrac{AD}{THY}$	$\dfrac{GU}{CY}$	Recovery† (per cent)
	NaCl molarity	NH₃ molarity	Thymine	Guanine	Cytosine			
Original			0.97	0.77	0.77	1.03	1.00	95
50–1, 53–4	0.20–0.29		0.91	0.61	0.81	1.10	0.75	91
55–7	0.29–0.31		0.88	0.64	0.84	1.14	0.76	89
59–64	0.34–0.39		0.94	0.71	0.82	1.06	0.87	90
147–161	2.0	TRIS, pH 9.5	0.97	0.73	0.83	1.03	0.89	92
197	2.0	0.1	0.88	0.67	0.74	1.14	0.91	89
199–200	2.0	0.1	0.95	0.64	0.74	1.05	0.87	98
206	2.0	0.1	1.01	0.75	0.79	0.99	0.95	95
236–7	2.0	0.25	0.98	0.63	0.74	1.02	0.85	100
239	2.0	0.35	0.95	0.68	0.72	1.05	0.95	95
242	2.0	0.45	0.98	0.78	0.78	1.02	1.00	99
244	2.0	0.53	0.94	0.86	0.90	1.06	0.96	104
I	0.29–0.40		1.01	0.64	0.70	0.99	0.91	
III	—	pH 10–10.8	1.03	0.83	0.77	0.97	1.08	
IV	—	0.5M NaOH	0.99	0.78	0.79	1.01	0.99	

* These values are the average of six determinations, except for the guanine of fraction number 147–161 which is the average of two analyses. Average deviation is less than 2 per cent. The last three entries (Fraction number I, III and IV) are from a separate experiment.

† $\dfrac{\text{Total } \mu\text{M of bases recovered}}{\text{Total } \mu\text{M of P in hydrolysate}} \times 100.$

6-methylaminopurine may replace as much as 20 per cent of the thymine in *E. coli* DNA, and commented on the inability of so rigid a model to accommodate such cases. Since the mathematical exactitude required by the Watson-Crick model is not followed in some cases, the question is raised as to whether or to what extent exact replication of the DNA structure occurs during cell division. That the molecule must be replicated in its biologically essential features is evident from its role in the transmission of hereditary characteristics. It is then pertinent to ask what essential features are necessary to assure genetic continuity. Apparently some residues in the nucleic acid chain can be replaced by other purine or pyrimidine bases. The exchange of 5-bromouracil for thymine residues in *E. coli* has been reported by Zamenhof, *et al.* (1956c), and perhaps it can be reasoned that certain thymine residues are not essential for genetic transmission, but play a role only in the maintenance of the gross structural integrity of the DNA molecules. Thus it could be imagined that these particular sites in the macromolecule can be occupied by compounds which may or may not be structural analogs without interfering with the genetic function. The base ratios presented in Table 1 indicate that certain DNA fractions from the column have structural features other than that prescribed by the Watson and Crick model. It would appear that a detailed study of the base composition of highly fractionated DNA might lead to a better understanding of which structural features are essential to the maintenance of the genetic function of DNA, and which features contribute secondarily in retaining the architectural balance of the molecules and their specific configuration.

APPLICATION TO PNEUMOCOCCAL TRANSFORMING DNA

A chromatogram of pneumococcal transforming DNA is given in Figure 9, and the streptomycin transforming activities of some of the fractions are recorded in Table 2. The pattern given by the mixture of pneumococcal RNA and transforming DNA is shown in Figure 10. The quantitation of transformation involves a complex biological system which is as yet incompletely understood. A discussion of some aspects of the assay should, therefore, aid in the evaluation of the significance of the results.

The maximum number of cells capable of being transformed is different for each culture. However, at low concentrations of DNA the number of cells transformed is directly proportional to the amount of DNA added (Marmur and Fluke, 1955; Thomas, 1955). For assay purposes, approximately the same amount of DNA (0.036 to 0.047 μg) of each of the fractions was added to one ml of culture. A control containing 0.040 μg DNA of the original unfractionated material was assayed simultaneously. These levels of DNA were well below those found necessary for maximum transformation. The number of transformed cells in each tube was determined (Hotchkiss and Marmur, 1954) and the specific activity calculated as the number of cells transformed per μg DNA. Relative activities were calculated by dividing the

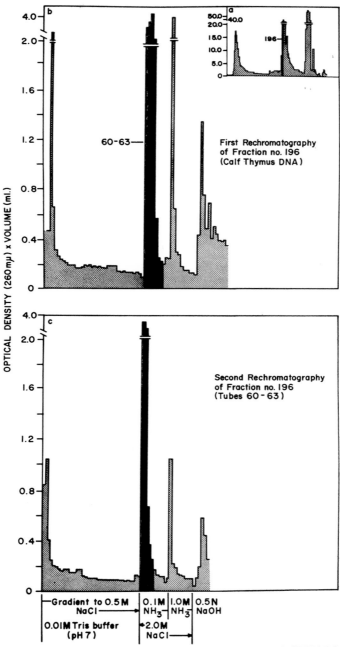

FIGURE 8. Rechromatography of calf thymus DNA fraction obtained from an ECTEOLA column: (a) original pattern (insert) obtained from chromatography of 70 mg of DNA on a 10 gm column of ECTEOLA. Fraction #196 was eluted with 0.1 M.NH₃ in 2.0 M NaCl; (b) rechromatography (upper left chart) of fraction #196 after dialysis against 0.01 M Tris buffer, pH 7; 58% of the original fraction #196 was eluted at the same solute concentration as in (a); (c) rechromatography of fractions #60–63 from (b) after dialysis as before; 54% of the DNA was again eluted (lower chart) at the same concentration of solute as in (a). The elution schedules for (b) and (c) were the same, but differed from that used in (a) in that discontinuous elution was used after the main peak which is shown in black had been eluted from the column.

specific activity of the fraction by the specific activity of the original DNA. Despite wide variations in specific activities with different cultures (from about 20,000 to over 180,000 for the unfractionated DNA), relative activities of the different

fractions determined at various times were reasonably consistent (Table 2).

As can be seen from Table 2, relative activities of the fractions vary greatly, some fractions (173 and 260; Fig. 9) possessing at least 50 times

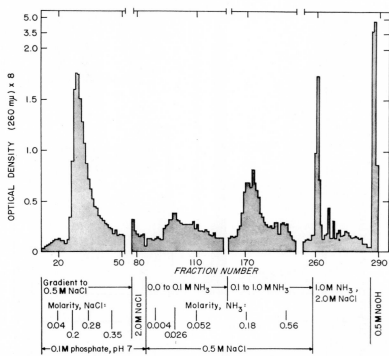

FIGURE 9. Fractionation (at 3°C) of four-marker pneumococcal transforming DNA on ECTEOLA. 3.2 mg of DNA placed on a 0.5 gm column (0.8 × 5.1 cm). Flow rate 8 ml/hr. See Table 2 for the streptomycin transforming activities of selected column fractions.

TABLE 2. STREPTOMYCIN TRANSFORMING ACTIVITIES OF CHROMATOGRAPHIC FRACTIONS OF PNEUMOCOCCAL DNA*

Fraction No.	Composition of Eluent		pH of Eluate	Relative Transforming Activity†		
	NaCl M	NH₃ M				
Original			7.0	1.0	1.0	1.0
25	0.17		7.0	0.7	0.8	0.7
27	0.19		7.0	0.2	0.4	0.2
29	0.21		7.0	0.5	0.6	0.4
32	0.25		7.0	0.4	0.1	0.04
35	0.28		7.0	1.2	0.8	1.9
40	0.32		7.0	0.9	0.7	1.2
67	0.45		7.0	0	0.1	0.06
78	0.47		7.0	0	0.1	0.03
99	0.50	0.02	8.4	1.9	1.8	2.0
173	0.50	0.22	9.5		5.1	4.2
190	0.50	0.56	10.4	1.1	1.0	
260	2.00	1.0	11.0		5.1	4.8

* See Figure 9 for the chromatographic profile of the pneumococcal DNA preparation used in this experiment.

$$† = \frac{\text{Transformants per } \mu\text{g DNA Fraction}}{\text{Transformants per } \mu\text{g DNA original}} \text{ (DNA de-}$$
termined by U.V. absorption.) The activities listed in the three columns were determined on separate days.

the activity of others (67 and 78; Fig. 9). The most active fractions measured were approximately five times as active as the original material. These fractions (173 and 260) were among those most tightly bound to ECTEOLA, and were eluted in the alkaline range. Fraction 260 required 1.0 M NH₃ (2.0 M NaCl) at pH 11.0 for elution and was kept at this pH in the refrigerator for several weeks before assay. It is possible that so alkaline a pH also destroys activity, and therefore fractions eluted in this region may have been initially more active than reported here.

Using a kieselguhr-histone column, Ephrussi-Taylor (1955b) has also obtained certain fractions from pneumococcal DNA which were about five times as active as the starting material. The fractions with the highest specific activity were among the first to be eluted, while in the present investigation, the most active fractions were eluted late. Lerman (1955) has used methylated bovine serum albumin to fractionate isotopically-labeled (P³²) pneumococcal transforming DNA, and has obtained fractions about twice as active as the original. Unfortunately it was assumed that the DNA contents of the fractions were proportional to the amount of P³² present. This assumption suffers from two major deficiencies: 1) DNA is heterogeneous and it cannot therefore

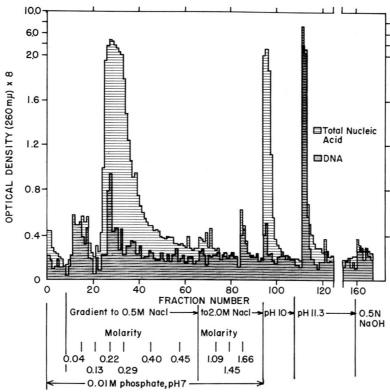

FIGURE 10. Chromatography of the mixed RNA and DNA from pneumococcus on ECTEOLA. 3.5 mg of mixed nucleic acids, of which 0.9 mg was transforming DNA, was added to a 0.5 gm, 0.8 × 5.1 cm column, flow rate 8 ml/hr. The horizontally shaded area shows the total nucleic acid in each fraction as measured by optical density at 260 mμ whereas the more deeply shaded areas indicate the amount of DNA as determined by the Ceriotti (1955) reaction. The difference between the two values represents the amount of RNA present. The chromatography was carried out at 3°C.

be assumed that the DNA-P^{32} content of all column fractions is equal, and 2) no correction was made for RNA-P^{32} contained in the fractions, or other P^{32}-containing impurities.

The molecular weight of the transforming factor has been investigated to some extent. Studies on the inactivation of isolated pneumococcal transforming substance by ionizing radiation have been used to calculate its molecular weight. Ephrussi-Taylor and Latarjet (1955) calculated a value of about 700,000 from X-ray inactivation data. Marmur and Fluke (1955), in studies of four transforming factors of pneumococcus, found that part of the activity showed a radiosensitive molecular weight of 0.5×10^6 to 10^6, while another part showed a radiosensitive molecular weight of of 2×10^6 to 8×10^6. In our studies, fraction 25 (Table 2; Fig. 9), which showed a relative streptomycin transforming activity of about 0.7, was found by sedimentation studies to have a mean molecular weight of 430,000, while the most active fractions (173 and 260; Table 2; Fig. 9) had mean molecular weights of about 7×10^6. These results suggest, as was found by Marmur and Fluke, that transforming activity may be associated with molecules of varying sizes.

The number of cells transformed with increasing DNA concentration was studied with the original material and with fractions 32, 173, and 260 (Table 2; Fig. 9). Although the relative activities of these fractions varied from an average of 0.2 for fraction 32 to 5.0 for fraction 260, the use of an excess of any of these DNA fractions transformed the same number of cells. This is interpreted to indicate that the lower relative activity of fraction 32 is not due to the presence of an inhibitor, but rather to a decreased proportion of DNA molecules possessing streptomycin transforming activity. Conversely, it would appear that the higher activities of fractions 173 and 260 (Table 2; Fig. 9) are due to increased proportions of active molecules. These results are consistent with the concept that the chromatographic fractionation has resulted in an actual fractionation of biological activity. Other markers are now under investigation. Preliminary results from another experiment have indicated that streptomycin and penicillin activities may be separable. Although active fractions completely lacking one or the other activity were not obtained, some fractions had high relative streptomycin activities associated with low penicillin activities, for others the relative activities were reversed, and in still others essentially equal activities were obtained.

Some Thoughts and Speculations

That DNA from many sources is heterogeneous is today quite firmly established. This concept of the heterogeneity of DNA has evolved slowly from the simpler idea held at one time that all nucleic acids were identical. As biochemical techniques were refined and thinking became somewhat more precise, the original idea was modified to one in which it was thought that all plant nucleic acids were the same and all animal nucleic acids were alike, each group, however, being different from the other. These sweeping generalizations were replaced in turn by the tetranucleotide hypothesis and by the concepts of constancy of composition and content of DNA per cell. The recent and perhaps most restrictive of the modern concepts, from which is derived our current ideas concerning the reduplication of genetic determinants, postulates duplication of genetic determinants, postulates the specific pairing of certain purine and pyrimidine bases.

There is a tendency to disregard those data which do not conform in all respects with the current hypotheses of DNA composition and structure. For example, if the composition of a DNA preparation shows a deviation from unity for the ratio of adenine/thymine or guanine/cytosine, the method of preparation or analysis is seriously questioned. In this connection it is well to recall a passage from Gulland's paper (1947) delivered at these same Symposia shortly before his untimely death: "As long as the nucleic acid molecule was believed to be small in size and to consist of only four mononucleotide molecules, small divergences from the statistical tetranucleotide ratio could be ignored as arising probably from experimental error or traces of impurity in the material being examined. It is obvious, however, that in a large polynucleotide molecule of high molecular weight deviations, even if slight, can be of considerable significance." Possible explanations have been presented above for the frequent inability to obtain the unity ratios such as have been reported in much of the earlier literature. We believe that the most important single factor for these discrepancies appears to be the fact that all DNA specimens, which have thus far been examined for this purpose, have been found to consist of mixtures.

Many procedures for the isolation and preparation of DNA used for the purpose of analytical or crystallographic studies (Wilkins, 1956) yield material which represents only a part (sometimes a small part) of the total DNA. Such studies have not ordinarily been carried out on those other portions of the DNA which have frequently been disregarded. It may be that only that portion of the DNA which very nearly gives perfect unity base ratios, as well as the beautiful X-ray diffrac-

tion patterns[7], is the genetically significant material. The remainder may consist of breakdown products, incompletely organized molecules, or materials involved in processes other than genetic. The fractionation procedure described here has yielded fractions at various places in the chromatogram which show significant deviations from unity ratios (Table 1) while other fractions (242 and IV, Table 1) have nearly "ideal" ratios. However, the latter required either 0.45 M ammonia or 0.5 M NaOH for their removal from the column, and these might thus be considered "mistreated" fractions. In the case of pneumococcal DNA, fractions from many regions throughout the chromatogram possess biological activity (Table 2). The biological properties of several of these fractions might not have been investigated had there been a strict adherence to certain of the modern restrictive concepts of DNA chemistry.

The pneumococcal DNA endowed with transforming activity behaves on the column in much the same fashion as do the other DNA's studied. It has been presumed that the multiple biological functions of DNA are a reflection of this heterogeneity. However, it is also conceivable that heterogeneity may exist among DNA molecules possessing a single biological function. In this connection it should be recalled that although the transforming DNA in this investigation was prepared from a culture obtained from a single cell isolate, the ability to transform receptor cells to streptomycin resistance was associated with many of the fractions which were obtained after its fractionation on ECTEOLA. Very early fractions (25; Table 2; Fig. 9) as well as some late ones (260; Table 2; Fig. 9) possessed transforming activity. This observed physico-chemical heterogeneity of a single transforming activity suggests at least two interpretations.

One possibility is that heterogeneous DNA molecules may each contain one or more specific, fixed sites which are the loci of the biological activity. An analogous situation may exist in other biologically active materials. For example, substances with equal blood group A activity may vary in their fucose contents (Kabat, 1956a), and enzyme molecules with a single defined specificity may be heterogeneous (Bier and Nord, 1953; Hirs, et al., 1953; Martin and Porter, 1951).

Another interpretation is that a given active site may not be located in the same relative position in all molecules. In addition, there may be variations in the specific structure of sites which possess the same function. McElroy and Swanson (1951), for example, have suggested that a gene may exist in several states with the same phenotypic activity. A parallel may be drawn from the field of immunochemistry in which it has been

---

[7] It has not yet been established that the fibers themselves which are drawn from DNA gels for crystallographic studies also possess unity ratios.

found that antibodies to a single antigen may vary in the strengths of their combination with antigen (Jerne, 1951), in their cross-reactions (Kabat, 1953), and in the size and nature of their combining sites (Kabat, 1956a, b), all of which indicate a heterogeneity of these reactive loci.

It has generally been assumed that DNA molecules are duplicated exactly during cell multiplication, and that mutation results from an occasional error in this process (Watson and Crick, 1953a, b). In view of the fact that DNA molecules with a single demonstrable transforming activity appear to be heterogeneous, the possibility that reduplication may frequently be inexact must be considered. If the active site represents only a small portion of a large molecule, the low incidence of a given mutation may be explained by the rare occurrence of inexact reduplication of this restricted specific area. If the structure at the specific site is different in individual molecules, inexact duplication may occur even in this locus without necessarily resulting in phenotypically-expressed mutation. Recent investigations on the incorporation or occurrence of purine and pyrimidine analogs in bacterial DNA's (Dunn and Smith, 1954, 1955; Zamenhof and Griboff, 1954; Zamenhof, et al., 1956a) offer some support for the concept that duplication of DNA is not always exact. Unstable genes (Zamenhof, et al., 1956b) or pre-mutants (Auerbach, 1951) might be explicable in these terms.

The essential reproducibility of the chromatographic patterns lends much credence to the differences seen among patterns given by DNA from different sources. Thus the differences in the patterns for brain and kidney DNA, or T6r and T6r+ phage DNA can be taken as reflecting intrinsic differences in these biological materials. In the last mentioned instance, a single genetic change is involved, and a significant (but not understood) difference in chromatographic profile is seen. From the results of the experiments reported here, it is expected that more detailed studies of the chemical, physical and biological properties of the individual column fractions will assist in a selection among the interpretations discussed above or, perhaps, may suggest additional possibilities.

It is therefore hoped that this new parameter, the chromatographic profile of DNA, will aid in further understanding of genetic phenomena and serve, perhaps, as does the "fingerprint" region in infra-red spectra in the elucidation of chemical problems.

ACKNOWLEDGEMENTS

The authors take pleasure in expressing their appreciation to the following persons for their interest in, and stimulating discussions of, various aspects of the material presented herein: Dr. George B. Brown, Dr. Rollin D. Hotchkiss, Dr. Jacques R. Fresco, and Dr. Solon A. Ellison. It is also a pleasure to thank Mr. Herbert S. Rosenkranz, Mrs. Grace Korngold, Miss Marion T. Dowling and Mr. Percy J. Russell, Jr., for competent assistance.

REFERENCES

ADA, G. L., and PERRY, B. T., 1955a, Infectivity and nucleic acid content of influenza virus. Nature, Lond. *175:* 209–210.

1955b, Specific differences in the nucleic acids from A and B strains of influenza virus. Nature, Lond. *175:* 854–855.

AUERBACH, C., 1951, Problems in chemical mutagenesis. Cold Spr. Harb. Symp. Quant. Biol. *16:* 199–213.

AVERY, O. T., MacLeod, C. M., and McCarty, M., 1944, Studies on the chemical nature of the substance inducing transformation of pneumococcal types. J. Exp. Med. *79:* 137–158.

BENDICH, A., 1952, Studies on the metabolism of the nucleic acids. Exp. Cell Res. *3,* suppl. 2: 181–199.

1956, Heterogeneity of deoxyribonucleic acid (DNA). In: Essays in Biochemistry, S. Graff, Ed., pp. 14–21, New York, John Wiley.

BENDICH, A., RUSSELL, P. J., JR., and BROWN, G. B., 1953, On the heterogeneity of the desoxyribonucleic acids. J. Biol. Chem. *203:* 305–318.

BENDICH, A., FRESCO, J. R., ROSENKRANZ, H. S., and BEISER, S. M., 1955, Fractionation of deoxyribonucleic acid (DNA) by ion exchange. J. Amer. Chem. Soc. *77:* 3671–3673.

BENDICH, A., PAHL, H. B., and BROWN, G. B., 1956, Chromatographic fractionation of *E. coli* DNA containing 5-bromouracil-2-C^{14}. (Manuscript in preparation.)

BIER, M., and NORD, F. F., 1953, Crystalline trypsin. Nature, Lond. *171:* 1022–1023.

BRADLEY, D. F., and RICH, A., 1956, The fractionation of ribonucleic acids on Ecteola-cellulose anion exchangers. J. Amer. Chem. Soc. (in press).

BROWN, G. L., and MARTIN, A. V., 1955, Fractionation of deoxyribonucleic acid of T2r bacteriophage. Nature, Lond. *176:* 971–972.

BROWN, G. L. and WATSON, M., 1953, Heterogeneity of deoxyribonucleic acids. Nature, Lond. *172:* 339–342.

CERIOTTI, G., 1955, Determination of nucleic acids in animal tissues. J. Biol. Chem. *214:* 59–70.

CHARGAFF, E., 1955, Isolation and composition of the deoxypentose nucleic acids and of the corresponding nucleoproteins. In: The Nucleic Acids, I. E. Chargaff and J. N. Davidson, Eds. pp. 307–371, New York, Academic Press.

CHARGAFF, E., CRAMPTON, C. F., and LIPSHITZ, R., 1953, Separation of calf thymus deoxyribonucleic acid into fractions of different composition. Nature, Lond. *172:* 289–292.

COHEN, S. S., 1955, Comparative biochemistry and virology. Adv. Virus Res. *3:* 1–48, New York, Academic Press.

1956, Molecular bases of parasitism of some bacterial viruses. Science *123:* 653–656.

CRAMPTON, C. F., LIPSHITZ, R., and CHARGAFF, E., 1954, Studies on nucleoproteins II. Fractionation of deoxyribonucleic acids through fractional dissociation of their complexes with basic proteins. J. Biol. Chem. *211:* 125–142.

DIERMEIER, H. F., DiStephano, H. S., and BASS, A. D., 1955, The effect of alloxan on liver DNA of the rat. J. Pharm. Exp. Therap. *115:* 240–245.

DUNN, D. B., and SMITH, J. D., 1954, Incorporation of halogenated pyrimidines into the deoxyribonucleic acids of *Bacterium coli* and its bacteriophages. Nature, Lond. *174:* 305–306.

1955, Occurrence of a new base in the deoxyribonucleic acid of a strain of *Bacterium coli.* Nature, Lond. *175:* 336–337.

EPHRUSSI-TAYLOR, H., 1955a, Genetic function and molecular structure of DNA. In: Conférences et Rapports, 3e Congr. Intern. Biochimie, Bruxelles, p. 333–339.
— 1955b, Current status of bacterial transformations. Adv. Virus Res. *3:* 275–307, New York, Academic Press.

EPHRUSSI-TAYLOR, H., and LATARJET, R., 1955, Inactivation par les rayons X, d'un facteur transformant du pneumocoque. Biochim. Biophys. Acta *16:* 183–197.

FRAENKEL-CONRAT, H., 1956, The role of the nucleic acid in the reconstitution of active tobacco mosaic virus. J. Amer. Chem. Soc. *78:* 882–883.

GIERER, A., and SCHRAMM, G., 1956, Infectivity of ribonucleic acid from tobacco mosaic virus. Nature, Lond. *177:* 702–703.

GULLAND, J. M., 1947, The structures of nucleic acids. Cold Spr. Harb. Symp. Quant. Biol. *12:* 95–103.

HARBERS, E., and BACKMANN, R., 1956, Untersuchungen über den Einfluss von Röntgenstrahblen auf die Desoxyribonucleinsaure im Walker-carcinom der Ratte. Exp. Cell Res. *10:* 125–131.

HIRS, C. H. W., MOORE, S., and STEIN, W. H., 1953, A chromatographic investigation of pancreatic ribonuease. J. Biol. Chem. *200:* 493–506.

HOTCHKISS, R. D., 1954, The genetic chemistry of the pneumococcal transformations. Harvey Lectures *49:* 124–144.
— 1952, The role of desoxyribonucleates in bacterial transformations. Phosphorus Metabolism *2:* 426–436, Baltimore, Johns Hopkins Press.
— 1955, The biological role of the deoxypentose nucleic acids. In: The Nucleic Acids II, E. Chargaff, and J. N. Davidson, Eds., pp. 435–473, New York, Academic Press.

HOTCHKISS, R. D., and MARMUR, J., 1954, Double marker transformations as evidence of linked factors in desoxyribonucleate transforming agents. Proc. Nat. Acad. Sci. Wash. *40:* 55–60.

JERNE, N. K., 1951, A study of avidity. Acta. Path. Microbiol. Scand., Suppl. *87:* 1–183.

KABAT, E. A., 1953, The unity and diversity of antibodies. N. Y. Acad. Med., Section on Microbiology, Symp. *5:* 102–110.
— 1956a, Blood Group Substances: Their Chemistry and Immunochemistry; p. 147–148, 227–228; New York, Academic Press.
— 1956b, Heterogeneity in extent of the combining sites of human anti-dextran. (in press).

KAY, E. R. M., SIMMONS, N. W., and DOUNCE, A. L., 1952, An improved preparation of sodium desoxyribonucleate. J. Amer. Chem. Soc. *74:* 1724–1726.

LERMAN, L. S., 1955, Chromatographic fractionation of the transforming principle of the pneumococcus. Biochim. Biophys. Acta *18:* 132–134.

LIPPINCOTT, J. A., and COMMONER, B., 1956, Reactivation of tobacco mosaic virus infectivity in mixtures of virus protein and nucleic acid. Biochim. Biophys. Acta *19:* 198–199.

LUCY, J. A., and BUTLER, J. A. V., 1954, Fractionation of deoxyribonucleoprotein by successive extraction with constant salt concentration. Nature, Lond. *174:* 32–33.
— 1956, Fractionation of deoxyribonucleoprotein. Bull. Soc. Chim. Belg. *65:* 133–139.

MARKHAM, R., 1953, Virus nucleic acids. Adv. Virus Res. *1:* 315–332, New York, Academic Press.

MARMUR, J., and FLUKE, D. J., 1955, Uniformity of ionizing radiation action on several transforming factors of pneumococcus. Arch. Biochem. Biophys. *57:* 506–514.

MARTIN, A. J. P., and PORTER, R. R., 1951, The chromatographic fractionation of ribonuclease. Biochem. J. *49:* 215–218.

MCELROY, W. D., and SWANSON, C. P., 1951, The theory of rate processes and gene mutation. Quart. Rev. Biol. *26:* 348–363.

PETERSON, E. A., and SOBER, H. A., 1956, Chromatography of proteins I. Cellulose ion-exchange adsorbents. J. Amer. Chem. Soc. *78:* 751–755.

SCHRAMM, G., SCHUMACHER, G., and ZILLIG, W., 1955, An infectious nucleoprotein from tobacco mosaic virus. Nature, Lond. *175:* 549–550.

SCHWANDER, H., and SIGNER, R. 1950, Darstellung von hoch-molekularem Natrium-thymonucleinat aus Kalbsthymus. Helv. Chim. Acta *33:* 1521–1526.

SCHWERDT, C. E., 1954, Paper presented at meeting of Amer. Assoc. Adv. Sci., Berkeley, Calif.

SEVAG, M. G., LACKMAN, D. B., and SMOLENS, J., 1938, The isolation of the components of streptococcal nucleoproteins in serologically active form. J. Biol. Chem. *124:* 425–436.

SHERRATT, H. S. A., and THOMAS, A. J., 1953, The nucleic acid fractions of a strain of *Streptococcus faecalis*. J. Gen. Microbiol. *8:* 217–223.

SINSHEIMER, R. L., 1954, The action of pancreatic desoxyribonuclease I. Isolation of mono- and dinucleotides. J. Biol. Chem. *208:* 445–459.
— 1955, The action of pancreatic deoxyribonuclease II. Isomeric dinucleotides. J. Biol. Chem. *215:* 579–583.

SHOOTER, K. V., and BUTLER, J. A. V., 1955, Apparent heterogeneity of deoxyribonucleic acid: Sedimentation experiments at low concentrations. Nature, Lond. *175:* 500–502.

SMITH, J. D., and WYATT, G. R., 1951, The composition of some microbial deoxypentose nucleic acids. Biochem. J. *49:* 144–148.

THOMAS, R., 1955, Recherches sur la cinétique des transformations bactériennes. Biochim. Biophys. Acta *18:* 467–481.

WATSON, J. D., and CRICK, F. H. C., 1953a, Molecular structure of nucleic acids: A structure for deoxyribose nucleic acid. Nature, Lond. *171:* 737–738.
— 1953b, The structure of DNA. Cold Spr. Harb. Symp. Quant. Biol. *18:* 123–131.

WILKINS, M. H. F., 1956, Physical studies on the molecular structure of deoxyribose nucleic acids and their biological consequences. Cold Spring Harbor Symposia Quant. Biol. *21:* 75–90.

WYATT, G. R., and COHEN, S. S., 1953, The bases of the nucleic acids of some bacterial and animal viruses: the occurrence of 5-hydroxymethyl cytosine. Biochem. J. *55:* 774–782.

ZAMENHOF, S., and GRIBOFF, G., 1954, Incorporation of halogenated pyrimidines into the deoxyribonucleic acids of *Bacterium coli* and its bacteriophages. Nature, Lond. *174:* 306–308.

ZAMENHOF, S., GRIBOFF, G., and MARULLO, N., 1954, Studies on the resistance of desoxyribonucleic acids to physical and chemical factors. Biochim. Biophys. Acta *13:* 459–470.

ZAMENHOF, S., REINER, B., DE GIOVANNI, R., and RICH, K., 1956a, Introduction of unnatural pyrimidines into deoxyribonucleic acid of *Escherichia coli*. J. Biol. Chem. *219:* 165–173.

ZAMENHOF, S., LEIDY, G., HAHN, E., and ALEXANDER, H. E., 1956b, Inactivation and unstabilization of the transforming principle by mutagenic agents. J. Bact. *71:* (in press).

ZAMENHOF, S., RICH, K., and DE GIOVANNI, R., 1956c, Thymine-5-bromouracil "exchange" in deoxyribonucleic acid of *Escherichia coli:* Federation Proc. *15:* 390.

DISCUSSION

LERMAN: We have been applying a somewhat different system of chromatography to DNA from pneumococcus, with apparently different results. Both our extraction and chromatographic procedures have been restricted to those conditions of temperature, salt concentration, pH, etc. which may be expected to insure minimum degradation or denaturation; removal of RNA is effected by treatment with Norit following exposure to a low concentration of ribonuclease. It may be noted that in contrast with other reports, we find very little adsorption of RNA to Norit before ribonuclease digestion. The resulting material is found to be highly active for transformation to streptomycin resistance. Chromatography is carried out on a column consisting of insoluble methylated bovine serum albumin supported on Celite. The eluting solution is sodium perchlorate buffered at pH 6.7 in a concentration which rises linearly at a rate of about 0.002 M/ml from an initial concentration of 0.04 M. Elution of DNA commences at about 0.17 M and is virtually concluded within an extremely narrow band at a salt concentration only 10 per cent greater (see Fig. 1). We have searched the fractions comprising this band for evidence of fractionation by two procedures, the rechromatography of selected fractions, and the assay of fractions separately and in pools for transforming activity with respect to streptomycin resistance, mannitol utilization, and the double transformation to both of these. The transforming activities per microgram DNA of the various fractions and the original preparation show no significant variations either in dependence on DNA concentration in the proportional region or in maximum yield at the plateau.

In a previous report (Lerman, 1955, Biochim. Biophys. Acta *18:* 132) the considerable resolving power of this system of chromatography was demonstrated by rechromatographing one fraction and even further fractionating the resulting distribution. With the present preparations, repeated chromatography of any one fraction merely reproduces, with reasonable precision, the original chromatogram. It is evident by both the biological and the physical-chemical tests that no genuine fractionation has been obtained

The differences between these results and those of the earlier report (Lerman, 1955) are attributable to improved methods of preparation with the consequent higher purity of the more recent DNA samples. The distribution of transforming activities in the earlier chromatograms corresponds closely to the present distribution of DNA.

We have evidence (to be published shortly) that the adsorption and elution of DNA is by no means a simple ion exchange process with methyl albumin, although methyl albumin functions as an ion exchanger for simpler anions.

It must be concluded that substantially different processes are involved in Dr. Bendich's procedure and our own.

BENDICH: Use of the chromatographic procedures employing columns of kieselguhr-histone (Brown and Watson, 1953) and the substituted-cellulose ECTEOLA have demonstrated that a gross heterogeneity exists in the DNA from a large number of unrelated sources. Both procedures have also demonstrated a heterogeneity of transforming factors (DNA) from pneumococcus.

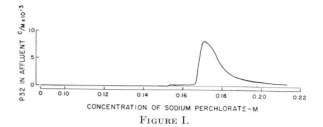

FIGURE I.

We therefore considered the published report (Lerman, 1955) of a fractionation of pneumococcal transforming factor employing methylated serum albumin to constitute independent confirmation of these findings. But, as we see now, that report has not been confirmed on re-examination. The present failure to fractionate pneumococcal transforming factor with methylated serum albumin may merely be a reflection of its lack of resolving power for this DNA, or perhaps for others. It would be of interest to determine whether or not the methylated serum albumin can be used to fractionate any of the other preparations of DNA which have already been shown to be heterogeneous by at least four independent techniques.

MOSES: There is always a difficulty in interpreting biochemical results obtained from a population of cells. In most tissues of higher organisms, varying numbers of histologically differentiated cell types are bound to be included. Even in a sample of one cell type, varying metabolic states may be represented. Any interpretation of the DNA heterogeneity that Dr. Bendich has reported must take into account the heterogeneity of the biological sample. On the other hand, in the case of phage where there is no reason to suspect sample heterogeneity, this problem is probably negligible.

BENDICH: It is widely believed that the DNA of the various tissues of, for example, a given mammalian species is the same. That is, the composition of the DNA of different cells is considered to be constant. We had occasion a few years ago to re-examine this question; we studied the base composition of the DNA from a number of different organs of the rat and found that the composition in fact varied from organ to organ. Preliminary results of such studies have been presented (Bendich, 1956). We have found the chromatographic profiles of the DNA from different tissues of the rat also to be different. It is therefore important, in interpreting biochemical results which bear on this question, to consider whether or not one is dealing with single cell types or with mixtures (that is, cell heterogeneity). This would not be important, of course, if it were really true that the DNA of the various cells of a particular species was the same. We found differences in the composition and in the chromatographic profile of the DNA from different organs of the rat, but it may also be true that the physiological state of the animal or the metabolic state of the cells of a given tissue may also affect either the DNA composition or the chromatographic profile. We are currently engaged in studies on this latter point. At first sight, there is perhaps no reason to suspect sample heterogeneity in the case of bacteriophage. But the question may be raised as to whether or not all phage particles are actually identical. After all, DNA is very complex and it may be that such huge macromolecules are really never duplicated in every detail. In addition, it is possible I suppose that some phage particles may contain DNA molecules of different states of completion and perhaps this may be another reason why a heterogeneous pattern is seen when phage DNA is examined.

The Nucleus as a Site of Biochemical Activity

A. E. Mirsky, Syozo Osawa and V. G. Allfrey

The Rockefeller Institute, New York

The experiments about to be described deal with the metabolic activity of isolated cell nuclei, and with their capacity to incorporate isotopically-labeled amino acids into their proteins. It will be shown that the deoxyribonucleic acid of the nucleus plays a role in this incorporation; that protein synthesis virtually ceases when the DNA is removed from the nucleus, and that the uptake of amino acids resumes when the DNA is restored.

Some observations on the conditions necessary for amino acid incorporation, on the effects of various inhibitors, and on the role of nucleic acid components in protein synthesis will also be made. Finally, evidence will be presented to show that nuclear activity also includes the capacity to synthesize energy-rich bonds by a process of oxidative phosphorylation. (Preliminary accounts of some of these experiments have been published (Allfrey, 1954; Allfrey *et al.*, 1955).

Some Properties of Isolated Thymus Nuclei

Most of the experiments to be described were performed on nuclei isolated from calf thymus tissue in 0.25 M sucrose solution containing a small amount of calcium chloride. The procedure is rapid and simple, and it provides nuclei of high purity in good yield.

Since some form of standardization is essential for all work on isolated cell components, thymus nuclei isolated in sucrose have been compared with those isolated in non-aqueous media (Allfrey *et al.*, 1952; Stern and Mirsky, 1953). The purpose of this comparison is to test whether the aqueous isolation procedure extracts water-soluble nuclear components, or whether it leads to excessive contamination with the water-soluble proteins of the cytoplasm. Many such comparisons have shown that thymus "sucrose" nuclei are the equivalent of the standard "non-aqueous" nuclei in many respects. Their DNA content is the same (2.5 per cent DNA-P), as is their overall protein composition and enzymic constitution (Stern and Mirsky, 1953).

When preparations of thymus nuclei isolated in sucrose solution are examined under the light microscope, either stained or unstained, they seem a beautiful preparation. One observes great numbers of free nuclei, a few whole cells, and occasional red cells. Staining reveals occasional strands of cytoplasm attached to some of the nuclei. The overall extent of this cytoplasmic contamination can be estimated chemically (*e.g.* by nucleic acid analyses) and the conclusion was reached that these nuclei are better than 90 per cent pure.

Since many intact thymocytes have only a thin halo or crescent of cytoplasm, the possibility was considered that many objects believed to be free nuclei under the light microscope might be intact cells with scanty or negligible amounts of cytoplasm. To investigate this possibility two preparations were examined under the electron microscope. (This was made possible through the generous cooperation of Drs. M. Watson and G. Palade of the Rockefeller Institute.) Electron microscopy makes it evident that there is some cytoplasmic contamination, but this is also evident in stained preparations under the light microscope. The advantage of the electron microscope in these studies is the ease of detection of small thymocytes. Cell counts on random fields selected from the two preparations gave 45 cells per thousand nuclei in the first preparation and 77 per thousand in the second. Even more convincing evidence for the absence of appreciable whole cell contamination was obtained in studying the effect of deoxyribonuclease. These experiments are described in detail below.

Amino Acid Incorporation into the Proteins of Isolated Nuclei

When thymus nuclei are suspended in a buffered sucrose medium and incubated at 37°C, in the presence of isotopically-labeled amino acids, there is a rapid and considerable incorporation of the isotope into the proteins of the nucleus. Figure 1 shows the time course of incorporation of alanine-1-C[14] into the mixed proteins of isolated calf thymus nuclei. The lower curve shows the incorporation observed into lymphoma nuclei isolated by a similar procedure. (The lymphoma tissue was generously supplied by Dr. John Kidd of Cornell University Medical College.) After an initial "lag" period of about 10 to 15 minutes, the C[14]-uptake proceeds linearly for about 90 minutes and then begins to taper slowly off.

Because a few whole cells are inevitably present in preparations of thymus nuclei, the possibility was considered that the observed amino acid uptake was due to the cells and not to the nuclei. To test this possibility a radioautograph was made of a smear of the nuclear suspension after incubation with C[14]-alanine and acid-fixation to remove the soluble amino acid. The distribution of silver grains produced in an overlaying photographic emulsion was then examined under the microscope, and it was observed that all components of

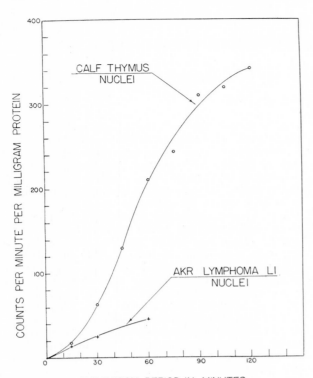

FIGURE 1. The time course of alanine-1-C^{14} incorporation into the proteins of isolated nuclei. The specific activity of the total nuclear protein is plotted against the time of incubation of the nuclear suspension. The upper curve shows the incorporation into thymus nuclei. The lower curve shows the rate of alanine-C^{14} uptake by nuclei isolated from an AKR lymphoma.

Time Course of C^{14}-Amino Acid Incorporation

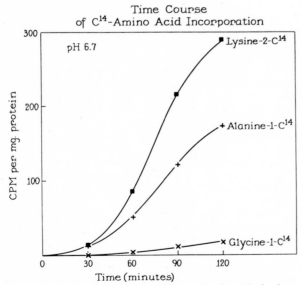

FIGURE 2. The time course of incorporation of alanine-1-C^{14}, glycine-1-C^{14}, and lysine-2-C^{14} into the proteins of isolated thymus nuclei. In this plot the data have been "normalized" to show the relative uptakes for equivalent amounts of the different amino acids, where each has the same specific activity in mc per mM.

the suspension were radioactive. The uptake was not simply due to the few cells present in the smear. Similar work in other laboratories also makes it plain that individual nuclei incorporate the radioactive amino acid (Errera, unpub.).

Figures 2 and 3 show the time course of alanine-1-C^{14}, glycine-1-C^{14}, lysine-2-C^{14}, and methionine-S^{35} incorporations. In these and in most of the experiments to be described below, the uptake was followed by measuring the radioactivity of the total mixed proteins of the nucleus. The results are expressed as counts per minute per mg. of protein. The protein was prepared first by extensively washing the nuclei with trichloroacetic acid (TCA), removing the nucleic acids with hot TCA and finally removing the lipides with warm ethanol, ethanol-ether-chloroform mixtures, ether, and acetone. The protein residue was then homogenized in acetone and filtered off on filter-paper planchets. Radioactivity was determined using a Geiger-Muller tube and scaling circuit, and the measurements were subsequently corrected for self-absorption (Schweitzer and Stein, 1950).

To test whether the radioactivity measured was actually in the protein and not merely adsorbed or bound by ester linkages, the protein was treated with alkali and with ninhydrin. In the case of incorporated alanine-1-C^{14}, more than 94 per cent of the activity remained after treatment with 0.25 N NaOH for two hours, and more than 89 per cent remained after reaction with ninhydrin. Seventy-six per cent of the incorporated methionine-S^{35} was stable to alkali. When the different proteins of the nucleus are fractionated before counting, the label remains throughout the fractionation and can be detected in such well-defined nuclear components as the "arginine-rich" and "lysine-rich" histones.

The nature of the lag in the uptake of radioactive alanine into the proteins of the nucleus was investigated by experiments which are summarized in Figure 4. Nuclei were pre-incubated at 37° for 10, 20, or 30 minutes before adding the isotopic alanine. The time course of C^{14}-incorporation by such pre-incubated nuclei was compared with that of "control" nuclei which had received the isotope at time zero. It is evident that pre-incubation diminishes the lag period without affecting the subsequent rate of C^{14}-alanine incorporation. These findings suggest that an activation of some sort occurs during pre-incubation. Further evidence for such activation will be presented below in connection with the inhibitory effects of benzimidazole derivatives. The lag in C^{14}-alanine uptake may also be due, in part, to the existence of a pool of unlabeled alanine in the nuclei; a pool which must be depleted before isotopic alanine is then up. This would be analogous to the interesting situation described by Bolton (unpub.) of fixed amino acid pools in bacteria. No evidence for a lag period in methionine-S^{35} uptake has been found in thymus nuclei. This, too, has a parallelism in bacterial systems (Bolton, unpub.).

There are a number of experiments now to be described which deal with the conditions necessary for amino acid incorporation, and with the inhibition of nuclear protein synthesis.

The uptake of amino acids is an aerobic phenomenon which does not occur in a nitrogen atmosphere and which is inhibited by a number of substances which are known to block oxidative phosphorylation (Table 1). Cyanide, azide, dinitrophenol, janus green B, dicumarol, and Antimycin A all inhibit alanine uptake. However, methylene blue, a substance which inhibits oxidative phosphorylation in mitochondria, has only a small effect on nuclear isotope incorporation. The nature of the oxidative phosphorylation in preparations of isolated thymus nuclei is discussed in detail later in this paper.

Adding metabolites, such as glucose, fructose, or α-ketoglutarate to the nuclear suspension has little effect on the incorporation of amino acids (Table 2). Added glucose may at times raise the alanine uptake by about ten per cent. An attempt to block glycolysis by the addition of fluoride did not result in inhibition of alanine incorporation.

It was shown by Gale and Folkes (1953) that chloramphenicol blocks protein synthesis in bacteria. This substance has little effect on glycine-1-C[14], alanine-1-C[14], or methionine-S[35] uptake by isolated nuclei (Table 3). The table also summarizes some experiments using p-fluorophenylalanine, an amino acid antagonist which was shown by Halvorson and Spiegelman (1952) to

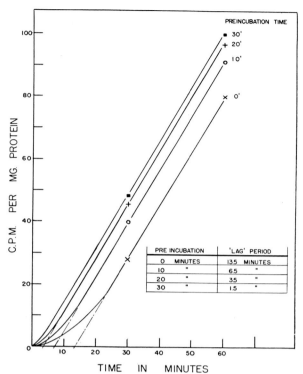

FIGURE 4. The effect of pre-incubation of thymus nuclei upon the subsequent incorporation of alanine-1-C[14]. The nuclear suspension was pre-incubated for 10, 20 or 30 minutes before adding the isotopic alanine. The time course of C[14] incorporation by such pre-incubated nuclei is compared with that of "control" nuclei which received the isotope at time zero. Note that pre-incubation diminishes the "lag" period without affecting the subsequent rate of C[14]-alanine incorporation.

block protein synthesis in bacteria. We were unable to test this compound at the higher concentrations used in Halvorson's experiments, but at 5×10^{-3} M it inhibited alanine uptake by only 15 per cent. Similarly, added ethionine (1.5×10^{-4} M) had no effect on the incorporation of methionine-S[35] or lysine-2-C[14], and it reduced alanine uptake by only 14 per cent.

In considering possible inhibitors of nuclear protein synthesis, our attention was directed to the remarkable observation that repeated injections of cortisone lead to involution of the thymus gland (Santisteban and Dougherty, 1954). When tested on thymus nuclei, *in vitro*, small amounts of cortisone lead to greatly reduced alanine-C[14] uptakes (Table 3).

Among the inhibitors tested, a series of substituted benzimidazoles were of greatest interest. Typical of this class of compounds is the substance 5,6-dichloro - β - D - ribofuranosyl - benzimidazole (DRB). This structural analog of a purine riboside was found by Tamm and Horsfall to retard influenza virus multiplication in the mouse and in tissue culture (Tamm, 1954; Tamm *et al.*, 1954, 1956). When tested on isolated thymus nuclei it

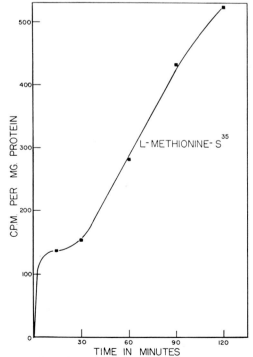

FIGURE 3. The time course of methionine-S[35] incorporation into the proteins of isolated thymus nuclei.

TABLE 1. EFFECT OF ANOXIA AND OF SEVERAL INHIBITORS UPON C[14]-AMINO ACID INCORPORATION BY ISOLATED CALF THYMUS NUCLEI

Conditions of Experiment	Isotope Administered as	Specific Activity of Nuclear Protein	Degree of Inhibition
		c.p.m. per mg	*per cent*
1. Nuclei in O_2	glycine-1-C[14]	71	—
Nuclei in N_2	glycine-1-C[14]	15	80
2. Nuclei in O_2	DL-alanine-1-C[14]	72	—
Nuclei in N_2	DL-alanine-1-C[14]	10	85
3. "Control" nuclei	DL-alanine-1-C[14]	72	—
Nuclei in 2×10^{-4} M dinitrophenol	DL-alanine-1-C[14]	11	84
4. "Control" nuclei	DL-alanine-1-C[14]	131	—
Nuclei in 2×10^{-4} M janus green B	DL-alanine-1-C[14]	3	97
5. "Control" nuclei	DL-alanine-1-C[14]	54	—
Nuclei in 1×10^{-3} M NaCN	DL-alanine-1-C[14]	13	76
Nuclei in 1×10^{-3} M NaN_3	DL-alanine-1-C[14]	5	91
Nuclei + 0.05 mg dicumarol per ml	DL-alanine-1-C[14]	8	85
Nuclei + 1 μg antimycin A per ml	DL-alanine-1-C[14]	6	89

TABLE 2. EFFECT OF FLUORIDE AND OF ADDED METABOLITES UPON C[14]-AMINO ACID INCORPORATION BY ISOLATED CALF THYMUS NUCLEI

Conditions of Experiment	Isotope Administered as	Specific Activity of Protein
		c.p.m. per mg
1. "Control" nuclei	DL-alanine-1-C[14]	62
Nuclei in 1×10^{-3} M Na F	DL-alanine-1-C[14]	57
2. Nuclei without added metabolite	DL-alanine-1-C[14]	40
Nuclei + 40 μM glucose	DL-alanine-1-C[14]	44
Nuclei + 40 μM fructose	DL-alanine-1-C[14]	40
3. Nuclei without added metabolite	glycine-1-C[14]	86
Nuclei + 40 μM glucose	glycine-1-C[14]	99
Nuclei + 40 μM α-ketoglutarate	glycine-1-C[14]	109

effectively inhibits the uptake of alanine-1-C[14]. Tests of this and similar compounds (synthesized by C. Shunk and K. Folkers of the Merck Research Laboratories) are summarized in Table 4. It is of special interest that the inhibitions observed in the isolated nuclei closely parallel those found in tests of viral growth. The ribosyl benzimidazole is an effective inhibitor while the corresponding arabinose derivative is not. Effective inhibition also requires that the ribose exist in the furanose, not the pyranose form, and that the glycosidic linkage between the sugar and the benzimidazole ring should have the β-, and not the α-, configuration.

A remarkable feature of these inhibitors in the viral growth system is the limitation of their time of action. They effectively retard virus multiplication only if they are present at the time of infection or shortly afterward, and much of their effectiveness is lost if they are administered several hours after infection has occurred. This limitation on the time of action is also evident when benzimidazole derivatives are tested on isolated thymus nuclei. The experiments summarized in Figure 5 show that when 5,6-dichloro-β-D-ribofuranosyl-benzimidazole (DRB) is added together with the isotopic alanine, the uptake is inhibited from the outset, and for the duration of the experiment. However, when the DRB is added 30 or 60 minutes after adding the C[14]-alanine there is no appreciable inhibition of the amino acid uptake. The findings suggest that DRB interferes with a preliminary activation of nuclear protein synthesis, and that once this activation has occurred the inhibitor is no longer effective. This agrees with the conclusions drawn previously from the study of the lag phase in alanine-1-C[14] incorporation.

One of the most striking effects on nuclear amino acid incorporation is that produced by sodium ions. Nuclei isolated in sucrose need a sodium supplement in order to incorporate amino acids actively. Figure 6 shows the effect of varied sodium concentration on the level of glycine-1-C[14] uptake. There is a well defined maximum at about 0.07 M under our test conditions. The sodium requirement seems to be specific. An attempt was made to substitute all or part of the sodium in the medium with an equivalent amount of potassium. In these experiments the total salt concentration was kept constant and the ratio NaCl/KCl was varied. When all the sodium is replaced by potassium the uptake falls to 15 per cent of the

TABLE 3. EFFECT OF CHLORAMPHENICOL, CORTISONE AND AMINO ACID ANTAGONISTS UPON C14-AMINO ACID INCORPORATION BY ISOLATED CALF THYMUS NUCLEI

Conditions of Experiment	Isotope Administered as	Specific Activity of Nuclear Protein	Change in C14 or S35 Uptake
		c.p.m. per mg	*per cent*
1. "Control" nuclei	DL-alanine-1-C14	97	—
Nuclei in 3.2×10^{-4} M chloramphenicol	DL-alanine-1-C14	97	0
2. "Control" nuclei	glycine-1-C14	21	—
Nuclei in 1.6×10^{-4} M chloramphenicol	glycine-1-C14	19	−10
3. "Control" nuclei	L-methionine-S35	137	—
Nuclei in 1.6×10^{-4} M chloramphenicol	L-methionine-S35	136	0
4. "Control" nuclei	DL-alanine-1-C14	43	—
Nuclei in 1×10^{-3} M p-fluorophenylalanine	DL-alanine-1-C14	37	−14
5. "Control" nuclei	DL-alanine-1-C14	37	—
Nuclei in 5×10^{-3} M p-fluorophenylalanine	DL-alanine-1-C14	31	−15
6. "Control" nuclei	DL-alanine-1-C14	65	—
Nuclei in 1.5×10^{-4} M ethionine	DL-alanine-1-C14	56	−14
Nuclei in 1.5×10^{-3} M ethionine	DL-alanine-1-C14	51	−21
7. "Control" nuclei	DL-lysine-C14	23	—
Nuclei in 1.5×10^{-4} M ethionine	DL-lysine-C14	22	−4
Nuclei in 1.5×10^{-3} M ethionine	DL-lysine-C14	22	−4
8. "Control" nuclei	L-methionine-S35	221	—
Nuclei in 1.5×10^{-4} M ethionine	L-methionine-S35	215	−3
Nuclei in 1.5×10^{-3} M ethionine	L-methionine-S35	194	−12
9. "Control" nuclei	DL-alanine-1-C14	217	—
Nuclei + 0.063 mg cortisone	DL-alanine-1-C14	138	−36
Nuclei + 0.125 mg cortisone	DL-alanine-1-C14	122	−54

TABLE 4. EFFECT OF BENZIMIDAZOLE DERIVATIVES ON ALANINE-1-C14 UPTAKE BY ISOLATED NUCLEI

Derivative Tested	Amount	Specific Activity of Nuclear Protein	Inhibition of Uptake	Relative Inhibition of Virus Multiplication*
	mg.	*c.p.m. per mg.*	*per cent*	
"Control"	—	50	—	—
5,6-dichloro benzimidazole, 1-β-D Arabino-pyranoside	0.1	45	10	3.1
5,6-dichloro benzimidazole, 1-β-D Ribo-pyranoside	0.1	36	28	15
5,6-dichloro benzimidazole, 1-β-D-Ribo-furanoside	0.1	26	48	92
4,5,6-trichloro benzimidazole, 1-α-D-Ribo-furanoside	0.01	46	8	165
4,5,6-trichloro benzimidazole, 1-β-D-Ribo-furanoside	0.01	36	28	760

* Work of Tamm *et al.*, 1954, 1956; Tamm, 1954.

optimal value. Increasing the sodium to potassium ratio gives a corresponding increase in the amount of amino acid incorporated (Fig. 7). When the sodium concentration is optimal, the addition of small amounts of potassium (chloride) does not influence the uptake.

The extreme dependence of the capacity of the nucleus to incorporate amino acids upon sodium ion concentration makes it necessary to control rather rigorously the sodium level of the incubation medium. This introduces a related problem, namely the osmotic balance between nuclear structures and the suspending medium. It was soon found that nuclei exposed to high sucrose concentrations lost their ability to incorporate amino acids into protein. A more detailed study of this dependence of uptake upon sucrose concen-

tration is presented in Figure 8. The peak of activity under our test conditions occurs at about 0.20 M. The medium also contains sodium phosphate buffer (0.025 M), glucose (0.02 M), and NaCl (0.03 M). Although the effects described bear some resemblance to the osmotic properties of semi-permeable membranes, it should be pointed out that thymus nuclei are not enveloped by an intact, semi-permeable membrane, and that they are freely permeable to large molecules, such as ribonuclease, deoxyribonuclease, histones, protamines and basic dyes. The marked effects of sucrose concentration upon nuclear activity suggest that the fine structure necessary for nuclear protein synthesis is in osmotic balance with its environment, and that nuclear function can vary with that balance. This is reminiscent of experi-

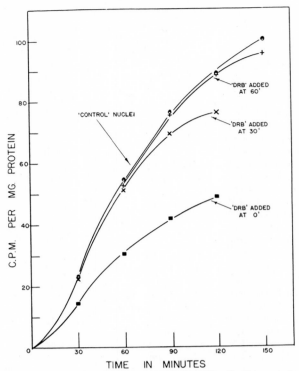

FIGURE 5. The effect of 5,6-dichloro-β-D-ribofuranosyl-benzimidazole (DRB) on alanine-1-C¹⁴ incorporation into the proteins of isolated thymus nuclei. The time course of C¹⁴ incorporation in the presence of DRB is compared with that observed in "control" nuclei (upper curve). Note that DRB added together with the isotopic alanine (at time zero) is an effective inhibitor, whereas DRB added 30 or 60 minutes later is far less effective.

ments on the extended and contracted states of interphase chromosomes (Ris and Mirsky, 1949).

Although it is a simple matter to control the sucrose concentration and sodium level of the incubation medium, there are other factors which influence nuclear amino acid uptake which are not readily subject to control. In working with tissue obtained from commercial packers one finds variations in the age of the thymus, and in the sex and physiological condition of the animal. Weather and feeding, too, can vary the synthetic activity of the nucleus in ways which cannot be predicted or controlled. Thus the actual amount of amino acid incorporated in a given time varies from one nuclear preparation to another, and it is necessary to run daily controls when comparisons are being made.

The synthetic activity of the isolated nucleus can be readily destroyed by heating, by freezing and thawing, or by breaking in a high-speed blendor. Nuclei removed from sucrose to salt solutions, or washed with 0.1 M phosphate buffer prior to incubation in a sucrose medium, lose their ability to incorporate amino acids. Nuclei stored at 2°C gradually lose their synthetic activity. The rate of decline in activity with storage varies con-

siderably in different preparations, but in most cases the ability to incorporate amino acids into nuclear protein is well retained for four to six hours and is almost entirely lost after 24 hours at 2°.

SYNTHESIS *vs.* EXCHANGE

There are several experiments now to be described which make it clear that the uptake of labeled amino acids into nuclear proteins represents an essential aspect of protein synthesis, and is not simply a random, non-specific exchange reaction involving a few labile groups of the nucleus.

The first of these experiments is the demonstration that only the L-isomer of the administered DL-alanine-1-C¹⁴ is incorporated into nuclear protein. The ability of the nucleus to distinguish between D and L forms of the amino acid is indicated by the experiments summarized in Figure 9. In these tests increasing amounts of unlabeled D-alanine or unlabeled L-alanine were added to the incubation medium together with the DL-alanine-1-C¹⁴. If both the D and L forms of the C¹⁴-alanine were utilized by the nucleus then both unlabeled isomers should compete with isotopic molecules for acceptance by the nucleus, and the C¹⁴-activity of the nuclear protein should be correspondingly lowered. Actually, the addition of unlabeled D-alanine has no such effect; only the L-isomer competes for incorporation. It follows, therefore, that only the L-form of the C¹⁴-alanine adminis-

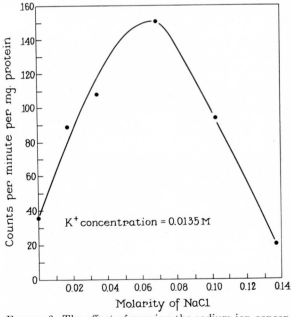

FIGURE 6. The effect of varying the sodium ion concentration of the incubation medium on the ability of thymus nuclei to incorporate glycine-1-C¹⁴. The specific activity of the nuclear protein after 60 minutes incubation in the presence of glycine-C¹⁴ is plotted against the sodium concentration of the medium.

tered is utilized for protein synthesis by the nucleus.

A second experiment was designed to test whether amino acid once incorporated is in constant exchange with other amino acid molecules in the medium. If the uptake of amino acids is indeed reversible then C[14]-alanine once incorporated into nuclear proteins should be exchanged with unlabeled L-alanine added to the medium after incorporation has occurred. This was tested in the experiments summarized in Figure 10. Incorporation of C[14]-alanine was allowed to proceed for 60 minutes. At that time the nuclei were centrifuged down and the isotopic alanine was removed. The nuclei were then resuspended in the presence of a 200-fold excess of unlabeled L-alanine. Samples of the nuclei were removed at 30 minute intervals and the carbon-14 activity of the nuclear protein measured in the usual way. It is evident from the curves that the specific activity of the nuclear proteins remains essentially constant for three hours even in the presence of a great excess of unlabeled alanine. It follows that the C[14]-alanine incorporated into nuclear protein is not subject to selective replacement by unlabeled alanine in the medium. The figure also shows that when addi-

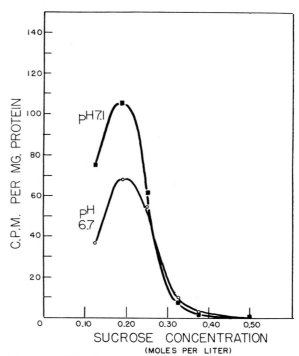

FIGURE 8. The effect of varying the sucrose concentration of the medium upon the ability of thymus nuclei to incorporate alanine-1-C[14]. The specific activity of the nuclear protein after 60 minutes incubation is plotted against the sucrose concentration of the incubation medium.

tional C[14]-alanine is added to the nuclei in such experiments, incorporation proceeds in the usual way. Thus the nuclei will continue to incorporate C[14]-amino acid under conditions where they will not give it up. Similar experiments have been performed using S[35]-labeled methionine and parallel results were obtained. It follows that the incorporation of isotopic amino acids into the proteins of isolated nuclei is essentially irreversible, and the possibility can be excluded that a few active centers in the nuclear protein are in constant amino acid exchange with the medium.

It should be noted, however, that experiments of this kind do not exclude the possibility of a slow, random turnover involving a large number of amino acid residues, all equally subject to replacement; because if a great number of the alanine or methionine residues in the nucleus are able to exchange, and only a few of these turn over in the three or four hour experimental period, then the rate of loss of C[14]-alanine or S[35]-methionine once incorporated will be too small to be followed experimentally.

It may be of value at this point to clarify our usage of the term "protein synthesis." In all experiments where one measures the incorporation of labeled amino acids into proteins, the question naturally arises as to the relationship between the uptake observed and the synthetic process. In the

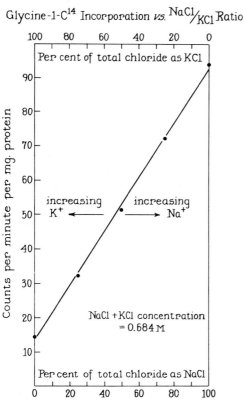

Glycine-1-C[14] Incorporation vs. $\frac{NaCl}{KCl}$ Ratio

FIGURE 7. The effect of varying sodium/potassium ratio on glycine-1-C[14] incorporation by isolated thymus nuclei. The specific activity of the nuclear protein after 60 minutes incubation is plotted against the ratio of sodium to potassium ions in the medium, the total salt concentration being held constant.

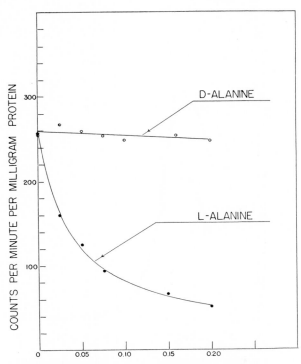

MG. UNLABELED D- OR L—ALANINE ADDED

FIGURE 9. The effect of unlabeled D- and L- alanines upon incorporation of DL-alanine-1-C¹⁴ by isolated thymus nuclei. The specific activity of the nuclear protein after 60 minutes incubation is plotted against the amount of unlabeled D- or L- alanine added to the medium. Note that added D-alanine has no effect on C¹⁴-uptake, whereas L-alanine competes with isotopic molecules for acceptance by the nucleus. It follows that only the L-isomer of the administered C¹⁴-alanine is utilized for nuclear protein synthesis.

strictest sense "synthesis" can be applied only in cases where a net production of new protein molecules can be demonstrated. When such synthesis occurs in the presence of isotopically labeled amino acids the protein formed will be labeled. However, the incorporation of isotopic amino acids does not, in itself, constitute a proof that new protein molecules have been synthesized. Although in these experiments on isolated nuclei, a net synthesis of new protein has not been directly demonstrated, a number of observations make it most probable that we are dealing with a very direct aspect of the synthetic mechanism:

1). The uptake of amino acids is energy dependent.

2). The amount of amino acid incorporated into definite proteins increases with time. When the proteins of the nucleus are fractionated before counting (see below), one observes a progressive time course of amino acid uptake into such well-defined protein fractions as the arginine- and lysine-rich histones.

3). The relative rates of amino acid uptake into different nuclear proteins *in vitro* are in accord with the rates observed in *in vivo* experiments.

4). Isotopic amino acid molecules once incorporated are not rapidly lost by exchange with unlabeled molecules in the medium.

From the amount of isotopic alanine incorporated an estimate can be made of the amount of new protein which may be formed. In a typical experiment 30 mg of nuclei incorporate 0.6 μg (2.4 per cent) of the administered C¹⁴-alanine in one hour. If the average nuclear protein contains about 7.6 per cent alanine (Daly and Mirsky, 1955), this uptake corresponds to the formation of about 8 μg of protein per hour, an amount too small to be demonstrated directly by methods now available to us. Nevertheless, the extent of the synthesis can be better appreciated from the calculation that each nucleus synthesizes 22 molecules of protein of average MW 50,000 every second.

Attempts have been made to increase the extent of incorporation of isotopic alanine and glycine by the addition of a supplement of mixed L-amino acids to the nuclear suspension. No stimulation was observed, which leads to the conclusion that, if the uptake of labeled amino acids represents a net synthesis of protein, the other amino acids required must be present in the nuclei. That this is indeed the case for thymus nuclei isolated by the Behrens' procedure has been recently shown by Kay (1956).

THE ROLE OF DEOXYRIBONUCLEIC ACID IN PROTEIN SYNTHESIS

The notion originally suggested by Brachet and by Caspersson that ribonucleic acids play a role in protein synthesis is now widely accepted as demonstrated. The most direct evidence in its favor stems from the work of Gale and Folkes on amino acid uptake by bacterial cell residues (Gale and Folkes, 1953), and from work in this laboratory on amino acid incorporation by a ribonucleoprotein complex of the liver (Allfrey et al., 1955). In both cases ribonuclease acts to suppress amino acid incorporation.

The isolated cell nucleus affords a unique opportunity to test the role of the deoxyribonucleic acids in the process of protein synthesis, and the results have a special interest because they ultimately bear on the mode of action of the gene, and on the chemical relationships between the nucleus and the cytoplasm.

A number of experiments which relate deoxyribonucleic acid to the process of protein synthesis in the nucleus will now be described. Several of these experiments deal with the effect of deoxyribonuclease on the uptake of labeled amino acids. When isolated nuclei are treated with crystalline pancreatic deoxyribonuclease before adding isotopic amino acids, the incorporation of the latter is markedly impaired. The degree of impairment becomes more serious as more and more of the deoxyribonucleic acid is removed. Experiments showing the relationship between loss of DNA and

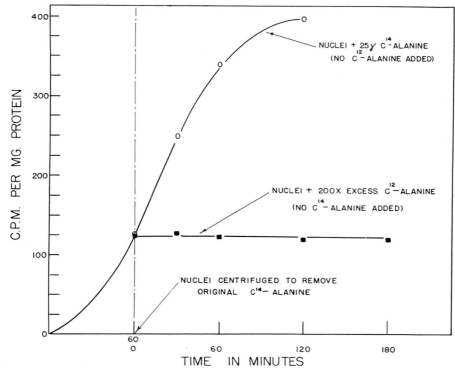

FIGURE 10. The retention of incorporated alanine-1-C[14] following addition of a large excess of unlabeled L-alanine (see text). The specific activity of the nuclear protein at different intervals after adding the unlabeled alanine is plotted against time. The upper curve shows that the nuclei in these experiments are still able to incorporate C[14]-amino acid.

inhibition of alanine-1-C[14] and lysine-2-C[14] uptakes are summarized in Figure 11. At the outset there is roughly a 1:1 correspondence between the per cent DNA removed and the per cent inhibition of the uptake. The inhibition becomes more marked when 30 to 80 per cent of the DNA is removed. Beyond that point the loss of DNA has little effect on the uptake, which remains constant at about 15 to 20 per cent of that observed in control experiments. This sensitivity of the nucleus to treatment with deoxyribonuclease is further evidence for the absence of appreciable whole cell contamination, because intact cells are not sensitive to treatment with this enzyme. Thymus tissue slices or minces, for example, show only a very slight inhibition of alanine-1-C[14] uptake following treatment with deoxyribonuclease, and the inhibition observed (about 15 per cent) could easily be attributed to enzyme attack of cells which had been damaged mechanically.

The foregoing experiments suggest that deoxyribonucleic acid plays a direct role in nuclear protein synthesis. Additional support for this conclusion arises from experiments which test whether the synthetic activity of nuclei treated with deoxyribonuclease can be restored by the addition of supplementary DNA. In these experiments the nuclei were treated with deoxyribonuclease until 70 per cent or more of the DNA had been released into the medium. The nuclei were then centrifuged

down, and the medium containing the DNA hydrolysis products was removed. The nuclei were then resuspended in the presence of a calf thymus DNA preparation: isotopic amino acid was supplied and incorporation allowed to proceed for 60 minutes. The specific activity of the protein in nuclei which had received the deoxyribonucleic acid supplement was then compared with the protien "activities" in control nuclei which had been treated with the enzyme in the same way but which had not received any additional deoxyribonucleic acid. The data in Table 5 make it clear that added calf thymus DNA does, in fact, restore much, and at times, nearly all of the original activity of the nucleus. Other experiments were performed to measure the amount of added nucleic acid taken up by DNAase-treated nuclei (Table 6). The results show that under the conditions used in all the "restoration" experiments, 30 to 40 per cent of a 5 mg DNA supplement enters the nuclei.

It is a matter of some interest that when thymus nuclei in sucrose solution are treated with DNAase, they lose 90 per cent of their DNA and yet no more than 15 per cent of the histone is released; although histones are water-soluble and known to be attached to the DNA in the nucleus. This contrasts strongly with the properties of the same nuclei in a saline medium, for when DNA is

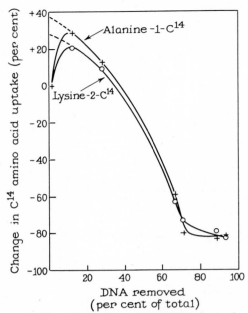

FIGURE 11. The effect of removing DNA from thymus nuclei upon the subsequent incorporation of alanine-1-C^{14} and lysine-2-C^{14}. Nuclei were pretreated with DNAase to remove increasing amounts of their DNA. They were subsequently incubated for 60 minutes in the presence of the isotopic amino acid. The decrease in specific activity of the nuclear protein in treated nuclei, relative to that observed in untreated, "control" nuclei, is plotted against the per cent removal of the DNA.

removed and sucrose is not present, half of the histone is released from the nuclei.

This ability of the thymus nucleus in sucrose to retain its histones despite the removal of DNA may account for the ease with which added DNA is taken up by DNAase-treated nuclei, and it suggests that the proteins of the chromosome are still arranged in a specific and functional configuration.

Pretreatment of isolated thymus nuclei with deoxyribonuclease affects the uptake of different amino acids to different extents (Table 7). Methionine-S^{35} incorporation, for example, was reduced by only 42 per cent under conditions where alanine-1-C^{14} uptake was inhibited 75 per cent. But, despite this difference, the addition of a DNA supplement seems to restore the lost activity equally in both cases.

Several experiments were performed to test whether chemically or physically modified DNA could restore the uptake in DNAase-treated nuclei. It was found that DNA denatured by treatment with alkali (pH 12.2 for 16 hours; Doty, 1955) was just as effective as the original DNA preparation. Apurinic acid, while not as effective as intact DNA, does produce an appreciable stimulation of uptake in the DNAase-treated nuclei. The non-dialyzable DNA "core" which remains after exhaustive digestion of thymus DNA with deoxyribonuclease (Zamenhof and Chargaff, 1950), and the dialyzable split products of the digestion are both able to replace the "whole" DNA in this system (Table 5).

Since even degraded thymus DNA can function in restoring amino acid uptake, it was also a matter of considerable interest to test whether nucleic acids other than calf thymus deoxyribonucleic acid can restore the synthetic capacity of DNAase treated nuclei. We first compared calf thymus DNA with the DNA of wheat germ and found the latter to be far less effective than the former. However, when the study was extended to include DNAs from other sources, it was found that all the other nucleic acids tested were quite comparable to thymus DNA in their ability to restore C^{14}-amino acid incorporation. A number of such experiments are summarized in Table 8. Even sea urchin sperm DNA was as effective as the DNA of the thymus.

The next step was to test the effect of ribonu-

TABLE 5. EFFECT OF SUPPLEMENTARY THYMUS DNA IN RESTORING C^{14}-ALANINE UPTAKE IN DNAase-TREATED NUCLEI

Supplement Tested	Specific Activity of Nuclear Protein			Activity Lost	Activity Regained	Recovery of Lost Activity
	"Control" nuclei	DNAase-treated nuclei	Treated nuclei + supplement			
	cpm/mg	*cpm/mg*	*cpm/mg*	*cpm/mg*	*cpm/mg*	*per cent*
1. Thymus DNA	99	15	55	84	40	48
2. Thymus DNA	135	21	93	114	72	64
3. Thymus DNA	99	33	101	66	68	103
Thymus DNA alkali-denatured	99	33	104	66	71	108
4. Thymus DNA	40	10	29	30	19	63
Thymus DNA apurinic acid	40	10	17.4	30	7.4	25
5. Thymus DNA	38	7.5	28	30.5	20.5	67
Thymus DNA "core" after DNAase digestion	38	7.5	24.5	30.5	17	56
Thymus DNA dialyzable products of DNAase digestion	38	7.5	29	30.5	21.5	70

TABLE 6. COMBINATION OF NUCLEIC ACIDS WITH DNAASE-TREATED NUCLEI

Conditions of Experiment	Amount of DNA in Nuclei	Amount of Added DNA Combined	Per Cent of Added DNA Combined
	mg	*mg*	
"Control" nuclei	11.2	—	—
Nuclei treated with DNAase	2.6	—	—
DNAase-treated nuclei + 5 mg. thymus DNA	4.13	1.63	33
DNAase-treated nuclei + 10 mg. thymus DNA	4.6	2.0	20
DNAase-treated nuclei + 5 mg. alkali-denatured DNA	4.5	1.9	38
DNAase-treated nuclei + 10 mg. alkali-denatured DNA	5.0	2.4	24
DNAase-treated nuclei + 5 mg. yeast RNA	4.3	1.7	34
DNAase-treated nuclei + 10 mg. yeast RNA	5.6	3.0	30

cleic acids on amino acid uptake by DNAase-treated nuclei. Two preprations were tested, one from calf liver, and the other from yeast. Both were just as effective as the DNA of the thymus (Table 9). Since RNA could replace DNA in this system an attempt was made to substitute a mixture of mononucleotides for the RNA. This mixture was made up of the nucleoside 2' or 3' phosphates in the same proportions in which they occur in yeast RNA. These did not restore uptake. By the same token, RNA hydrolyzed in dilute alkali to yield the mononucleotides could not restore alanine incorporation in DNAase-treated nuclei.

Other compounds tested without effect included AMP, ADP, and ATP, and mixtures of the purine and pyrimidine bases. Several dinucleotides prepared from yeast RNA were made available to us through the generosity of Dr. R. B. Merrifield of the Rockefeller Institute. These included adenylic-adenylic dinucleotide, adenylic-guanylic dinucleotide, adenylic-uridylic dinucleotide, and guanylic-cytidylic dinucleotide. None of these compounds could restore uptake in DNAase-treated nuclei.

Although fragments as small as dinucleotides do not seem to be active in our system (with the reservation that only a few of the possible dinucleotides were tested), it was found that the dialyzable split products of RNA digestion by RNAase were partially effective; and it has already been pointed out that the dialyzable split products of DNA digestion by DNAase were quite effective. Both these findings suggest that relatively simple, low-molecular-weight compounds,

TABLE 7. EFFECT OF DNAASE TREATMENT ON ALANINE-1-C^{14} AND METHIONINE-S^{35} INCORPORATION BY ISOLATED NUCLEI

Conditions of Experiment	Isotope Administered as	Specific Activity of Nuclear Protein	DNAase Control	Activity Lost	Activity Regained	Recovery
		c.p.m./mg	*per cent*	*cpm/mg*	*cpm/mg*	*per cent*
"Control" nuclei	DL-alanine-1-C^{14}	40	—	—	—	—
Nuclei pretreated with DNAase	DL-alanine-1-C^{14}	10	25	30	—	—
DNAase-treated nuclei + thymus DNA	DL-alanine-1-C^{14}	29	—	30	19	63
"Control" nuclei	L-methionine-S^{25}	141	—	—	—	—
Nuclei pretreated with DNAase	L-methionine-S^{25}	82	58	59	—	—
DNAase-treated nuclei + thymus DNA	L-methionine-S^{35}	119	—	59	37	63

TABLE 8. EFFECT OF DIFFERENT DNAS IN RESTORING C^{14}-ALANINE UPTAKE IN DNAASE-TREATED NUCLEI

Supplement Tested	Specific Activity of Nuclear Protein			Activity Lost	Activity Regained	Recovery of Lost Activity
	"Control" nuclei	DNAase-treated nuclei	Treated nuclei + supplement			
	cpm/mg	*cpm/mg*	*cpm/mg*	*cpm/mg*	*cpm/mg*	*per cent*
1. Thymus DNA	145	69	101	76	32	42
Wheat germ DNA	145	69	86	76	17	22
2. Thymus DNA	91	25	70	66	45	68
Calf kidney DNA	91	25	70	66	45	68
Chicken erythrocyte DNA	91	25	60	66	35	53
Paracentrotus sperm DNA	91	25	72	66	47	71
3. Thymus DNA	135	21	93	114	72	63
Trout sperm DNA	135	21	89	114	68	60

TABLE 9. EFFECT OF RIBONUCLEIC ACIDS AND RIBONUCLEOTIDES ON C[14]-ALANINE
UPTAKE BY DNAASE-TREATED NUCLEI

Supplement Tested	Specific Activity of Nuclear Protein			Activity Lost	Activity Regained	Recovery of Lost Activity
	"Control" nuclei	DNAase-treated nuclei	Treated nuclei + supplement			
	cpm/mg	cpm/mg	cpm/mg	cpm/mg	cpm/mg	per cent
1. Calf liver RNA	92	54	80	38	26	68
Calf thymus DNA	92	54	81	38	27	71
2. Thymus DNA	68	23	54	45	31	69
Yeast RNA	68	23	58	45	35	78
Yeast RNA, hydrolyzed in 0.3 N NaOH	68	23	23	45	0	0
Yeast RNA, dialyzable after RNAase digestion	68	23	36	45	13	29
A, G, U, C, mononucleotide mixture	68	23	23	45	0	0
3. Thymus DNA	83	14	46	69	32	46
Yeast RNA	83	14	45	69	31	45
Adenylic-adenylic dinucleotide	83	14	18	69	4	6
Adenylic-guanylic dinucleotide	83	14	18	69	4	6
Adenylic-uridylic dinucleotide	83	14	18	69	4	6
Guanylic-cytidylic dinucleotide	83	14	18	69	4	6

perhaps of the order of trinucleotides, are able to substitute for DNA in mediating or facilitating amino acid incorporation. Further fractionation studies are now in progress in an attempt further to characterize and isolate the active dialyzable material.

That intact nucleic acids have a high degree of specificity in biological systems is evident both from the role of DNA in bacterial transformation (Avery, MacLeod and McCarty, 1944), and of RNA in tobacco mosaic virus infection (Gierer and Schramm, 1956; Fraenkel-Conrat and Williams, 1955; Lippincott and Commoner, 1956). In the amino acid incorporation system which we have described there is, as yet, no inkling of such specificity. On the contrary, the findings in nuclei deprived of their original DNA suggest a rather generalized ability of polynucleotide fragments to facilitate amino acid incorporation. In the intact nucleus this ability is very probably linked with factors of specificity in the intact DNA. Yet the ability of other DNAs, DNA fragments, and RNA to substitute for thymus DNA in these experiments introduces some questions of considerable interest. Does specificity reside in the chromosomal protein as well as in the DNA? Evidence has already been presented to show that even the smaller proteins of the chromosome are retained by DNAase-treated nuclei. If the proteins originally associated with DNA retain their specific configurations, then added polynucleotide may be taken up only to conform with the original spatial arrangement of the native DNA. If this is the case, then the proteins synthesized by 'restored' DNAase-treated nuclei might be the same, regardless of the source of added nucleic acid. On the other hand, if specificity resides only in the nucleic acid, then the possibility exists that added nucleic acids lead to the synthesis by the nucleus of different proteins. This would be analogous to bacteriophage DNA dominating and modifying the metabolism of the cell which it infects. This possibility that different proteins are made in the presence of different nucleic acids is being investigated. An alternate possibility, of course, is that the nucleus uses added polynucleotides for the synthesis of its own, characteristic DNA (but cannot use nucleoside 2' or 3' phosphates). The ability of isolated nuclei to synthesize nucleic acids from small precursors is demonstrated below.

The ability of RNA to restore alanine uptake in nuclei deprived of their DNA naturally raises the question of the role of ribonucleic acid in nuclear metabolism. Attempts to relate the ribonucleic acid of the thymus nucleus directly to nuclear protein synthesis have not so far been successful. Treatment of the isolated nuclei with ribonuclease before adding C[14]-amino acids has no effect on the uptake of the latter. However, this result does not permit the conclusion that ribonucleic acid has no part in nuclear protein synthesis, because in the experiments mentioned only 54 per cent of the nuclear RNA could be released by the action of the enzyme.

It was previously noted that the uptake of isotopic amino acids into the proteins of thymus nuclei is not a rapidly reversible, exchange-type reaction. This conclusion was obtained from experiments which showed that labeled amino acids once incorporated into nuclear proteins are not readily replaced by non-labeled amino acids in the medium. Similar experiments were performed on DNAase-treated nuclei which were supplemented with either thymus DNA or yeast RNA. These tests are summarized in Figure 12. In both cases the uptake was apparently irreversible: The nuclei

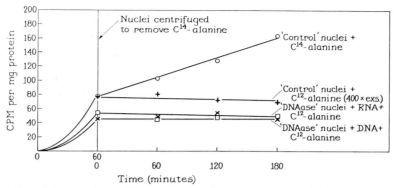

FIGURE 12. The retention of the alanine-1-C^{14} incorporated into the proteins of DNAase-treated nuclei which were "restored" by adding thymus DNA or yeast RNA (see text). The nuclei were treated with DNAase, then given a nucleic acid supplement and incubated in the presence of C^{14}-alanine. They were then centrifuged down and reincubated in the presence of a great excess of unlabeled L-alanine. The specific activity of the nuclear protein at different intervals after adding the unlabeled alanine is plotted against time. The upper curve shows that the nuclei in these experiments are still able to incorporate C^{14}-amino acid.

TABLE 10. EFFECT OF METHYL GREEN, PROTAMINE AND A HISTONE UPON
C^{14}-AMINO ACID INCORPORATION BY ISOLATED CALF THYMUS NUCLEI

Conditions of Experiment	Isotope Administered as	Specific Activity of Nuclear Protein	Change in C^{14} Uptake
		cpm per mg	*per cent*
1. "Control" nuclei	DL-alanine-1-C^{14}	154	—
Nuclei + 0.125 mg methyl green	DL-alanine-1-C^{14}	167	+8
Nuclei + 0.25 mg methyl green	DL-alanine-1-C^{14}	162	+5
Nuclei + 0.50 mg methyl green	DL-alanine-1-C^{14}	116	−25
2. "Control" nuclei	glycine-1-C^{14}	205	—
Nuclei + 0.25 mg methyl green	glycine-1-C^{14}	251	+22
3. "Control" nuclei	glycine-1-C^{14}	89	—
Nuclei + 0.50 mg methyl green	glycine-1-C^{14}	64	−28
4. "Control" nuclei	DL-alanine-1-C^{14}	154	—
Nuclei + 0.375 mg protamine	DL-alanine-1-C^{14}	168	+9
Nuclei + 0.75 mg protamine	DL-alanine-1-C^{14}	159	+3
Nuclei + 1.50 mg protamine	DL-alanine-1-C^{14}	164	+6
5. "Control" nuclei	glycine-1-C^{14}	79	—
Nuclei + 1.5 mg protamine	glycine-1-C^{14}	70	−11
Nuclei + 1.5 mg histone (lysine-rich)	glycine-1-C^{14}	76	−4

did not lose isotopic amino acid once it was incorporated. The failure to "exchange" cannot be the result of a loss of activity because such nuclei given C^{14}-alanine show an extensive C^{14} uptake into their proteins.

Since, in the intact nucleus, deoxyribonucleic acid is required for protein synthesis the question naturally arises as to how the DNA participates in amino acid incorporation. Several experiments were performed to test whether the action of deoxyribonucleic acid requires the active participation of its free phosphate groups. The results of these experiments are summarized in Table 10. The procedure used was to add varying amounts of basic compounds which are known to combine with the free phosphoric acid groups of deoxyribonucleic acid. The compounds selected included the basic dye, methyl green, and two basic proteins, protamine, and a lysine-rich histone prepared from calf thymus. It is clear that the addi-

tion of small amounts of methyl green, protamine or histone to the nuclei before adding the isotopic amino acid has little effect on the uptake. Larger amounts lead to a partial impairment of carbon-14 incorporation; but the impairment may reflect osmotic or other damage to the system, since large amounts of added serum albumin also decrease the uptake. The results suggest that some of the free phosphate groups of the DNA can be blocked without affecting the uptake of labeled amino acids.

WHICH NUCLEAR PROTEINS BECOME LABELED?

The answer to this question depends at the outset upon the existence of a dependable and meaningful scheme of fractionating the proteins of the nucleus. This is a field of endeavor which is now in its earliest stages of development, though it promises to become a major topic of biochemical investigation.

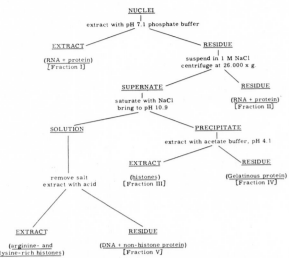

FRACTIONATION OF THE PROTEINS OF
ISOLATED CALF THYMUS NUCLEI

FIGURE 13. Flow-Sheet for the fractionation of the proteins of isolated thymus nuclei (see text).

We have developed a provisional fractionation procedure which is applicable to the proteins of thymus "sucrose" nuclei, and which permits the separation of several classes of proteins of different properties and considerable biological interest. In its essentials the procedure is as follows (see Flow-Sheet in Fig. 13):

1). The nuclei are incubated in buffered sucrose solution in the presence (in these experiments) of C^{14}-alanine. After uptake has occurred the nuclei are centrifuged down. The protein released into the medium is precipitated with trichloroacetic acid (TCA). The amount of this protein in the medium increases with the time of incubation, but it has a very low specific activity relative to the other proteins of the nucleus. The uptake into this fraction does not seem to be dependent upon DNA since pre-treatment of the nuclei with DNAase does not affect it; nor does RNAase have any effect.

2). The nuclei are next extracted with 0.1 M potassium phosphate buffer at pH 7.1. The extract contains some RNA and a small amount of protein, the yield of which seems to diminish as the incubation is prolonged. This protein [Fraction I] has considerable interest because at times it is the most actively labeled fraction of the nucleus. Moreover, the uptake of isotope into this fraction is almost completely abolished by pre-treating the nuclei with DNAase. It is not affected by pre-treatment with RNAase.

3). The nuclei are then suspended in 1 M sodium chloride solution, in which they swell and largely dissolve. The opalescent solution is centrifuged at 26,000 × g to sediment the undissolved material. This residue [Fraction II] comprises about ten per cent of the nuclear mass and con-

tains one-third of the nuclear ribonucleic acid. There is evidence to suggest that this fraction contains the nucleoli (Bessis, 1954).

4). The supernatant after high speed centrifugation contains the bulk of the protein of the nucleus, and all of the deoxyribonucleic acid. It can be fractionated to yield different histones, a gelatinous protein, and an unfractionated residue. The protein in the latter is firmly attached to the DNA (Allfrey, et al., 1955).

The distribution of C^{14}-activity in these different protein fractions is a matter of some interest (Table 11). (It should be mentioned that the total alanine contents of the protein fractions are very similar, so that differences in carbon-14 concentration reflect differences in the metabolic activity of the various proteins.) It was found that the protein most closely associated with the DNA is more active than all other proteins of the nucleus, with the occasional exception of the small fraction extractable in pH 7.1 buffer. This result lends further support to the conclusion drawn from deoxyribonuclease experiments that the DNA plays a direct role in protein synthesis. A second point of interest is the fact that the level of isotope incorporation into the histone proteins is relatively low. This result agrees with earlier in vivo experiments in which it was noted that the incorporation of N^{15}-glycine into the histones of mouse liver, pancreas, and kidney is much lower than the uptake into the residual proteins of the chromosome (Daly et al., 1952).

A final point deals with the effect of pH upon amino acid incorporation into the different protein fractions of isolated nuclei. When nuclei are incubated at pH 6.7, the uptake of C^{14}-alanine into the DNA-attached protein is only about half of that observed following incubation at pH 7.3. In contrast, the uptake into the proteins of the "pH 7.1 extract" is slightly higher when the nuclei are incubated at pH 6.7.

NUCLEIC ACID SYNTHESIS

The question now arises as to whether the isolated thymus nucleus can synthesize nucleic acid by itself. This was tested by incubating the nuclei in the presence of C^{14}-labeled glycine, a substance known to be a precursor of the purine ring in nucleic acid biosynthesis. Table 12 summarizes some preliminary experiments in which incorporation was demonstrated in three ways. In the first, the total nucleic acid was extracted with dilute KOH and prepared by zone electrophoresis. It may contain a trace of adsorbed protein. In the other experiments the nucleotides and the purines were separated on ion-exchange resins. In all cases, a detectable amount of isotope appeared in the nucleic acid. (In a recent communication, Friedkin and Wood, 1956, report the incorporation of C^{14}-thymidine by isolated rabbit thymus nuclei. In their experiments the presence of DNAase lowers the incorporation.) The effect of the nucleases on glycine-1-C[14] uptake into the nucleic acids has not yet been tested.

Oxidative Phosphorylation in Isolated Nuclei

It has been shown that the uptake of amino acids into nuclear proteins is an energy-dependent, aerobic process. One of the questions which naturally arises is how the nucleus meets the energy requirement for the synthetic process. Since it has been generally accepted that in the cytoplasm energy-rich compounds such as ATP and related nucleotides participate in numerous synthetic processes, one might suppose that such compounds are involved in protein synthesis within the nucleus. This would fit in with the previous observations that amino acid incorporation is an oxidative process which is blocked by certain uncoupling reagents which are known to inhibit the synthesis of ATP in mitochondria. We have therefore investigated the nucleotide system of the nucleus.

Our first step has been to show that quantitatively and qualitatively much the same complement of acid-soluble mononucleotides occurs in the nucleus as in the cytoplasm. Then it has been found that within the nucleus these nucleotides can be phosphorylated to the energy-rich triphosphate form. As to the nature of the phosphorylation, there exist certain resemblances as well as differences between the nucleus and mitochondria. Another aspect of the problem that has been investigated concerns the way in which nucleotides are held in the nucleus. Finally, attempts have been made to elucidate the role of the nuclear mononucleotides in the synthesis of protein as it occurs in the nucleus. The work which will be mentioned below has been done on calf thymus nuclei isolated in sucrose-CaCl$_2$, unless otherwise specified.

Presence of Nucleotides in the Nucleus

When one investigates water-soluble substances such as mononucleotides in isolated nuclei, it is important to use preparations isolated in such a way that loss or adsorption of these substances is prevented during the course of the nuclear isolation. Nuclei isolated in non-aqueous media (so-called Behrens' type nuclei) meet these requirements. Analyses of nucleotides were therefore first performed on isolated "non-aqueous" nuclei of calf thymus, and the results were compared with those obtained in thymus tissue (which had been treated with the same solvents to which the nuclei had been exposed during their isolation). Cold two per cent perchloric acid extracts of "non-aqueous" nuclei and tissue were fractionated by Dowex-1 ion-exchange chromatography as described by Cohn and modified by Hurlbert et al. (1954). A typical chromatogram is illustrated in Figure 14. It is seen that calf thymus nuclei contain quantitatively and qualitatively nearly the same complement of nucleotides as the whole

TABLE 11. ALANINE-1-C[14] INCORPORATION INTO DIFFERENT PROTEIN FRACTIONS OF THYMUS NUCLEI

Protein Fraction	Incubation Time	Specific Activity
	min.	*cpm/mg*
1. Total nuclear protein.................	90	107
Fraction I (protein soluble in pH 7.1 buffer).............................	90	179
Fraction II (residue after extraction in extraction in 1 M NaCl)............	90	117
Fraction III (histones)...............	90	36
Fraction IV (gelatinous protein)......	90	157
Fraction V (non-histone protein associated with DNA)...................	90	243
2. Protein released to medium during incubation...........................	30	5
	60	8
	90	16
Fraction I........................	30	10
	60	66
	90	105
Arginine-rich histones................	30	2.3
	60	4.5
	90	6.7
Lysine-rich histones..................	30	—
	60	5.6
	90	6.9
3. "Control" nuclei		
Protein released to medium during incubation......................	90	41
Fraction I........................	90	323
Other fractions combined...........	90	64
DNAase-treated nuclei		
Protein released to medium during incubation......................	90	47
Fraction I........................	90	25
Other fractions combined...........	90	5

TABLE 12. INCORPORATION OF GLYCINE-1-C[14] INTO THE PROTEINS AND NUCLEIC ACIDS OF ISOLATED CALF THYMUS NUCLEI

Nuclear Component	Specific Activity
	cpm per mg
Total nuclear protein	117
Nucleic acid prepared by zone electrophoresis	19
Nucleotides prepared on Dowex-1	11
Purines prepared on Dowex-50	57

tissue. Mononucleotides of adenine, guanine, cytosine, and uracil, together with several uridine diphosphate derivatives and diphosphopyridine nucleotide were identified; one of the striking features here being the predominating amount of adenine nucleotides. Only a trace of cytidine nucleotides was found. In a two per cent perchloric

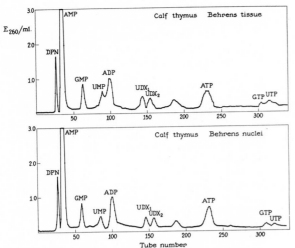

FIGURE 14. Acid-soluble nucleotides of calf thymus "non-aqueous" nuclei and the corresponding whole tissue (see also the top column of Table 13). Note the predominance of monophosphates over di- and triphosphates.

acid extract more than 80 per cent of ultraviolet absorbing material at 260 mμ is found to consist of nucleotides, either by adding up all nucleotide peaks on the chromatogram, or by measuring at 260 mμ the quantity of light-absorbing material which did not combine with Dowex-1 resin. The quantity of nucleotides in "non-aqueous" thymus nuclei is about 1.7 per cent of the total nuclear mass. Practically the same content of nucleotides in the nucleus as in the cytoplasm was also found in the case of calf liver, and of chicken erythrocytes.

The overall concentration of nucleotides in the nucleus is however different from one type of tissue to another. Nuclei from metabolically active tissues such as calf thymus, or calf liver have a higher content of nucleotides than is found in nuclei of such metabolically inert cells as chicken erythrocytes or trout spermatozoa (Table 13).

When analyses of nucleotides are performed on calf thymus nuclei isolated in 0.25 M sucrose-0.002 to 0.003 M CaCl$_2$, it is found that they usually retain 60 to 80 per cent of their original acid-soluble nucleotide content. However the ability to retain the nucleotides in sucrose nuclei from different calf thymus tissues at different times of the year varies considerably. Such nucleotides as are retained after isolation of nuclei remain in the nuclei even after repeated washings with cold sucrose-CaCl$_2$ solution (Table 14). This is rather surprising because of the diffusible nature of nucleotides in aqueous media, and because the nuclear membrane of nuclei isolated in a sucrose solution is not a barrier to the passage of even much larger molecules. The way in which nucleotides are retained in the nucleus will be discussed later.

Chromatographic analyses (Fig. 15, Table 13) revealed that sucrose nuclei have a pattern of nucleotide distribution similar to that found in "non-aqueous" nuclei, with an important exception which will be dealt with in the next section.

Even before the analyses of nucleotides on isolated nuclei that have just been described were made, there were observations suggesting the presence of these substances in nuclei: Davies (1954), and Walker and Yates (1952) in the course of their microspectrophotometric observation on nuclei in tissue culture, reported that there are substances which absorb ultraviolet light and are soluble in acid-alcohol fixatives. The English authors supposed that their "lower nucleotides" are precursors of DNA. However their procedure

TABLE 13. ACID SOLUBLE ADENINE NUCLEOTIDES IN TISSUES AND NUCLEI

Material Analysed	E$_{260}$ per g Lipid Free Dry Matter Present as				
	Total E$_{260}$	AMP	ADP	ATP	Total adenine nucleotides
Calf thymus tissue* (Behrens preparation)........	500	102	56	43	201
Calf thymus Behrens nuclei*.....................	500	93	58	44	195
Calf thymus Behrens nuclei......................	420	80	19	14	113
Calf thymus tissue.............................	580	119	29	15	163
Calf thymus tissue.............................	580	118	33	20	171
Calf thymus sucrose nuclei......................	306	28	23	46	97
Calf thymus sucrose nuclei......................	390	34	22	58	104
Calf thymus sucrose nuclei......................	460	39	29	89	157
Calf liver tissue (Behrens preparation)...........	382	—	—	—	—
Calf liver Behrens nuclei........................	350	—	—	—.	—
Chicken erythrocytes (Behrens preparation).......	92.0	3.2	9.3	15.8	28.3
Chicken erythrocyte Behrens nuclei..............	95.4	6.1	14.0	14.1	34.2
Brown trout sperm.............................	170	—	—	—	—
Rainbow trout sperm...........................	171	—	—	—	—

* Derived from the same thymus gland.

does not permit identification of each nucleotide. Naora and Takeda (1954) recognized the occurrence of labile phosphate compounds, which they assumed to be ATP, in the rat liver nuclei isolated by the Behrens' procedure. Although possible contamination of glucose-1-phosphate which is also acid-labile (LePage, 1951) and is known to occur in the nuclei should be considered, at least a part of their "labile phosphate" must be ATP. Edmonds and LePage (1955) reported the presence of various nucleotides in the sucrose nuclei obtained from Flexner-Jobling tumor cells. Kay and Davidson (1955) noted the occurrence of acid-soluble nucleotides in "non-aqueous" nuclei from various tissues. Now their chemical nature has been established and it is likely that nuclear mononucleotides, as cytoplasmic ones, play a part in numerous processes, including the synthesis of protein that occurs in the nucleus.

Phosphorylation of Nucleotides in the Nucleus

The predominance of nucleotide monophosphates in thymus tissue and in thymus nuclei prepared by the "non-aqueous" procedure should not be taken to indicate the actual condition *in vivo*, or an artifact due to the action of non-aqueous media. We have repeatedly observed that so-called "fresh" calf thymus tissue has a similar predominance of monophosphates over di- and triphosphates (Table 13). It seemed probable to us that the predominance of these low energy forms is simply a reflection of anoxia resulting from the death of the animal. Evidence to support this conclusion is derived from a series of nucleotide analyses of rat thymus tissues which can be excised from the animal after death with a speed that cannot be achieved in the case of a slaughterhouse animal such as the calf. Some of the rat tissues were frozen in liquid nitrogen immediately upon excision; others were incubated at 30°C for five, ten, and twenty minutes. As can be seen in Figure 16, in the immediately frozen tissue, ATP predominates over ADP and AMP, and during the course of incubation the amount of ATP sharply drops with a simultaneous increase of AMP, ADP content remaining relatively unchanged. The same sort of changes were observed in the uridine and guanine nucleotides. A comparison of nucleotide distribution in "non-aqueous" nuclei and sucrose nuclei reveals an interesting difference between them: the predominance of low energy forms in "non-aqueous" nuclei and of high energy forms in sucrose nuclei. This is taken to indicate that during the preparation of sucrose nuclei in the cold, the monophosphate characteristic of the excised tissue is largely converted back to the energy-rich triphosphate form which predominates in the living tissue. The post-mortem predominance of nucleotide monophosphates in thymus tissue seems therefore to afford a unique opportunity to study the mechanism of their phosphorylation in the nucleus.

| | E_{260} per g Lipid Free Dry Matter | | |
	Exp. 1	Exp. 2	Exp. 3
Original sucrose nuclear preparation..	264	198	100
After 1st washing....................	234	177	90
After 2nd washing...................	232	—	—

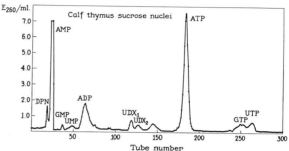

FIGURE 15. Acid-soluble nucleotides of calf thymus sucrose nuclei. Note the predominance of triphosphates over di- and monophosphates.

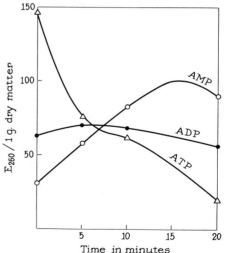

FIGURE 16. Post-mortem changes of adenine nucleotides in rat thymus tissue. Excised thymus tissue was incubated at 30° C for 5, 10, 15, and 20 minutes.

The formation of high energy phosphate bonds is presumably the result of extensive aeration of the homogenates and nuclear suspensions during the isolation procedure. To determine whether this phosphorylation involves participation of the cytoplasmic fraction in the homogenate, or whether it is an intranuclear phenomenon, two types of experiments were carried out.

TABLE 15. PHOSPHORYLATION IN ISOLATED CALF THYMUS SUCROSE NUCLEI

Material Analysed	Total E_{260} in 1 g Dry Matter	Per Cent of Total E_{260} Present as			
		AMP	ADP	ATP	Total adenine nucleotides
Sucrose nuclei after rapid isolation (25 min. at 2° C)	308	19.0	10.5	7.6	37.1
Above nuclei stirred at 2° C for 50 min. after isolation	308	3.5	5.7	24.5	33.7
Sucrose nuclei after rapid isolation (28 min. at 2° C)	295	14.2	8.5	7.6	30.3
Above nuclei stirred gently at 2° C for 60 min. after isolation	300	4.6	5.6	20.4	30.4
Calf thymus tissue	—	18.8	5.8	3.7	28.3
Sucrose nuclei prepared rapidly from above tissue (28 min. at 2°C)	240	16.0	7.9	6.7	30.6
Above nuclei stirred gently at 2° C for 60 min. after isolation	233	6.3	6.4	16.6	29.3

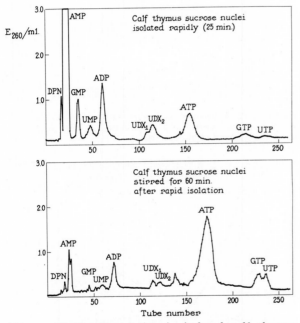

FIGURE 17. Phosphorylation in isolated calf thymus sucrose nuclei. Acid-soluble nucleotides of sucrose nuclei isolated rapidly (in 25 minutes) at 2°C (above), and of the same nuclei stirred gently in the cold for an additional 50 minutes (below). Note the increase in amount of triphosphates after 50 minutes.

TABLE 16. SYNTHESIS OF ATP IN THE SUCROSE HOMOGENATES OF CALF THYMUS TISSUE WITH SEPARATION INTO NUCLEAR AND CYTOPLASMIC FRACTIONS

Material Analysed	Per Cent of Total E_{260} Present as					
	Unadsorbed to Dowex-1	AMP	ADP	ATP	Total adenine nucleotides	Unadsorbed + total adenine nucleotides
Homogenate	18.0	14.5	3.1	1.5	19.1	37.1
Cytoplasm	28.0	7.7	2.3	1.0	11.0	39.0
Nuclei	18.0	2.5	3.2	14.4	20.1	38.1

1). Nuclei were isolated as quickly as possible (at 2°C in 25 to 28 minutes). At this time most nucleotides are still present in the monophosphate form. Such a nuclear preparation was then gently stirred for an additional 50 to 60 minutes in the cold. At the end of this time a large part of the monophosphates had been converted into triphosphates (Table 15, Fig. 17).

2). A thymus tissue homogenate in sucrose-CaCl$_2$ solution was stirred gently for 95 minutes at 4°C. This homogenate was then fractionated into nuclear and cytoplasmic components. As indicated in Table 16, the original homogenate at the beginning of the experiment contained a large amount of AMP but almost no ATP. It is obvious that during the incubation of the homogenate in the cold under the prevailing experimental conditions, phosphorylation of AMP took place in the nuclear but not in the cytoplasmic fraction, and the same may be said of the guanine and uridine nucleotides. The decrease of AMP content in the cytoplasmic fraction was probably the result of phosphatase action. This phosphatase does not seem to act on the nuclear nucleotides (Table 16).

The two experiments that have just been described show that phosphorylation of nucleotides occurs within the nucleus. The next experiments were arranged to enable us to compare nuclear phosphorylation with mitochondrial oxidative phosphorylation, which has been extensively investigated. An important characteristic of phosphorylation in mitochondria is that considerable quantities of nucleotides can be added to a mitochondrial preparation and that the nucleotides so added become phosphorylated. A distinctive feature of nuclear phosphorylation is that only intranuclear monophosphates seem to be phosphorylated, for added AMP is not acted upon. In an experiment to show whether nuclei act upon added nucleotides, thymus sucrose nuclei were isolated rapidly so that most nucleotides were still in the form of mononucleotides. At this point, to the concentrated nuclear suspension, about twice as much AMP as total intranuclear nucleotides was added with and also without the appropriate amount of inorganic phosphate. The suspension

TABLE 17. EFFECTS OF METABOLIC INHIBITORS ON PHOSPHORYLATION OF
NUCLEOTIDES IN ISOLATED CALF THYMUS SUCROSE NUCLEI

Inhibitor	Concentration	Change in Phosphorylation due to Added Inhibitor (%)	Inhibitory Effect on		References for Mitochondrial Data
			Nuclear phosphorylation	Mitochondrial phosphorylation	
Sodium cyanide	1×10^{-3} M	−100	+	+	—
Carbon monoxide	100 per cent	−100	+	+	—
2,4-Dinitrophenol	2×10^{-4} M	−100	+	+	Loomis and Lipmann (1948)
Sodium azide	1×10^{-3} M	−100	+	+	Loomis and Lipmann (1949)
Antimycin A	1 µg/ml	−61	+	+	Potter et al. (1952)
Dicumarol	1×10^{-4} M	0	−	+	Martius et al. (1953)
Janus Green B	2×10^{-5} M	+6	−	+	Dianzani et al. (1956)
Methylene Blue	2×10^{-5} M	+30	−	+	Lehninger (1949)
	2.5×10^{-4} M	+21			
Calcium ions	2×10^{-3} M	0	−	+	Lehninger (1949)
	3×10^{-3} M	0			
	4×10^{-3} M	0			

was then stirred for an additional 120 minutes in the cold. At the end of the experiment, exactly the same amount of AMP that had been added to the suspension was recovered as AMP, whereas the amount of ADP, and the amount of synthesized ATP were just the same in the material to which AMP had been added and in the control to which no AMP had been added. It should be noted that the phosphate required for phosphorylation is available inside the nucleus; in no experiments on nuclear phosphorylation has the addition of phosphate been required. We have made some preliminary observations in this connection; sucrose nuclei when isolated rapidly contain less inorganic phosphate than is required for the phosphorylation of nuclear mononucleotides, and during the course of phosphorylation inorganic phosphate actually increases in amount. It is therefore probable that the phosphate available for the nuclear phosphorylation is derived from some organic phosphates in the nucleus.

When the effects of metabolic inhibitors are tested, one can see certain resemblances as well as differences between nuclear and mitochondrial phosphorylation (Table 17). Nuclear, like mitochondrial phosphorylation is completely inhibited by some common inhibitors such as sodium cyanide, carbon monoxide, sodium azide and dinitrophenol (Loomis and Lipmann, 1948, 1949). Considering the mode of action of these inhibitors it is probable that the phosphorylation concerned is oxidative, and involves electron transport by means of cytochrome whereby energy-rich phosphate bonds are synthesized. Antimycin A (Potter and Reif, 1952) blocked this process by 60 per cent. Calcium ions are necessary in our system in order to maintain the nuclear structure. Varying calcium concentrations, from 2×10^{-3} M to 4×10^{-3} M, did not influence the rate of phosphorylation. That no phosphorylation takes place in the cytoplasmic fraction under our experimen-

tal conditions has been mentioned already. Phosphorylation in the cytoplasmic fraction is probably prevented by the presence of calcium ions, a known potent inhibitor of mitochondrial oxidative phosphorylation (Lehninger, 1949). Certain reagents which block phosphorylation in mitochondria, namely dicumarol, janus green B and methylene blue have no effect or if any, a slightly accelerative effect on nuclear phosphorylation (Lehninger, 1949; Martius and Nitz-Litzow, 1953; Dianzani and Scuró, 1956). These observations may be taken as additional evidence against the participation of mitochondria in the phosphorylation occurring in preparations of isolated nuclei. In all inhibitor experiments, the adenine, uridine and guanine nucleotides behaved in a parallel fashion.

Nuclei do not seem to contain the equipment for ordinary terminal oxidation as found in mitochondria, such as cytochrome c oxidase, cytochrome c and the flavoproteins including cytochrome c reductases (Hogeboom et al., 1954; Stern and Timonen, 1954). In the case of calf thymus it has been reported that cytochrome c oxidase is sharply localized in the mitochondrial fraction; no detectable amount of this enzyme was found in the nuclei. The evidence that cytochrome c oxidase is absent from the nuclei is, however, perhaps not as decisive as would appear. The fact that the cytochrome c added to nuclei is not oxidized should be considered in relation to the fact that added AMP is also not acted upon. And yet in the latter case we know that nuclei actually phosphorylate the AMP already within them. It is, accordingly, worth considering that nuclei may contain cytochrome c, possibly in low concentration, which they are able to oxidize. Experiments on DPN cytochrome c reductase are unfortunately not decisive (Stern and Timonen, 1954). If sucrose nuclei do not in fact contain any cytochrome c oxidase, it may be supposed that nuclear phosphorylation proceeds through a respiratory chain which differs from that present in mitochondria. One such difference might be the occurrence of different cytochromes, and in this connection it has already been shown that the cytochromes of microsomes differ from those of mitochondria (Strittmatter and Ball, 1954; Chance and Williams, 1954). Although inhibitor experiments indicate a difference between nuclear and mitochondrial phosphorylation, they do not yet throw any light on the details of the nuclear system.

Considering the fact that cyanide, carbon monoxide, azide and dinitrophenol block nuclear phosphorylation the involvement of glycolysis in this process is unlikely.

Although most inhibitors which block nuclear phosphorylation also stop amino acid uptake in the nucleus, at least one reagent, namely dicumarol, which does not affect phosphorylation does inhibit protein synthesis. This result might indicate that dicumarol blocks the energy transfer from the nucleotide system to the synthesis of protein.

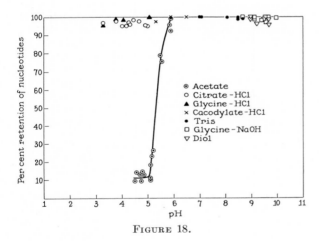

FIGURE 18.

TABLE 18. EFFECT OF SOME SUBSTANCES ON THE RETENTION OF NUCLEOTIDES IN CALF THYMUS SUCROSE NUCLEI

Substances 0.02 M in Sucrose	pH of Media	Per Cent Loss
Formate	4.65	98
Acetate	4.45	90
Acetate	5.90	1.9
Propionate	4.32	95
Monochloroacetate	4.35	99
Ethyl alcohol	4.25	2.8
Acetaldehyde	4.40	4.1
Citrate-HCl	4.45	2.5
Glycine-HCl	4.10	0
Succinate	4.35	0
Acetone	4.35	0
Acetone	7.45	0

Retention of Nucleotides in the Nucleus

The ability of sucrose nuclei to retain nucleotides is really quite surprising. It has been mentioned already that the bulk of the nucleotides is retained in the sucrose nuclei after their isolation. The nucleotides of isolated nuclei are well retained for at least 24 hours in the cold, or after repeated washings of nuclei with cold sucrose-$CaCl_2$ solution. Treatment of sucrose nuclei with 0.5 M sucrose, or with 0.25 M sucrose-0.003 M $CaCl_2$ containing 0.14 M NaCl has almost no effect on nucleotide retention.

Nucleotide retention in the nuclei is, however, dependent on the presence of sucrose, for as soon as sucrose is replaced by a buffer solution in water at any pH, all nucleotides are completely lost from the nuclei. Citric acid nuclei, sucrose nuclei treated with 0.01 M citric acid without sucrose, or sucrose nuclei treated with saline in the absence of sucrose do not contain the nucleotides. One of the interesting features about nucleotide retention may be its irreversibility. Once nuclei lose their nucleotides by any means we have tried, nucleotides added to the medium cannot be taken up.

As long as there is sucrose in the medium, nuclei can be subjected to dilute buffer solutions over a wide pH range without loss of nucleotides (Fig. 18). In such experiments, to one volume of nuclear suspension, nine volumes of 0.022 M buffer in 0.25 M sucrose-0.003 M $CaCl_2$ were stirred and kept in the cold for 30 minutes. After centrifuging, the pH and extinction at 260 mμ of the supernatant were measured. At least 95 per cent of nucleotides were retained over the whole pH range tested (pH 3.25 to 10.0). Buffers used included glycine-HCl, citrate-HCl, cacodylic acid-NaOH, 'Tris,' 'Diol,' and glycine-NaOH.

When sucrose nuclei were treated with a series of acetate buffers in sucrose solution, a surprising observation was made. Dilute acetate buffer (0.02 M) removed 85 to 90 per cent of the nucleotides from the sucrose nuclei below pH 5.1. In order to learn how specific acetate is in releasing nucleotides from nuclei in a sucrose medium, some related substances were tested. The results are included in Table 18. It is clear that certain simple fatty acids such as formic, propionic, and monochloroacetic have a similar ability to release nucleotides. However ethyl alcohol, acetaldehyde, citrate, glycine-HCl, succinate, and acetone have no effect on the removal of nucleotides from the sucrose nuclei.

As to the effect of acetate, it is obvious from Figure 18 that there is a sharp boundary of effective pH of acetate between pH 5.1 and pH 5.9. In this pH range, the quantity of nucleotides released by acetate gradually increases as the pH drops. At pH 5.9 there is no loss of nucleotides by acetate; at pH 5.1 the maximum loss occurs.

A time course study on the effect of dilute acetate (0.005 M) at pH 4.5 (see Fig. 17) revealed that 90 per cent of the nucleotides were released within less than 2 minutes without further increase over 30 minutes; at pH 5.9 there is no sign of nucleotide release by acetate even after 30 minutes. These facts clearly indicate that release of nucleotides from the nuclei by acetate is pH dependent. Release of nucleotides by propionic acid, formic acid or monochloroacetic acid show the same pH dependence as acetate (Fig. 19). Since the dissociation constants of formic, acetic, propionic, and monochloroacetic acids differ considerably from each other, the effect of pH on release of nucleotides seems to be due not to the effect of pH on the reagents added but rather to the effect of pH on a component of the nuclei with which acetate and the other substances react.

To study the quantitative relationship between acetate and the removal of nucleotides from the nuclei, buffers were prepared containing a mixture of acetate and citrate at pH 4.5 in which the total

molar concentration was kept constant but in which the acetate concentration was varied. It is evident from Figure 20 that increasing concentration of acetate results in a corresponding increase in amount of nucleotides removed from the nuclei. In other experiments the amount and concentration of acetate were held constant but the amount of nuclear material was varied over a three-fold range. It was found that the quantity of nucleotides released was proportional to the amount of nuclear material present. Under these conditions, therefore, the concentration of acetate is the determining factor in releasing the nucleotides at the effective pH even when relative amounts of acetate and nuclei are varied. In further experiments on the acetate effect, we are planning to use C^{14}-labeled acetate to study the combination of acetate with nuclear constituents.

Our colleague, Dr. R. Lorente de Nó, has called our attention to some remarkable observations of

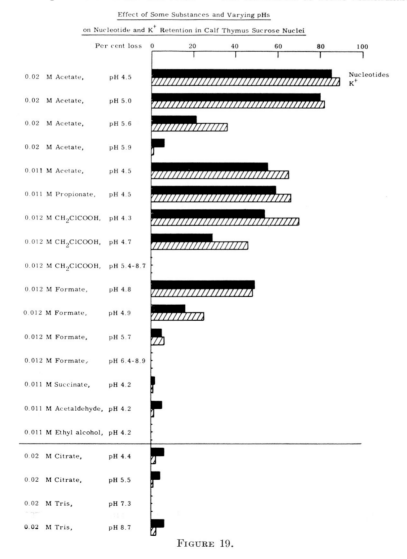

FIGURE 19.

Effect of Varying Acetate: Citrate Ratio
on Nucleotide Retention in Calf Thymus Sucrose Nuclei
pH 4.4; buffer concentration 0.0166 M in sucrose-CaCl₂

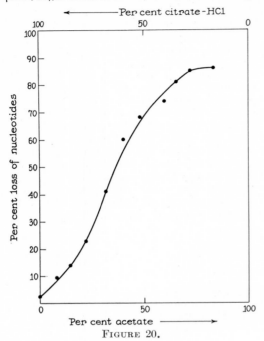

FIGURE 20.

his on the irreversible damage done to nerve fibers by a low concentration of acetate in a slightly acid medium (Lorente de Nó, 1946). The analogy with the acetate effect on nuclei is suggestive.

It should be mentioned in passing that when nuclei are treated with acetate buffer at pH 4.5 in sucrose-CaCl₂, nucleotide triphosphates and diphosphates are largely converted to the monophosphate form. This dephosphorylation does not seem to have any relation to the specific effect of acetate in releasing nucleotides from the nuclei, for it was found that citrate buffer at the same pH (which does not release the nucleotides) also tends to dephosphorylate tri- and diphosphates.

It was found that when nucleotides are released from sucrose nuclei by acetate and other reagents, potassium in the nuclei is also released at the same time. All the potassium analyses to be mentioned were done by Dr. Shinji Itoh. Sucrose nuclei usually retain somewhat less than 50 per cent of the potassium present in the "nonaqueous" nuclei. This potassium is well preserved even after repeated washing of nuclei with cold sucrose-CaCl₂ solution (Itoh and Schwartz, unpub.). Figure 19 includes the results of experiments in which the effects of a number of substances at various pHs on the retention of nucleotides and potassium were tested. One can see that there is a remarkable correlation between the retention of nucleotides and of potassium; over a wide range of pH as well as in the various kinds of reagents, both substances are in each instance released at the

same time. It is not likely that the potassium released is combined with the nucleotides because the molar ratio of potassium to nucleotide removed is about twenty. The facts suggest rather that both substances are part of a common complex in the cell nuclei; acetate and other effective reagents disturb this complex in some way so that nucleotides and potassium are released.

We now have reasons to suppose that the nucleotides of the nucleus are held in some complex structure and that only such nucleotides are involved in the metabolism of the cell nucleus. The evidence for this is: (1) Nucleotides are firmly held in the nucleus under a variety of conditions, and some special reagents such as acetate can release them together with potassium from the sucrose nuclei; (2) once nuclei lose their nucleotides, added nucleotides are not taken up; (3) only intranuclear nucleotides are phosphorylated—added nucleotides cannot be acted upon; (4) added AMP, ADP, or ATP have no effect on the synthesis of protein by isolated sucrose nuclei, whereas upon removal of nucleotides and potassium protein synthesis is seriously impaired; (5) under our experimental conditions intranuclear nucleotides, especially their triphosphates are held to a considerable extent during the course of protein synthesis.

Relation of Nucleotides and Potassium to Protein Synthesis in the Nucleus

The effect of removal of nucleotides and potassium on the process of amino acid uptake in the nucleus has been studied. Since this involves exposing the nuclei to media in which the pH has been decreased, the effect of such exposure (without removal of nucleotides and potassium) was first investigated. After treating the nuclei with a sucrose solution containing an acid buffer (citrate or cacodylate) the nuclei were then washed with a sucrose-pH 6.7 phosphate mixture and the uptake of C¹⁴-alanine into nuclear protein was measured under standard conditions. The way in which protein synthesis was reduced by exposure to acid media is shown in Figure 21, the curve on the left. The release by acetate of nucleotides and potassium from nuclei occurs quite sharply as the pH is decreased and fortunately the point at which the release happens is at a higher pH than that at which severe inactivation of protein synthesis by acid takes place. Exposure of nuclei to acetate prevents protein synthesis, when the nuclei are subsequently placed in a sucrose-pH 6.7 phosphate mixture, as shown in Figure 21, curve on the right. The release of nucleotides and potassium from nuclei by acetate and the destructive effect of acetate on protein synthesis in nuclei occur at a pH distinctly higher than that at which acidity *per se* greatly diminishes synthesis. These experiments demonstrate a correlation between the loss of nucleotides and potassium from nuclei and the impairment of protein synthesis in nuclei. Such a correlation is not, of course, a proof that the presence of nucleotides is required for protein synthesis.

Throughout this paper and the preceding one there have been comments on the role of sucrose in maintaining the integrity of the nucleus. It is well known that the microscopic appearance (in the light microscope) of an isolated nucleus is different when it is in a sucrose medium from what it is in a saline medium. If in a given preparation the medium is changed repeatedly from sucrose to saline and then back to sucrose the microscopic appearance of the nucleus changes with each change of medium; the alterations in microscopic appearance are readily reversed. The conditions within the nucleus which are preserved by sucrose solutions, and which have been significant for the present investigation, are different from those that have been recognized hitherto. The intranuclear conditions to which we now refer and the maintenance of which depends upon sucrose, when the nucleus is isolated, cannot be recognized by examination with the light microscope; and, furthermore, when these conditions within the nucleus are disturbed, restoration has not been possible. We are here dealing with what we must suppose are changes in the fine structure of the nucleus, changes which affect the metabolic activity of the nucleus.

That intranuclear conditions depend upon keeping isolated nuclei in a sucrose medium is shown by the following facts: (1) Synthesis of protein stops if sucrose is removed and is not restored if the nuclei are again placed in a sucrose medium; (2) mononucleotides are released when isolated nuclei are placed in a medium not containing sucrose and nucleotides are not again taken up by the nuclei when they are returned to a sucrose medium; (3) when sucrose nuclei are treated with DNAase they lose as much as 80 to 90 per cent of their DNA and yet only 15 per cent of their histone is released, although histone, a water-soluble protein, is attached to DNA in the nucleus; on the other hand, when nuclei are in a saline medium (containing no sucrose) at the same time that DNA is removed by the action of DNAase about 50 per cent of the histone is released from the nuclei.

In our preparations the nuclei have been in isotonic sucrose, 0.25 M. If the sucrose concentration is raised to 0.50 M synthesis of protein no longer occurs, nor does it occur if the nuclei are returned to 0.25 M sucrose; apparently hypertonic sucrose causes an irreversible change in the fine strucure of the nucleus. Retention of nucleotides in nuclei is not impaired by raising the sucrose concentration from 0.25 M to 0.50 M.

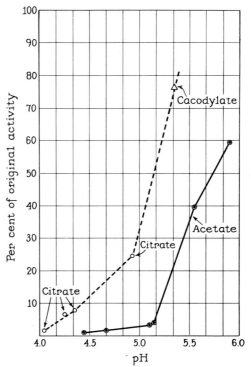

FIGURE 21. Effect of the exposure of calf thymus sucrose nuclei to acidic buffer solutions on the subsequent synthesis of protein.

Sucrose nuclei were exposed to the buffers in sucrose-$CaCl_2$ indicated in the figure. After 30 minutes, the nuclei were washed with 0.02 M sodium phosphate buffer in sucrose-$CaCl_2$ at pH 6.7, and tested for the incorporation of C^{14}-alanine into the nuclear proteins. Loss of nucleotides by the acidic buffer treatment from the nuclei was: in the citrate and cacodylate series, reading points on the curve from left to right, 6.1, 6.1, 5.1, 6.1, and 2.3 per cent of the control; in the acetate series, reading points on the curve from left to right, 90.5, 90.5, 84.0, 77.5, 26.5, and 9.3 per cent of the control.

Abscissa represents the pH of the buffer solution measured after the treatment of nuclei.

SUMMARY

1. Nuclei prepared from calf thymus nuclei in a sucrose medium actively incorporate labeled amino acids into their proteins. This is an aerobic process which is dependent on nuclear oxidative phosphorylation.

2. Evidence is presented to show that the uptake of amino acids represents nuclear protein synthesis.

3. The deoxyribonucleic acid of the nucleus plays a role in amino acid incorporation. Protein synthesis virtually ceases when the DNA is removed from the nucleus, and uptake resumes when the DNA is restored.

4. In the essential mechanism of amino acid incorporation, the role of the DNA can be filled by denatured or partially degraded DNA, by DNAs from other tissues, and even by RNA. Purine and pyrimidine bases, monoribonucleotides, and certain dinucleotides are unable to substitute for DNA in this system.

5. When the proteins of the nucleus are fractionated and classified according to their specific activities, one finds the histones to be relatively

inert. The protein fraction most closely associated with the DNA has a very high activity. A readily extractable ribonucleoprotein complex is also extremely active, and it is tempting to speculate that this may be an intermediary in nucleo-cytoplasmic interaction.

6. The incorporation of amino acids seems to require a preliminary "activation" of the nucleus. This can be blocked by certain benzimidazole derivatives (which also block influenza virus multiplication; Tamm *et al.*, 1954).

7. The isolated nucleus can incorporate glycine into nucleic acid purines.

8. Together with earlier observations on the incorporation of amino acids by cytoplasmic particulates, these results show that protein synthesis can occur in both nucleus and cytoplasm.

9. It has been demonstrated by ion-exchange chromatography that the cell nucleus contains mononucleotides of adenine, guanine, cytosine, and uracil, together with diphosphopyridine nucleotide, and several uridine diphosphate derivatives; the adenine nucleotides predominating in amount. Nucleotide components in the cell nucleus are in close agreement quantitatively and qualitatively with those found in the cytoplasm.

10. In calf thymus "sucrose" nuclei, nucleotide monophosphates can be phosphorylated to the energy-rich triphosphate form *without* participation of cytoplasmic components. As to the nature of the phosphorylation, it has been shown that there exist certain differences as well as resemblances between nuclei and mitochondria. A distinctive feature of nuclear phosphorylation is that only intranuclear monophosphates seem to be phosphorylated. The process is completely inhibited by cyanide, azide, dinitrophenol, and carbon monoxide. However certain reagents which block oxidative phosphorylation of mitochondria, namely dicumarol, janus green B, methylene blue, and calcium ions, have no effect on phosphorylation within the nucleus.

11. The bulk of mononucleotides is preserved within thymus nuclei after their isolation in sucrose. Nucleotides are surprisingly well retained by nuclei in a sucrose medium whether or not electrolytes are present and in buffers ranging from pH 3 to 10; under all conditions sucrose is required for retention.

12. Dilute acetate in sucrose releases nucleotides from the nucleus below pH 5.1. As to the effective pH of acetate, there is a sharp boundary between pH 5.1 and pH 5.9. At pH 5.9, and above, acetate does not remove nucleotides from the nucleus. The effects of propionate, formate, and monochloroacetate on the nuclei are the same as that of acetate.

13. When nuclei are exposed to a wide variety of conditions a close correlation is found between the retention in the nucleus of nucleotides and of potassium. This suggests that both substances are part of a common complex in the cell nucleus.

14. It has been shown that upon removal of nucleotides and potassium from calf thymus sucrose nuclei by acetate, the ability to incorporate C^{14}-alanine into nuclear protein is greatly impaired.

REFERENCES

ALLFREY, V. G., 1954, Amino acid incorporation by isolated thymus nuclei. I. The role of desoxyribonucleic acid in protein synthesis. Proc. Nat. Acad. Sci. Wash. *40:* 881–885.

ALLFREY, V. G., MIRSKY, A. E., AND OSAWA, S., 1955, Protein synthesis in isolated cell nuclei. Nature Lond. *176:* 1042–1049.

ALLFREY, V. G., DALY, M. M., AND MIRSKY, A. E., 1955, Synthesis of protein in the pancreas. II. The role of ribonucleoprotein in protein synthesis. J. Gen. Physiol. *37:* 157–175.

ALLFREY, V. G., STERN, H., MIRSKY, A. E., and SAETREN, H., 1952, The isolation of cell nuclei in non-aqueous media. J. Gen. Physiol. *35:* 529–554.

AVERY, O. T., MacLEOD, C. M., AND McCARTY, M., 1944, Studies on the chemical nature of the substance inducing transformation of pneumococcal types. J. Exp. Med. *79:* 137–157.

BESSIS, M., 1954, In: Traité de Cytologie Sanguine. Masson et Cie, Paris, p. 83.

CHANCE, B., and WILLIAMS, G. R., 1954, Kinetics of cytochrome b_5 in rat liver microsomes. J. Biol. Chem. *209:* 945–951.

DALY, M. M., ALLFREY, V. G., AND MIRSKY, A. E., 1952, Uptake of glycine-N^{15} by components of cell nuclei. J. Gen. Physiol. *36:* 173–179.

DALY, M. M., and MIRSKY, A. E., 1955, Histones with high lysine content. J. Gen. Physiol. *38:* 405–413.

DAVIES, H. G., 1954, The action of fixatives on the ultra-violet-absorbing components of chick fibroblasts. Quart. J. Micr. Sci. *95:* 433–457.

DIANZANI, M. U., AND SCURO, S., 1956, The effects of some inhibitors of oxidative phosphorylation in the morphology and enzymic activities of mitochondria. Biochem. J. *62:* 205–215.

DOTY, P., 1955, The characterization, denaturation and degradation of DNA. Rts. 3ᵉᵐᵉ Cong. Intern. Biochimie, Bruxelles: 135–139.

EDMONDS, N., AND LePAGE, G. A., 1955, The incorporation of glycine-2-C^{14} into acid-soluble purines. Cancer Res. *15:* 93–99.

FRAENKEL-CONRAT, H., and WILLIAMS, R. C., 1955, Reconstitution of active tobacco mosaic virus from its inactive protein and nucleic acid constituents. Proc. Nat. Acad. Sci. Wash. *41:* 690–698.

FRIEDKIN, M., AND WOOD, H., 1956, Utilization of thymidine-C^{14} by bone marrow cells and isolated thymus nuclei. J. Biol. Chem. *220:* 639–651.

GALE, E. F., and FOLKES, J. P., 1953, Amino acid incorporation by fragmented staphylococcal cells. Biochem. J. *55:* xi.

GALE, E. F., AND FOLKES, J. P., 1953, The assimilation of amino-acids by bacteria. 15. Actions of antibiotics on nucleic acid and protein synthesis in *Staphylococcus aureus*. Biochem. J. *53:* 493–498.

GIERER, A., and SCHRAMM, G., 1956, Die Infektiosität der Nucleinsäure aus Tabak-mosaikvirus. Zeit. Natur. *11b:* 138.

HALVORSON, H. O., and SPIEGELMAN, S., 1952, The inhibition of enzyme formation by amino acid analogues. J. Bact. *64:* 207–221.

HOGEBOOM, G. H., SCHNEIDER, W. C., AND STRIEBICH, M. J., 1954, Cytochemical studies V. On the isolation and biochemical properties of liver cell nuclei. J. Biol. Chem. *209:* 945–951.

HURLBERT, R. B., SCHMITZ, H., BRUMM, A. F., and POTTER, V. R., 1954, Nucleotide metabolism. II. Chromatographic separation of acid-soluble nucleotides. J. Biol. Chem. *209:* 23–29.

JUDAH, J. D., and WILLIAMS-ASHMAN, H. G., 1951, The inhibition of oxidative phosphorylation. Biochem. J. *48:* 33–42.

KAY, E. R. M., 1956, Incorporation of C[14]-formate into free amino acids and proteins of cell nuclei of various tissues of the rabbit. Federation Proc. *15:* 107.

KAY, E. R. M., AND DAVIDSON, J. N., 1955, Acid-soluble nucleotide derivatives in cell nuclei isolated in a non-aqueous medium. Experientia *11:* 439–440.

LEHNINGER, A. L., 1949, Esterification of inorganic phosphate coupled to electron transport between dihydrodiphosphopyridine nucleotide and oxygen. J. Biol. Chem. *178:* 625–644.

LEPAGE, G. A., 1951, In: Manometric Techniques and Tissue Metabolism. Umbreit *et al.* 2nd Edition. Minneapolis, Burgess.

LIPPINCOTT, J. A., AND COMMONER, B., 1956, Reactivation of tobacco mosaic virus infectivity in mixtures of virus protein and nucleic acid. Biochim. Biophys. Acta *19:* 198–199.

LOOMIS, W. F., and LIPMANN, F., 1948, Reversible inhibition of the coupling between phosphorylation and oxidation. J. Biol. Chem. *173:* 807–808. 1949, Inhibition of phosphorylation by azide in kidney homogenate. J. Biol. Chem. *179:* 503–504.

LORENTE DE NÓ, R., 1946, A study of nerve physiology. Studies Rockefeller Inst. Med. Res. *131:* 1–496, especially p. 181.

MARTIUS, C., and NITZ-LITZOW, D., 1953, Über den Wirkungamechanismus des Dicumarols und verwandter Verbindungen. Biochim. Biophys. Acta. *12:* 134–140.

NAORA, H., and TAKEDA, S., 1954, Occurrence of labile phosphate in rat liver nuclei. Biochim. Biophys. Acta. *13:* 360–364.

POTTER, V. R., and REIF, A. E., 1952, Inhibition of an electron transport component by antimycin A. J. Biol. Chem. *194:* 287–294.

RIS, H., and MIRSKY, A. E., 1949, The state of the chromosomes in the interphase nucleus. J. Gen. Physiol. *32:* 489–502.

SANTISTEBAN, G. A., AND DOUGHERTY, T. F., 1954, Comparison of the influences of adrenocortical hormones on the growth and involution of lymphatic organs. Endocrinol. *54:* 130–146.

SCHWEITZER, G. K., and STEIN, B. R., 1950, Measuring solid samples of low energy beta emitters. Nucleonics *7:* 65–72.

SIEKEVITZ, P., 1952, Uptake of radioactive alanine *in vitro* into the proteins of rat liver fractions. J. Biol. Chem. *195:* 549–565.

SIEKEVITZ, P., and ZAMECNIK, P. C., 1951, In vitro incorporation of 1-C[14]-DL-alanine into proteins of rat liver granular fractions. Federation Proc. *10:* 246.

STERN, H., and MIRSKY, A. E., 1953, Soluble enzymes of nuclei isolated in sucrose and non-aqueous media. J. Gen. Physiol. *37:* 177–187.

STERN, H., and TIMONEN, S., 1954, The position of the cell nucleus in pathways of hydrogen transfer: Cytochrome C, flavoproteins, glutathione, and ascorbic acid. J. Gen. Physiol. *38:* 41–52.

STRITTMATTER, C. F., and BALL, E. G., 1954, The intracellular distribution of cytochrome components and of oxidative activity in rat liver. J. Cell. Comp. Physiol. *43:* 57–78.

TAMM, I., 1954, Inhibition of influenza and mumps virus multiplication by 4,5,6-trichloro-1-β-D-ribofuranosyl-benzimidazole. Science *120:* 847.

TAMM, I., FOLKERS, K., and SHUNK, C. H., 1956, High inhibitory activity of certain halogenated ribofuranosylbenzimidazoles on influenza B virus multiplication. J. Bact. *72:* 54–58.

TAMM, I., FOLKERS, K., SHUNK, C. H., and HORSFALL, F. L., 1954, Inhibition of influenza virus multiplication by N-glycosides of benzimidazioles. J. Exp. Med. *99:* 227–249.

WALKER, P. M. B., and YATES, H. B., 1952, Ultra-violet absorption of living cell nuclei. Symp. Soc. Exp. Biol. *6:* 266–276.

ZAMENHOF, S., and CHARGAFF, E., 1950, Dissymmetry in nucleotide sequence of deoxypentose nucleic acids. J. Biol. Chem. *187:* 1–14.

DISCUSSION

BRAUN: As you know, within the last couple of years Skoog, Miller, Strong and their associates at the University of Wisconsin have isolated and studied a compound derivable from DNA which controls cell division in plants. This compound, which is 6-furfuryl amino purine or kinetin, was found by us to have a striking selective toxicity for bacterial cells of different genotypes. For example, we observed that nonsmooth cells of *Brucella abortus* or of unencapsulated cells of *Pneumococcus* are inhibited in the presence of as little as 0.001 γ kinetin per ml whereas smooth or encapsulated cells are not inhibited. These effects disappear when the concentration of kinetin is increased above one γ/ml. Have you had an opportunity to test the effects of this interesting compound on your material?

MIRSKY: No, we have not but we should like to test it.

HAUROWITZ: The lack of a latent period for methionine may be due to binding by means of the sulfur atom, or to the fact that methionine is bound directly to protein whereas the other amino acids may be bound first to histone, then to protein.

MIRSKY: Our observations on the rate and level of incorporation of amino acids into histones and other proteins of the nucleus show that incorporation into histones does not precede that into other histones.

HAUROWITZ: Can you replace DNA by polyphosphoribose?

MIRSKY: We have not done this experiment but we are planning to.

Physical Studies of the Molecular Structure of Deoxyribose Nucleic Acid and Nucleoprotein

M. H. F. WILKINS

Medical Research Council, Biophysics Research Unit, King's College, London

INTRODUCTION

It may be useful at this time to consider how much we know about DNA structure and how much we do not know. It is about six years since clear X-ray diffraction photographs of DNA were first obtained, and three years since Watson and Crick (1953) built their molecular model of DNA (then described by Watson at the Symposium here), and proposed a hypothesis to explain how DNA molecules could be replicated *in vivo*. We have now much data to show that their general idea for the structure is correct, but evidence bearing on the biological hypothesis is somewhat conflicting. It seems necessary to stress that correctness of the structure does not imply correctness of the biological hypothesis. In the next decade we can expect that an increasing number of molecular structures will appear and become part of biology, and, as the derivation of such structures is not easily understood by biologists, it may be of interest to discuss the background for the finding of the DNA molecular configuration and use it to illustrate the nature of the methods employed.

THE ROLE OF MOLECULAR MODELS IN THE DETERMINATION OF MOLECULAR STRUCTURES

The X-ray photographs taken in our laboratory (Wilkins *et al.*, 1953; Franklin and Gosling, 1953) followed the earlier work of Astbury (1947) and provided the means of determining the 3-dimensional molecular configuration of the DNA molecule; in particular, it was clear at an early stage in our work that the molecule was very likely to have a helical configuration, and Astbury had pointed out that the nucleotides were probably arranged like "a pile of pennies." This kind of physical approach, however, would be of little use without the fundamental chemical knowledge which was built up at about the same time and made clear the system of covalent bonds linking the chemical groups in DNA (in other words, the chemists determined the structure in a chemical sense) and also gave information about the weaker links—the hydrogen bonds. Physico-chemical techniques also gave helpful information: they demonstrated the thread-like shape of the molecule and the arrangement of the bases at right angles to its length. What X-ray diffraction did

was to indicate the arrangement in space of the chemical groups in the molecular thread. It is very convenient (and probably genetically necessary) that the DNA molecule has a well-defined and in some ways simple configuration which stays intact during extraction from living things, and thus may then be studied by physical methods.

It is probably worth stressing that X-ray diffraction, for most molecules which are not very small, is the only technique which can establish their configuration; on the other hand, only very rarely can it be used to determine the chemical structure of such molecules before this has been achieved by chemical methods. But when a small molecule is being studied, X-ray diffraction may be used by itself to determine the position, size, and weight of the atoms in the molecule. The extent to which it is profitable to combine stereochemical methods with the X-ray technique increases with the complexity of the molecules studied.

To find the structure of very large molecules it is necessary to know the form of the small chemical groups of which it is composed. The structures of these groups are found by studying crystals of simple compounds. Molecular models are then built using inter-atomic distances and arrangements already known to occur in crystals, and a search is made for a structure which would give a diffraction pattern similar to that observed with X-rays. The structure can be established only by close combination of model-building and X-ray diffraction.

THE BACKGROUND OF THE WATSON AND CRICK MOLECULAR MODEL

The more important information available as a guide in the building of the Watson and Crick model was as follows. The covalent linkages in the polynucleotide chain were firmly established and knowledge of the dimensions and shapes of the chemical groups was fairly complete. X-ray diffraction data gave the main dimensions of the helix and provided important suggestions about its internal structure (*e.g.* the "pile of pennies") and showed that the molecule was almost certainly composed of more than one polynucleotide chain. The equalities found in the base analyses suggested that the bases occurred in pairs, and titration studies showed that the bases were probably

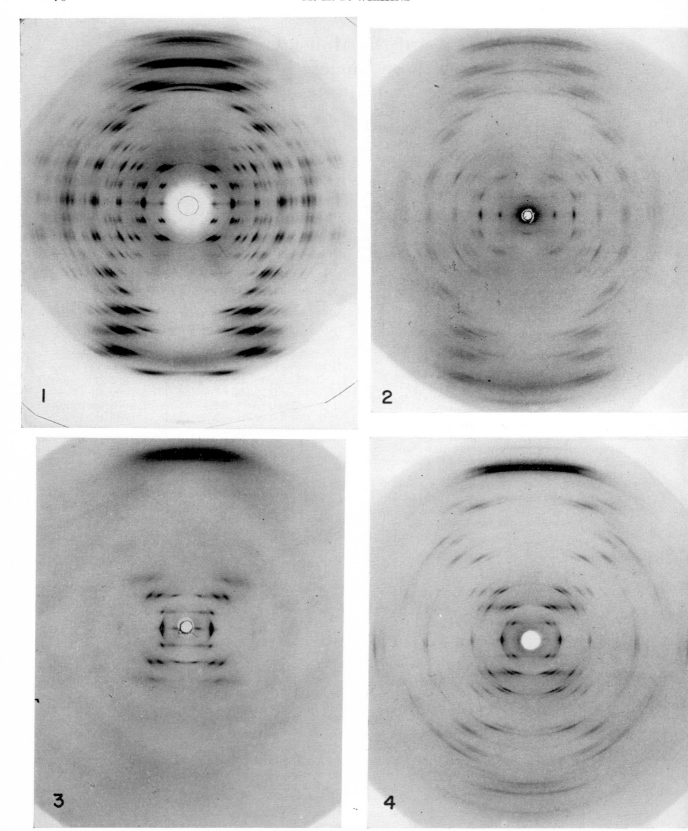

FIGURES 1–4

joined by hydrogen bonds. The difficulty about DNA structure was that a regular helix had to be built from four nucleotides of different shape and size. This paradox was resolved by Watson and Crick. They made the important assumption that the number of polynucleotide chains in the molecule was two; and they so arranged the hydrogen bonds between the bases that they achieved the elegant result of having two pairs of bases such that in both pairs the bonds joining the base to the sugar ring were the same distance apart and inclined to each other at the same angle and were symmetrically arranged. This symmetry and equivalence made it possible to build a helical molecule with the sugar and phosphate portions regularly arranged but with any complicated sequence of bases along the length of the molecule.

Although many of the dimensions of the model were indicated by X-ray diffraction data, the precise dimensions and much of the internal configuration of the structure were largely derived by the actual process of building the model so that it conformed with available stereochemical data. It may be seen therefore, that the structure was somewhat hypothetical insofar as it was not derived entirely or directly from experiment (Crick and Watson, 1954). In fact, calculation of the diffraction pattern produced by the structure showed that it did not agree adequately with detailed X-ray data, and it remained to be shown that a molecular model of this type could be built which would agree well with the data.

REFINED STRUCTURE FOR DNA

1. Use of the Lithium Salt of DNA

About a year ago we described a modified structure (Feughelman et al., 1955) which was in satisfactory agreement with the experimental data, the main modification being to place the nitrogen bases closer to the helix axis than in the Watson and Crick model and to reduce the diameter of the helix. Since then more rigorous proof of the correctness of the structure has become possible; first, because more accurate X-ray data have been obtained, and second, because models have been built using new stereochemical data.

The unpublished X-ray diffraction and model-building results which I will describe are the joint work of Dr. W. E. Seeds, Dr. H. R. Wilson, Mr. R. Langridge, Mr. C. W. Hooper and myself at King's College, London, in collaboration with Dr. L. D. Hamilton and Dr. R. K. Barclay of the Sloan-Kettering Institute, New York, who supplied new materials. The earlier X-ray pictures of the sodium salt of DNA (e.g. Fig. 5) in the B configuration (Fig. 9), although fairly sharp, were still sufficiently diffuse to make really reliable measurements of the diffracted X-ray intensity impossible. The new lithium salt of DNA made by L. D. Hamilton crystallizes in the B configuration and the X-ray photograph consists of sharply defined spots (Fig. 4) which may be measured accurately. Another advantage of the lithium salt is that the lithium ion scatters about three times less X rays than the sodium ion and may be ignored in the calculation of the diffracted intensities from the molecular model. When sodium is used, the possibility of appreciable error exists because the position of the metal ion in the structure is uncertain. The new stereochemical data used in building the model consists of bond lengths and angles in a phosphate di-ester (dibenzyl-phosphoric acid) (Dunitz and Rollett, 1956) and the configuration of thymidine (Huber, 1956).

The micro-crystals in the fibre of Li DNA are orthorhombic and, at about 66 per cent relative humidity, the unit cell dimensions are: a. 22.8 Å; b. 31.7 Å; c. 33.6 Å. The axes of the helical molecules are in the direction which is parallel to the fibre axis, and two DNA molecules pass through the unit cell, one molecule being displaced relative to the other along its axis by one third of the helix pitch length. The distance between centres of the molecules which make contact on the same level is 22.8 Å, but where the contact is between molecules at different levels, the distance is as small as 19.1 Å.

Model building confirms that the molecules are in contact, and that displacement of the molecules by one third of the pitch length allows them (on account of being double and not single helices) to come more closely in contact than when on the same level. There are exactly ten nucleotide pairs in the molecule per turn of the helix. As the symmetry of the lattice may reflect the symmetry of the molecule, one expects tenfold helices to pack in orthorhombic manner if crystallization is perfect. Crystallization of the B configuration in a hexagonal form (Feughelman et al., 1955) is necessarily imperfect.

The correspondence between diffraction intensities calculated from the model and as observed is satisfactory and is shown in Figure 10, and the configuration of the molecule is shown in Figure 11. (This configuration still requires some refining but the actual structure cannot be very different from it.) The sugar ring has the O atom $\sim \frac{1}{4}$ Å

FIGURE 1. X-ray diffraction pattern of Na DNA in the A configuration at 75% relative humidity. The sharp spots indicate a high degree of crystallinity.

FIGURE 2. X-ray diffraction pattern of Rb DNA in the A configuration at 75% relative humidity. The inner spots on the first and second layer-lines are weaker than in Na DNA, and a spot not present in Na DNA is visible at the centre of the first layer-line.

FIGURE 3. X-ray diffraction photograph of Na DNA in the B configuration at 92% relative humidity. Spots are visible near the centre of the pattern only; this indicates crystallinity is imperfect. The spots are clearer than those obtained in another specimen (Fig. 5).

FIGURE 4. X-ray diffraction photograph of Li DNA in the B configurarion at 66% relative humidity. The sharp spots in all parts of the pattern indicate a high degree of crystallinity.

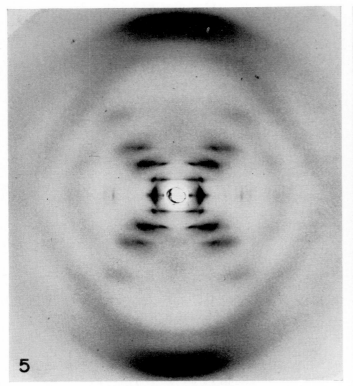

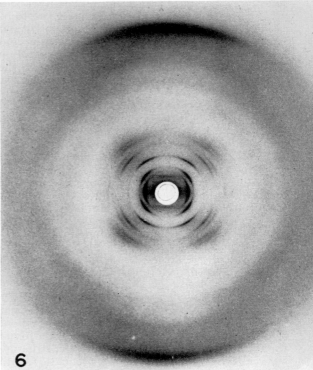

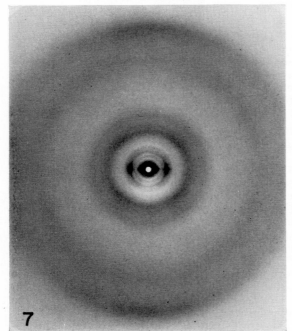

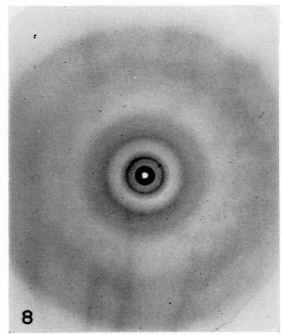

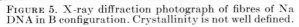

FIGURE 5. X-ray diffraction photograph of fibres of Na DNA in B configuration. Crystallinity is not well defined.

FIGURE 7. X-ray photograph of fibres of nucleohistone extracted from calf thymus. The diagonal cross pattern characteristic of the DNA helix is visible and the 2nd and 3rd layer-lines can be distinguished. The first layer-line is not visible.

FIGURE 6. X-ray diffraction photograph of fibres of oriented *Sepia* sperm. The pattern resembles that of DNA (*e.g.* Fig. 5) except that the first layer-line (see Fig. 18) is stronger.

FIGURE 8. X-ray photograph of intact sperm heads of *Arbacia*. The pattern is unoriented but otherwise is indistinguishable from that of extracted nucleohistone.

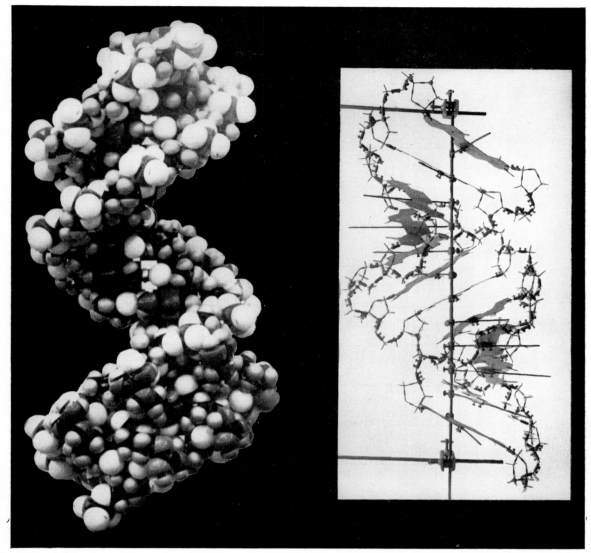

FIGURE 9. Molecular models of DNA. The model on the left shows the molecule in the B configuration and the shape and size of the atoms. On the lower groove of the model a polyarginine group has been added to show how protamine can combine compactly with DNA. The model on the right shows the molecule in the A configuration; this type of model made with wire is the kind mainly used in this research—the centres of atoms occur at the junctions in the wires and the nitrogen base-pairs are represented by metal plates; interatomic distances may be measured accurately.

out-of-plane but this value could be altered if the bond-angles and lengths in the phosphate-ester chain were adjusted slightly. The distances between atoms in contact are about the same as in previous models (Feughelman *et al.*, 1955) and the diffraction pattern was calculated from the model by the same procedure as before.

2. Use of Sodium and Rubidium Salts of DNA

The certainty with which the correctness of a molecular structure may be established is increased when the molecule can be studied in more than one configuration. Fortunately this is possible with DNA. The sodium salt crystallizes with the helical molecules in the A configuration (Fig. 9) where the attractive forces between the ions have caused the helix to shrink in length and eleven nucleotide pairs are packed in one turn of the helix and the planes of the nitrogen bases become tilted at $\sim 70°$ to the helix axis. As eleven is an odd number the crystal form is monoclinic; there is one molecule passing through the unit cell. The dimensions of the unit cell at ~ 75 per cent relative humidity are: a. 21.9 Å; b. 40.4 Å;

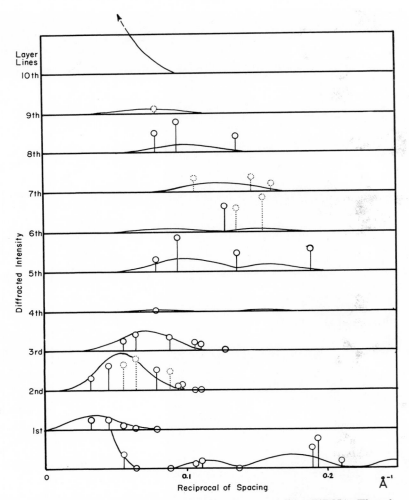

FIGURE 10. Observed and calculated intensities of diffraction for crystalline LiDNA. The observed intensities are shown by circles (the values for full circles are more reliable than for dotted circles); the smooth curve is calculated from the model. The curve on the 10th layer-line rises to a higd level off the diagram and the corresponding very strong observed intensities are not shown.

c. 28.4 Å; β. 97.15°. In the crystallites the molecules are arranged in contact and are at slightly different levels to allow closest approach. The correspondence between calculated and observed intensities of diffraction is satisfactory and is shown in Figure 12. It is only possible to obtain this correspondence if the sodium ions are placed in certain positions near the phosphate groups. These particular positions are not stereochemically unique and it is very desirable to confirm their correctness. This may be achieved by making use of the sodium, potassium, and rubidium salts of DNA which were prepared by L. D. Hamilton and R. K. Barclay. These salts are isomorphous and, as the effective X-ray scattering from the rubidium ion is about 3.5 times that of sodium, the intensities of the spots on the X-ray picture change greatly when sodium is replaced by

rubidium. The calculated and observed intensities agree very satisfactorily, all the large changes being accounted for (see Fig. 13).

INEXACT FIT OF OBSERVED AND CALCULATED DIFFRACTION INTENSITIES

Certain parts of the DNA X-ray diffraction pattern are determined by the basic characteristics of the molecular structure and are not affected much by changes in structural details. If the structure is to be established it is necessary that observed and calculated intensities of diffraction agree well in these regions. Such agreement exists. The first significant region is in the centre of the pattern on the first four-layer-lines where the strong diffraction defines the main shape and dimension of the helix. The other important region is on the tenth layer-line on the B pattern, and on the sixth, seventh and eighth layer-lines on the A pattern, where the strong diffraction defines the way the nitrogen bases are piled on top of one another. Agreement may be poor for other parts of the pattern but this does not matter for the diffraction in those parts is determined by details of configuration. We cannot expect to predict these details because we do not know accurately the correct values to use for many bond lengths and angles, nor can we predict the detailed arrangement of the water molecules surrounding the DNA.

THE LIMITATIONS IN KNOWLEDGE OF DNA STRUCTURE OBTAINED BY X-RAY DIFFRACTION

All the atoms in a fibre of DNA diffract X rays, and if the structure in the molecule is repeated periodically and if the molecules are packed regularly side-by-side (*i.e.* the arrangement is crystalline), the energy of the diffracted waves is concentrated in certain directions, and spots appear on the X-ray photograph. Regular double-helix molecules packed irregularly in the fibre will produce diffuse rings on the photograph; distorted molecules will produce even more diffuse rings. Such diffuse rings will not show clearly on the photograph and are not amenable to study. Our attention has been concentrated on the crystalline portions of the fibre. We now know that these regions consist of double-helix molecules, but we also know that density and water content measurement combined with X-ray diffraction gives a value of ~2.5 for the number of polynucleotide chains in the molecule with the B configuration. Such discrepancy occurs in the study of fibres and is explained by postulating the existence in the fibre of non-crystalline regions where the molecules are packed more closely than in the crystalline parts. Existence of these amorphous regions, which probably constitute half or more of the fibre, is also required to explain infra-red dichroism measurements as well as the measurements, made by Dr. Harold Wyckoff, of mechanical properties of DNA fibres. (I would like to say here that Dr. Wyckoff, has single-handed, in unpublished work, paralleled much of the earlier X-ray studies on DNA carried out by our team.)

If X-ray diffraction has told us nothing of the amorphous regions in the DNA fibre, the question arises as to whether molecules with structure other than the double helix might exist in these regions. However, it is unlikely that other structures exist to any great extent, because analysis of whole fibres shows unity ratios of base content, and absence of non-hydrogen-bonded bases, and a non-double helix structure which satisfies these analyses and hydrogen-bonding conditions is not easily conceived.

Measurement of the ratio of amorphous to crystalline material in DNA fibres is difficult and unreliable; hence we have made no attempt to

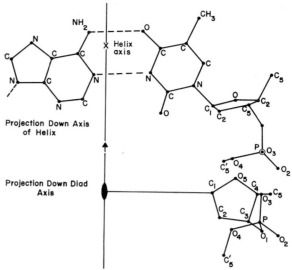

FIGURE 11. The B configuration of DNA.

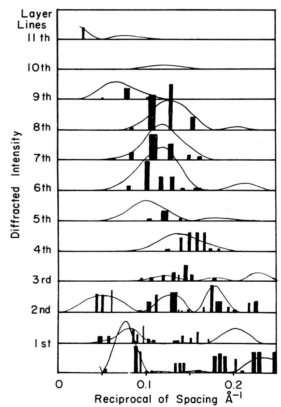

FIGURE 12. Observed and calculated intensities of diffraction for crystalline Na DNA. The observed intensities are shown by the heights of the black rectangles and the smooth curve is calculated from the model.

find how this ratio varies with the type of cell from which the DNA is prepared. However, we have found no difference in X-ray photographs of DNA isolated from rapidly and slowly dividing

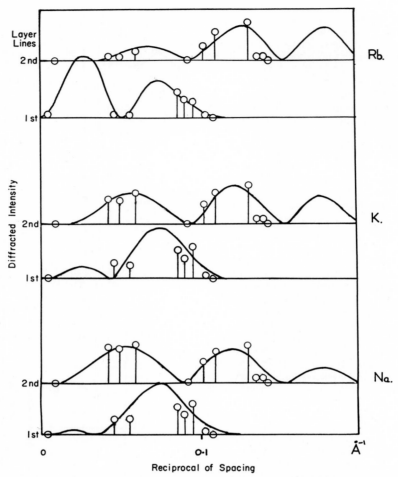

FIGURE 13. The difference of intensity of diffraction in isomorphous Na, K, and Rb salts of DNA. The smooth curve is calculated from the model; observed intensities are shown by circles. The main differences as the mass of the ion is increased are: On the first layer-line the first point on the left becomes of appreciable intensity only for Rb, and the second pair of points decreases almost to zero; on the second layer-line, the ratio of the first two peaks changes considerably.

cells, that is, with a high and low rate of DNA turnover, and from cells with high and low rates of protein synthesis.

Apart from lack of knowledge of the amorphous material, information about the molecules in the crystalline regions is also limited. We cannot exclude the possibility that there are occasional branches or breaks in the molecule. All we know is that the molecule is on the average a regular helix for about 20 turns (*i.e.* molecular weight $\sim 70,000$). We do not know whether the molecule is regular over a greater length; the diffraction provides no evidence about discontinuities placed farther apart than about 20 turns.

THE DNA MOLECULE CONSIDERED AS A TEMPLATE

In considering how DNA might act as a template, the sugar and phosphate part of the mole-cule are not of primary interest as they are regularly arranged; also it is quite likely that there are few breaks or branches in the poly-nucleotide chain, and therefore, one expects all specificity to be mainly associated with the nitrogen bases. These, in the B configuration which exists *in vivo*, lie fairly well exposed to outside influence, at the bottom of the 2 helical grooves on the molecule (Fig. 9). The surface of these grooves is fairly smooth, for example, interchange of a purine by a pyrimidine or a hydrogen atom by a methyl or amino group causes a difference in position of the bottom of the groove of 1.5 Å or less. Hence, from a space-filling point of view, the template character of DNA is not very marked. In particular, DNA does not look like a template for amino acids because the volume differences between amino acids are larger than those between purines and pyrimidines.

The difference in chemical reactivity between the various nitrogen bases is also small. The more reactive groups are hydrogen-bonded to link the bases in pairs. Only one of the four bases has a free amino group (and even it might be hydrogen bonded); this is on guanine in the shallower of the two grooves on the molecule. There is also little difference between the number of hydrogen-bonding sites on the two pairs of bases, though the positions of these sites differ. In the shallow groove both base-pairs have two sites, and the guanine-cytosine pair has an extra site on the amino group of guanine. In the deep groove both base-pairs have three sites and there is a methyl group on thymine in the same position as a hydrogen on cytosine. One may expect to find template action expressed in the slight differences of shape of the bases and exact positions of hydrogen-bonding sites. It is clearly possible for a suitably-shaped molecule to be held firmly, and with a high degree of specificity, in either of the grooves on DNA, by the combined effect of the pattern of hydrogen bonds and the total action of van der Waals forces acting over a large surface area in the grooves.

Polynucleotides would in principle possess ideal characteristics for templating to DNA; but, although polypeptides appear unlikely in this role, there are other possibilities in this connection which should not altogether be forgotten. Glucose has been found attached to hydroxymethyl cytosine in T2 bacteriophage DNA and it seems possible that other groups may also be found attached to the bases. If these attachments are labile, much attached matter may exist and yet remain undetected because it has been removed during purification. The presence of the unknown groups would of course enormously increase the templating possibilities of DNA, and Crick (1956) has suggested that specific templates might exist which link DNA and amino acids. In any case, as Chargaff (1955) has pointed out, it would be a mistake to let acceptance of ideas of DNA structure discourage further analytical research.

Hypothesis Concerning Replication of DNA Molecules

The Watson and Crick hypothesis about DNA replication has shown a kind of way biological processes may be interpreted in terms of precise molecular structure and is of much significance for this reason if for none other. Several experimental studies are in progress in an attempt to find if the hypothesis is correct or not, and at the moment the situation is not clear: Drs. Plaut and Mazia have results on plant cells, and different kinds of studies on bacteriophages have been carried out by Dr. Levinthal, Dr. Stent and Dr. Hershey.

Some Remarks on Molecular-Model Schemes in Biology

The hypothesis of Watson-Crick, and the suggestion of Gamow (1954) that groups of nucleotides could act as templates for 20 amino acids considered relevant to protein synthesis, have stimulated much speculation about molecular biology. Some schemes published have begun by being based on sound stereochemical ideas but, when these ideas were found unsuitable for the scheme, they were modified in a way stereochemically unlikely or impossible. It should be recognized that the work of Watson and Crick is seriously regarded because in it they adhered carefully to accepted stereochemical standards. When considering molecular model schemes, accurate 3-dimensional molecular models should be built and, among other things, the interatomic distances should be measured to make sure they are not too small. Molecular model building is a precise and often tedious discipline and need not be the fanciful expression of half-formed ideas. Most X-ray crystallographers are competent to advise those interested in these matters.

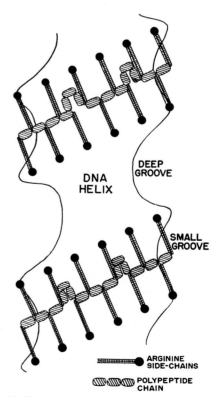

Figure 14. Diagram showing how protamine binds to DNA. The polypeptide chain winds around the small groove on the DNA helix. The phosphate groups are at the black circles and coincide with the basic ends of the arginine side-chains. Non-basic residues are shown in pairs at folds in the polypeptide chain.

STRUCTURE OF DEOXYRIBOSE NUCLEOPROTEINS

Nucleoprotamine

We hope that a study of the structure of nucleoproteins can cast light on the functional relationship of nucleic acids and proteins. The simplest basic protein to combine with DNA is protamine, and the mode of combination is known with a fair degree of certainty (Feughelman *et al.*, 1955). The polypeptide chain in nucleoprotamine is in a fully-extended form and winds helically around the DNA molecule and over, or in, the small groove on it (Fig. 14). The side-chains reach out from the polypeptide chain at about right-angles so that, on alternate sides, their basic end-groups can combine with the phosphate groups of the DNA. One-third of the residues in protamines are non-basic and these residues probably occur at folds in the polypeptide chain so that all the basic groups are able to combine with phosphates. A single residue cannot form a fold, but two together can; sequence analysis shows that the non-basic residues do in fact occur in pairs and not singly (Felix *et al.*, 1956). However, we do not know yet whether the folds point inwards towards the nitrogen bases or outwards.

It would seem that the possibility of folding can be large in basic proteins. The X-ray photographs (Fig. 15) of complexes of DNA with protamine and with polylysine (supplied by Prof. Katchalski) show no significant difference from those with lysine-rich histone (70 per cent non-basic residues) supplied by Dr. Mirsky and from naturally occurring nucleoprotein in sperm heads of *Sepia* or of *Loligo* which contain proteins with 70 per cent non-basic residues (Hamer, 1955) (see also Fig. 16). Molecular model-building

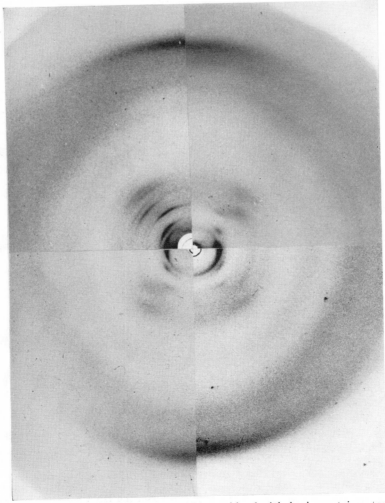

FIGURE 15. Comparison of the X-ray photographs of DNA combined with basic proteins: top left, intact oriented *Sepia* sperm; top right, DNA recipitated with lysine-rich histone; bottom left, nucleoprotamine extracted from *Salma trutta* sperm; bottom right, DNA precipitated with protamine.

shows that the polypeptide chain can fit snugly into the small groove on the DNA molecule (Fig. 9). We have also confirmed, more thoroughly than in earlier experiments, that the X-ray picture from *Loligo* sperm heads is not the result of artifact. Dr. D. B. Carlisle of the Marine Biological Laboratory at Plymouth supplied us with live spermatophores from a large species of *Loligo*. We obtained in four hours, from an intact spermatophore (enclosed in a mica cell to prevent drying) X-ray photographs which showed all the features previously observed using dried fibres of sperm.

Nucleohistone

Nucleoprotamines have been found in sperm heads (of many species but not all) and not in nuclei of other kinds of cell. The genetic material in sperm heads is probably in an inert state, being stored before beginning its genetical function in the egg. We have studied nucleoprotamine because it appeared to be the simplest combination of DNA and protein. The structure of nucleoprotein in cells which are growing, differentiating, or synthesizing protein might be more directly connected with dynamic relations between DNA and protein. In such cells—at least in higher organisms—DNA is, in the chromosomes, somehow in association with histone, non-basic protein, and possibly RNA. We thought the molecular structure of chromosomes in a functional state might be too complex to respond to direct study. Certain cells, for example, thymocytes and fowl erythrocytes, have nuclei which consist largely of nucleohistone and contain a minimum of non-basic protein and RNA. We thought these nuclei might have a simpler structure than those containing more non-basic protein and we have therefore, begun our work on these nuclei although the biological activity of erythrocyte nuclei may be low.

We have found that substantially the same X-ray diffraction photograph is obtained from calf thymus and from fowl erythrocyte nuclei, *Arbacia* sperm heads (Fig. 8) (which contain a basic protein which resembles histone more than protamine; Hamer, 1955) and calf thymus nucleohistone extracted with water (Fig. 7). (We are grateful to Dr. G. L. Brown of our laboratory for providing most of the extracted materials.) Evidently nucleohistone has a characteristic molecular morphology which may be preserved intact during extraction. Extracted material, or a jelly of coalesced nuclei, may be stretched into fibres in which the thread-like molecules tend to lie parallel to the length of the fibre. The X-ray photographs obtained from such fibres (Fig. 7) are, apart from orientation, the same as those from the unoriented material. The picture is not so well defined as when DNA or nucleoprotamine is used, but it is clear that much of the DNA in nucleohistone exists in its usual helical configu-

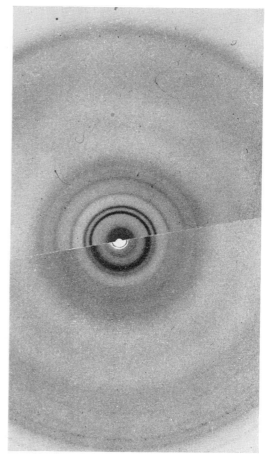

FIGURE 16. Comparison of the X-ray diffraction photographs of sperm heads of *Salvelinus* containing nucleoprotamine and *Loligo* (non-oriented) containing a nucleoprotein with a higher proportion of non-basic amino acids. The rings are less clearly defined in the photograph of *Salvelinus* and this means that the arrangement of the molecules is more disordered than in *Loligo*; otherwise no difference is apparent. (*Salvelinus* and *Salmo* sperm were kindly supplied by Prof. K. Felix.)

ration. Because nucleoprotamine consists of a polypeptide wrapped around the small groove on the DNA molecule, the first layer-line (Fig.17 and 18) of the nucleoprotamine X-ray diagram is stronger compared to the second layer-line than is the case for DNA alone. This strong first layer-line does not appear on the X-ray pictures of nucleohistone fibres, and it therefore seems that histone is not combined with DNA in the same way as in nucleoprotamine. An arrangement of histone which would be compatible with the relative intensities of the layer-lines is that in which histone polypeptide chains are wrapped around both grooves (Fig. 19) on the DNA molecule. We can eliminate also the possibility that all protein in the nucleohistone specimens is equally distributed between the DNA molecules

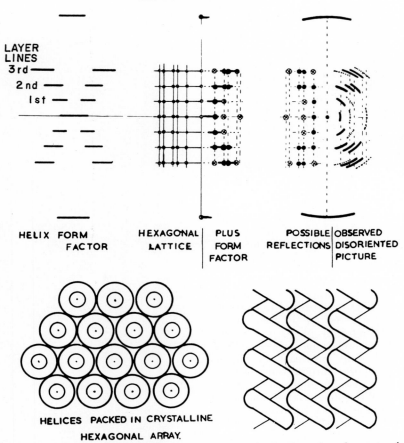

FIGURE 17. Diagrams showing how the X-ray diffraction photograph of oriented nucleoprotamine in sperm heads is produced. The diffraction spots (or reflections) occur where the crystal lattice points superimpose on the calculated diffraction (or form-factor). The molecules in the specimen are slightly disoriented and as a result the X-ray spots are enlarged into arcs of circles.

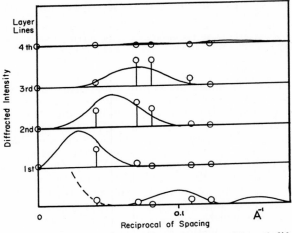

FIGURE 18. Observed and calculated intensities of diffraction from nucleoprotamine. The observed intensities are shown by circles and the smooth curve is calculated from the model. The dotted part of the curve and the observed point on it have been reduced in height 10 times.

and wrapped around them; for if this were so, the X-ray spacings at right angles to the fibre length would, in partly dried specimens, be larger than those observed. These spacings increase when the fibres are wetted, until a value of $\sim$38 Å is reached. The molecules are then disoriented, possibly owing to coiling of the chromonemata which had been straightened out in the stretched fibres. The 38 Å spacing is also observed in unfixed nuclei (Fig. 20) and even in whole thymocyte cells. It appears likely, that in the living interphase nucleus, nucleoprotein molecules lie parallel and equally spaced in groups of at least several dozen. The 38 Å spacing would correspond to a distance of 45 A between centres of the molecules if they are packed hexagonally. In one direction at least, the molecules are only about 25 Å across, and hence, in the living nucleus there is a space of about 20 A, filled largely with water, between adjacent molecules. Possibly this space is necessary to enable large molecules to move between the nucleoprotein threads.

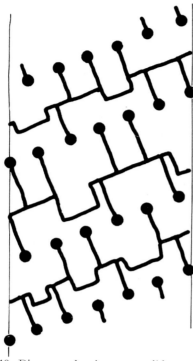

FIGURE 19. Diagram showing a possible way histone might bind to DNA. The black circles show the position of the phosphate groups on the DNA helix; the lines trace the polypeptide chain, the folds in it, and the side-chains of arginine and lysine.

There is, on the X-ray photographs of the various kinds of nucleohistone mentioned, a strong X-ray spacing at about 60 Å (Fig. 21). In fibres this spacing is at right angles to their length. We have not yet eliminated the possibility that the spacing corresponds to a periodicity in lipid associated with the nucleohistone, but this appears rather unlikely in view of the fact that the spacing is also observed in nucleohistone which has been purified by precipitation from aqueous solution with 0.14 Molar sodium chloride. If it is assumed that all the spacings arise from one kind of nucleohistone, they could be explained by the idea that DNA molecules occur in pairs joined together by protein. Such an interpretation is, however, at the moment very uncertain. The nucleohistone we study is known to contain many different proteins, some described as histone and others not. The fractionation and study of these components has only begun, and until much more is known of the chemistry of the nucleus, it is unlikely that physical studies by methods such as X-ray diffraction will yield results which can be interpreted without ambiguity. It is, however, clear that the interphase nucleus is largely composed of fine threads containing one or two DNA molecules, and that these threads lie parallel, packed together in groups. It seems probable that X-ray diffraction is here showing us the ultimate fibrillar structure of polytenic chromosomes.

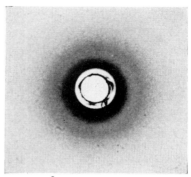

FIGURE 20. The 38 Å ring in the X-ray diffraction photograph of unfixed nuclei from fowl erythrocytes.

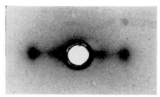

FIGURE 21. The 60 Å diffraction spots in the X-ray picture of oriented extracted calf thymus nucleohistone.

ACKNOWLEDGMENTS

I am most grateful to my colleagues at King's for help in preparing the illustrations for this paper and to Dr. L. D. Hamilton for help with the manuscript.

REFERENCES

ASTBURY, W. T., 1947, X-ray studies on nucleic acids. Symp. Soc. Exp. Biol. *1:* 66–76.

CHARGAFF, E., 1955, Isolation and composition of the deoxypentose nucleic acids and of the corresponding nucleoproteins. In: The Nucleic Acids, New York, Academic Press, Vol. 1. Chapter 10: 307–368.

CRICK, F. H. C., 1956, Conference on nucleic acids and protein synthesis, Biochem. J. (in press).

CRICK, F. H. C., and WATSON, J. D., 1954, The complementary structure of deoxyribosenucleic acid. Proc. Roy. Soc. *223:* 80–96.

DALY, M. M., and MIRSKY, A. E., 1955, Histones with high lysine content. J. Gen. Physiol. *38:* 405–413.

DOTY, P., 1956, The characterization, denaturation and degradation of desoxyribose nucleic acid. Proc. 3rd Intern. Congr. Biochem.: 135–139.

DUNITZ, J. D., AND ROLLETT, J. S., 1956, The crystal structure of dibenzylphosphoric acid. Acta. cryst. Camb. *9:* 327–334.

FELIX, K. FISCHER, H., and KREKELS, A., 1956, Progress in Biophysics. London, Pergamon Press, p. 1.

FEUGHELMAN, M., LANGRIDGE, R., SEEDS, W. E., STOKES, A. R., WILSON, H. R., HOOPER, C. W., WILKINS, M. H. F., BARCLAY, R. K., HAMILTON, L. D., 1955, Molecular structure of deoxyribose nucleic acid and nucleoprotein. Nature, Lond. *175:* 834–836.

FRANKLIN, R. E., and GOSLING, R. G., 1953, Molecular configuration in sodium thymonucleate. Nature, Lond. *171:* 740–741.

GAMOW, G., 1954. Possible relation between deoxyribonucleic acid and protein structure. Nature, Lond. *173:* 318.

HAMER, D., 1955, The composition of the basic proteins of echinoderm sperm. Biol. Bull., Wood's Hole *10:* 35–39.

Huber, M., 1956, Acta. cryst. Camb. (in press).
Watson, J. D., and Crick, F. H. C., 1953, A structure
    for deoxyribose nucleic acids. Nature, Lond. *171:*
    737–738.
    1953, Genetical implications of the structure of deoxy-
    ribose nucleic acid. Nature, Lond. *171:* 964.
Wilkins, M. H. F., Stokes, A. R., and Wilson, H. R.,
    1953, Molecular structure of desoxypentose nucleic
    acids. Nature, Lond. *171:* 738–740.

DISCUSSION

Plaine: You have stated that the structure of the DNA molecule *is* continuous. From their analysis of terminal phosphate groups, Dekker and Schachman concluded that the structure consisted of interrupted strands, with the breaks occurring about every fifty nucleotides but being staggered in the two chains of the molecule. Such an interrupted-two-strand structure might be more flexible than a continuous one and might possibly be more applicable for explaining some of the genetic and cytogenetic phenomena. Would you please explain why you object to, or what is wrong with, the interpretation of the interrupted structure?

Wilkins: Until recently there existed much evidence from dye-binding and titration studies

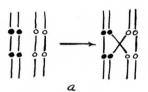

Figure 1a.

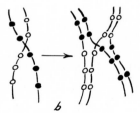

Figure 1b.

Figure 1c.

Figure 1d.

which indicated that there was in DNA one secondary phosphoryl group per 20–30 nucleotides (*e.g.* Peacocke, 1955). It was suggested that these phosphoryl groups were at the ends of branches attached to the main polynucleotide chains.

Dekker and Schachman (1954) preferred to interpret their results in terms of breaks in the phosphate-ester chains in the double-helix DNA molecule, and they produced experimental evidence to show that, when the hydrogen bonds linking the chains in the double-helix molecule were broken by heating, the molecular weight of DNA fell to that of 20–30 nucleotides. However, Doty and Rice (1955) have shown that when hydrogen bonds in DNA are broken by heat or low pH, the molecular weight is unaltered. It is not clear to me to what extent differences of conditions of heating in the two sets of experiments or differences in initial intactness of the DNA explain the disagreement in these results. However, Peacocke (1956), one of the main workers studying the question of secondary phosphoryl groups in DNA, now claims that neither dye-binding nor titration experiments give evidence of secondary phosphoryl groups. It appears therefore, that there is not much reason for supposing that the suggestion of Dekker and Schachman is correct. Furthermore, it seems rather unlikely that the regularity and rigidity of the double-helix molecule would be preserved when breaks occur in the phosphate-ester chain for, at such breaks, the helix would be held intact only by van der Waals forces. (Refs.: Dekker, C. A., and Schachman, H. K., 1954, Proc. Nat. Acad. Sci. Wash. *40:* 894–909; Doty, P., and Rice, S. A., 1955, Biochim. Biophys. Acta *16:* 446–448; Peacocke, A. R., 1955, La Ricerca Sci., Suppl. Simp. Intern. Chim. Macromol., Oct. 1954, and 1956, J. Chem. Soc. in press.)

Weinstein: I wonder whether Dr. Wilkins would care to say anything about the relation between the structure of DNA or of other substances in the chromosomes and crossing over.

The classical theory of crossing over, which goes back to Janssens and Morgan, implies, from a chemical point of view, that connections between atoms in the same chromatid are replaced by connections between atoms in different chromatids. (Fig. 1a). The necessity for such a change is avoided in Belling's theory, because some of the new genes are formed on one of the old chromatids and some on the other, as the two old chromatids lie across each other (Fig. 1b). But the avoidance is only for crossovers between homologous strands; because to account for 3-strand (progressive) and 4-strand (digressive) crossovers, Belling's theory must be modified to allow exchanges to occur between sister chromatids. A sister exchange, if it occurs after the new genes have become linked in a chain, implies a change of two bonds. (See fig. 1c.) If, when it occurs, the new genes are not yet linked in a chain, there is only one longitudinal bond to be altered. (See fig. 1d.) Therefore the genetic evidence implies that at least in some cases of crossing over, connections between old genes are replaced by connections between old and new genes; and we might expect some indication of this in the chemistry of the chromosomes.

WILKINS: The only substance about which we know much in chromosomes is DNA and hence it would seem best to confine speculations to this substance. There is, of course, no difficulty in envisaging a supply of energy in the cell sufficient to cause polynucleotide or polypeptide chains to break and afterwards to reform in other ways which might then give rise to recombination. It is not easy, however, to suggest a scheme for recombination which arises naturally from the structure of DNA. Most theories would involve the idea that crossing over and replication took place simultaneously, but in higher organisms it is uncertain whether crossing over occurs during DNA synthesis or afterwards when chiasmata formation is observed. It seems likely that crossing over in higher organisms differs from that in bacteriophage. Possibly this difference is due to bacteriophage processes probably taking place on a molecular level, whereas the chromosomes of higher organisms have a more complicated organization (*e.g.*, contain many strands). In such chromosomes the molecular changes may be substantially the same as in bacteriophages, but the expression of these changes may appear different. The first problem in devising a molecular theory is to find a mechanism for homologous pairing. No one appears to have obtained a really satisfactory solution in terms of DNA molecules only, but I understand that this question will be discussed at the Symposium on the Chemical Basis of Heredity, about to take place at the Johns Hopkins University.

I would like to mention here some points which are relevant to Dr. Weinstein's question insofar as they illustrate the kind of difficulty which arises in speculation about the molecular processes in biology. (These points have arisen at this Symposium out of discussion with Dr. Levinthal, Dr. Stent and others; while I make no claim to these ideas, I may be responsible for any errors involved.)

First, let us consider one of the main objections to the Watson and Crick hypothesis of DNA replication. The argument is that, if the hydrogen bonds between the two polynucleotide chains in a DNA molecule are broken, the two parts cannot easily separate because they are intertwined. Unwinding of the two chains is considered to be an unlikely process because of interaction between the chains. This argument, however, seems to involve the assumption that some unspecific process such as Brownian motion would unwind the chains. There is no difficulty in unwinding the chains if a directed process of separation begins at one end of the molecule and travels along it. As an example of such a process, it has been suggested that, as the two chains separate, nucleotides condense on them to form two new DNA molecules. (It is necessary, of course, to explain why the reaction proceeds forwards and not backwards.) Thus, while duplication of the original molecule is taking place, the two new partly-formed molecules are joined to the portion of the original molecule which has not yet duplicated. The junction moves until the original molecule has split along its whole length and two complete separate new molecules have been formed. The helical molecular strands rotate about their axes during this duplication, but Dr. Levinthal has made a calculation which shows that the energy required to overcome the viscous forces involved is quite small. Many rather unsatisfying schemes for DNA replication have been suggested in order to avoid the difficulty of unwinding, and it seems that such schemes only deserve attention if it can be shown that the difficulty of unwinding really exists.

This kind of argument about the helical nature of DNA may be taken a stage farther by suggesting that the helical nature, rather than being an impediment, may in fact be of considerable help to the molecule in its functioning. Let us confine the discussion to DNA replication according to the Watson and Crick hypothesis. We know that the hydrogen bonds in DNA can be readily broken by heating, but the value of the activation energy of this process indicates that the bonds reform unless they are broken in about 15 consecutive base-pairs (Doty, 1956). Bond repair also seems to take place when ultraviolet light is absorbed by the bases. It seems likely that *in vivo* the hydrogen bonds in DNA may be breaking and reforming, a process like melting and solidifying. This conclusion is not surprising if we accept the idea that any templating actions of DNA, replication or otherwise, are determined primarily by hydrogen bonds to the nitrogen bases. If it is necessary at one stage during the templating process for the two molecular components to be held together, it is equally necessary for them soon afterwards to come apart freely. This might be easily achieved if the hydrogen bonds were close to their "melting point." If the phosphate-ester chains in the DNA molecule were straight, or consisted of adjacent and non-intertwined helices, the two chains might, on account of their flexible nature, begin accidentally to separate whenever the hydrogen bonds melted locally. The intertwined helical structure of DNA is semi-rigid because the configuration is determined not only by the hydrogen bonds pairing the bases, but also by van der Waals forces; and hence, the polynucleotide chains cannot separate locally unless a sufficiently large region of the hydrogen-bonding system is melted to enable the helical configuration in that region to become seriously disordered. However, as we have said above, if the bonds are broken at one end of the molecule, and systematic rearrangement of the bases prevents them from reforming, the two poly-nucleotide chains might be separated readily.

It has often been commented that, while much is known about the structure of DNA and of its biological activity, almost nothing is known of its biochemical activity. This absence of knowledge, however, is only to be expected if the activity of DNA consists of transient hydrogen bonding to highly specific substances.

ALFERT: Dr. Wilkins presented evidence that sperm protamines are attached to DNA in a manner different from that of histones found usually combined with DNA in somatic nuclei. A difference in the configuration of nucleoprotein complexes is also reflected in a particular cyto-chemical property of DNA, namely its relative basophilia in various types of nuclei. Lison (1955, Acta Histochem. *2:* 47) has recently shown that the basic dye-binding capacity of rat sperm nuclei greatly decreases during maturation of the sperm while the nuclear protein increases in basicity. By means of similar cytophotometric de-terminations of nuclear Feulgen/methyl green staining ratios on sections of guinea-pig testis we have obtained data in accord with those of Lison, also showing a substantial relative decrease in the basophilia of sperm DNA as compared to that of other nuclear types in the testis. While Lison postulates that the high arginine content of sperm protein is responsible for its ability to suppress the dye-binding capacity of DNA-phos-phate groups, the same cytochemical effect on DNA can apparently be produced in other systems by a very different mechanism: this is shown by the findings of Bloch and Godman (1956, J. Biophys. Biochem. Cytol. *1:* 531) which suggest that a partial staining inhibition of nuclear DNA in physiologically active somatic cells may be produced by its association with a non-basic protein fraction.

Genetic Significance of the Transfer of Nucleic Acid from Parental to Offspring Phage[1]

A. D. Hershey and Elizabeth Burgi

Department of Genetics, Carnegie Institution of Washington, Cold Spring Harbor, New York

Putnam and Kozloff (1950) first demonstrated that labeled atoms derived from a parental generation of phage particles were partly conserved among the viral offspring. Subsequent work showed that the conserved atoms were derived from and transferred to deoxyribonucleic acid (DNA), chiefly or exclusively (Hershey and Chase, 1952; Kozloff, 1953; French, 1954). What can this phenomenon tell us about genetic replication and recombination?

The selective transfer of DNA is not itself very informative: most of the viral protein fails to enter the cell at the time of infection and is unavailable for transfer (Hershey and Chase, 1952). Moreover, the same selectivity is observed when one examines the utilization of labeled bacterial constituents for viral growth: only the DNA is utilized efficiently (Kozloff *et al.*, 1951; Hershey *et al.*, 1954). Considering the two results together one can invoke metabolic accident, or perhaps nuclear localization of viral growth, but certainly not direct expression of a presumed genetic role for DNA.

Kozloff (1952, 1953) listed three reasons for suspecting that the material transfer from parental phage to offspring had nothing to do with genetic function. First, the transfer was variable and incomplete. Second, phosphorus atoms seemed to be transferred more efficiently than DNA-nitrogen atoms. Third, bacteria infected with a mixture of irradiated, presumably genetically impotent phage particles and normal phage particles yielded viral offspring containing atoms derived from the irradiated parent.

More recent work has followed two main directions. On the one hand it was necessary to improve the techniques of the transfer measurements, mainly in order to refine Kozloff's ingenious experiments. On the other hand it was necessary to invent methods for examining the distribution of parental atoms among offspring phage particles. Current developments along both lines are summarized below.

The Meaning of Incomplete Transfer

Improved methods for measuring the transfer of phosphorus from parental to offspring phage

raised the observed efficiency to 40 or 50 per cent (Watson and Maaløe, 1953; Hershey, 1953). For a time it appeared that there might be a theoretical upper limit at about 50 per cent, suggesting separation of the viral DNA into transferrable and nontransferrable portions, possibly corresponding to the two strands of the duplex DNA structure (Watson and Crick, 1953).

Maaløe and Watson (1951) first tested this idea by carrying the transfer measurement through two successive cycles of viral growth. They reasoned that if the transferred atoms represented a special part of the viral DNA, labeled atoms should tend to concentrate in that part during a first cycle of growth, and transfer with greater efficiency during a second cycle. Instead, they found only the usual efficiency of transfer in both cycles. Thus the transferred DNA served as precursor to both transferrable and nontransferrable portions of the DNA in the offspring. In effect, the transferred atoms represent a random sample of the parental atoms. Either the viral DNA consists of a single functional species, or of two or more each of which is conserved with equal efficiency.

A closer look at the chemistry of transfer leads to the same conclusion. Phosphorus and purine carbon are transferred with equal efficiency (Watson and Maaløe, 1953). All four purine and pyrimidine residues are transferred equally (Hershey *et al.*, 1954). The unequal transfer of phosphorus and DNA nitrogen reported by Kozloff (1953) remains unexplained.

In Table 1 we present in detail a recent experiment describing the conservation of C^{14}-labeled bases. It shows that the individual purines and pyrimidines are transferred with an efficiency close to 50 per cent, similar to that observed for phosphorus under the same conditions. It also shows that unlabeled thymidine and uridine added to the culture medium fail to suppress the transfer of pyrimidines. Similar results have been reported for single competitors (Hershey *et al.*, 1954). These results suggest transfer as intact DNA or polynucleotides, as opposed to transfer through intermediates of smaller size. The partial transfer again resembles a random sample of the whole parental DNA.

If the transfer is random, the loss is random. How does this loss occur? We believe that most of it can be explained in terms of the hazards, technical and biological, of the transfer measure-

[1] Supported in part by a grant (C 2158) from the National Cancer Institute, National Institutes of Health, Public Health Service. Isotopes were supplied by the Oak Ridge National Laboratory on allocation from the Atomic Energy Commission.

TABLE 1. TRANSFER OF C[14] FROM PARENTAL
TO OFFSPRING T2

Sample	Phage per B	Whole DNA	Sum of Bases	Per Cent Distribution of C[14]			
				g	h	a	
		cpm	*cpm*				
Total label	—	35500	13500	18	19	30	33
			14300	19	19	28	34
		34200	11900	19	18	29	33
			13000	18	18	28	36
Phage blank	2	3660	1360	17	17	29	37
			lost				
		4280	1510	18	18	30	34
			1620	19	18	31	32
Phage yield (no competitor)	277	22600	7510	20	20	30	31
			9455	19	18	29	35
		22900	8600	18	16	30	37
			8850	20	16	29	35
Phage yield (thymidine + uridine)	289	21400	8700	18	17	31	34
			8970	19	18	30	34
		22400	8760	17	18	27	38
			7590	20	18	29	33

A suspension of 4×10^{10} bacteria (glucose-ammonia medium, 36°C) was infected with 1.5×10^{11} uniformly C[14]-labeled phage (0.05 μc/μg C) and centrifuged to remove unadsorbed C[14] (21 per cent). The infected cells were resuspended in fresh culture medium and transferred to two culture tubes, one of which contained 0.2 mg/ml each of thymidine and uridine. Samples were immediately removed for analysis of total labeled DNA. Other samples were removed at 12 minutes (phage blank) and 90 minutes (phage yield). These samples were lysed with cyanide and carrier phage, and the reisolated phage was analysed for labeled DNA. DNA was isolated by the Schmidt-Thannhauser method (Hershey et al., 1953). Labeled purines and pyrimidines were assayed after separation by paper chromatography (Hershey, 1954). Cultural conditions and fractionation of lysates are described by Hershey and Melechen (1956). Results are expressed in counts per minute per 9 ml of culture, with per cent distributions among guanine, hydroxymethylcytosine, adenine, and thymine. They represent duplicate chromatograms from duplicate 9 ml culture samples of each kind.

Similar results were obtained with deoxycytidine and deoxyadenosine competing. In another experiment with thymidine (added before infection) overall transfer was reduced slightly, but not the relative transfer of thymine.

ment. To understand these, it is necessary to know something about the technology of experimentation with phage.

The first problem is to prepare viable phage particles labeled with P[32]. The optical cross section (cm²/phage) at 260 mμ, that is, the optical density per centimeter divided by the plaque count per milliliter of a purified phage preparation, is a convenient index of viability. The best preparations of T2 measure about 7×10^{-12} cm²/phage (Luria et al., 1951; Hershey et al., 1953); our worst radioactive preparations measure four times higher. The dead phage particles in such preparations adsorb to bacteria but fail to inject their DNA. Needless to say, the measured transfer of P[32] to offspring is strongly dependent on the viability of the labeled phage particles.

An optical cross-section not exceeding 8×10^{-12} cm²/phage is readily obtained if one observes the following precautions during the preparation of stocks. First, the specific radioactivity of the incorporated phosphorus is kept as low as convenient to minimize effects of radiation. Second, phage growth is interrupted at 40 minutes after infection. Later phage yields contain many noninfective particles (Lanni and Lanni, personal communication; Hershey and Melechen, 1956). Third, the culture is lysed in a medium of low salt concentration containing indole to prevent inactivation of phage by adsorption to bacterial debris (Sagik, 1954). Fourth, the bacterial debris is promptly removed after lysis by filtration through a porcelain candle. Fifth, the phage particles are sedimented quickly in the presence of peptone to protect against effects of radiation in the pellet. Sixth, the transfer measurement is made, in our experiments within 48 hours, before further radiation damage can accumulate.

The transfer measurements themselves present four difficulties. First, the best phage preparations undoubtedly contain inviable particles (Luria et al., 1951). Second, phage particles attaching to bacteria already infected one minute or so earlier fail to contribute P[32] to the viral progeny. About half such particles fail to inject; the DNA of the other half is released into the medium in acid-soluble form (French et al., 1952; Watson and Maaløe, 1953; Hershey et al., 1954). This loss can be minimized by using a low ratio of phage to bacteria or by ensuring rapid adsorption of phage to bacteria. Third, some means must be employed to prevent lysis of the infected cells before all the labeled precursors have been incorporated into offspring phage particles. Fourth, some means must be employed after lysis to prevent loss of phage by adsorption to bacterial debris, and otherwise to ensure complete recovery of viral progeny.

Watson and Maaløe (1953) developed several methods for minimizing the known losses. They, and afterwards Hershey (1953), obtained 40 to 50 per cent transfer of P[32] from parental to offspring phage. Recently we have employed the method described in Figure 1, which gives about 58 per cent transfer. In this method we make use of the fact that lysis of infected bacteria is prevented by continuous reinfection (Doermann, 1948). Two bacterial cultures are infected with phage at 10 minute intervals, the first with nonradioactive phage, the second with radioactive phage. About 25 minutes after infection some of the cells in the first culture lyse, and the liberated virus particles attach to other bacteria and postpone their lysis. Before this time the two cultures are mixed, so that the first wave of lysis among cells of the second culture is largely prevented.

We interpret the results shown in Figure 1 in the following way. Some of the parental phage particles fail to inject. They contribute to the radioactivity of low and high speed pellets at ten minutes, and account for about 12 per cent of the total P^{32}. Radioactive phage progeny begin to form about ten minutes after infection. On fractionation, most of the phage progeny go into the high speed pellet. However, eleven per cent are recovered by titration of the low speed pellet and about two per cent in the final supernatant, compared to the titer before fractionation. The main fraction thus contains about 87 per cent of the phage particles titratable in the lysate. Only part of the rise in radioactivity of the low speed pellet can be attributed to infective phage particles. Another part of it, as well as the rise in acid-soluble P^{32}, must reflect phage particles released by premature lysis of cells in the growing culture, all of which would be lost by readsorption to bacteria. Prematurely lysing cells also release into the medium radioactive DNA that can be detected by comparing acid-soluble P^{32} produced in cultures with and without added deoxyribonuclease (Hershey, 1953). This is in addition to the P^{32} in the pellet fractions, which are always treated with the enzyme after lysis and before centrifugation.

The total DNA balance can be summarized as follows: about 12 per cent lost as noninjecting phage; about 12 per cent lost by readsorption of viral offspring after premature lysis (rise in acid-soluble after 10 minutes plus part of rise in low speed pellet); about ten per cent lost as DNA sensitive to deoxyribonuclease before massive lysis; and about 58 per cent transfer (rise in high speed pellet divided by 0.87). This leaves only eight per cent of the labeled DNA to be accounted for by unspecified biological accidents, such as cells that do not lyse prematurely but produce few or no viral offspring.

The details of this interpretation are somewhat arbitrary. Their plausibility is increased by many similar experiments performed under conditions in which the transfer is less efficient, which always show larger losses among the recognizable categories. We conclude that the partial transfer is easily explained by random losses of the kinds described, and that it has nothing to do with the mechanism of transfer.

THE MEANING OF EARLY TRANSFER

Parental phosphorus, like all other viral DNA precursors present in the cell during early stages of infection, tends to concentrate in the first phage particles to be formed (Weed and Cohen, 1951; French *et al.*, 1952; Stent and Maaløe, 1953; Watson and Maaløe, 1953). In fact, one can iden-

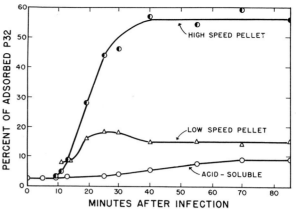

FIGURE 1. Transfer of radiophosphorus from parental to offspring phage. Bacteria were grown in glucose-ammonia medium to 5×10^8 per ml, centrifuged, and resuspended in fresh medium at 2.5×10^9 per ml. P^{32}-labeled T2, specific activity 0.1 mc/mg P, were added at a ratio of 3 particles per bacterium. After warming 5 minutes, the mixture was centrifuged, and the supernatant, containing 5 per cent of the total P^{32}, was discarded. The infected cells were resuspended in fresh medium at 5×10^8 cells per ml and added (at 0 minute) to two volumes of bacterial culture that had been infected with nonradioactive phage 10 minutes earlier. Samples were then taken at intervals for determination of acid-soluble and acid-insoluble P^{32}. Other samples were lysed and fractionated centrifugally (Hershey and Melechen, 1956). The high speed pellet contains the phage particles, except for about 11 per cent in the low speed pellet and 2 per cent lost in the final supernatant. The total adsorbed P^{32} is computed from the average of sums for 10 measurements of acid-soluble and insoluble portions, with less than 10 per cent range of variation.

tify one or more pools of preformed phage-precursor DNA, in which labeled parental DNA is metabolically equivalent to labeled DNA from other sources (Hershey, 1953). The size of these pools can be altered by experimental interference and when this is done the average concentration of parental atoms in the offspring phage particles is correspondingly altered (Hershey and Melechen, 1956). Under the conditions described in Figure 1, the pool contains 25 to 50 phage equivalent units of DNA (1 unit = 2×10^{-10} micrograms). Except for losses of the type already discussed, all the DNA present in the cells and having the composition characteristic of virus particles is contained in this pool. The first phage particles formed receive, on the average, two per cent each of the labeled parental atoms. Particles formed later receive less and less until, after the first 100, the supply of labeled precursors runs out. The distribution of parental atoms among the offspring measured in this way is an average distribution. It tells us that the synthesis of phage precursor DNA and the formation of phage particles proceed at equal rates and that the two processes are separated by a certain interval of time. It thus characterizes the replicating population, not the process of replication.

The unit of replication seems to be free DNA, that is, molecules of DNA confined only by the bacterial cell, not by smaller particles (Watanabe *et al.*, 1954; Hershey and Melechen, 1956). If so, the formation of particles resembling finished phages is terminal to replication. This circumstance seems to set phage growth apart from more conventional examples of DNA synthesis, in which replication is presumably bound up with complex patterns of chromosomal and nuclear behavior. Just how real this difference is, and whether it will simplify any basic problems, remains to be seen.

The Microscopic Distribution of Transferred Atoms

The manner in which the number of parental phosphorus atoms per offspring phage particle varies from particle to particle may be spoken of as the microscopic distribution. Like the average distribution, it might be time-dependent, for any of three reasons. First, if the transferred atoms all pass through a pool of intermediates of small size on their way to offspring particles, the microscopic distribution might resemble the average distribution. If part of the atoms are transferred in this way, two or more distributions would be superimposed. Second, if replication takes place by a mechanism that partitions parental atoms equally between two daughters (Delbrück, 1954), the microscopic distribution would reflect the number of generations of descent, strongly time dependent. The mode of the distribution for early particles (5 or 6 generations) would be similar to the average (2%), but first generation particles containing 50 per cent of the parental atoms would not be excluded. The only clear alternative to this type of replication is one that produces a time-independent distribution of large pieces of parental DNA as suggested, for example, by the model of Watson and Crick (1953). Third, if the process recognized as genetic recombination calls for fragmentation of completed parental strands, an additional time-dependent distribution will result. The number of mating acts is supposed to equal the number of generations (Visconti and Delbrück, 1953; Levinthal and Visconti, 1953). For this and other reasons most phage geneticists prefer to think that recombination is part of the replication process itself (reviewed by Hershey, 1956). If so the two need not be considered separately in the distribution problem, and both can be imagined to occur without producing a time-dependent fragmentation of the parental genetic material. These ideas were first clearly stated by Levinthal (1955, 1956) and are discussed in greater detail by Delbrück and Stent (1956).

The distribution problem is of interest chiefly in terms of what light it might shed on the mechanisms of replication and recombination. For a long time it has been clear that the light would be dim indeed unless both processes together produced a time-independent distribution of the parental DNA, a circumstance that generates a strong bias in favor of models possessing this property. A preliminary experiment by Garen was disappointing for this reason (Hershey *et al.*, 1954). He found that during mixed infection parental atoms pass abundantly from particles of one genotype to those of a second, implying dispersion of some kind. However, a new consideration has been introduced by Levinthal (1956). He proposes that phage particles contain two kinds of DNA, one dispersed among the progeny in small pieces, the other in large. Thus it is possible to suppose that the small pieces account for Garen's result, and the large pieces only engage in genetic processes. Unfortunately, the reverse situation, among other alternatives, is not yet excluded.

We summarize below four independent methods of attacking these questions. All of them represent technical developments of a very high order. None of them has yet been adequately studied.

The Autograph Method

Levinthal (1955, 1956) first obtained radiographs of individual phage particles labeled with radiophosphorus. The radioactive particles are dispersed between two layers of radiosensitive photographic emulsion, in which single Beta emissions will form a track. The film is allowed to dry on a slide, aged to permit decay of P^{32}, and developed. Radiation emanating from point sources produces star-shaped figures. The number of tracks in a star depends in a statistically predictable way on the number of P^{32} atoms in the source, and on the time of exposure. Accurate counts can be made of stars showing 5 to 20 tracks, and matters are arranged so that the average number of tracks per star lies in this range. From the counts one obtains the number of sources per sample, the average number of P^{32} atoms per source, and information about the variation of this number from source to source.

For reference purposes, it should be recalled that one phage particle contains about 2×10^{-10} micrograms of DNA, which corresponds to an aggregate molecular weight of 1.2×10^8. The preliminary results obtained by the autograph method may be summarized in terms of fractions of this phage equivalent unit (Levinthal, 1956).

First, if uniformly labeled phage particles are subjected to osmotic shock, and the liberated DNA is examined, one finds large pieces, uniform in size and approximately one per phage particle, corresponding in size to about 0.4 of the phage-equivalent unit. The remainder of the DNA does not produce visible stars, and must be dispersed as fragments smaller than 0.1 of a unit.

Second, if the offspring from labeled particles are examined, one finds that a few of them, approximately one per parent, each contain about 0.2 of a unit of parental DNA. The P^{32} in these particles does not disperse upon osmotic shock.

The remainder of the particles do not contain sufficient P^{32} to be detected by the method.

Third, if the particles described above are passed through a second cycle of growth, the large fragments of parental DNA do not diminish appreciably in size or number.

Levinthal (1956) interprets his results in the following way. Phage particles contain a single large piece of DNA, of molecular weight about 50 million, and many smaller pieces. The large piece is duplex in structure, and passes into the progeny by halves. On the average only one of the halves is conserved, presumably owing to random losses. The recipient particle thus contains a new duplex piece, one half of which is of parental origin. On further replication, the halves of duplexes retain their integrity as before, and no further fragmentation of parental pieces is observed.

Furthermore, since the 0.4 unit piece may be the only one large enough to account for linkage data (Benzer, 1955), it should be identifiable with the phage chromosome, an hypothesis subject to test. If this hypothesis proves to be correct, both replication and genetic recombination would have to be explained by mechanisms that do not fragment the parental DNA after the first generation.

We consider Levinthal's hypothesis an extremely useful one, because it makes very specific predictions concerning the outcome of many experiments that might not otherwise seem promising. Some examples of these will be mentioned below. On the other hand it would, in our opinion, be a mistake to regard the hypothesis as established by the present data, both because of uncertainty about their accuracy, and because important sources of error are difficult to exclude.

Two sources of error should be mentioned. The extraction of DNA from phage particles by osmotic shock is, according to general experience, a complicated process not at all understood. Under the usual conditions, a large part of the DNA remains associated with the protein portion of the phage particles. Experiments of the type described by Levinthal should be accompanied by proof that the DNA has first been isolated.

The second source of error is applicable to all experiments involving isotope transfer from parental to offspring phage, and becomes more important, the higher the specific radioactivity of the parental generation. Highly radioactive stocks are likely to contain several noninfective particles for each infective particle. The noninfective particles adsorb to bacteria but do not inject their DNA. They tend to be liberated again when the infected bacteria lyse, and so contaminate the final progeny. Under certain conditions, at least, they can readsorb specifically when again brought in contact with bacteria. Nothing is known about the possibility of partial loss of DNA from such particles. However, the discrimination between isotope in offspring particles and isotope in remnants of parental particles is a perennial technical problem that, in our experience, has no general solution.

THE RADIOACTIVE DECAY METHOD

Hershey, Kamen, Kennedy, and Gest (1951) proposed to study the microscopic distribution problem in terms of the fact that phage particles containing radiophosphorus die at a rate proportional to the number of radioactive atoms they contain. This proposal came to nothing when it was found that the offspring of highly radioactive particles are stable. Stent and Jerne (1955) inferred that the transferred atoms of radiophosphorus must be concentrated in very few of the offspring particles, so few that their loss by radioactive decay is undetectable. They also devised a method for testing this inference. They looked for the death of a few highly radioactive particles among the offspring by measuring the progressive loss in transferability, in experiments performed on successive days, from first cycle offspring to second cycle offspring. The results showed that some of the transferred phosphorus was, in fact, concentrated in a few particles subject to radioactive decay.

Subsequent experiments add further information (Stent, Jerne, and Sato, 1956). It now appears that the few particles subject to radioactive decay contain only half the transferred phosphorus. The others, although they seem to contain considerable amounts of radiophosphorus, are stable. Furthermore, the distribution of radiophosphorus between particles that decay and particles that are stable is not appreciably different among the offspring from first and second cycles of growth, suggesting a time-independent distribution.

Two interpretations can be entertained. One may suppose that the transferred DNA is of two kinds: one sensitive to radioactive decay, and one resistant, the two fractions being of approximately equal size. The time-independent distribution then implies that both kinds of DNA are transmitted to progeny with equal efficiency and at least one of them without progressive fragmentation. This interpretation, without further assumptions, does not permit any inference about the distribution of transferred atoms. Its general features resemble Levinthal's hypothesis.

The second interpretation is different. One assumes that the rates of death among the offspring and among the parents are identical measures of P^{32} content. Then some individual particles among the offspring contain 20 per cent or less, in fixed or variable amount, of parental phosphorus. On this interpretation some of the apparent radiophorus content of the stable particles probably should be attributed to radioactive contaminants that adsorb reversibly to bacteria. Thus the data are compatible with a variety of hypotheses, the most restrictive fact being the time-independent character of the microscopic distribution.

The hint of a functionally bipartite DNA suggested to Stent, Jerne, and Sato (1956) the following experiment. Bacteria were infected with one highly radioactive particle of phage and ten nonradioactive particles differing from the minority parent by four distantly linked genetic markers. The yields of virus from individual bacteria contained particles of the genotype of the minority parent in less than ten per cent of the cases. In other words, the genetic results alone suggested that the parental chromosome had been frequently destroyed in the act of producing genetic recombinants. Moreover, particles of the genotype of the minority parent, even in those yields containing only one such particle, were not subject to radioactive decay at an appreciable rate. Both results tend to disagree with predictions of the Levinthal hypothesis. The experiment requires further study, however.

The experiments of Levinthal and of Stent *et al.* show two common features. First, the transferred DNA is found to be concentrated, in part, in very few offspring particles. Second, these particles seem to contain DNA of parental origin that is not subject to further fragmentation during continued replication. The functional status of the material possessing these properties is not yet clear, but the question should yield to further experiments.

TRANSMISSIBLE LESIONS CAUSED BY ULTRAVIOLET IRRADIATION

Kozloff (1952) reported experiments of the following type. Bacteria were simultaneously infected with radioactive phage particles that had been subjected to ultraviolet irradiation and normal nonradioactive particles. The viral progeny issuing from such bacteria, presumably the offspring of nonradioactive particles, were found to contain radiophosphorus in appreciable amounts. For a long time this result furnished the strongest evidence that the transfer from parental to offspring phage in general might reflect genetically unspecific metabolic processes, like the transfer of atoms from bacterial to viral DNA in infected cells. As it now turns out, quite the opposite conclusion can be drawn.

Kozloff's experiments left three questions undecided. First, what is, in fact, the extent of genetic contribution from irradiated particles to viral growth under the conditions employed? Second, how does the efficiency of transfer of radiophosphorus from irradiated particles compare with that from nonirradiated particles? Third, does the radiophosphorus derived from irradiated particles end up in viable or inviable offspring?

The first question has been studied by Doermann *et al.* (1955), who propose the following hypothesis. The effects of ultraviolet light can be ascribed largely to the production of localized lesions in the genetic material of the particles. A particle containing one such lesion is noninfective by itself, but can contribute genetic markers to the offspring of a mixed infection provided the locus of the lesion and the locus of the marker can be separated by genetic recombination. The lesion itself cannot replicate; like an atom of P^{32}, it must occupy a singular position in the genetic material of the phage but, unlike authentic genetic markers, cannot be mapped. Its localized nature is inferred from the facts that distantly linked genetic markers are inactivated independently of each other, apparently by single quantum acts, and closely linked markers tend to be inactivated together.

To understand the quantitative facts underlying this hypothesis, the methods of measurement must be clearly visualized. Consider two types of measurement. First, samples from a population of phage particles are subjected to varying doses of ultraviolet light, and their ability to multiply is tested by infecting bacteria *singly* with the irradiated particles. The loss of ability to multiply measured in this way proves to be an approximately exponential function of dosage, and the results can be described in terms of an average lethal dose that inactivates 63 per cent $(1-1/e)$ of the phage particles. Second, other irradiated samples of the same population are tested by infecting bacteria simultaneously with single irradiated particles plus three unirradiated particles differing from the irradiated particles by several genetic markers. Yields of phage from these bacteria are scored with respect to presence or absence of genetic markers from the irradiated parent. The results can be described in terms of an average dose of irradiation that inactivates a specified marker in 63 per cent of the irradiated phage particles, which proves to be approximately the same for different markers, and to be strictly exponential down to a few per cent survival.

The first measurement estimates a qualitatively unspecified inactivating dose of radiation, the second a knockout dose for a specified marker. The second dose proves to be 10 to 13 times larger than the first for several markers in either T2 or T4 (Doermann, personal communication; Hershey, unpublished). The factor increases for small survival fractions, but this need not concern us here. The practical conclusion is that *irradiation with 10 to 20 phage-inactivating doses of ultraviolet light should largely suppress genetic contribution from the great majority of phage particles in mixed infection with live particles.* An even smaller dose should suffice if different specified knockouts are not produced entirely independently of each other. This has not yet been checked in a perfectly general manner.

Is the transfer of radiophosphorus from irradiated particles to the offspring of a mixed infection with unirradiated particles independent of radiation dosage? Our experiments confirm Kozloff's conclusion that it is, but there are several technical difficulties.

If bacteria are infected with five particles each of irradiated and nonirradiated phage, many of the bacteria will not produce phage, the fraction of productive bacteria decreasing as the radiation dose is raised. In the range in which we are interested, 10 to 20 inactivating doses, only about half the bacteria are productive. This decreases the isotope transfer from parents to offspring, and greatly reduces the accuracy of measurement The complication can be minimized in several ways.

First, one can reduce the input of irradiated particles to one or less per bacterium. Under these conditions the transfer from the irradiated parent to the issue of the mixed infection is close to normal and virtually independent of radiation dosage.

Second, in mixed infection with several particles of each kind, one can compare the transfer to offspring from the irradiated parent with that from the nonirradiated parent in otherwise identical experiments in which the label is reversed. When this is done the transfer from the irradiated parent is appreciably lower than the transfer from the unirradiated parent, but this can be attributed to selection since the bacteria that yield phage will tend to be those infected with less than the average number of irradiated particles.

Third, one can compare the specific radioactivity (P^{32} per phage particle) of the progeny with that of the labeled parent, independently of the overall transfer. The relation, progeny : parent for early phage yields is approximately 0.02 m, where m is the average number of labeled parents per productive bacterium. It is not appreciably affected by ultraviolet irradiation of the labeled parent in mixed infection, but is subject to numerous errors.

We conclude that the transfer from ultraviolet irradiated parents to the offspring of mixed infection with live parents is virtually independent of dosage of radiation, and probably independent of number of infecting particles per bacterium, except for the side effects mentioned. (This conclusion probably does not apply to ionizing radiations, the effects of which have not been carefully investigated; see Hershey et al., 1954.)

We turn now to the question as to whether radiophosphorus originating from the irradiated parent of a mixed infection ends up in live or dead particles among the offspring. The test is two-fold. First, one measures the transfer from first to second cycle progeny in bacteria mixedly infected with particles of the test phage and normal, nonradioactive particles. This transfer proves to be 40 per cent under the conditions of test, and tells us that the radiophosphorus in the first cycle offspring is contained in particles that adsorb to bacteria and inject their DNA in normal fashion, independently of the ultraviolet dose administered

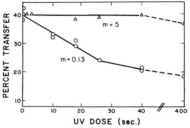

FIGURE 2. Second cycle transfer of P^{32} from irradiated parents. The first cycle offspring came from bacteria infected with an average of 5 particles each of ultraviolet-irradiated, radioactive phage and live nonradioactive phage. The 18 second dose on the abcissa corresponds to 10^{-3} survival of irradiated phage (7 inactivating doses). The curves show efficiency of transfer of P^{32} from first to second cycle offspring, measured in single infection (0.13 viable phage per bacterium) and in mixed infection with live phage particles (5 per bacterium). Each point is an independent measurement calling for an abridged version of the experiment described in Figure 1.

to the parental particles. Second, one measures the transfer from first to second cycle offspring in bacteria singly infected with the test phage. Here the result depends on the exposure to ultraviolet light of the parental phage. For unirradiated parents, the transfer from first to second cycle offspring is 40 per cent, as usual. For large ultraviolet doses, it is only about 20 per cent. For increasing doses of ultraviolet light, the effect rises to a maximum at about ten phage lethal doses, and then remains constant. Typical results are illustrated in Figure 2.

The result described shows that the offspring from mixed infection with irradiated and unirradiated parents contain dead phage particles resembling in important respects the irradiated parents themselves. They adsorb to bacteria and inject their DNA, but do not pass it on to viral offspring unless they are helped out by normal phage particles growing in the same bacterium. Presumably they do not produce offspring at all without such help. This result is surprising since it means that the complicated process by which phage particles are formed does not discriminate between normal DNA and DNA containing lethal damages. (The formation of inviable phage particles containing 5-bromouracil, described by Dunn and Smith in 1954, may be analogous.) It tends to confirm the hypothesis of Doermann et al. (1955), that ultraviolet light produces local lesions in the genetic material of irradiated particles without destroying genetic function as a whole.

About 50 per cent of the transferred radiophosphorus originating from irradiated parents ends up in dead particles: the remainder is in live particles (Fig. 2). This result requires about ten phage-lethal damages per parental particle, but is independent of ultraviolet dosage above this point. This suggests that the viral DNA consists of photo-sensitive and insensitive parts, and recalls Levinthal's hypothesis.

TABLE 2. EFFECTS OF VARYING PHAGE:BACTERIUM RATIO ON PROPORTION OF TRANSFERRED P³² IN VIABLE OFFSPRING FOLLOWING MIXED INFECTION WITH LIVE PLUS IRRADIATED PARENTS

Parental Input		Per Cent of Transferred P³² in Viable Offspring
Irradiated	Live	
1*	2.5	62
1*	9	59
5*	5	50
10*	2.5	33–46
10*	0	30–45
0	5*	100
5	5*	85
10	2.5*	70

The parental input is expressed as phage particles of each kind per bacterium. Asterisks identify the radioactive parent. The irradiated parent received 12 to 15 inactivating doses of ultraviolet light in all experiments. The per cent of transferred P³² in viable offspring is the fractional transfer during a second cycle following single infection divided by the fractional transfer during a second cycle following mixed infection with live phage, times 100. The ranges shown indicate verified results of different experiments: the transfer measurements themselves are reproducible. Systematic errors in experiments with multiple input of irradiated parents are difficult to exclude, however.

The following controls show that most of the dead particles are dead because they receive DNA from the irradiated parent. If radiophosphorus is introduced with the live parent only, or from the culture medium only, not more than 10 or 20 per cent of the label in the offspring is in dead particles.

How does the result depend on the number of irradiated and nonirradiated particles per bacterium used for the first cycle infection? Data bearing on this point are summarized in Table 2. The effects are not large, but are consistent with the idea that the number of dead offspring particles, which cannot be measured directly, increases with increasing numbers of irradiated parents.

How does the result depend on the time after infection at which the first cycle yield is harvested? One systematic experiment showed that radiophosphorus derived from the irradiated parent and transferred into both live and dead offspring was similarly concentrated in the first phage particles to be formed. Samples lysed before any viable offspring had been formed yielded only traces of radiophosphorus in what behaved like dead phage particles, presumably representing contamination with very small numbers of irradiated parental particles.

How are these results to be interpreted? We mention only two ways, since even these remain to be discriminated. One may imagine that the irradiated particles all behave alike, and contain two kinds of DNA, one that distributes at random between live and dead particles, another that produces dead particles. The proportion of dead particles among the labeled offspring can then be estimated from the proportion of P³² derived from the unirradiated parent and ending up in dead particles: 10 to 30 per cent apparently dependent on the number of irradiated parents per bacterium used for the initial infection (Table 2). Attempts to measure numbers of dead particles directly in terms of their presumed ability to kill bacteria to which they adsorb are consistent with this estimate. Unfortunately, neither method is exact enough to do more than show that the proportion of dead particles is small.

The second possible interpretation is less interesting. One supposes that only half the irradiated parental particles participate in viral growth in any sense: most of the radiophosphorus from these particles ends up in live offspring. The remaining half of the particles are excluded from genetic and metabolic participation in growth, and their DNA is used intact to form dead offspring particles. On this hypothesis, the radiophosphorus derived from the culture medium or the unirradiated parent that appears in dead particles would have to be ascribed to metabolic effects, caused by the presence of irradiated DNA in the cells, that produce dead particles independently of the source of the DNA they receive. This second mechanism could also explain the effects of increasing ratio of infection with the irradiated parent.

These alternatives probably cannot be distinguished by the types of experiment referred to above.

RADIOPHOSPHORUS AS A GENETIC MARKER

All types of experiment so far discussed point to a distribution of parental DNA to offspring particles characterized in part by large pieces in very few phage particles. The experiments employing ultraviolet light suggest further, in view of the hypothesis of Doermann et al. (1955), that the large pieces in this instance represent damaged genetic material. The defect of these experiments lies in our failure to show that the radiation damage is not itself responsible for the preservation of the large pieces. We turn therefore to experiments in which an authentic genetic marker is substituted for the uncertain effect of ultraviolet light.

Needless to say, these experiments have their own peculiar limitations. The difficulty is to separate phage particles of differing genotype. Only one tested procedure, already used by Garen (Hershey et al., 1954), is known. It depends on the property of host-range mutants to adsorb to certain strains of bacteria that do not adsorb wild-type phage.

The experiments call for a mixed infection with genetically and isotopically marked phages, for example, P^{32} h^+ and P^{31} h particles, which may be thought of as a $P^{32} \times h$ cross in which we look for reassortment of P^{32} atoms with respect to the h marker. Unfortunately, phages carrying this marker are subject to the phenomenon known as phenotypic mixing (Streisinger, 1956), which means that among the issue of the cross there is little correspondence between genotype and phenotype. To eliminate this confusion, the progeny from the cross must be put through a second cycle of growth in unmixed infection: the resulting particles adsorb to bacteria with the specificity characteristic of their genotype. For the purposes of this experiment, the second cycle of growth can be thought of as a random sampling procedure for analyzing the progeny of the cross itself. Possible technical complications are largely excluded by the finding that the cross P^{32} $h \times P^{31}$ h^+ yields the same result as the reverse cross P^{31} $h \times P^{32}$ h^+.

The result is found to depend strongly on the input ratio of the two kinds of phage entering the cross. If this is equal (5 particles of each type per bacterium), about two thirds of the transferred P^{32} ends up in particles of the genotype of the labeled parent. If it is extremely unequal (1 labeled to 9 unlabeled) about one third of the transferred P^{32} remains associated with the genotype of the labeled parent. If the result is interpreted in terms of a fraction, x, of isotope that is linked to h, and a fraction, 1 − x, that is randomly dispersed, x amounts to about 30 per cent of the transferred isotope, with no marked tendency to fall when transfer from a minority parent is measured.

To test further the hypothesis mentioned, two crosses with reverse label and equal input were carried through a second cycle of mixed infection, followed by a third cycle of single infection to eliminate phenotypic mixing. Samples of the first cycle progeny were also put through a second cycle of single infection for comparison. Results are given in Table 3. They show that if there is a fraction of the transferred DNA that is inseparably linked to the genetic marker, this fraction does not exceed 20 per cent after two cycles of mixed infection followed by one unmixed. If the association between P^{32} and genetic markers is measuring the transfer of P^{32} in the form of large, genetically specific pieces of DNA, the results suggest either progressive dispersion of these pieces during growth, or discrimination against them during transfer. Since these alternatives cannot be distinguished in the experiments cited, the most important conclusion is as follows. Some preferential association of parental phosphorus with parental genotype persists even after repeated crossing, and with respect to a minority parent, two conditions that are known to encourage reassortment of genetic markers. Most of

TABLE 3. LINKAGE BETWEEN TRANSFERRED P^{32} AND PARENTAL GENOTYPE DURING SUCCESSIVE CYCLES OF MIXED GROWTH

Labeled Parent	z	Progeny 1		Progeny 2	
		y	x	y	x
h	0.43	0.65	0.39	0.53	0.18
h^+	0.55	0.71	0.36	0.64	0.20

z = fraction of offspring with genotype of labeled parent.

y = fraction of transferred P^{32} contained in offspring with genotype of labeled parent.

$x = (y - z)/(1 - z)$, theoretical fraction of transferred P^{32} linked to genetic marker if the remainder is randomly dispersed.

Initial infection with approximately 5 particles each of h and h^+ genotype. Progeny 1 is the issue from the initial infection passed through a second cycle of single infection. Progeny 2 is the issue from a second cycle of mixed infection (10 particles of first cycle progeny per bacterium) followed by a third cycle of single infection. The final stages of single infection serve to eliminate phenotypic mixing. The fraction z reflects the relative parental input, and does not change significantly during successive cycles of growth.

the transferred atoms, however, are not linked to the single genetic marker used.

The following experiment suggests a possible relation between the transferred DNA linked to the parental marker, and the DNA derived from irradiated parents that carries radiation damage. Bacteria were infected with five particles each of P^{32}-labeled h parents and nonradioactive h^+ parents, all the parental particles having been irradiated with about 13 inactivating doses of ultraviolet light. The production of phage progeny under these conditions calls for cooperation among the individually noninfective particles (Luria and Dulbecco, 1949). For present purposes this experiment can be considered equivalent to infection with irradiated and unirradiated parents insofar as production of viable and inviable progeny is concerned. The practical difference is in the genetic result: under the conditions specified one gets equal numbers of h and h^+ offspring, in addition to nonviable offspring. The purpose of the experiment is to measure the distribution of transferred P^{32} among these three categories.

The proportion of transferred P^{32} contained in dead particles was measured, as previously described, in terms of the transfer of P^{32} from first to second cycle offspring in single versus mixed infection. The respective transfer values were 13 per cent and 40 per cent, indicating 67 per cent of the transferred P^{32} in dead particles among the first cycle offspring.

A second cycle offspring was then prepared following single infection with particles of the first cycle offspring. This served to eliminate the dead particles and to permit expression of the h genotype among offspring from the viable particles. The second cycle offspring could then be fractionated by adsorption to appropriate bacterial cells. Their P³² was found to be distributed virtually at random with respect to genotype.

This result is also susceptible of at least two interpretations. One can suppose that the transferred P³² normally remaining in association with particles of the genotype of the labeled parent has, in this instance, passed exclusively into the inviable offspring; that is, that the photosensitive DNA and the genetically specific DNA represent a single fraction, the remainder entering viable offspring at random with respect to genotype.

Alternatively, one can suppose that the DNA from some of the parental particles has passed intact into inviable offspring, and that only the remainder of the parental particles have participated in viral growth. The random distribution of P³² among the viable offspring of these particles could then be ascribed to a second effect of ultraviolet light, namely, to increase the frequency of genetic recombinants (Jacob and Wollman, 1954; De Mars, unpub.).

These experiments, therefore, like the others described, fail to resolve the main questions.

DISCUSSION AND SUMMARY

In the first part of this paper we assess old and new experiments bearing on the chemistry of the transfer of DNA from parental to offspring phage, and reach the conclusion that the transfer occurs in the form of polynucleotides, and that the basic transfer process is highly efficient. The relatively low efficiency of the measured transfer is ascribed to random losses inherent in the techniques of measurement.

The remainder of the paper is concerned with the manner in which the transferred DNA is dispersed among the offspring. Levinthal (1956) and Delbrück and Stent (1956) have discussed the relation of this question to possible mechanisms of replication and genetic recombination. We reduce the numerous alternatives to two. The processes mentioned, considered together, might cause progressive fragmentation of the parental DNA, or might produce a dispersion with time-independent features. The second alternative is interesting not only because of the light it might throw on the underlying processes, but also because it admits the possibility of distinguishing between DNA responsible for genetic continuity and DNA possibly concerned with other functions (Levinthal, 1956).

Four recently developed methods are available for examining the distribution of parental DNA among offspring phage particles. The first and most direct relies on radioautography of individual particles (Levinthal, 1956). The second depends on the sensitivity to radioactive decay of offspring particles containing large amounts of radiophosphorus (Stent and Jerne, 1955; Stent, Jerne and Sato, 1956). The third utilizes the fact, first reported here, that much of the radiophosphorus derived from ultraviolet irradiated parental phages is incorporated into inviable offspring particles. The fourth, first employed by Garen, measures the association between radiophosphorus and a single genetic marker among the progeny of crosses between isotopically and genetically marked parents (Hershey et al., 1954; and this paper).

Results of the first method, as interpreted by Levinthal, suggest that the viral DNA consists of two kinds. One kind, made up of a single large piece in the parental particle, produces a time-independent distribution of labeled half pieces among the offspring particles. The second kind consists of smaller pieces that are dispersed among the offspring. Levinthal assumes that the large piece is the functional chromosome, containing functionally equivalent halves.

Results of the second method strongly support two conclusions reached by Levinthal: dispersion of the parental DNA into large and small pieces among the offspring, and the time-independent character of this dispersion. The method does not directly measure size, however, and a preliminary genetic experiment throws doubt on the identification of the large conserved piece with the intact parental chromosome.

Results of the third method likewise call for the transmission of large pieces of parental DNA, marked by persistent lesions caused by ultraviolet light, into a few inviable particles among the offspring. The size of the photosensitive fraction, 40 per cent, is in agreement with Levinthal's hypothesis. Insofar as the lesions resemble genetic damages (Doermann et al., 1955), the large pieces can be identified as genetic material. The possibility that the photochemical damage itself affects dispersion has not been excluded, however.

Results of the fourth method show that approximately the amount of parental DNA called for by Levinthal's hypothesis, or possibly a little less, remains associated with a single genetic marker during mixed growth of two genetically marked parents. Preliminary experiments do not confirm that this association is time-independent, however.

By combining the third and fourth methods, one can show that DNA derived from an ultraviolet irradiated parent and transmitted to viable offspring is not specifically associated with a single genetic marker from the labeled parent. This could mean that the DNA incorporated into inviable offspring, only, represents the hereditary material of the parents, or that the irradiation has modified the dispersion of parental material during transfer.

We conclude that Levinthal's hypotheses and the new experimental techniques summarized in this paper tie together several questions about function of DNA and mechanisms of genetic recombination and replication in a way that should contribute materially to their solution.

REFERENCES

BENZER, S., 1955, Fine structure of a genetic region in bacteriophage. Proc. Nat. Acad. Sci. Wash. *41:* 344–354.

DELBRÜCK, M., 1954, On the replication of desoxyribonucleic acid. Proc. Nat. Acad. Sci. Wash. *40:* 783–788.

DELBRÜCK, M., and STENT, G. S., 1956, On the mechanism of DNA replication. Symposium on Chemical Basis of Heredity, McCollum-Pratt Institute, Baltimore.

DOERMANN, A. H., 1948, Lysis and lysis-inhibition with *Escherichia coli* bacteriophage. J. Bact. *55:* 257–276.

DOERMANN, A. H., CHASE, M., and STAHL, F. W., 1955, Genetic recombination and replication in bacteriophage. J. Cell. Comp. Physiol. *45:* Suppl. 2: 51–74.

DUNN, D. B., and SMITH, J. D., 1954, Incorporation of halogenated pyrimidines into the deoxyribonucleic acids of *Bacterium coli* and its bacteriophages. Nature, Lond. *174:* 305–306.

FRENCH, R. C., 1954, The contribution of protein from parent to progeny in T2 coliphage. J. Bact. *67:* 45–49.

FRENCH, R. C., GRAHAM, A. F., LESLEY, S. M., and VAN ROOYEN, C. E., 1952, The contribution of phosphorus from T2 bacteriophage to progeny. J. Bact. *64:* 597–607.

HERSHEY, A. D., 1953, Nucleic acid economy in bacteria infected with bacteriophage T2. II. Phage precursor nucleic acid. J. Gen. Physiol. *37:* 1–23.

1954, Conservation of nucleic acids during bacterial growth. J. Gen. Physiol. *38:* 145–148.

1956, Bacteriophages as genetic and biochemical systems. Advances in Virus Research IV, in press.

HERSHEY, A. D., and CHASE, M., 1952, Independent functions of viral protein and nucleic acid in growth of bacteriophage. J. Gen. Physiol. *36:* 39–56.

HERSHEY, A. D., DIXON, J., and CHASE, M., 1953, Nucleic acid economy in bacteria infected with bacteriophage T2. I. Purine and pyrimidine composition. J. Gen. Physiol. *36:* 777–789.

HERSHEY, A. D., GAREN, A., FRASER, D. K., and HUDIS, J. D., 1954, Growth and Inheritance in bacteriophage. Yearb. Carnegie Instn. *53:* 210–225.

HERSHEY, A. D., KAMEN, M. D., KENNEDY, J. W., and GEST, H., 1951, Mortality of bacteriophage containing assimilated radioactive phosphorus. J. Gen. Physiol. *34:* 305–319.

HERSHEY, A. D., and MELECHEN, N. E., 1956, Synthesis of phage-precursor nucleic acid in the presence of chloramphenicol. Virology, in press.

JACOB, F., and WOLLMAN, E., 1954, Genetic study of a temperate bacteriophage of *Escherichia coli* III. Effect of ultraviolet irradiation on genetic recombination. Ann. Inst. Pasteur 88: 724–749.

KOZLOFF, L. M., 1952, Biochemical studies of virus reproduction VII. The appearance of parent nitrogen and phosphorus in the progeny. J. Biol. Chem. *194:* 95–108.

1953, Origin and fate of bacteriophage material. Cold Spring Harbor Symp. Quant. Biol. *18:* 209–220.

KOZLOFF, L. M., KNOWLTON, K., PUTNAM, F. W., and EVANS, E. A., JR., 1951, Biochemical studies of virus reproduction. V. The origin of bacteriophage nitrogen. J. Biol. Chem. *188:* 101–116.

LEVINTHAL, C., 1955, The mechanism of DNA replication and genetic recombination in phage. Rendiconti di Scienze, Instituto Lombardo *89:* 192–199.

1956, The mechanism of DNA replication and genetic recombination in phage. Proc. Nat. Acad. Sci. Wash., in press.

LEVINTHAL, C., and VISCONTI, N., 1953, Growth and recombination in bacterial viruses. Genetics *38:* 500–511.

LURIA, S. E., and DULBECCO, R., 1949, Genetic recombinations leading to production of active bacteriophage from ultraviolet inactivated bacteriophage particles. Genetics *34:* 93–125.

LURIA, S. E., WILLIAMS, R. C., and BACKUS, R. C., 1951, Electron micrographic counts of bacteriophage particles. J. Bact. *61:* 179–188.

MAALØE, O., and WATSON, J. D., 1951, The transfer of radioactive phosphorus from parental to progeny phage. Proc. Nat. Acad. Sci. Wash., *37:* 507–513.

PUTNAM, F. W., and KOZLOFF, L. M., 1950, The fate of the infecting virus particle. J. Biol. Chem. *182:* 243–250.

SAGIK, B. P., 1954, A specific reversible inhibition of bacteriophage T2. J. Bact. *68:* 430–436.

STENT, G. S., and JERNE, N. K., 1955, The distribution of parental phosphorus atoms among bacteriophage progeny. Proc. Nat. Acad. Sci. Wash. *41:* 704–709.

STENT, G. S., JERNE, N. K., and SATO, G., 1956, see DELBRÜCK and STENT, 1956.

STENT, G. S., and MAALØE, O., 1953, Radioactive phosphorus tracer studies on the reproduction of T4 bacteriophage. II. Kinetics of phosphorus assimilation. Biochim. Biophys. Acta *10:* 55–69.

STREISINGER, G., 1956, Phenotypic mixing of host range and serological specificities in bacteriophages T2 and T4. Virology, in press.

VISCONTI, N., and DELBRÜCK, M., 1953, The mechanism of genetic recombination in phage. Genetics *38:* 5–33.

WATANABE, I., STENT, G. S., and SCHACHMAN, H. K., 1954, On the state of the parental phosphorus during reproduction of bacteriophage T2. Biochim. Biophys. Acta *15:* 38–49.

WATSON, J. D., and CRICK, F. H. C., 1953, The structure of DNA. Cold Spring Harbor Symp. Quant. Biol. *18:* 123–131.

WATSON, J. D., and MAALØE, O., 1953, Nucleic acid transfer from parental to progeny bacteriophage. Biochim. Biophys. Acta *10:* 432–442.

WEED, L. L., and COHEN, S. S., 1951, The utilization of host pyrimidines in the synthesis of bacterial viruses. J. Biol. Chem. *192:* 693–700.

Mutation and Recombination at the Host Range Genetic Region of Phage T2[1]

GEORGE STREISINGER[2] AND NAOMI C. FRANKLIN[3]

California Institute of Technology, Pasadena, California

Studies of the genetic fine structure of a functional unit occupying a short region in phage can be expected to yield manifold information concerning the nature of mutation and recombination. Specifically, the size of mutated sites and the distances between mutated sites can be described in terms of recombination frequency, and an attempt can be made to translate them into molecular terms. By comparing the site of back mutations to the site of the original mutation, information may be gained concerning the potential configurations that give rise to a functional product. The ability of a genetic region to produce a functional product can, in addition, be investigated by comparing the function of genetic information at a given region when present in "cis" versus "trans" arrangements. If the product of a region can be identified and isolated, it should be possible to compare the information carried by the genetic material with the information carried by the product. By the use of very closely situated sites the place of recombination can be localized, and recombinants between two close sites can be examined for any unexpected features which may aid in the construction of models or recombination.

Fine structure analysis of bacteriophage was initiated by Benzer (1955) on the r_{II} region of phage T4. We have undertaken a similar analysis using mutations concerning the host range (h) region of T2L (Luria, 1945) partly in order to discover to what extent the findings concerning fine structure within the r_{II} region could be generalized to other regions, and partly because the h region possesses certain unique advantages:

1) Phage particles with either one of the alleles (h or h^+) at this region can be scored selectively in the presence of very large numbers of particles with the opposite allele. Thus there is a high degree of resolution for potential recombinants between various "forward" *and* "reverse" mutants.

2) Differences at the h region are thought to control differences of protein of the phage tail. It may thus be possible eventually to establish a correspondence between genetic changes at the h region and differences in the protein product.

THE h REGION

The h region of phage T2 controls the adsorptive specificity of the phage: wild type T2 h^+ adsorbs to and infects *Escherichia coli* strain B, but not the mutant strain B/2; the phage mutant T2 h infects both strains.

The derivation of various mutants is illustrated in Figure 1. An h mutant (Luria, 1945), obtained from the original h^+ strain of phage T2L, is labelled h_0O. Strains with the host range characteristics of h^+ were selected from h_0O by picking turbid plaques observed when h_0O is plated on a mixture of strains B and B/2 (B + B/2). The proportion of these h^+ types is found to be about 10^{-4}. It can be increased by adsorbing out about 90 per cent of the h phage on young cells of B/2 and removing these cells by centrifugation. Selection of independently occurring h^+ mutations was accomplished by isolating only one h^+ type from each of many single plaque isolates of h_0O.

The types selected by the above procedure are separable into two classes on the basis of plaque morphology when plated on B + B/2. Some give turbid plaques with clear centers (perhaps similar to the h^t of Hershey, 1946). These h^t strains adsorb to B/2 and are thus not host range mutants with respect to adsorbability. The h^t loci are not closely linked to h and these strains will not be discussed further here.

Other isolates show no clearing of plaque centers, though they may show randomly scattered clear areas presumably due to reverse mutation. These are h^+ strains, similar to the original h^+ strain of T2L. The h^+ strains did not adsorb at a measurable rate on strain B/2, either reversibly of irreversibly. The original h^+ strain was labelled h^+O, and mutant h^+ strains were labelled serially h^+1, h^+2, etc. Generically the different h^+ strains will be referred to as h^+i, h^+j, etc.

The various h^+ mutants differ with respect to stability at 65° and with respect to the reversion index (Benzer, 1955), that is, the mean proportion of h particles in stocks of a given h^+ strain (Table 1). This reversion index varied from more than 10^{-3} to less than 10^{-7}. At least one of the h^+ strains adsorbed to the host strain B at a lower rate than the others.

[1] Aided by a grant from the National Foundation for Infantile Paralysis.

[2] Fellow of the National Foundation for Infantile Paralysis; present address: Department of Genetics, Carnegie Institution of Washington, Cold Spring Harbor, N. Y.

[3] Postdoctoral Public Health Service Research Fellow of The National Cancer Institute; present address: Max-Planck-Institut für Biologie, Tübingen, Germany.

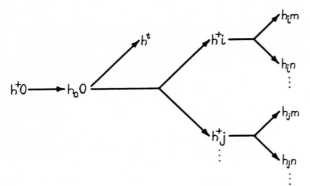

FIGURE 1. Scheme of mutations.

MAPPING OF THE h^+ MUTANTS

Frequency of h recombinants in $h^+i \times h^+j$ crosses. Fourteen h^+ mutants with low reversion indices were crossed to each other as well as to the original h^+0 in order to determine recombination frequencies. The scoring of h types in the progeny from crosses of two h^+ strains on *E. coli* B was accomplished by preadsorbing[4] the progeny on B and by plating on B/2/5 (a B strain resistant to T2 and to T5) with added phage T5. This prevents the masking of genotypes as a result of phenotypic mixing (see below) and permits the removal of uninfected B cells by adding phage T5 to the plate. Plaques of h particles were produced in frequencies characteristic for the pair of h^+ strains used. The frequencies of h progeny obtained in various crosses are given in Table 2.

The frequency of h genotypes in a lysate is corrected in several ways to give an estimate of the frequency of h recombinants: 1) for mutation (by comparison with a multiple infection lysate of each parent); 2) for possible recombination in the scoring procedure (by reconstruction experiments with mixtures of the parents); 3) for low or unequal multiplicity (Lennox *et al.*, 1953); 4) for efficiency of plating of h on B/2/5 as compared with B. These corrections altogether usually amounted to less than 20 per cent of the recombination value.

The results can be summarized as follows: crosses of most pairs of h^+ mutants gave h recom-

4 Recent results of Edgar (1956) indicate that the frequencies of observed recombinants are higher when the progeny of a two factor cross is preadsorbed to a sensitive host and then plated on an indicator strain, than if the plating is done directly on the indicator strain. This result is interpreted as being due to the persistence of heterozygotes (Hershey and Chase, 1951), which in the course of replication in the sensitive cells produce additional recombinants. The h recombinants are scored by preadsorbing the progeny of an $h^+i \times h^+j$ cross to B, and subsequently plating on B/2. It is unlikely, however, that additional recombinants, formed from persistent heterozygotes during the preadsorption step, would be scored in our system, since recombinants formed from such heterozygotes would probably be present in small clones (see $hr_{13} \times h^+r^+$ heterozygotes, Hershey and Chase, 1951) and would predominantly be h^+ phenotypically (because of phenotypic mixing).

TABLE 1. PROPERTIES OF h^+ STRAINS

Strain Number	Map Position	k Values for Heat Inactivation at 65°C	Reversion Index
h^+11	+1.8	>1	<3 × 10⁻⁷
h^+23	+0.31	>1	<3 × 10⁻⁷
h^+10	+0.29	0.07	<3 × 10⁻⁷
h^+37	±0.004	>1	5 × 10⁻⁷
h^+0	0	0.04	1 × 10⁻⁶
h^+34	not mapped	not determined	>10⁻³
h^+41	not mapped	not determined	>10⁻³

The strains used were selected for low reversion indices. The map position refers to the distance from h^+0. The heat inactivation constant k is derived by the equation $P/P_0 = e^{-kt}$, where P is the plaque titer after t minutes of exposure at 65° in tryptone broth and P_0 is the titer of initial phage. The reversion index is estimated from the frequency of h genotype in two or three lysates prepared from inocula of less than 100 particles. The frequency of particles with h genotype was measured by preadsorbing the progeny on strain B and plating on B/2/5 with added phage T5. The preadsorption step (necessary to eliminate phenotypic mixing) limits the size of the population tested, so that frequencies of h particles lower than 10⁻⁷ cannot be measured accurately. Reversion indices greater than 10⁻³ cannot be measured accurately by this technique because the inocula may already contain mutant h particles.

binants with frequencies characteristic for the pair used. All of the frequencies were low (less than 1%), indicating that the h^+ mutations all occurred within a region of two recombination units.

Four h^+ mutants gave no measurable recombinants when crossed to h^+11, two gave no recombinants when crossed to h^+23, and one gave no recombinants when crossed to h^+10. These strains will be crossed with one another and with other strains to determine whether they are repeat mutations.

In order to check whether the h genotypes recovered from $h^+i \times h^+j$ crosses were allelic to the h_0O genotype two strains of recombinant h were selected from each of two different crosses. These recombinant h strains were crossed back to the standard h_0O strain. The frequency of h^+ phage in these $h \times h$ crosses was less than 0.2 per cent. Clearly the h recombinants are not produced by changes at sites measurably distinct from the h region.

An additional test of the recombinant nature of the h progeny from the crosses was made by measuring the frequency of h progeny in a cross between h^+37 and h^+0 using U.V. irradiated parents. It had been shown by Jacob and Wollman (1955) for phage λ, and confirmed by DeMars (personal communication) for phage T2, that irradiation of the parent phage increases the frequency of recombinants. We found that the pro-

TABLE 2. RESULTS OF $h^+i \times h^+j$ CROSSES

Cross	Number of Crosses	% of h Observed among Progeny × 2	Corrected Map Distance	% of r+ in Total Lysate	% of r in Total Lysate	Expected Frequency of Recombinants between h and r22 in %	Found Frequency of Recombinants between h and r22 (% of r+ or r among %h Progeny)	Excess Recombination in %
$h^+11 \ r^+ \times h^+24 \ r$	4	0.43	0.05 ± 0.05	54		33	43 ± 4	10 ± 2
$h^+11 \ r^+ \times h^+23 \ r$	3	1.48	1.59 ± 0.29	43		28	41 ± 1	13 ± 2
$h^+11 \ r \times h^+23 \ r^+$	3				55	33	47 ± 3	14 ± 5
$h^+11 \ r^+ \times h^+10 \ r$	4	1.67	1.76 ± 0.35	43		28	40 ± 4	12 ± 4
$h^+11 \ r \times h^+10 \ r^+$	3				58	35	56 ± 6	21 ± 7
$h^+11 \ r^+ \times h^+37 \ r$	5	1.37	1.57 ± 0.14	46		29	40 ± 3	11 ± 5
$h^+11 \ r \times h^+37 \ r^+$	4				56	34	48 ± 4	14 ± 4
$h^+11 \ r^+ \times h^+0 \ r$	2	1.57	1.68 ± 0.28	43		28	38 ± 1	10 ± 1
$h^+11 \ r \times h^+0 \ r^+$	2				49	31	54 ± 5	23 ± 6
$h^+24 \ r \times h^+10 \ r^+$	3	0.95	1.03 ± 0.15	50		31	44 ± 4	13 ± 6
$h^+24 \ r \times h^+37 \ r^+$	3	1.09	1.29 ± 0.20	47		29	44 ± 3	15 ± 3
$h^+24 \ r \times h^+0 \ r^+$	3	1.00	1.19 ± 0.06	50		31	48 ± 1	17 ± 1
$h^+23 \ r^+ \times h^+10 \ r$	2	0.017	0.019 ± 0.001	44		29	35 ± 2	6 ± 1
$h^+23 \ r \times h^+10 \ r^+$	2				56	34	38 ± 3	4 ± 2
$h^+23 \ r^+ \times h^+37 \ r$	3	0.29	0.34 ± 0.05	49		31	43 ± 2	12 ± 3
$h^+23 \ r \times h^+37 \ r^+$	3				54	33	42 ± 2	9 ± 3
$h^+23 \ r^+ \times h^+0 \ r$	1	0.32	0.33 ± 0.03	43		28	40	12
$h^+23 \ r \times h^+0 \ r^+$	1				57	35	56	21
$h^+10 \ r^+ \times h^+37 \ r$	2	0.25	0.26 ± 0.035	51		32	42 ± 2	10 ± 1
$h^+10 \ r \times h^+37 \ r^+$	2				54	34	45 ± 2	11 ± 3
$h^+10 \ r^+ \times h^+0 \ r$	3	0.27	0.29 ± 0.03	44		28	38 ± 2	10 ± 3
$h^+10 \ r \times h^+0 \ r^+$	3				60	37	50 ± 2	13 ± 1
$h^+37 \ r^+ \times h^+0 \ r$	3	0.0033	0.004 ± 0.0015	45			not determined	not determined
$h^+37 \ r \times h^+0 \ r^+$	1				45		not determined	not determined

Crosses were performed on bacteria of strain B grown to 10^8 per ml, washed and resuspended in buffer, and aerated for 90 minutes (Benzer, 1952). The cells were infected in buffer with equal multiplicities (5 to 10) of each of the parents. After a period sufficient for at least 95% phage adsorption a dilution was made into salt-free broth. The infected bacteria were aerated for two hours at 37° to assure lysis. Burst sizes varied from 40 to 100. In each cross 100 to 400 recombinant plaques were scored. The per cent of h progeny observed was corrected as described in the text to obtain the frequency of recombinants. The expected frequency of recombinants between h and r_{22} was calculated from equation 8 of Visconti and Delbrück (1953). The variability from experiment to experiment is expressed as the mean deviation for each set of crosses.

portion of h particles from a cross of $h^+0 \times h^+37$ was increased almost tenfold by irradiation of the parents (Table 3). The proportion of h mutants in control experiments with each parent alone was not increased by irradiation.

The order of the h^+ sites. The order of the h^+ sites within the h region was obtained from three-factor crosses of the type $r_{22}h^+i \times r^+h^+j$, where r_{22} is 24 units from h as measured in two factor crosses. If the order is, for example, r-h^+i-h^+j, more of the recombinant h particles would be expected to be r^+ than r. Crosses between most pairs of h^+ mutants were done with the r marker both in coupling and repulsion. (The relative order of the mutants h^+37 and h^+0 could not be determined from crosses of the type $h^+37 \ r \times h^+0 \ r^+$ and $h^+37 \ r^+ \times h^+0 \ r$ since the frequency of h mutants from these h^+ strains, as judged from control platings of the parental stocks, is 10% of the frequency of the h recombinants, and thus high enough to prevent any precise measurement of recombination between r and h.)

A map of the various h^+ sites as determined from three factor crosses is given in Figure 2. As can be seen from the map, the distances between the markers, in terms of recombination units (these being twice the per cent of h recombinants) are compatible with the order as determined from three factor crosses. The map is additive in that the sum of the distances between a series of markers equals approximately the distance between the outside markers. The variability from experiment to experiment is such, however, that deviations from additivity of the order of 20 per cent would not have been observed.

Two markers, h^+17 and h^+49, gave anomalous results in some crosses and had not been accurately mapped. Further study of these mutants may reveal genetic changes of more complex types.

THE MUTATION h^+i TO h

The above results demonstrate that mutational events leading from the h to the h^+ phenotype occur at any one of a number of sites within

TABLE 3. EFFECT OF U.V. IRRADIATION ON THE
FREQUENCY OF RECOMBINANTS
FROM $h^+0 \times h^+37$ CROSSES

Calculated Survival of Parents	% of h Progeny in Lysate
1	2.2×10^{-3}
1	3.0×10^{-3}
2.3×10^{-3}	5.3×10^{-3}
2.0×10^{-5}	1.1×10^{-2}
1×10^{-8}	2.2×10^{-2}

Crosses were performed as described in Table 2 except that the parents were irradiated to give the indicated survivals. The two control crosses, performed at
this same time, are included in Table 2.

the h region. A preliminary recombination analysis of mutants in the reverse direction, from h^+ to h,
was undertaken to determine the nature of this
change. One could imagine that mutation from h^+
to h restoring the h function could occur at suppressor loci removed from the h region, or at a
number of sites within the h region, or else only at
or very near, the site of the original h to h^+ change.

It is possible to decide between these alternatives by selecting various mutants (h_in, h_im . . .
from strain h^+i, h_jn, h_jm . . . from strain h^+j and
so on; see Fig. 1) and crossing these h mutants
to h_0O (the strain from which the various h^+
mutants were selected).

Several independent h mutants were obtained
from each of the strains h^+0, h^+37, h^+10, h^+34, and
h^+41. The last two h^+ strains have high reversion
indices (of the order of 10^{-3}) and have not yet
been mapped.

Crosses were performed using ultraviolet irradiated stocks in order to increase any recombination which may occur between different h sites.
The progeny of $h \times h$ crosses were plated on a
mixture of $B + B/2$. Recombinant h^+ particles,
if present, would appear as turbid plaques.

No recombinants were found among the progeny
of crosses of h_0O with $h_{\circ7}$, h_{10}, h_{34}, and h_{41}
strains; this corresponds to a frequency of less
than 0.5 per cent. Since the frequency of any re-

combinants would have been increased by a factor
of about ten due to U.V. irradiation of the parents,
this result indicates that the sites of the mutation
h^+i to h_i were less than 0.1 per cent from the site
of the mutation h to h^+i. This conclusion was
strengthened by the fact that no recombinants
were found in pairwise crosses of the type $h_in \times
h_im$ (using four different h_0 strains, four h_{37} strains,
four h_{10} strains, ten h_{34} strains, and six h_{41} strains).

The resolution of this system can be increased
about a hundredfold by selectively removing non-
recombinant h progeny from $h \times h$ crosses by
adsorption with $B/2$; more precise results will be
gained by the use of this system. In addition, the
various h strains obtained from h^+ mutant
strains can be compared to the original h with
respect to other characters such as stability at
high temperatures. In this way it should be possible to determine whether reverse mutations
entail a precise restoration of the original genotype.

The frequency of the h^+ mutants in the original
h_0O stock is of the order of 10^{-4}. This represents
the sum of the frequencies of mutation at many
sites. The frequency of the h mutants is different
for various h^+ strains and varies from more than
10^{-3} to less than 10^{-7}. The occurrence of a high
frequency of mutation to h, at a number of h^+
sites, shows that the genetic configuration determining the h phenotype is genetically more stable
than many of the mutant configurations determining h^+.

THE h REGION AS A FUNCTIONAL UNIT

Phage particles attach to sensitive bacterial
cells by their tail tips (Anderson, 1953). The
attachment site seems to consist of protein, since
the adsorptive capacities of certain strains of
phage T4 can be activated by agents such as
urea with kinetics resembling those of protein
denaturation (Sato, 1956), and since blocking the
amino groups of phage T2 prevents their attachment to bacteria (Puck and Tolmach, 1954).
There is evidence that inactivating antibody acts
on the tail tip, and perhaps on the rest of the tail
itself (Lanni and Lanni, 1953).

The h region seems to control the specificity of
the attachment site by which the phage adsorbs
to the host cell. Serological differences (between
the related phages T2 and T4) with respect to
inactivating antibody have been shown to be
controlled at the h region (Streisinger, 1956a). In
addition, a comparison of different h^+ mutants
with respect to stability at 65° showed significant
differences. Although a direct demonstration that
heat-inactivated particles do not adsorb to host
cells (and thus that various h^+ mutants differ
with respect to the heat sensitivity of the receptor)
has not yet been accomplished, we have found
that heat-inactivated particles do not kill cells,
are unable to produce lysis from without at

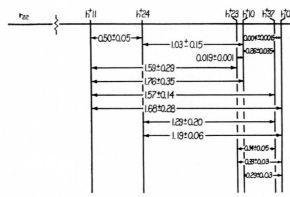

FIGURE 2. Map of the h^+ mutants.

phage-to-cell ratios of up to one thousand, and do not measurably contribute genetic markers when added to bacteria infected with untreated particles.

Such differences in the structure of the receptor sites, affecting their antigenicity and heat stability, would not be expected if the h region controlled only their production and not their specific details of structure.

The unity of function of the h region was examined by means of a cis-trans type of test. The method applied, similar in principle to the heterokaryon test used with fungi, makes use of the phenomenon of phenotypic mixing. It has been observed (Novick and Szilard, 1951; Hershey et al., 1951) that progeny of crosses between T-even phages or T2 and T2 h yield particles with phenotypes different from their genotypes with respect to host range. The material for the receptor sites of phage particles appears to be produced in a pool and to become associated more or less randomly with the genetic material (Streisinger, 1956b). Thus in a cross of $h \times h^+$ particles some of the genetically h particles will be phenotypically h^+ although after a further cycle of multiplication the progeny of these particles will have phenotypes identical with their genotypes.

The proportion of phenotypically h particles depends on the proportion of the h parent (Hershey, personal communication). Thus the amount of h genotype produced can be measured by measuring the proportion of h phenotype among the genetically h particles.

By use of this phenomenon, the ability of the h region to produce h phenotype could be compared in $h \times h^+$ crosses ("cis" configuration)[5] and in $h^+i \times h^+j$ crosses ("trans" configuration). In several $h^+i \times h^+j$ crosses, using different pairs of h^+ mutants, it was found that only one to three per cent of the recombinant h particles were phenotypically h. In contrast, about 60 per cent of the h progeny of $h \times h^+$ crosses was phenotypically h. It can be concluded that h sites in trans configuration are not efficient at the production of the h phenotype. The h phenotype can be produced only if all of the sites within the region are in the h state.

These results can be compared with those of Benzer (1955) on mutants within the r_{II} region. Benzer found that this region can be subdivided into two adjacent subregions, each of which acts as a unit of function in a similar cis-trans test.

RECOMBINATION

The experiments on recombination between h^+ mutants carrying markers outside the h region show that recombination between two h^+ sites is accompanied by excess recombination between the h region and the r_{22} marker.

The map distance between r_{22} and h is 24 units. In three-factor crosses the frequency of recombination in a given region is expected to be greater among particles selected as recombinants in another region than among an unselected sample of particles because these recombinants are particles which have mated more frequently than average with genetically heterologous particles (Visconti and Delbrück, 1953). The expected frequency of recombinants between r_{22} and h among recombinants for two closely linked sites would be 31 per cent. As can be seen from Table 2, the frequency of recombination between r and h is greater than expected, averaging 44 per cent. This excess recombination brings the frequency close to the theoretical maximum of 50 per cent. Before concluding, however, that the excess recombination is due to a higher frequency of multiple recombinational events at a single mating, rather than to other possible factors not considered by the Visconti-Delbrück theory, experiments with a series of markers outside the h region should be performed. Results on the r_{II} region, bearing on this same problem, are reported by Edgar (1956).

DISCUSSION AND CONCLUSIONS

The h region in some features resembles systems controlling the production of enzymes in other organisms. In the mutation from h to h^+ the ability to adsorb to B/2 can be completely lost by any one of several mutational events within one functionally related region. This is similar to the behavior of the td locus of Neurospora where any one of many mutations, distinguishable by physiological properties and by their behavior in the presence of a number of suppressor mutants, results in inability (or very limited ability) to produce active tryptophan synthetase (Yanofsky, 1956).

In addition to causing losses of functional enzymes, mutations have been observed to produce enzymes with decreased stability at high temperatures (Maas and Davis, 1952). Several of the h^+ mutations confer to the phage an increased temperature sensitivity, the increment being of the same order as that observed for the thermolabile tyrosinase of Neurospora (Horowitz and Fling, 1953).

The mutations h to h⁺. Mutations from h to h^+ can occur at any one of a number of sites as determined by recombination analysis. The ordering of the mutant sites can be accomplished by means of three factor crosses and a more or less additive map is obtained.

The closest sites observed in the h region are 0.004 recombination units apart,[6] the next closest

---

[5] Double mutants with two h^+ sites have not yet been isolated, thus $h^+i \times h^+j$ crosses are compared to $h^+i \times h$ and $h^+j \times h$ crosses rather than to $h^+i\ h^+j \times h$ crosses.

[6] The two mutants giving the smallest recombination distance are h^+0 and h^+37. It cannot be excluded that one of these mutants is, in fact, a double mutant, the two members of which span the other mutant. Strain h^+0 is the one from which h_00 was obtained, the other h^+ mutants in turn being derived from h_00. The stock h_00

0.02 units apart. Benzer (1955) on the basis of a number of assumptions concerning the total number of nucleotides of the DNA of T2 which is thought to carry the genetic information, and the length of the linkage map in terms of the total number of units of crossing over, concluded that the minimal recombination frequency, corresponding to the distance between two contiguous nucleotides, would be of the order of the frequencies observed in our system.

The total length of the h region is about two units, as compared to four units for each of the two sections of the r_{II} region studied by Benzer (1955).

The sites of the mutations h^+ to h. The mutations in the direction from h^+ to h occur at (or at least very near) to the site of the particular h^+ mutation from which a given h mutant had originated. Thus it appears that the information necessary for the production of the h phenotype corresponds to a unique configuration, or at least to a very limited number of configurations, within the h region. The terms "forward" and "reverse" mutation appear to be meaningful in this system.

The fact that all h mutations from a particular h^+ occur at the same site is remarkable in light of the observation that the frequency of h mutation from any one of a number of h^+ mutants may be several orders of magnitude higher than the sum of all the mutations h to h^+. This suggests that some of the mutated h^+ sites have configurations which are more mutable than *any* of the configurations present in the unmutated h region.

The functional unity of the h region. Mixed infection of a bacterium with phage particles which collectively (but not individually) carry all the information necessary for the production of the h phenotype does not lead to efficient production of any phage with h phenotype. Thus, the whole region must apparently act as a single unit to give what may be a single product.

Other loci involved in the control of host range. Loci not closely linked to the h region control the specificity of adsorption in ways which have not yet been studied. A suppressor of the h locus ($=su$-h), which is not closely linked to h, can be introduced into T2L from the related phage T4 (Streisinger, 1956a). Particles of the genetic constitution h su-h are phenotypically like h^+ particles. In another strain, T2H, we found that mutations of h to h^+ (turbid plaques on B + B/2) can occur at either one of two not closely linked regions. Mutations of the strain T2H with respect to the infection of resistant bacteria (strain 2bc) occur at a number of loci distributed over the whole genetic map (Baylor, personal communication). The details of the mechanism involved in this system have not yet been worked out.

Our experiments show that analysis of genetic

had been obtained by Luria in 1945; it is possible that the h^+0 strain has accumulated an additional h^+ mutant during subcultures since that time.

fine structure is possible at the h region. It seems likely that the adsorption elements controlled by this region can be isolated (Kellenberger and Arber, 1955; Kozloff and Henderson, 1955; Williams and Fraser, 1956) and analyzed. It should be possible eventually to study a point by point correspondence between genetic changes at the h region and structural changes in the product protein.

ACKNOWLEDGEMENTS

The authors wish to express their indebtedness to Drs. M. Delbrück, R. Dulbecco, and S. E. Luria for their stimulating criticisms, and to Dr. S. E. Luria for his aid in the redaction of this paper.

REFERENCES

ANDERSON, T. F., 1953, The morphology and osmotic properties of bacteriophage systems. Cold Spr. Harb. Symp. Quant. Biol. *18:* 197–203.

BENZER, S., 1952, Resistance to ultraviolet light as an index to the reproduction of bacteriophage. J. Bact. *63:* 59–72.

1955, Fine Structure of a genetic region in bacteriophage. Proc. Nat. Acad. Sci., Wash. *41:* 344–354.

EDGAR, R., 1956, Discussion of the paper of G. Streisinger and N. C. Franklin. Cold Spr. Harb. Symp. Quant. Biol. *21:* 109.

HERSHEY, A. D., 1946, Spontaneous mutations in bacterial viruses. Cold Spr. Harb. Symp. Quant. Biol. *11:* 67–76.

HERSHEY, A. D., and CHASE, M., 1951, Genetic recombination and heterozygosis in bacteriophages. Cold Spr. Harb. Symp. Quant. Biol. *16:* 471–479.

HERSHEY, A. D., ROESEL, C., CHASE, M., and FORMAN, S., 1951, Growth and inheritance in bacteriophage. Yearb. Carneg. Instn. No. *50:* 195–200.

HOROWITZ, N. H., and FLING, M., 1953, Genetic determination of tyrosinase thermostability in *Neurospora*. Genetics *38:* 360–374.

JACOB, F., and WOLLMAN, E. L., 1955, Étude génétique d'un bactériophage tempéré d'*Escherichia coli*. III. Effet du rayonnement ultraviolet sur la recombinaison génétique. Ann. Inst. Pasteur *88:* 724–749.

KELLENBERGER, F., and ARBER, W., 1955, Die Structur des Schwanzes der Phagen T2 und T4 und der Mechanismus der irreversiblen Adsorption. Z. Naturf. *10b:* 698–704.

KOZLOFF, L. M., and HENDERSON, K., 1955, Action of complexes of the zinc group metals on the tail protein of bacteriophage T2 r^+. Nature, Lond. *176:* 1169–1171.

LANNI, F., and LANNI, Y. T., 1953, Antigenic structure of bacteriophage. Cold Spr. Harb. Symp. Quant. Biol. *18:* 159–168.

LENNOX, E. S., LEVINTHAL, C., and SMITH, F., 1953, The effect of finite input in reducing recombinant frequency. Genetics *38:* 508–511.

LURIA, S. E., 1945, Mutation of bacterial viruses affecting their host range. Genetics *30:* 84–99.

MAAS, W. K., and DAVIS, B. D., 1952, Production of an altered pantothenate-synthesizing enzyme by a temperature sensitive mutant of *Escherichia coli*. Proc. Nat. Acad. Sci., Wash. *38:* 785–797.

NOVICK, A., and SZILARD, L., 1951, Virus strains of identical phenotype but different genotype. Science *113:* 34–35.

PUCK, T. T., and TOLMACH, L. J., 1954, The mechanism of virus attachment to host cells. IV. Physicochemical studies on virus and cell surface groups. Arch. Biochem. Biophys. *51:* 229–245.

SATO, G., 1956, The effect of urea on cofactor requiring bacteriophage. Thesis, California Institute of Technology, Pasadena, California.

STREISINGER, G., 1956a, The genetic control of host range and serological specificity in bacteriophages T2 and T4. Virology 2: 377–387.

1956b, Phenotypic mixing of host range and serological specificities in bacteriophages T2 and T4. Virology 2: 388–398.

VISCONTI, N., and DELBRÜCK, M., 1953, The mechanism of genetic recombination in phage. Genetics 38: 5–33.

WILLIAMS, R. C., and FRASER, D., 1956, Structural and functional differentiation in T2 bacteriophage. Virology 2: 289–307.

YANOFSKY, C., 1956, Gene Interactions in Enzyme Synthesis. In: Enzymes: Units of Biological Structure and Function. New York, Academic Press. Pp. 147–160.

DISCUSSION

RIZKI: In the absence of information regarding the genetic changes such as deficiencies and duplications, do you consider phenotypic expressions and differences in linkages of h^+'s are adequate attributes for classifying them as sites of a functional unit? This question is asked particularly in view of the unusual kind of heterozygosity you have just reviewed, for which there is no parallel in the higher organisms suitable for cytogenic analysis.

STREISINGER: Recombination data indicate that our h^+ mutants are at different sites. Three-factor crosses give an additive map, indicating that we are dealing with ordinary mutational events. Benzer finds that some of the mutational sites within the r_{II} region extend over large areas and may be deletions. Two of the h^+ mutants we have examined (h^+49 and h^+17) may involve complex changes since they showed complications in mapping.

EDGAR: We have been studying recombination in the r_{II} region of T4. Many mutants located in this region have been isolated, and the bacterial host K-12(λ) permits the selective recovery of the r^+ recombinants from crosses between these mutants (Benzer, 1955). Chase (personal communication) has developed a replica plating technique for recovering the double mutants from such crosses which has made feasible closely linked three- and four-factor crosses. In certain crosses of this type, the r^+ recombinants must arise by double or triple recombination events. Unusually great negative interference is found in such crosses. This negative interference is interpreted as due to multiple recombinations occurring in small regions. Certain of the crosses indicate that the negative interference extends over a region approximately four recombination units in length (Chase and Doermann, personal communication).

In order to account for this negative interference, the hypothesis is suggested that the source of the negative interference is the overlap (heterozygous) region. One possible explicit formulation of this idea would be that distantly linked markers are recombined by the mechanism which

Levinthal (1954) suggested. However, when closely linked markers are employed (i.e., $r227$-$r320 \times r205$), most of the particles formed which are heterozygous in this region will be of the non-recombinant type (i.e., $r227$-$r320/r205$). It is suggested that such heterozygotes persist and produce non-heterozygous progeny which are highly recombinant in the region of the overlap.

To test this model the following experiment was performed. The progeny from the cross $r227$-$r320 \times r205$ were adsorbed to E. coli B under conditions of single infection and the infected bacteria plated on K-12(λ). In this cross the r^+ recombinants must arise by two recombination events occurring within a region 0.5 recombination units in length. This experiment is compared to adsorbing to K-12(λ) and plating on K-12(λ) and to appropriate controls. A 35-fold increase in plaque-formers resulted from the B preadsorption. If the heterozygotes were no more efficient in the production of recombinants than the two parents, a two-fold increase would be expected. The excess is interpreted as being due to the presence of these non-recombinant heterozygotes among the progeny, which, although unable to grow in K-12(λ), are capable of growth in B. During this time they produce r^+ recombinants with great efficiency, characteristic of the negative interference region. The results of this and a similar experiment with a two-factor cross are given in Table A.

Experiments to investigate this phenomenon and to test various models are in progress.

(References: Benzer, S., 1955, Proc. Nat. Acad. Sci. Wash. 41: 344–354; Levinthal, C., 1954, Genetics 39: 169–184; Stahl, F. W., 1956, Virology 2: 206–234.)

LITMAN: I should like to report on some recent work done in collaboration with Dr. A. B. Pardee at Berkeley, concerned with mutant production in

TABLE A

	$r227$-$r320$ $\times$ $r205$	$r168 \times r145$
A. % of progeny preadsorbed on B which plates on K-12(λ)	0.35	0.50
B. % of progeny preadsorbed on K-12(λ) which plates on K-12(λ)	0.01	0.073
C. Assumed % of progeny which are non-recombinant heterozygotes*	0.75	0.75
D. % non-recombinant heterozygotes yielding r^+ during growth in B $\left(\dfrac{a-b}{c}\right)$	45.2	57.2
E. % B infected with the two parents which yield r^+	1.4	11.6+

* Assuming that the frequency of non-recombinant heterozygotes in these crosses is equal to the frequency of heterozygotes for one pair of alleles.

† Calculated from Stahl, 1956.

bacteriophage. About a year ago we performed experiments with the purpose of incorporating the pyrimidine derivative 5-bromouracil (5-BrU) into the DNA of T2 phage, and we noticed that a large number of a variety of plaque type mutants had appeared among the progeny. These mutants amounted to about 15 per cent of the total plaques produced. To our knowledge the only chemical previously known to increase spontaneous mutations in phage is proflavin, which was shown by De Mars to increase mutations to another plaque type some 40-fold.

To obtain 5-BrU incorporation into the DNA of E. coli and T2, one must grow these organisms under conditions of thymine deficiency. This can be achieved either by working with a thymine deficient strain of E. coli as Zamenhof has done (1954), or by adding sulfanilamide (sulfa) to the medium, a method employed by Dunn and Smith (1954) and also adopted in our experiments (Litman and Pardee, in press). In the presence of either sulfa or 5-BrU alone, no phage mutants were produced. 5-chlorouracil and 5-iodouracil, in the presence of sulfa, were as effective in mutant production as was 5-BrU.

The appearance of mutants during growth in the presence of 5-BrU and sulfa could be attributed either to a mutagenic action or to a selective enrichment by the medium of the mutants already present in the T2 stock at a background frequency of 10^{-3}. The possibility of selection was eliminated by the following two experiments. First we performed a one-step growth experiment in the synthetic medium plus sulfa and 5-BrU, and as usual followed the increase in phage number from before to after lysis. We found that while the total number of phages had increased only 18 times, the total number of plaque type mutants had increased 500-fold. To explain this result as due to selection, one would have to postulate a burst of 500 for each pre-

existing mutant. In the 5-BrU medium, however, the mutants had burst sizes and latent periods of the same magnitude as the original stock.

Secondly we performed a single cell burst experiment again in the medium containing sulfa and 5-BrU. The results are given in Table B.

Any pre-existing mutant should have developed into a clone of mutant progeny. This was not observed; rather, of the 13 plates containing mutant plaques, 12 had one mutant per plate and one had two mutants. A is calculated from the number of bacteria originally infected with phage. B is obtained from the number of plates containing no plaques using a normal Poisson distribution formula. The ratio of B to A, the fraction of infected bacteria which released phage, is equal to 1, and therefore, every infected bacterium produced infective phage. C is calculated from the number of plates which contained no mutant plaques again using the Poisson formula. The ratio of C to B is the fraction of infected bacteria which released mutant phage. Since in the original infection mixture, only one out of every 10^3 bacteria was infected with a mutant phage, the mutants appearing after lysis from one in every four bacteria must have arisen through mutation and not selection.

Many of the plaque type mutants that were obtained from sulfa and 5-BrU action have been picked and replated three or more times on broth agar, and in almost all cases they remained mutant. However, some of these induced mutants appeared to be unstable, that is, on replating they exhibited more than one plaque type, and a few showed a constant and rather large frequency of reversion to the original stock. Zamenhof and coworkers (personal communication) have evidence for a similar instability regarding the colony morphology of a thymine deficient strain of E. coli after growth in 5-BrU. It would seem, therefore, that mutations can be caused both during the process of introduction of 5-BrU into the DNA and also during its replacement by normal components.

More recently we have been investigating the production of host range mutants, and we have been able to cause the appearance of 50 per cent h mutants after growth of a T2 h^+ strain in sulfa and 5-BrU. This represents an increase in these mutants of at least 10^7-fold.

The most obvious explanation for the mutagenic effect of 5-BrU is that its incorporation into the DNA is directly responsible for the production of phage mutants. Both Dunn and Smith (1954) and ourselves have found that a large proportion of the phages containing 5-BrU are non-infectious. The amount of thymine replaced by 5-BrU seemed to depend on the 5-BrU concentration in the medium at the time of infection, but as yet we can make no correlation between the amount of 5-BrU incorporated into the DNA and the percentage or the number of mutants produced. We

TABLE B

No. of Plates	No. of Plaques/Plate	No. Plates with Mutants
28	0	—
11	1–5	2
13	6–9	4*
9	10–21	4
5	22–85	3

A. Infected cells/plate (calculated from input)... 0.75
B. Infected cells/plate (calculated from Poisson
     law).. 0.86
   Ratio of B to A............................. 1.1
C. Infected cells/plate yielding mutants (calcu-
     lated from Poisson law).................... 0.22
   Ratio of C to B............................. 0.26
   Ratio of C to B............................. 0.26

* One plate contained 2 mutants.

have obtained a phage preparation whose thymine was completely replaced by 5-BrU, but nine per cent of the total phages still formed plaques of normal and mutant type. This means that the viable phages do contain 5-BrU and probably to the same extent as do the "dead" ones. These non-infectious or "dead" phages are unable to kill bacteria, but we have not yet determined their adsorptive capacities.

It is more likely that mutant production is the result of a combination of the manifold effects that 5-BrU and sulfa have on DNA metabolism as well as DNA structure. Coughlin and Adelberg (in press) and also Weinberg have evidence to show mutagenesis resulting from thymine starvation in *E. coli* 15 T⁻. In our system, aside from its incorporation into DNA, 5-BrU in the presence of sulfa inhibits thymine utilization, is reversed by thymidine competitively, and inhibits uracil formation or utilization.

In summary, we have found that 5-BrU in the presence of sulfa has a very strong mutagenic action in bacteriophage, that this action may possibly create an instability in the entire genome of the phage, and that its incorporation into DNA is apparently insufficient to explain its mutagenic effect.

(References: Zamenhoff, S., and Griboff, G., 1954, Nature, Lond. *174:* 306; Dunn, D. B., and Smith, J. D., 1954, *ibid.* 305.)

A Comparative Study of Certain Gene Loci in *Salmonella*[1]

M. DEMEREC

Carnegie Institution of Washington, Department of Genetics, Cold Spring Harbor, New York

During the past three years research workers in our laboratory, using various auxotrophic mutants of *Salmonella typhimurium*, have accumulated a considerable body of data pertaining to the structure and organization of gene loci. Although these data are not yet adequate to give us a clear picture of a gene or of the mutation process, they seem to be sufficient to justify their use in the development of a model to serve as a guide in planning further work. It is my intention here to present an evaluation of the findings from this point of view. I should like to call attention to the fact that the material to be discussed represents work done by several members of our group, and that some of it has not yet been published.

METHODS

The transduction process, discovered by Zinder and Lederberg (1952), was used in our genetic analyses. The mechanism of this process is as follows. A phage particle carries a bacterial chromosome fragment, presumably acquired at random, from the bacterium in which it grew, and deposits it in the bacterium which it infects. A fraction of such phage-transported fragments are incorporated into the chromosomes of the offspring of the infected bacteria. Results of experiments by Witkin and Lacy (1954) show that a certain percentage of the offspring of every transduced bacterium carry the original chromosome of the recipient bacterium in unchanged form, whereas the rest of the offspring carry a chromosome in which a small region has been replaced by a homologous region introduced by the phage. Using known genetic markers in chromosomes of recipient and donor bacteria, we have shown (Demerec and Demerec, 1956) that this incorporation is accomplished through a process similar to crossing over.

Thus the transduction phenomenon makes it possible to induce duplication of a short region of a bacterial chromosome, and to investigate recombination between the duplicated region and the whole chromosome. It is evident that, since single, triple, and other odd classes of crossovers produce deficiencies (except when a terminal region is involved), only even crossover classes can be recovered.

[1] The work described in this paper was supported in part by a grant-in-aid from the American Cancer Society upon recommendation of the Committee on Growth of the National Research Council.

TERMINOLOGY

The terms and symbols we use in this work have been discussed in detail in a separate paper (Demerec, 1956). Because we employ certain terms in a more specific sense than is generally implied in their usage, the system will be outlined briefly here, in order to avoid misunderstanding.

There is now abundant evidence to indicate that a gene can be subdivided by crossing over into smaller, lineally arranged units, which we call *sites*. Thus a gene occupies a linear section of chromosome, which we call a *gene locus*, or simply *locus*. The different forms in which a gene may exist are called *alleles*. They may be *nonidentical* if due to mutations at different sites of a gene locus, or *identical* if due to mutations at homologous sites. This does not necessarily imply that two independent mutations occurring at the same site give rise to mutants of identical chemical structure or identical phenotype.

Each symbol in the mutant nomenclature we have adopted includes an abbreviation of the distinctive phenotype of the mutant (*try* for tryptophan-requiring mutant, *hi* for histidine-requiring, *ad* for adenine-requiring, etc.), and a number that identifies the particular mutant, in the order in which it was found, among those of similar phenotype (*try-1*, *try-2*, ⋯ ; *hi-1*, *hi-2*, ⋯ ; *ad-1*, *ad-2*, ⋯). When the locus of a mutant has been determined, a capital letter designating the locus is inserted in the symbol (*tryD-1*, *tryC-3*, *tryB-2*, *tryA-8*, etc.). A locus designation is not an essential part of a symbol.

SENSITIVITY OF THE TRANSDUCTION METHOD

Frequency of crossing over between two genes is usually expressed as the ratio of the number of recombinations to the total number of chances for occurrence of crossing over. Thus the sensitivity of an experimental system for the detection of rare crossover classes depends on its capacity to produce a large total number of all possible recombinant and parental classes. In work with *Drosophila*, for example, this factor depends on the number of flies raised in any one experiment; and since that number is readily determinable, the degree of sensitivity of a test is easily established. In our material, however, the total number of chances for occurrence of crossing over—which we might call the "base line" for determining the sensitivity of the method—cannot be ascertained directly. I shall describe three indirect approaches to an estimate of this base line.

The first approach rests on the following assumptions: (a) that each phage particle used in an experiment carries a bacterial chromosome fragment; (b) that these fragments represent random portions of chromosome; and (c) that a certain fraction of them participate in transduction. Then, to estimate the value of the base line it is necessary to know the number of phage particles used in an experiment, which can easily be determined by assay, and the fraction that carry the chromosomal portion we are interested in. This fraction can be estimated only roughly, by assuming that each fragment carries approximately the same number of genes, and by estimating the total number of genes present in a bacterium.

We have experimental evidence, in the case of the tryptophan region of the *Salmonella* chromosome, that a fragment may include four closely linked *try* loci and the *cysB* locus, and that they are arranged in the following order: *tryD—tryC—tryB—tryA—cysB*. Judging by the frequencies of recombination between them, *tryA* and *cysB* are farther apart than *tryD* and *tryA*. Thus, in the region between *tryA* and *cysB* there is room for more than four additional loci the size of the *try* loci. Furthermore, from the frequency of simultaneous transductions involving *tryD* and *cysB* it can be inferred that an average transducing fragment is considerably longer than the distance between *tryD* and *cysB*. It seems reasonable to assume, therefore, that the minimum number of genes included in such a fragment is not less than ten; and, since linkage between genes controlling unrelated reactions is very rare, it may be concluded that the maximum number of genes in a fragment is probably not more than twenty.

The number of genes present in a bacterium can only be guessed. If it is assumed that *Drosophila* has about 5000 genes, it is a fair guess that the bacterium has no less than 1000 and no more than 5000.

On the assumption, then, that the average transducing fragment includes between 10 and 20 genes, and that the total number of genes in a bacterium is between 1000 and 5000, it can be computed that a fragment comprising any particular region of a chromosome will be carried by $\frac{1}{500}$ to $\frac{1}{50}$ of phage particles. The results of Ozeki's (1956) study of abortive transduction indicate that only a small percentage of the fragments introduced by phage into recipient bacteria participate in stable transduction by being incorporated into the chromosomes of the bacterial offspring, whereas a larger number are not incorporated and thus remain inactive as far as transduction is concerned. For mutants *athC-5* and *-14*, studied by Ozeki, the active portion is about one-tenth the inactive portion. Taking this into account, we may estimate that the fraction of transducing fragments representing any one region of chromosome is smaller by a factor of about 10 than the fraction of phage particles carrying such fragments, or $\frac{1}{5000}$ to $\frac{1}{500}$ the total number of particles used in an experiment. According to this estimate, in our usual experiments, in which we employ 10^8 phage particles per Petri plate, the approximate number of phage particles carrying any one specific fragment and participating in stable transduction is between 2×10^4 and 2×10^5 per plate. This represents the total number of chances for occurrence of crossing over, or the base line for calculating its frequency.

The second approach, suggested independently by A. D. Hershey and by Hermann Moser, estimates the maximal fraction of phage particles that may carry a particular fragment on the basis of the approximate number of particles that are produced per bacterium. According to studies made by N. D. Zinder and Alan Garen (personal communication), the average number of phage particles released by one lysed bacterium, under the experimental conditions that we have used, is 700. Since the average number of nuclei per bacterium, before infection, is four, and since it seems reasonable to assume that each chromosome is represented only once in every nucleus, it follows that only four phage particles originating in the same bacterium can carry similar chromosome fragments. Therefore it may be expected that no more than one in 175 phage particles will carry a fragment representing any particular region of chromosome. Taking abortive transduction into account, we may estimate our base line as $\frac{1}{1750}$ of the total number of phage particles used in an experiment.

The third approach to an estimate of this base line uses data from linkage experiments involving the *try* loci and the *cysB* locus. In the experiment *tryD-10 cysB-12* ($\times$) *tryA-8*, for example, the numbers of crossovers occurring in the regions of the chromosome between the markers were as follows (see Demerec and Hartman, 1956, table 12):

region 1-2,	207
regions 3-4 and 2-4,	825
regions 1-2-3-4-,	19

If crossing over occurs at random, it is to be expected that the frequency of quadruple crossovers (1-2-3-4) will be a product of the frequencies of double crossovers (1-2 $\times$ 3-4). The data of this experiment do not give a value for the 3-4 class alone, but show the combined values for classes 3-4 and 2-4. From the results of numerous experiments involving the *try* and *cysB* markers, however, we would expect the 2-4 class to be about one-third the 1-2 class, or 69. Deducting this from the combined values for the 3-4 and 2-4 classes, we obtain 756 as an estimate of the value for the 3-4 class.

These data come from one experiment, in which approximately the same total number of phage particles was used in obtaining each of the different classes of recombinants, and thus all classes should have the same "base line." If we call this base-line value x, the frequency of quadruple crossovers is $\frac{19}{x}$ and the frequencies of the two double-crossover classes are $\frac{207}{x}$ and $\frac{756}{x}$. Then, assuming random occurrence of crossing over, we can express the relation among these three classes as follows: $\frac{19}{x} = \frac{207}{x} \times \frac{756}{x}$. Thus $x = \frac{207 \times 756}{19} = \frac{156,492}{19} = 8236$. This reasoning indicates that in the material used there were 8236 chances for detection of 19 quadruple crossovers, and consequently about 1.56×10^5 chances of detecting one quadruple crossover. Further, since about 4×10^8 phage particles were used on four plates, it is calculated that about 4×10^4 transducing phage particles per plate (per 10^8 phage particles) carried the fragment including the *try–cysB* region of the chromosome.

The value obtained by this method of computation is within the range of values obtained by the previously described methods. Since the length of a fragment carrying both *tryD* and *cysB* is greater than the length of region necessary to include two more closely linked markers, this method of computation underestimates the value of x in examination of the linkage relation between two alleles.

According to the first method of estimate described, between 1/5000 and 1/500 of phage particles carry any one particular chromosomal fragment that will participate in stable transduction; according to the second method, this fraction is 1/1750; and according to the third, it is 1/2500. These estimates are in fair agreement with one another. Therefore it seem reasonable to assume that at least 1 per 3000 phage particles used in an experiment carries a fragment capable of transducing a specific region of chromosome; and according to this assumption, since we routinely use about 10^8 particles per plate in our experiments, the total number of chances for occurrence of crossing over within such a region is approximately 3.3×10^4 per plate. It is possible to increase the number of phage particles per plate about one hundred fold.

Our experience indicates that as a rule the transduction method is sufficiently sensitive to detect recombination between two markers if there is a possibility of its occurring. We have observed that if no recombinants are found when approximately 10^9 phage particles are used in an experiment none are found if the number of particles is increased by a factor of ten or even a hundred. Benzer (1955) made a similar observation in re-

combination experiments with bacteriophages. Although his method is sensitive enough to detect recombinants occurring with a frequency of about 10^{-8}, it was not necessary to use more than about 10^4 phage particles to detect every recombinant class. This finding suggests that there is a definite limit to the size of a region within which crossing over can occur, and that the methods used by Benzer and by us are entirely adequate to detect crossovers within such a region.

It should be mentioned that the efficiency of transduction may vary considerably among experiments in which different mutant markers are used as recipients. Higher than average efficiency, for example, is associated with most of the histidine mutants, whereas with some other mutants like *cysE-2*, *-6*, and *-8*, the efficiency is very low. These differences have not yet been explained. They introduce another variable, however, which has to be taken into account in tests of whether or not crossing over occurs between two markers.

COMPLEX STRUCTURE OF GENE LOCI

The analysis of a large number of auxotrophic mutants has shown that on the basis of two criteria, namely, their linkage relations and the positions of their biosynthetic blocks, mutants of similar phenotypes can be divided into well-defined groups. Mutants belonging to any one group are closely linked, and they exhibit the effect of a block at a particular point in the chain of biochemical reactions leading to the synthesis of the required growth factor. This is interpreted to mean that the members of such a group are nonidentical alleles.

In studies involving about 400 auxotrophs, the following numbers of gene loci have been identified:

tryptophan	4	serine	2
histidine	4	proline	2
cystine	5	phenylalanine	2
methionine	5	tyrosine	2
leucine	2	purines	9
isoleucine-valine	3	galactose	2

Thus 42 gene loci in all have been identified so far. In 36 of these cases, we have two or more alleles available for study; and in every instance either all the alleles or a large percentage of them have been found to be nonidentical. This finding indicates that nonidentical allelism is not a special feature of certain gene loci, but a general property of all loci.

VARIATION AMONG DIFFERENT SITES OF THE SAME LOCUS

P. E. Hartman (1956) observed considerable differences in reaction to purines among the eight nonidentical alleles of the *hiA* locus. He found that the nutritional deficiency of *hiA-32*, and to a lesser extent that of *hiA-6*, can be satisfied also by any one of several purines, whereas the other six known alleles of the *hiA* locus show no detectable reaction to purines. His analysis indicates that in these two mutants purines allow growth by sparing a common precursor or by supplying a readily utilizable source of the carbon-2 of histidine, rather than by serving as direct precursors in the synthesis of L-histidine by an alternate pathway. It shows also that *hiA-32* and *hiA-6* are not adjacent to each other on the genetic map of the *hiA* locus but are separated by at least five other sites. These results reveal a considerable degree of differentiation among alleles of the same locus with respect to nutritional requirements, and indicate that sites responsible for similar reactions need not be located in the same part of a gene locus.

An interesting pattern of distribution of differentiated sites within a locus was analyzed by Yura (1956a) and Haruo Ozeki (unpub.) in the case of the *athA* locus, where the sites of nine alleles requiring adenine and thiamine have been identified. One of the characteristics of the *athA* locus is that the nutritional requirements of certain alleles can be modified so that pantothenate is able to replace thiamine. Thus it is possible to recognize phenotypically stable alleles, requiring adenine and thiamine, and unstable alleles, in which pantothenate can take the place of thiamine; and among the unstable alleles there are several degrees of instability, depending on the frequency with which modification occurs. Studies of the order of the alleles on a genetic map locate the site of *athA-4*, which is the most stable of the nine known alleles, near the center of the locus; the sites of *athA-8* and *athA-9*, which are the most unstable, at the two extreme ends; and those of the other alleles between *athA-4* and either of these two end positions, approximately in the order of their degree of stability, the more stable being near the center. Thus we have indication, in this case, of a polarity in the arrangement of sites, with a gradient from a stable center towards unstable ends. A similar pattern of distribution of sites was also observed in the case of the *athD* locus.

Another evidence of differentiation among alleles of the same locus is emerging from R. C. Clowes' studies (unpub.) of 12 nonidentical alleles of the *cysB* locus. The nutritional deficiency in all these alleles can be satisfied by cysteine. Four of them, however—namely, *cysB-18*, *-24*, *-25*, and *-10*—are able to utilize SO_3 compounds as well. Since the *cysB* locus is closely linked with the *try* loci, it is possible to determine the order of most of the *cysB* alleles with a considerable degree of precision by the use of three-point tests (Demerec and Hartman, 1956). Such determinations show that the site of *cysB-14*, which is one of the alleles satisfied only by cysteine, is at the left end of the locus, and that to the right of it, in the following

order, are the sites of three cysteine-or-SO_3 alleles (*-18*, *-24*, and *-25*), six cysteine-only alleles (*-12*, *-16*, *-27*, *-40*, *-41*, *-45*), one more cysteine-or-SO_3 allele (*-10*), and, farthest to the right, another cysteine-only allele (*-15*). Thus the sites of these two kinds of alleles are not distributed at random along the locus, nor is each kind segregated by itself, but there is an evident tendency towards grouping, with the two kinds of groups intermixed.

It has been observed that nonidentical alleles of the same gene locus often differ as to frequencies of mutation to prototrophy, either spontaneous or induced by treatment with ultraviolet radiation or other mutagens. An extensive study of alleles of one galactose and one serine locus, made by Zlata Hartman (1956), revealed a considerable amount of variation among them with regard to both spontaneous mutability and mutability induced by treatment with any one of five mutagens. It also showed that some of the alleles are mutagen stable whereas others are not. Similar results were obtained by Yura (1956a) in studies of spontaneous and U.V.-induced mutability in several alleles of three purine loci.

All this evidence shows that mutants resulting from changes at different sites of a locus, although they are affected primarily in one function, may differ from one another in respect to various other properties. The findings indicate that the sites of alleles possessing similar properties are not distributed at random within a locus, but tend to be grouped together; and they also suggest that differentiation among sites may be less extensive in certain regions of a chromosome than in others.

MULTIPLE-SITE MUTANTS

The results of our first transduction experiments to determine the allelic relations among cystine-requiring mutants (Demerec, Blomstrand, and Demerec, 1955) showed that *cys-20* failed to produce any recombinants in transduction tests with six of the other cystine mutants, namely, *cys-1*, *-3*, *-5*, *-13*, *-21*, and *-22*, whereas recombinants were obtained in all tests of these six mutants with one another. The frequencies of recombination indicated that the six mutants are closely linked; and it was concluded that they are non-identical alleles of one gene locus, which is now known as *cysA*. Subsequently, two more non-identical alleles belonging to the *cysA* locus were isolated (*cysA-32*, *-69*), and neither of these produces recombinants with *cys-20*. Thus it is evident that *cys-20* is different from the other *cysA* alleles, in that it covers all the known sites of that locus.

A similar case of a multiple-site mutant has been described by P. E. Hartman (1956). He found that *hiB-22* gave no recombinants in tests with any of the five known nonidentical alleles of the *hiB* locus (*hiB-29*, *-20*, *-14*, *-24*, and *-21*), but that it did produce recombinants with the eight known nonidentical alleles of the *hiA* locus, to the left of *hiB* on the chromosome map, and with the six known nonidentical alleles of the *hiC* locus, to its right. Thus it appears probable that *hiB-22* covers the sites of one locus, and that the sites of the two adjacent loci are not included.

Another multiple-site mutant was found by Yura (1956a) in studies of the *athA* locus. This is *athA-10*, which does not show recombination with any of the seven nonidentical alleles identified at that locus.

An interesting situation with regard to the occurrence of multiple-site mutation has been analyzed by Clowes (unpublished) in the *cysC* and *cysD* loci. These two loci are very closely linked, presumably adjacent to each other. They can be differentiated because the nutritional deficiency in *cysC* mutants is satisfied by either cysteine, thiosulfate, or sulfite compounds, whereas the deficiency in *cysD* mutants is satisfied only by cysteine or thiosulfate. Moreover, *cysD* mutants accumulate in the medium in which they grow a substance that supports the growth of *cysC* mutants; in other words, *cysD* mutants are able to feed *cysC* mutants. The approximate map order of four nonidentical alleles of *cysC* and four of *cysD* is as follows: *cysC-43*, ···· *-47*, *-7*, *-38*, *cysD-23*, *-51*, *-44*, *-46*. Judging by the frequencies of recombinants, *cysC-47*, *-7*, and *-38* are close together, with *-43* some distance to the left of them. All four *cysD* alleles are close together. So far, the order of such closely linked alleles can be determined only approximately. In addition to these eight mutants, six multiple-site mutants have been found, each including some of the known sites of the *cysD* locus plus *cysC-47*, *-7*, and *-38* but not *cysC-43*. Tests made by Clowes show that they do not feed *cysC* mutants. Recently, fourteen additional mutants have been found in the *cysC–cysD* region. An analysis carried out by B. Djordjevic shows that four are *cysC* mutants, four are *cysD* mutants, and six are multiple-site mutants covering some of the known sites of the *cysD* locus and all except *cysC-43* of the *cysC* locus. Thus it is evident that in the *cysC–cysD* region of the chromosome multiple-site mutants are detected with a high frequency.

The information now available about multiple-site mutants suggests that they are of a different type than the mutants usually found in our material. They are distinctive in the following respects:

1) As a rule, the frequency with which they are found in any one of the analyzed regions of bacterial chromosome is lower than the frequency of occurrence of single-site mutants. We have data concerning 24 gene loci, namely, two tryptophan, four cystine, four histidine, six purine, five methionine, one proline, one phenylalanine, and one tyrosine; and only in the *cysC–cysD* region has the frequency of multiple-site mutants been high.

2) They cover well-defined regions. The mutants *cysA-20*, *hiB-22*, and *athA-10* cover all the known sites of their respective loci; and the *cysC–cysD* mutants appear to cover certain sites of these two loci.

3) Neither *athA-10* nor any of the *cysC–cysD* mutants reverts to prototrophy. Small-colony-forming "revertants" appear with a low frequency when *cysA-20* bacteria are grown on minimal plates. An analysis of these now being made by Sheila Howarth, however, indicates that they are due to mutations at a suppressor locus, rather than to back mutations at the *cysA-20* locus. Similar small-colony revertants were observed by P. E. Hartman in his work with the *hiB-22* mutant, and although they have not yet been analyzed their small size, which is a characteristic property of suppressor revertants (Giles and Partridge, 1953), makes it appear probable that they also are due to mutations at a suppressor locus. Therefore it seems very likely that inability to revert to prototrophy is another common feature of multiple-site mutants.

4) P. E. Hartman's (1956) study of frequencies of crossing over between mutants of the four adjacent histidine loci has revealed lower values for crossing over between *hiB-22* and markers located to either side of it than between the other *hiB* mutants and these markers. The difference is less with more distantly located markers. These findings apply regardless of whether *hiB-22* is carried by the recipient bacteria or is introduced by the transducing phage. We have not been able to make similar studies with other multiple-site mutants because mutants representing adjacent loci have not yet been identified.

Thus the known properties of multiple-site mutants, briefly summarized, are as follows: they fail to produce recombinants with a number of closely linked markers; the frequency with which they are found at any one locus is, as a rule, lower than the frequency of occurrence of single-site mutants; they cover a well-defined region of chromosome; they do not revert to prototrophy; and, in the one case (*hiB-22*) in which it is possible to study crossing over with adjacent markers, a multiple-site mutant exhibits a lower frequency of crossing over than do single-site mutants of the same locus.

The failure to produce recombinants with closely linked markers suggests that we are dealing with a mutation which extends over a certain length of the chromosome, and that either (a) crossing over leading to viable recombinants cannot occur at all within that length, or (b) if it does occur the recombinants cannot be recognized because they do not have the wild-type phenotype. The (a) condition could be produced by chromosomal aberrations such as deletions, the (b) condition by simultaneous alterations at several adjacent sites.

When the accumulation of additional material

allows more extensive study of multiple-site mutants, we may be able to discover what mechanism is responsible for their origin. The evidence available at present favors a deletion mechanism, and critical information is supplied by the data concerning the frequency with which multiple-site mutants are found, particularly the exceptionally high frequency of such mutants observed in the *cysC–cysD* region of the chromosome.

Our reasoning finds support in observations made with *Drosophila*, which can be briefly summarized as follows. Lethals are the most frequently observed mutations, whether spontaneous or induced by radiation or some other mutagen. Cytological studies of lethal mutations occurring in chromosome regions favorable for such study indicate that a considerable proportion are deletions, detectable in salivary-gland chromosomes. For example, an analysis of 13 spontaneous and 48 X-ray-induced Notch mutations (Demerec and Fano, 1941) showed that nine of the spontaneous and 37 of the induced were deletions of various lengths, the spontaneous occurring within a region involving up to nine bands and the induced within a region involving up to 50 bands. Thus it was indicated that deletions are among the most frequently occurring of mutational events. Studies of lethals located in various regions of the X chromosome showed that regions differ in their importance to the performance of physiological functions in a cell. Lethal mutations, presumably deletions, in most of the regions investigated, were found to be lethal to even a few cells (cell lethal); lethals in a few regions were not cell lethal but were lethal to the organism as a whole; and, finally, a very few deletions were not lethal to the organism (Demerec, 1934, 1936, 1938). If similar conditions obtain in bacteria, that is, if a considerable portion of genetic changes are deletions and if, because of haploidy, only those can be detected which occur in regions of the chromosome not essential for the functioning of the genome, then it is to be expected that deletions will be observed with a high frequency only in the rare nonessential regions. In our material the *cysC–cysD* section of the chromosome would represent such a region. Rare survival of deletions in certain other regions—such as the *cysA*, *hiB*, and *athA* loci—could be explained by assuming that deletions in these regions have a strong detrimental, but not a lethal, effect on the functioning of the genome, and that, during the early divisions of cells carrying a deletion, mutation at some other locus compensated for the bad effect of the deletion.

In evaluating this proposed explanation it seems necessary to raise the question of why, since we are dealing with nutritional mutants, addition of the required nutrient to the medium should not be able to compensate for a deletion, as it is able to compensate for a nondeletional genetic change. A possible answer to this question is that a gene, in addition to controlling a specific function, also plays an important role in the general activity of the whole complex of genes—the genome—and that in relation to this activity the absence of certain genes cannot be offset.

The results of our experiments could also be explained, however, by assuming that the deficiency created by a deletion can be wholly compensated for by the addition of appropriate nutrient to the medium, and that the high frequency of multiple-site mutations observed in the *cysC–cysD* region is caused by a high frequency of occurrence of the events responsible for these mutations. We hope by further experimentation to find new evidence for analysis of the responsible mechanism.

IDENTICAL ALLELES

Interesting observations are available with regard to the repeated occurrence of mutations at the same site. Yura (1956a) found three mutants associated with one site of the *athA* locus, in which seven different sites in all have now been identified. Since each of these three mutants (*athA-1*, *-2*, *-3*) was isolated in a different culture, started from a small number of bacteria, they must have originated independently of one another; and since extensive transduction tests have failed to separate them, the assumption that they are due to independent alterations at the same site seems a reasonable one. These three mutants are very similar with respect to pattern of spontaneous and U.V.-induced reversions; they are all affected by a suppressor mutation that does not affect mutants belonging to other sites of the same locus (Yura, 1956b); and they are similar in their nutritional requirements, whereas other mutants of the *athA* locus show considerable differences. Thus *athA-1*, *-2*, and *-3* behave genetically as if they were due to alterations at the same site, and phenotypically they cannot be distinguished from one another by any criteria we have used.

Among the histidine mutants, P. E. Hartman (1956) found three pairs—namely, *hiD-1* and *-36*, *hiD-9* and *-17*, and *hiB-12* and *-24*—in which the two members of a pair could not be separated by transduction and so presumably were due to changes at the same site. He found, moreover, that *hiD-1* and *-36* were similar in all respects tested; that is, they appeared to be identical both genetically and phenotypically. But his tests also showed that the members of the other two pairs differed from each other. Mutant *hiD-9* displayed lower rates of both spontaneous and U.V.-induced mutability than *hiD-17*, and also produced slower-growing prototrophs; and *hiB-12* showed lower values for crossing over with the other *hi* markers than did *hiB-24*.

These analyses of four sets of mutants whose respective members could not be separated by crossing over revealed that in two cases the members of a set were phenotypically similar whereas in the other two cases there were detectable phenotypic differences between the members. If the mutants of each set were due to alterations occurring at the same site, these findings indicate that even at one site different changes may occur. On the other hand, it is possible that the two sets whose members showed differences represented multiple-site changes affecting a small region of a gene locus.

Distribution of Loci on a Chromosome

We have evidence that in *Salmonella* the distribution of genes along a chromosome may not be random and that there is a strong tendency for genes controlling related reactions to be grouped close together. In the extreme representation of such grouping, genes controlling related reactions are adjacent to one another and their order on a linkage map coincides with their sequence in respect to biochemical blocks in the chain of reactions they control. Two such cases of extreme grouping have been found so far. One involves four tryptophan loci (Demerec and Hartman, 1956) and the other four histidine loci (P. E. Hartman, 1956).

Examples of linkage sufficiently close to be detected by transduction tests have been found in several other series of mutants. Among five cystine loci, two are linked; among nine purine loci there are two linkage groups, one involving three loci and the other two; and, finally, both of the known leucine loci are linked.

That a similar nonrandom distribution of genes may occur in other species of bacteria is indicated by the current work of P. D. Skaar, which is summarized in the discussion following this paper. He has found that four tryptophan loci in strain B of *Escherichia coli*, which are homologous to the four tryptophan loci we have studied in *Salmonella*, are closely linked and appear to be arranged in a similar order.

As has been pointed out earlier (Demerec and Hartman, 1956), nonrandom distribution of genes could hardly exist unless certain gene arrangements conferred evolutionary advantage. Selective advantage as related to gene arrangement, however, may be different in different organisms, since in *Neurospora* four tryptophan and four histidine loci, which appear to be homologous to similar loci in *Salmonella*, are not linked.

Conclusions and Summary

Thanks to recent refinements in method, and particularly to the new techniques developed for work with microorganisms, we are now in a position to carry genetic analysis of the structure of genes, and of the relations between genes, considerably further than we were able to do only a few years ago. Although we are still in the early stages of such analysis with *Salmonella typhimurium*, the following facts are already evident.

1) Within a gene, smaller units or sites can be identified.

2) These sites have a definite minimum size.

3) Mutants representing changes at different sites of a gene locus, although they are affected primarily in one function, may differ from one another in various other properties.

4) Sites of alleles possessing similar properties are not distributed at random within a locus, but tend to be grouped together.

5) Genes are not distributed at random along a chromosome.

6) In *S. typhimurium* and *E. coli*—presumably in bacteria generally—there is a marked tendency for genes that control related reactions to be located close together, an indication that certain gene arrangements confer strong selective advantage.

References

Benzer, S., 1955, Fine structure of a genetic region in bacteriophage. Proc. Nat. Acad. Sci. Wash. *41*: 344–354.

Demerec, M., 1934, Biological action of small deficiencies of X chromosome of *Drosophila melanogaster*. Proc. Nat. Acad. Sci. Wash. *20*: 354–359.

1936, Frequency of "cell-lethals" among lethals obtained at random in the X chromosome of *Drosophila melanogaster*. Proc. Nat. Acad. Sci. Wash. *22*: 350–354.

1938, Eighteen years of research on the gene. In: Cooperation in Research. Carnegie Inst. Wash. Pub. *501*, pp. 295–314.

1956, Terminology and nomenclature. In: Genetic Studies with Bacteria. Carnegie Inst. Wash. Pub. *612*, pp. 1–4.

Demerec, M., Blomstrand, I., and Demerec, Z. E., 1955, Evidence of complex loci in *Salmonella*. Proc. Nat. Acad. Sci. Wash. *41*: 359–364.

Demerec, M., and Demerec, Z. E., 1956, Analysis of linkage relationships in *Salmonella* by transduction techniques. Brookhaven Symp. Biol. *8*: 75–84.

Demerec, M., and Fano, U., 1941, Mechanism of the origin of x-ray induced Notch deficiencies in *Drosophila melanogaster*. Proc. Nat. Acad. Sci. Wash. *27*: 24–31.

Demerec, M., and Hartman, Zlata, 1956, Tryptophan mutants in *Salmonella typhimurium*. In: Genetic Studies with Bacteria. Carnegie Inst. Wash. Pub. *612*, pp. 5–33.

Giles, N. H., and Partridge, C. W. H., 1953, The effect of a suppressor on allelic inositolless mutants in *Neurospora crassa*. Proc. Nat. Acad. Sci. Wash. *39*: 479–488.

Hartman, Philip E., 1956, Linked loci in the control of consecutive steps in the primary pathway of histidine synthesis in *Salmonella typhimurium*. In: Genetic Studies with Bacteria. Carnegie Inst. Wash. Pub. *612*, pp. 35–61.

Hartman, Zlata, 1956, Induced mutability in *Salmonella typhimurium*. In: Genetic Studies with Bacteria. Carnegie Inst. Wash. Pub. *612*, pp. 107–120.

Ozeki, Haruo, 1956, Abortive transduction in purine-requiring mutants of *Salmonella typhimurium*. In: Genetic Studies with Bacteria. Carnegie Inst. Wash. Pub. *612*, pp. 97–106.

Witkin, E. M., and Lacy, A. M., 1954, Bacterial genetics—II. Carnegie Inst. Wash. Year Book No. *53*: 241–246.

Yura, Takashi, 1956a, Evidence of nonidentical alleles in purine-requiring mutants of *Salmonella typhimurium*. In: Genetic Studies with Bacteria. Carnegie Inst. Wash. Pub. *612*, pp. 63–75.

1956b, Suppressor mutations in purine-requiring mutants of *Salmonella typhimurium*. In: Genetic Studies with Bacteria. Carnegie Inst. Wash. Pub. *612*, pp. 77–86.

ZINDER, N. D., and LEDERBERG, J., 1952, Genetic exchange in *Salmonella*. J. Bact. *64*: 679–699.

DISCUSSION

KREIG: The application of the "cis-trans" test by Ozeki constitutes a powerful additional tool for the analysis of the genetic structure of *Salmonella*. Has this test been applied to pairs of sites at neighboring loci, such as *hiA–hiB*?

DEMEREC: As you suggest, we hope by means of the abortive-transduction method worked out by Ozeki to be able to separate closely linked loci that have similar phenotypes. Observations made so far indicate that the method will be widely, although not generally, applicable. It has been found that abortive transductions cannot be recognized when the rate of residual growth of the recipient bacteria is high. Tests involving the histidine loci have not yet been made.

SPOFFORD: Could you compare the frequency of recombination between adjacent sites within loci and between adjacent loci in one of these complexes of loci, such as histidine?

DEMEREC: Yes. Hartman's data show that the frequency of recombinations is higher between *hiA-3* and *-32*, which are two nonidentical alleles of the *hiA* locus located close together, than between *hiA-32* and *hiB-29*, which are located in two adjacent gene loci.

ENGLESBERG: It seems quite clear that on the basis of accumulation and feeding experiments the nonidentical alleles Dr. Demerec has outlined cannot each be involved in the synthesis of a different enzyme in the defined biosynthetic pathways. It is true that the breaks have not been identified by enzymatic analysis and that a few no doubt involve more than one enzyme, but it does not seem probable that the single breaks postulated would actually involve a number of enzymes equal to the number of nonidentical alleles. Instead, it might be worth while to consider the nonidentical alleles as governing biosynthesis on a different level entirely, that is, on the level of the enzyme-forming mechanism itself.

SKAAR and DAVIDSON: Transductions among mutants of *Escherichia coli*, B/r, have been accomplished by means of a variant (P1*b*) of the temperate phage P1*kc* (Lennox, E. S., 1955, Virology *1*: 190–206). Nine independent tryptophan mutations were studied, representing blocks in four synthetic steps: before anthranilic acid (*tryA*), between anthranilic acid and indole (*tryB* and *tryC*), and between indole and tryptophan (*tryD*). All were closely linked, in agreement with findings in *Salmonella* (Demerec, M., *et al.*, 1955, Proc. Nat. Acad. Sci. Wash. *41*: 359–364).

Mutants of *E. coli*, B/r, which are resistant to coliphage T1, but not to T5, are usually tryptophan requirers (Anderson, E. H., 1946, Proc.

Nat. Acad. Sci. Wash. *32*: 120–128). They respond only to tryptophan. These two associated changes are pleiotropic effects of a single genetic event (Bryson, V., *et al.*, 1954, Ann. Report Biol. Lab., Cold Spring Harbor, N. Y., 1953–54, pp. 22–26). The mutation (here called *tryV*) is not closely linked to any of the well-known markers of strain K-12. All of four independent *tryV* mutations studied were found to be closely linked to the nine mutations cited above.

The following table gives percentages of wild-type transductants observed when various phage-bacteria mixtures were plated on minimal medium supplemented to permit recovery of the donor parental type. No value is based on examination of less than 1000 transductants.

Receptor	Donor .... Supplement	*tryA-2* Anthranilic acid	*tryB-1* Indole	*tryC-4* Indole
tryB-1		9.1	—	—
tryC-4		14.6	—	—
tryD-9		19.1	10.8	9.2
tryV-8		0	0	0

These data reveal that, although *tryA*, *tryB*, *tryC*, and *tryD* mutations (one example of each) are genetically separable, each of the first three acts as an allele of *tryV*. Transductions and sexual crosses involving the double mutants *tryAV*, *tryBV*, and *tryCV*, have led to the same conclusion. In addition, the allelism of *tryD-9* and *tryV-8* is indicated by the fact that cross-transductions on minimal medium fail to yield wild-type colonies. A plausible explanation of these apparently contradictory results is that *tryV* mutations consist of a deletion encompassing much of the region concerned with tryptophan synthesis.

This inference is supported by the following additional evidence: (1) the absence of reversions of *tryV*, (2) the poor growth of these mutants in minimal plus tryptophan (Anderson, 1946), (3) the failure of these mutants to accumulate any known precursor of tryptophan (Gots, J. S., *et al.*, 1954, J. Gen. Microbiol. *11*: 7–16), and (4) the fact that when *tryB* and *tryD* cells are made T1-resistant, *tryB* not only loses responsiveness to indole, but also ceases to accumulate anthranilic, whereas *tryD* ceases to accumulate indole (Gots *et al.*, 1954). It is suggested that deletions in regions of functionally related loci may be suspected in other situations where inconsistencies between growth requirements and accumulations exist.

SZYBALSKI: We have tried to re-examine the earlier work of Dr. Demerec on the fine structure of the streptomycin-dependence locus (*sd*) using the *Hfr* strain of *Escherichia coli*. This locus was chosen because of the ease with which a multitude of *sd* mutants could be isolated. Up to now all crosses between over 30 independently isolated *sd* mutants of the *Hfr* strain and their *F⁻* counterparts have not yielded any streptomycin-non-requiring recombinants, indicating the apparent homogeneity of this locus although the *sd* strains were not phenotypically identical (differences in colonial morphology, degree of dependence, rate of growth, etc.). The resolving power, however, is not very high in this system because the *Hfr* strain used shows a low frequency of recombination for the *sd* locus. Screening for a strain which will show a high frequency of recombination also for the *sd* marker, according to the method described by Jacob and Wollman, is under way. It will permit a great increase in the power of resolution in study of the fine structure of the *sd* locus.

Time, Temperature, and Protein Synthesis: A Study of Ultraviolet-Induced Mutation in Bacteria[1]

Evelyn M. Witkin

Department of Medicine, State University of New York College of Medicine at New York City, Brooklyn, New York[2]

About ten years ago (Demerec, 1946), it was reported that the yield of bacteriophage-resistant mutants induced by ultraviolet light in *Escherichia coli* increases as the irradiated population is allowed to multiply, until ten or twelve divisions are accomplished. Since that time, it has been observed repeatedly that maximal yields of many kinds of induced bacterial mutants, including auxotrophs (Davis, 1948), prototrophs (Davis, 1950; Demerec and Cahn, 1953) and streptomycin-independent variants (Labrum, 1953), are obtained only under conditions permitting more or less extensive periods of cell division after exposure to ultraviolet light. This "delayed appearance" of induced bacterial mutants has become one of the hardy perennials among the unsolved problems of microbial genetics.

Six possible mechanisms have been postulated to account for this phenomenon. Delayed mutation, phenotypic lag and segregation of multiple nuclei or multiple chromosomal strands were proposed by Demerec (1946). Newcombe and Scott (1949) added to the list the possible effect of irregularity of the growth pattern of irradiated cells, and Ryan (1954) suggested that delayed onset of division of newly induced mutant cells could account for the facts, in some cases. It has also been proposed that, in experiments with bacteriophage-resistant mutants, a methodological artefact may be responsible for exaggeration of the scope of delay (Newcombe, 1953). The complexity of the problem is exemplified by the multiplicity of the hypotheses offered to explain it, by the fact that they are by no means mutually exclusive, and by the possibility that the patterns of delay observed for different mutations may have their basis in different mechanisms. The hypotheses of segregation and irregularity of growth patterns have been satisfactorily eliminated, at least as primary factors, (Demerec and Cahn, 1953), but there has been conflicting evidence as to the part played by phenotypic lag (Newcombe and Scott, 1949; Ryan, 1955), and no decisive evidence in support of the possibility that induced mutations are often delayed in their occurrence for many generations (see, however, Witkin, 1951; Newcombe, 1953; Kaplan, 1952).

In the decade that has passed since the hypothesis of delayed mutation was proposed to account for the "delayed appearance" of induced mutants, it has become increasingly certain that the time interval between the absorption of radiant energy and the production of stable genetic changes can no longer be regarded as infinitesimal. The evidence that ultraviolet-induced mutations are irreversibly established only after an appreciable delay has come primarily from studies of postirradiation effects on the frequency of induced mutants, such as those of visible light (Kelner, 1949; Novick and Szilard, 1949; Newcombe and Whitehead, 1950), temperature (Witkin, 1953), and metabolites and metabolic inhibitors (Wainwright and Nevill, 1955a and b). Recent work (Anderson and Billen, 1955; Hollaender and Stapleton, 1956) suggests that mutations induced by ionizing radiations may also be susceptible to the influence of posttreatments. Information as to the duration of the period of susceptibility to postirradiation influences, limited as it is at the present time, does not, however, support the view that genetic instability persists for a number of cell generations after irradiation. The period of susceptibility to postirradiation temperature (Witkin, 1953; Berrie, 1953) for a variety of induced mutations in *E. coli* corresponds to a fraction of the time required for the first cell division after exposure to ultraviolet light. Newcombe (1955) has shown a relation between the period of susceptibility to photoreactivation in *Streptomyces* and the timing of the first nuclear division after irradiation. Thus, the evidence derived from studies of posttreatments suggests that the metabolic pathway leading from the absorption of energy to the establishment of induced mutations is associated with the first postirradiation cell division.

The experiments to be described in this report were begun in an effort to determine decisively the basis of the "delayed appearance" of ultraviolet-induced prototrophs, with the particular goal of obtaining information about the timing of the induced mutation process.

Materials and Methods

Bacterial strains. Most of the experiments were done with a tryptophane-requiring substrain (*try3*) of strain LT2 of *Salmonella typhimurium*, obtained from Dr. M. Demerec. Other auxotrophic substrains, each requiring a single growth factor, and

[1] This study was conducted in part under a grant from the National Science Foundation.
[2] Part of the work described in this report was done at the Carnegie Institution of Washington, Cold Spring Harbor, N. Y., while the author was a Staff Member of the Department of Genetics.

derived either from *S. typhimurium* LT2 or from *E. coli* B/r, were also used. Spontaneous rates of mutations to prototrophy were 10^{-8} or less, and all data presented in tables are corrected for spontaneous mutants.

Transducing Bacteriophage. In the experiments involving transduction, the temperate phage PLT22, obtained from Dr. N. Zinder, was used.

Culture Media. Difco nutrient broth and Difco nutrient agar were used as complete media. Synthetic medium "A" (Davis, 1950), consisting of inorganic salts and glucose, was used as minimal medium for strains derived from *S. typhimurium*, and was solidified with 1.5 per cent agar. The minimal medium used for strains derived from *E. coli* was medium "E," developed at Yale University by Vogel and Bonner (personal communication). Partial enrichment of minimal medium consisted of the addition of small amounts of nutrient broth, or small amounts of the specific growth factor required by the auxotrophic strain in use. The detailed description of the semi-enriched media will be given in connection with specific experiments.

Irradiation Procedure. Cultures to be irradiated were grown for 18 to 24 hours at 37°C, with aeration, in nutrient broth, unless otherwise specified. Ten-ml lots of culture were centrifuged, washed in saline or phosphate buffer, and resuspended in the same volume of saline or buffer for irradiation. The titer of the washed suspensions was usually between 1 and 3×10^9 cells per ml. The suspensions were irradiated in 7-ml portions in uncovered Petri dishes, with constant mechanical agitation during the exposure. The source of ultraviolet light was a G. E. Germicidal lamp. The dose used for *Salmonella* was 300 ergs/mm², and for *E. coli* B/r was 600 ergs/mm², giving survivals of between 10 and 20 per cent. Yellow light was used exclusively during and following irradiation to avoid uncontrolled photoreactivation.

Chloramphenicol was obtained from Charles Pfizer and Co.

EXPERIMENTAL RESULTS

PART I. THE "DELAYED APPEARANCE" OF INDUCED AUXOTROPHS

Induction delay compared with transduction delay. When strain *try3* of *S. typhimurium* is irradiated with ultraviolet light, induced prototrophs are obtained. The same genetic change can be brought about by infecting *try3* cells with transducing bacteriophage initially grown on an established stock of the ultraviolet-induced prototroph ($try3^{+uv}$). In these experiments, a comparison was made between the pattern of "delayed appearance" of the induced prototrophs (induction delay) and that of the prototrophs arising by transduction (transduction delay).

Since transduction is a parasexual process in which genetic properties are transferred from one bacterial strain to another (Zinder and Lederberg, 1952), the transduction from *try3* to $try3^{+uv}$ is essentially a recombination, and involves no mutagenic action. The same genetic change induced by ultraviolet light, however, is brought about by whatever events take place when one genetic specificity is altered by mutation to another. Thus, a comparison of the pattern of transduction delay with that of induction delay could provide critical evidence concerning the nature of the delay mechanism. Specifically, if the delayed appearance of induced mutants is primarily due to delayed mutation, it would be expected that prototrophs arising by transduction should exhibit no comparable delay. On the other hand, if phenotypic lag is the principal mechanism of induction delay, a similar delay should be found for transduction, since in both cases a physiological adjustment of the cell from tryptophane-dependence to independence must be effected.

In these experiments, a washed suspension of *try3* was irradiated, and the irradiated suspension divided into two portions. To the first portion (A), transducing phage (grown on a previously isolated $try3^{+uv}$ stock) was added; to the second portion (B), the same amount of nontransducing phage (the same phage strain, grown on *try3* itself, and thus incapable of transducing *try3* to prototrophy) was added. The two suspensions were thus identical in their previous growth history, in their exposure to ultraviolet light and in their state of infection with phage (except for the difference in the previous host of the infecting phage). Portion A is capable of giving rise to induced prototrophs and to prototrophs arising by transduction; portion B can give rise only to induced prototrophs. The pattern of delayed appearance of the prototrophs arising from each of the suspensions was measured by the method of increasing partial enrichment (Demerec and Cahn, 1953). Immediately after the addition of phage, the suspensions were placed in a 37°C water bath for ten minutes to allow adsorption to take place, and 0.1-ml aliquots were then spread on the surface of a series of minimal agar plates, some unsupplemented and others partially enriched with nutrient broth, the concentrations of nutrient broth in the plates ranging from 0.05 per cent to 2.5 per cent. Six platings from each suspension were made on each of the enrichment levels, and all of these plates were incubated for either 24 or 48 hours. The irradiated *try3* cells were able to undergo varying amounts of residual division on these plates, the amount of division being strictly dependent upon the enrichment level. In each experiment, the amount of residual division was determined by washing the cells from the surfaces of two plates of each enrichment level with 10 ml of saline, and assaying the wash fluid. These plate washes were performed after 24 hours of incubation, by which time the residual growth was completed, but before the colonies of prototrophs were large enough to be visible, or to contribute significantly to the total population on the plates. As a further precaution, the assays were plated on both minimal and complete media, so that differential counts could be used to eliminate the contribution of the prototrophs. After 48 hours of incubation, the colonies on the other four plates in each set were counted, and these data were used to construct "expression curves," relating the number of residual divisions undergone by the irradiated population (as determined by the level of enrichment) to the number of induced prototrophs (for suspension B), or to the number of prototrophs arising by transduction (for suspension A). Although suspension A gave rise to prototrophs by induction as well as by transduction, the frequency of the latter was much higher than that of the former under the conditions of these experiments, so that the induced mutants contributed very little to the plate counts in this series, and, in any case, their number was determined from the data in series B and subtracted from the A counts. Table 1 gives the results of a typical experiment, and the curves derived from a number of such experiments are shown in Figure 1.

It will be noted that the prototrophs arising by transduction are fully "expressed" on plates supporting only about two residual divisions, while the induced prototrophs continue to increase in numbers until an enrichment level supporting about six divisions is used. When corrections are made for the effects of irregularity of onset of division, as measured by the "checkerboard" respreading technique (Witkin and Thomas, 1955), it is found that the full yield of transductions is actually obtained after only one division, since these measurements show that only half the cells have actually divided when the population as a whole has doubled in number. A similar correction has very little effect on the pattern of delay shown by the induced mutants. The patterns of transduction delay and induction delay were compared for prototrophs derived from two other auxotrophs (adenineless and lysineless), and it was found in both cases that the maximum yield of transductions was obtained in one division, while the induced prototrophs continued to increase in numbers until enrichment levels supporting six residual divisions and at least ten residual divisions, for the two strains respectively, were used.

These results support the following conclusions concerning the mechanism of induction delay: 1) the "delayed appearance" of induced prototrophs cannot be primarily determined by phenotypic lag, which does not exceed one division; 2) irregularity of the growth pattern of irradiated cells cannot be primarily responsible for induction delay (nor can any other nongenetic effect of ultraviolet light), since the same irradiated suspension was used under comparable conditions of growth for the determination of transduction and induction delay patterns; 3) nuclear segregation can

TABLE 1. THE PATTERN OF "DELAYED APPEARANCE" OF PROTOTROPHS ARISING BY TRANSDUCTION COMPARED WITH THAT OF ULTRAVIOLET-INDUCED PROTOTROPHS

Culture used: 24-hour aerated broth culture of *try3*, washed and resuspended in buffer.

Ultraviolet treatment: 7 ml. of washed suspension irradiated with 300 ergs/mm² (survival 17%); irradiated suspension divided into two portions, A and B.

Bacteriophage: Transducing phage (previous host *try3⁺ᵘᵛ*) added to A; nontransducing phage (previous host *try3*) added to B; multiplicity of infection, ca. 5.

Number of viable cells plated: 4×10^7 per plate.

Enrichment of Minimal Agar	Number of Residual Div.	Number of Prototrophs per Plate	
		A, trans. + ind.	B, induced
% broth			
0.05	0.4	39, 48	0, 2
0.25	1.8	196, 226	4, 4
0.75	4.1	258, 267	17, 25
1.25	5.2	290, 276	72, 64
2.5	6.3	312, 288	79, 81

also be eliminated as a significant factor in induction delay, if the assumption is made that the probability of occurrence of either transduction or induced mutation in more than one nucleus of a multinucleate cell is negligible. The results are consistent with only two of the hypotheses that have been proposed, both attributing unique properties to the newly induced or potential mutant cell: delayed mutation, and delayed onset of division of cells in which a mutation has been actually or potentially produced. The next series of experiments was designed to test these possibilities.

The Clonal Increase of Newly Induced Prototrophs Compared with the Growth Rate of Previously Isolated Induced Prototrophs. Newcombe and Scott (1949) recognized that the possibility of delayed mutation as the major basis of induction delay carried with it the implication that mature

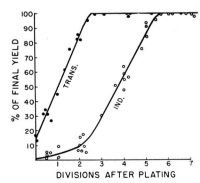

FIGURE 1. Expression curves of prototrophs obtained from *try3* by transduction and by induction with ultraviolet light.

colonies containing induced mutants should also contain the descendents of the unmutated sister cells of the original mutant. In other words, induced mutants should rarely be found as pure clones of the mutant type when the colonies in which they occur are detected without selection. Because of the difficulty of detecting most kinds of induced mutants in the absence of selective techniques, there has been only limited work done to analyze the composition of clones in which they arise. Ten such clones containing induced bacteriophage-resistant mutants in *E. coli* have been analyzed (Newcombe, 1953), six of which proved to be pure clones, and four were mixtures containing both sensitive and resistant cells. Since no special precautions were taken to control nuclear multiplicity, it is probable that some or all of the mixed clones arose simply through nuclear segregation. This seems all the more likely in view of the work with induced lactose-negative mutants in *E. coli* (Witkin, 1951; Newcombe, 1953), in which the composition of clones can be read directly from the colony color on indicator medium. In this case, when special methods were used to insure that the colonies containing induced lactose-negative mutants were derived from single nuclei, they were found to be pure clones of the mutant type much more frequently than mixed clones containing both lactose-positive and lactose-negative cells. These data, limited as they are, do not support the hypothesis of persistent genetic instability. They suggest, rather, that most of the induced mutations are established before the completion of the first postirradiation division. Since the frequency of induced prototrophs obtained from *try3* is relatively low, their detection without the use of a selective medium

did not seem practical. An indirect approach, using the respreading technique (Newcombe, 1949) was taken.

Three series of platings were made on the surface of semi-enriched (2.5 per cent broth) minimal medium: (1) the first series of plates was seeded with about 1×10^7 irradiated *try3* cells (which, if incubated without disturbance, would give rise to about 30 induced prototroph colonies); (2) the second series was seeded with about 30 *try3+uv* cells (from a previously isolated induced prototroph) which had been irradiated with the same dose, and (3) the third series was seeded with a mixture of about 30 *try3+uv* cells irradiated with the same dose plus about 10^7 ultraviolet-killed *try3* cells which had been more heavily irradiated than the others, and could not give rise to induced prototrophs. All three sets of plates were incubated, and at periodic intervals, four plates from each set were withdrawn from the incubator and respread with 0.1 ml of saline to redistribute the individual members of growing microcolonies. Since the medium is selective for prototrophs, a reading of these plates after 48 hours of reincubation will show, for the first series, the rate of increase of the average number of mutant cells per clone containing any newly induced mutants. The second and third series, for purposes of comparison, will show the growth rate of the established prototroph on the same medium, with or without a heavy background of ultraviolet-killed cells. Table 2 shows the results. It is obvious, first of all, that the growth of the established mutant is not affected by the presence of a heavy background of ultraviolet-killed cells, and either control series can be used as a standard for the growth rate of the established mutant. It will be seen also that the rate of increase of the average number of newly induced mutant cells per clone in which mutation has occurred lags behind the growth rate of the established mutant significantly, but to an extent which is not consistent either with the hypothesis that most of the induced mutations occur after a delay of several generations, or with the hypothesis that the potential mutant cell is more than slightly delayed in its onset of multiplication. Nuclear segregation could account for a discrepancy of the magnitude observed (Ryan, Fried and Schwartz, 1954). Since these experiments are based upon the average rate of increase of induced mutants, they do not rule out the possibility that a small fraction of mutations may be delayed, nor that a small fraction of potential mutants may start to multiply late, but there can be no doubt that neither of these mechanisms is characteristic of the majority of the induced mutations, nor can either of them account for the "delayed appearance" of the induced mutants as characterized by the expression curve.

The Dissociation of Residual Division from Induced Mutation Frequency. The results of the foregoing experiments led quite inescapably to the

TABLE 2. THE GROWTH RATE OF THE ESTABLISHED INDUCED PROTOTROPH (*try3+uv*) COMPARED WITH THE CLONAL INCREASE OF NEWLY INDUCED PROTOTROPHS

A. Plates seeded with irradiated *try3* (1×10^7 viable cells).

B. Plates seeded with irradiated *try3+uv* (30 viable cells).

C. Plates seeded with irradiated *try3+uv* (30 viable cells) plus 1×10^8 ultraviolet-killed *try3* cells.

Time of Incubation before Respreading	Colony Counts			Increase Factor		
	A	B	C	A	B	C
0	34	37	39	—	—	—
	42	28	27			
	42	28	28			
4 hr.	57	69	66	×1.5	×2.4	×2.2
	61	72	79			
	63	81	60			
5½ hr.	259	229	358	×7.7	×9.9	×9.7
	319	361	324			
	318	332	224			

conclusion that none of the hypotheses advanced to explain the "delayed appearance" of induced mutants could account for the expression curve of the prototrophs obtained from *try3*. There did not seem to be any reasonable possibilities other than those already eliminated, nor did there appear to be any basis for suspecting a methodological artefact in the experimental procedure used to obtain data for expression curves, as has been suggested in the case of bacteriophage-resistant mutants (Newcombe, 1953). A route of escape from this impasse, however, became evident in the course of reappraising the assumptions made in handling the data from such experiments. There is no doubt about the fact that the number of residual divisions undergone by the irradiated population increases as a function of the amount of nutrient broth added to the minimal agar. There is no doubt, also, that the number of induced mutations increases as the enrichment level is raised (up to a certain point). It does not necessarily follow, however, that the number of induced mutations must be a function of the number of residual divisions. It is quite conceivable, *a priori*, that increased residual division and increased mutation frequency could be parallel, but independent, consequences of increased enrichment. The assumption of a causal relation between induced mutation frequency and residual division is implicit in the way expression curves have been plotted, and it is this logically vulnerable assumption that was the next object of experimental analysis.

The experiments to be described were based upon the likelihood that induced mutations are established irreversibly before the completion of the first postirradiation division (as suggested by the duration of susceptibility to posttreatments, by the prevalence of pure mutant clones in the cases analyzed, and by the results of the respreading experiments described above). If this assumption is correct, the expression curve for the induced prototrophs obtained from *try3* could be interpreted as demonstrating that high yields of induced mutations are favored by the presence of high levels of enrichment *during the first division*, and conversely, that low yields of mutations are obtained when the enrichment level of the medium upon which the *first postirradiation division* occurs is low. Changes in the enrichment level after the completion of the first division should affect only the final amount of residual growth, but should have little or no influence on the mutation frequency.

In the first series of experiments, irradiated *try3* cells were incubated for three hours (corresponding to the time required for an average of one division on nutrient agar) on minimal medium without added enrichment, or with a relatively low level of enrichment. The enrichment level was then raised by lifting the entire disc of agar out of the Petri dish with a sterile spatula (bacteria

TABLE 3. "TRANSPLANTATION" OF IRRADIATED *try3* FROM LOW TO HIGH LEVELS OF ENRICHMENT

4.1 × 10⁷ viable cells plated on low enrichment level, incubated three hours at 37°C, transplanted to high enrichment level, incubated 48 hours.

Initial Plating on	"Transplanted" to	Final No. Resid. Div.	No. Induced Prototrophs	No. Viable Cells at Time of Transplantation*
Unsupplemented "A"	— (control)	0	0, 0	—
.05% n.b.	— (control)	1.1	10, 12	—
2.5% n.b.	— (control)	6.3	116, 108	—
Unsupplemented "A"	5% n.b.	6.2	0, 0	3.9 × 10⁷
.05% n.b.	5% n.b.	5.9	14, 11	4.3 × 10⁷

* Determined by plate-wash assays.

up) and placing it upon the surface of another minimal agar layer containing a relatively high amount of nutrient broth (5 per cent). Within one hour, the enrichment level is equilibrated by diffusion at the level of about 2.5 per cent, the maximum enrichment used in the previous experiments. The results of such a "transplantation" experiment are shown in Table 3. It will be seen that the number of prototrophs obtained on the transplant plates (incubated for three hours on unsupplemented "A" medium, or on "A" supplemented with 0.05 per cent broth, and then transplanted to "A" medium containing 5 per cent broth) is the same as the number of prototrophs obtained on the untransplanted low-enrichment controls. The residual division on the transplant plates, however, is the same as that on the high-enrichment controls having the maximal yield of induced prototrophs. Figure 2 shows the "expression" curve obtained by incubating irradiated *try3* on the standard series of enrichment levels for three hours, and then transplanting to agar enriched with 5 per cent broth. The curve obtained is indistinguishable from that obtained when the cells are incubated for the entire 48-hour incubation period on the initial enrichment levels, with no transplantation. The residual divisions ultimately achieved on the transplant plates was measured by platewashes after 24 hours of incubation, and was found to be uniform throughout, and to correspond to the level expected on the basis of the equilibrated enrichment level of about 2.5 per cent nutrient broth. It seems indisputable, therefore, that the number of induced mutations is determined by the enrichment level of the medium during the first three hours of postirradiation incubation (or some fraction of this period), and

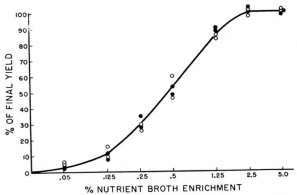

FIGURE 2. Expression of ultraviolet-induced prototrophs obtained from *try3* on minimal medium enriched
with different amounts of nutrient broth. Open circles,
irradiated cells plated on enrichment levels indicated,
and incubated 2 days. Closed circles, irradiated cells
plated on enrichment levels indicated, incubated 3
hours, then "transplanted" to plates enriched with 5%
nutrient broth and incubated two days.

is not critically related to the amount of residual
division.

In the next series of experiments, an effort was
made to determine more precisely the duration of
the sensitive period during which the amount of
nutrient broth added to the medium can still
influence the mutation frequency. Ideally, this
sort of experiment demands a method of instan-
taneous transfer of the irradiated cells from one
enrichment level to another, since the "transplantation" method involves a period of about an
hour before equilibration is completed. The use of
ultrafine filter membranes (Millipore filters) was
attempted, since bacteria growing on these membranes can be transferred quickly from the surface
of one plate to another. This technique was found
to be useless, however, since induced prototrophs
were never obtained on the filter membranes, in

spite of the fact that residual growth of the irradiated *try3* cells took place, apparently quite
normally. The probable reason for this unexpected
result will be considered in the Discussion. An
approximation of the timing of the sensitive period
was obtained using the transplantation method.
Irradiated *try3* cells were plated on low enrichment
levels (0.05 per cent broth), and transplanted to
plates containing minimal agar enriched with 5 per
cent broth after various periods of incubation
ranging from zero minutes to two hours. Table 4
shows the results. Immediate transfer results in a
significant depression of the mutation frequency
as compared with the control plated initially on
the highly enriched medium, and the maximum
depression (identical with the control plated initially on the low enrichment level) is obtained on
plates transplanted after 30 minutes. Since equilibration is complete after one hour, the duration
of the sensitive period can be set approximately
at between one and one and a half hours of incubation.

In the experiments just described, the change
in the enrichment level was that from low to high
enrichment, and it was found that one to one and
a half hours of incubation is sufficient to insure a
low mutation yield, regardless of the subsequent
increase in enrichment. Reciprocal experiments,
in which the initial incubation is on high enrichment levels, followed by transfer to unsupplemented minimal medium, should result in high
mutation yields, accompanied by low levels of
final residual division. Obviously, the transplantation method could not be used here, since the
equilibrated enrichment level after transplantation would differ too little from the initial high
level. In these experiments, therefore, the changes
in level of enrichment were made by washing the
bacteria from the surface of highly enriched plates
after one hour of incubation, concentrating and
washing the cells by centrifugation, and replating
on unsupplemented minimal medium. Low-to-high

TABLE 4. THE DURATION OF THE PERIOD OF SUSCEP-
TIBILITY OF INDUCED MUTATION FREQUENCY
TO CHANGES IN LEVEL OF ENRICHMENT

3.4×10^7 viable irradiated *try3* cells plated on low
enrichment level (0.05% n.b.), incubated for various
lengths of time, then "transplanted" to high enrichment
levels (5% n.b.). Equilibration of the enrichment level
at 2.5% n.b. is complete in about one hour.

Time on Low Enrichment Level	No. Viable Cells per Plate at Time of Trans.	No. Induced Prototrophs per Plate (48 hr. inc.)	Final No. Residl Div.
0 (plated directly on 2.5% n.b.)	—	126, 119	6.2
0 (immed. trans.)	3.3×10^7	32, 27	5.9
30 min.	3.6×10^7	0, 2	6.6
1 hr.	3.1×10^7	0, 1	5.7
2 hr.	3.7×10^7	0, 0	6.1
48 hr. (not trans.)	—	1, 2	1.6

TABLE 5. TRANSFER OF IRRADIATED *try3* FROM HIGH TO
LOW AND FROM LOW TO HIGH LEVELS OF ENRICHMENT
AFTER ONE HOUR OF INCUBATION

4.3×10^7 survivors plated on initial enrichment level,
incubated one hour at 37°C, washed from surface, concentrated by centrifugation, replated on final enrichment level, incubated 48 hours.

Low enrichment level: unsupplemented "A".
High enrichment level: 2.5% nutrient broth.

Enrichment Level		No. Viable Cells Replated	No. Induced Prototrophs per Plate	Final No. Resid. Div.
Initial	Final			
High	High	4.1×10^7	128, 127	6.5
High	Low	3.9×10^7	132, 122	1.5
Low	Low	4.3×10^7	2, 6	0.4
Low	High	4.0×10^7	4, 1	6.1

enrichment transfers were made by the same method. Table 5 shows the results, which provide further support for the conclusion that the frequency of induced prototrophs is determined by the amount of nutrient broth present in the medium during the first hour of postirradiation incubation, and is independent of the number of residual divisions.

The Generality of the Results. Since all of the experiments described above were done with a particular auxotrophic substrain of *S. typhimurium*, it seemed desirable to determine whether the behavior of other induced prototrophs, having expression curves previously interpreted as indicating extensive "delayed appearance", is similar to that of *try3*. Table 6 shows the results of transplantation from low to high enrichment levels after one hour of incubation for a number of different auxotrophic substrains of *S. typhimurium* and *E. coli*. In all cases, the results are in qualitative agreement with those obtained for *try3*. Table 7 shows the result of a more detailed analysis made with a tryptophane-requiring substrain of *E. coli* B/r, known as WP2. Reciprocal transfers from high to low, and from low to high levels of enrichment were made by the method of washing and replating. Again, it was found that the enrichment level present in the medium during the first hour after irradiation essentially determines the induced mutation yield, regardless of subsequent changes in the level of enrichment.

Thus, it appears to be generally true of ultraviolet-induced prototrophs in *E. coli* and *S. typhimurium* that the yield of mutations is independent of the number of residual divisions, but is determined by the amount of nutrient broth present in the minimal medium upon which the irradiated cells are incubated for approximately the first hour after irradiation, increasing as the amount

TABLE 6. "TRANSPLANTATION" OF IRRADIATED AUXOTROPHS FROM LOW TO HIGH LEVELS OF ENRICHMENT AFTER ONE HOUR OF INCUBATION

Strain	% Nutrient Broth in Medium		No. Induced Prototrophs per Plate
	Initially plated on	Transplanted to	
E. coli 12-33 (*meth-*)	0.05	—	77, 62
	2.5	—	562, 508
	0.05	5.0	59, 61
E. coli WP8 (*lys-*)	0.05	—	23, 25
	2.5	—	467, 441
	0.05	5.0	18, 29
E. coli 12-61 (*try-*)	0.05	—	34, 28
	2.5	—	1016, 884
	0.05	5.0	56, 37
S. typhimurium S1 (*pro-*)	0.05	—	0, 2
	2.5	—	76, 55
	0.05	5.0	1, 5

TABLE 7. TRANSFER OF IRRADIATED WP2 (*E. coli try-*) FROM HIGH TO LOW AND FROM LOW TO HIGH LEVELS OF ENRICHMENT AFTER ONE HOUR OF INCUBATION

4.1 × 10⁷ survivors plated on initial enrichment level, incubated one hour at 37°C, washed from surface, concentrated by centrifugation, replated on final enrichment level, incubated 48 hours.

Low enrichment level: Unsupplemented "E".
High enrichment level: 2.5% nutrient broth.

Enrichment Level		No. Viable Cells Replated	No. Induced Prototrophs per Plate	Final No. Resid. Div.
Initial	Final			
High	High	3.6×10^7	736, 673	7.1
High	Low	3.5×10^7	585, 619	1.6
Low	Low	3.8×10^7	55, 64	1.1
Low	High	3.4×10^7	72, 58	6.8

of broth increases up to a certain level. Changes in the concentration of nutrient broth after this time have no further influence on the frequency of induced mutations, although the residual growth responds to increased enrichment at any time during the incubation period.

PART II. THE INFLUENCE OF THE RATE OF POSTIRRADIATION PROTEIN SYNTHESIS ON THE YIELD OF INDUCED PROTOTROPHS

In Part I, it was shown that the frequency of induced prototrophs increases as a function of the concentration of nutrient broth present in the minimal medium during the first hour of postirradiation incubation. The effect of nutrient broth can be considered another example of a posttreatment capable of modifying the mutagenic action of ultraviolet light. The nutrient broth effect, like that of temperature (Witkin, 1953), differs from most other known posttreatments in that it affects quite specifically the yield of mutations, having no effect upon survival. The goal of the next series of experiments was to determine, as far as possible, the nature of the metabolic pathway through which the concentration of nutrient broth exerts its modifying action on the induced mutation frequency.

The Active Component of Nutrient Broth. Since nutrient broth was used throughout as the source of enrichment in the experiments previously described, the concentration of the growth-controlling amino acid, tryptophane in the case of *try3*, and those of all other components of nutrient broth were necessarily varied proportionately as the enrichment level was changed. The first step in this analysis, therefore, was to determine whether the active component was the required growth factor itself. Table 8 shows results of an experiment in which irradiated *try3* was plated on minimal agar supplemented with increasing quantities of tryptophane, resulting in a range of residual divisions from 0.7 to 5.8. Essentially no

TABLE 8. THE YIELD OF INDUCED PROTOTROPHS
OBTAINED FROM IRRADIATED *try3* ON MINIMAL
MEDIUM SUPPLEMENTED WITH TRYPTOPHANE

No. survivors plated: 3.9×10^7.

No. induced prototrophs on minimal agar enriched
with 2.5% nutrient broth: 122, 136, 111.

Enrichment	Number of Residual Divisions	Number of Induced Prototrophs/Plate
gamma tryptophane/ml		
0.01	0.7	0, 2, 0
0.05	2.3	0, 1, 1
0.1	3.3	0, 0, 0
0.25	4.3	1, 4, 0
0.5	5.8	2, 1, 0

induced prototrophs were obtained on plates
supplemented only with tryptophane, despite the
occurrence of extensive residual division. These
results demonstrate once again that the mutation
yield and the level of residual growth are independent responses to enrichment, and show also
that tryptophane, the factor that determines the
amount of residual division, is not the component
of nutrient broth that favors high yields of induced
mutations when present in the early postirradiation growth medium.

In the next experiments, minimal agar partially
enriched with tryptophane was further supplemented with metabolites known to be present in
nutrient broth. Table 9 shows the effects upon
the number of induced prototrophs of supple-
menting with a pool of purines and pyrimidines,
a pool of amino acids other than tryptophane, and
a pool of vitamins. Clearly, the amino acid fraction is the active component. It was further established that the presence of all other amino acids
in optimal concentrations, but without any tryptophane, results in failure to obtain induced prototrophs.

TABLE 9. THE YIELD OF INDUCED PROTOTROPHS OB-
TAINED FROM IRRADIATED *try3* ON MINIMAL MEDIUM
ENRICHED WITH VARIOUS METABOLITES PRESENT IN
NUTRIENT BROTH

No. survivors plated: 4.2×10^7.

Concentration of each vitamin: 2 γ/ml.

Concentration of each purine and pyrimidine: 20
γ/ml.

Concentration of each amino acid (except tryptophane): 20 γ/ml.

Minimal Medium Enriched with	No. Induced Prototrophs per Plate
.5 γ tryptophane....................	0, 0, 1
.5 γ/ml. tryp. + vitamin pool........	0, 3, 0
.5 γ/ml. tryp. + purine and pyrimidine pool..............................	1, 1, 0
.5 /ml. tryp. + amino acid pool......	154, 163, 149
amino acid pool (minus tryp.)........	0, 0, 0
2.5% nutrient broth..................	167, 138, 151

The "transplantation" experiments described
in Part I were repeated, using high and low concentrations of pooled amino acids instead of nutrient broth as the source of high or low enrichment
levels (always with a constant limiting amount of
tryptophane), and the results were duplicated
quite precisely. The nutrient broth effect is an
amino acid effect, and can be redescribed as follows: the yield of induced prototrophs is a function
of the concentration of amino acids (within a
certain range) present in the selective minimal
medium during the first hour of postirradiation
incubation.

Qualitatively comparable results were obtained
with a number of other auxotrophic substrains
of *S. typhimurium* and *E. coli*, including one strain
requiring adenine as a growth factor. In all strains
showing a pattern of "delayed appearance" according to former criteria, it was found that the
maximal yield of prototrophs was obtained when
a high concentration of amino acids (plus a limiting amount of the required growth factor) was
present during the early part of the postirradiation
lag phase.

The Specificity of the Amino Acid Effect. It has
been established that a pool of amino acids, present in the postirradiation growth medium during
the first hour of incubation, favors the production
of high yields of induced prototrophs. A preliminary study was made of the degree of specificity,
if any, of particular groups of amino acids. In
nutritional studies with microorganisms, amino
acids are often grouped for convenience into five
pools, the division being based upon biosynthetic
interrelationships. Table 10 shows the relative
effectiveness of each of these five pools individually, and in all possible combinations of two, three
and four pools, compared with the activity (already known) of all five pools. No single amino
acid pool approaches the effectiveness of the combination of all five. In general, the mutation frequency increases with the number of pools, although there is considerable variability, and pools
1, 2, 3 and 4, in combination, exceed the effectiveness of the combination of all five pools. The pattern is not one of great specificity, and a more
detailed investigation of this type was postponed
until the mechanism of the amino acid effect is
better understood.

The Role of the Preirradiation Culture Medium.
In all of the experiments previously described,
the auxotrophic cultures were grown initially in
nutrient broth. The finding that the presence of
amino acids during the early part of the postirradiation growth period favors the production of
high yields of induced prototrophs heightens the
possible significance of the previous history of the
irradiated cells with regard to amino acid metabolism. Specifically, it seemed important to determine whether *try3* cultures initially grown in
minimal medium supplemented with tryptophane,
and thereby adapted before irradiation to the

synthesis of other amino acids, would exhibit the same dependence upon an exogenous supply of amino acids in producing induced mutations. Table 11 shows the results of an experiment comparing the behavior of *try3* cultures grown initially in broth and in tryptophane-supplemented minimal medium. Whereas the broth-grown cells are unable to produce induced prototrophs on minimal plates supplemented only with tryptophane, the cells grown initially in tryptophane-supplemented minimal medium produce about half as many prototrophs on plates devoid of other amino acids as on plates supplemented with all amino acids. It is evident that the requirement for exogenous amino acids other than tryptophane for the production of induced prototrophs is less pronounced in bacteria initially "trained" to synthesize their own.

The Growth Rates of Irradiated Cells on Media of Various Enrichment Levels. The finding that the requirement for an exogenous supply of amino acids during the early postirradiation incubation period is less pronounced for bacteria previously adapted to the synthesis of amino acids suggests that the rate of protein synthesis during the criti-

TABLE 10. THE EFFECT OF ENRICHMENT WITH SINGLE AMINO ACID POOLS, AND WITH VARIOUS COMBINATIONS OF AMINO ACID POOLS, ON THE YIELD OF INDUCED PROTOTROPHS OBTAINED FROM IRRADIATED *try3*

No. of survivors plated: 3.8×10^7.

Pool 1 contains cysteine, methionine, argenine and lysine.

Pool 2 contains leucine, isoleucine and valine.

Pool 3 contains tyrosine and phenylalanine.

Pool 4 contains histidine, threonine, proline and glutamic acid.

Pool 5 contains serine, glycine, alanine and aspartic acid.

All plates contain 0.5 γ/ml tryptophane.

Final concentration of each other amino acid: 20 γ/ml.

Amino Acid Pools Added to Medium	No. Induced Prototrophs	Amino Acid Pools Added to Medium	No. Induced Prototrophs
1	5, 8	1 + 2 + 3	43, 52
2	14, 7	1 + 2 + 4	161, 189
3	8, 7	1 + 2 + 5	79, 127
4	16, 15	1 + 3 + 4	81, 94
5	11, 10	1 + 3 + 5	57, 40
1 + 2	31, 26	1 + 4 + 5	64, 58
1 + 3	14, 24	2 + 3 + 4	51, 67
1 + 4	23, 46	2 + 3 + 5	55, 35
1 + 5	38, 57	2 + 4 + 5	35, 49
2 + 3	23, 6	3 + 4 + 5	43, 26
2 + 4	65, 90	1 + 2 + 3 + 4	208, 199
2 + 5	41, 23	1 + 2 + 3 + 5	74, 119
3 + 4	21, 31	1 + 2 + 4 + 5	135, 117
3 + 5	31, 30	1 + 3 + 4 + 5	72, 72
4 + 5	24, 21	2 + 3 + 4 + 5	45, 54
		1 + 2 + 3 + 4 + 5	159, 143

TABLE 11. THE EFFECT OF THE PREIRRADIATION CULTURE MEDIUM ON THE YIELD OF INDUCED PROTOTROPHS OBTAINED FROM IRRADIATED *try3* ON MINIMAL AGAR WITH AND WITHOUT AMINO ACID ENRICHMENT

No. survivors plated: A, 2.3×10^7.
No. survivors plated: B, 2.6×10^7.

Preirradiation Culture Medium	No. Induced Prototrophs per Plate	
	On minimal agar + 0.5 γ/ml tryp.	On minimal agar + 0.5 γ/ml tryp. + amino acid pool*
Nutrient broth A......	0, 0, 2	102, 96, 116
Minimal medium + 20 γ/ml tryptophane B.................	122, 114, 121	240, 222, 231

* Each amino acid concentration: 20 γ/ml.

cal period may be the variable that is actually concerned in modifying the induced mutation frequency. This idea was given considerable support by measurements of the growth rates of irradiated *try3* cells on minimal agar enriched with various concentrations of nutrient broth. Figure 3 shows the growth curves obtained by incubating on various enrichment levels, and washing the cells from the surfaces of the plates after different periods of incubation. It is evident that the length of the lag phase and the slope during logarithmic growth, as well as the final level of residual growth, are functions of the amount of nutrient broth added to the minimal medium upon which the irradiated cells divide. Similar results were obtained when the plates were enriched with increasing concentrations of pooled amino acids (including tryptophane), using a pool containing 20 gamma/ml of each amino acid as the equivalent of undiluted nutrient broth. The fact that the growth rate under these conditions is limited by the concentration of amino acids in the medium suggests that the rate of protein synthesis is de-

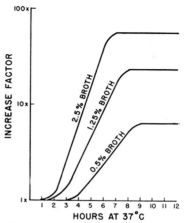

FIGURE 3. Growth curves of irradiated *try3* on minimal agar enriched with various amounts of nutrient broth.

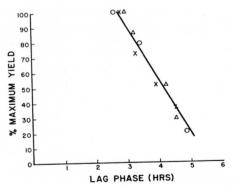

FIGURE 4. The relation between the length of the lag phase of irradiated auxotrophs (as determined by the enrichment level) and yield of induced prototrophs. Circles, *try3* (*S. typhimurium*); crosses, *WP2* (*E. coli*, tryptophaneless); triangles, *MS31* (*E. coli*, leucineless.)

creased, and becomes growth-limiting when the concentration of exogenous amino acids drops below a certain level.

The striking parallel between the effect of amino acid concentration on the growth rate of the irradiated cells and on the yield of induced mutations is shown in Figure 4. This curve shows the relation between the length of the lag phase (presumably a measure of the rate of protein synthesis, since it is shortened by increasing the concentration of amino acids) and the percentage of the yield of induced prototrophs obtained on minimal medium having various levels of enrichment, for two different auxotrophic strains of *E. coli*, as well as for *try3*. The results for all three strains, each having a very distinctive pattern of "delayed appearance" as measured in expression curves, show the same linear relationship between the length of the lag phase and the proportion of induced prototrophs obtained. It appears quite reasonable to infer that the yield of induced prototrophs is proportional to the rate of protein synthesis during the first hour of postirradiation incubation.

Further support for this hypothesis was obtained by analysis of a group of *E. coli* auxotrophs that showed no influence of amino acid concentra-

tion on the yield of induced mutations. These auxotrophs had no "delayed appearance," or, in revised terms, yielded as many induced prototrophs on unsupplemented minimal medium as on minimal medium supplemented with nutrient broth or with amino acids. An analysis of the postirradiation growth rates of these strains on unsupplemented minimal medium and on media supplemented with increasing amounts of amino acids showed no difference in the length of the lag phase nor in the generation time. In these strains, for reasons as yet not known, the rate of protein synthesis was not decreased in the absence of exogenous amino acids, nor was the yield of induced prototrophs.

The Effect of Posttreatment with Chloramphenicol. More direct support for the hypothesis that the frequency of induced prototrophs is determined by the rate of protein synthesis during the first hour of postirradiation incubation was obtained from experiments in which chloramphenicol, which is known to arrest bacterial division specifically by inhibiting the synthesis of proteins, without affecting the rate of RNA and DNA synthesis (Wisseman *et al.*, 1954; Hahn *et al.*, 1954) was used as a posttreatment. Irradiated cells of strains WP2 (try$^-$) and MS28 (leu$^-$) of *E. coli* were plated on optimally enriched plates containing 20 micrograms of chloramphenicol per ml, and were incubated on these plates for one hour. After this time, the cells were washed off the chloramphenicol plates and replated on optimally enriched medium without chloramphenicol. Controls were handled in the same way, except that chloramphenicol was omitted from the plates upon which the irradiated cells were incubated for the first hour. The results are shown on Table 12. It will be noted that one hour of incubation on plates containing chloramphenicol reduced the yield of induced prototrophs drastically with no appreciable effect upon the level of survival. The results with strain MS28 are of particular interest, since it is one of the exceptional strains described above that shows no response to amino acid concentration, with regard either to growth rate or to induced mutation frequency. Low concentrations of exogenous amino acids apparently do not decrease the rate of protein synthesis in this strain, hence there is no decrease in the yield of prototrophs. When an effective means of arresting protein synthesis, such as chloramphenicol, is used, this strain shows itself to be similar to the others, in that induced prototrophs are not obtained under these conditions.

According to the working hypothesis that has been adopted as a guide to further work, the effects of chloramphenicol and of low concentrations of amino acids have the same basis: their action in arresting or decreasing the rate of protein synthesis during the sensitive period. Since the period of susceptibility of induced mutation frequency to low concentrations of amino acids is known to

TABLE 12. THE EFFECT OF POSTTREATMENT WITH CHLORAMPHENICOL ON THE YIELD OF INDUCED PROTOTROPHS OBTAINED FROM IRRADIATED AUXOTROPHS

Strain	No. Viable Cells per Plate after One Hour		No. Induced Prototrophs per Plate	
	Chloramphenicol treated	Control	Chloramphenicol treated	Control
E. coli WP2 (try-)......	1.0×10^7	1.2×10^7	24, 20	216, 221
E. coli MS28 (leu-)......	5.5×10^6	6.0×10^6	6, 2	42, 39

be about one hour, it can be predicted that the period of susceptibility to chloramphenicol should also be about one hour. Table 13 shows the results of an experiment in which irradiated cells were incubated for various periods of time on optimally enriched minimal medium containing chloramphenicol, and then washed from the surface and replated on chloramphenicol-free medium. The yield of induced mutations is found to be reduced to a minimum after one to one and a half hours of incubation in the presence of chloramphenicol. The periods of susceptibility to the antimutagenic effects of chloramphenicol and of low concentrations of exogenous amino acids are approximately coincidental.

Table 14 shows the results of experiments in which irradiated cells were incubated on optimally enriched minimal plates without chloramphenicol for one hour, then washed off and plated on chloramphenicol plates, incubated for one hour, and then again washed off and replated on chloramphenicol-free plates. It is clear that the yield of induced prototrophs is not affected by incubation in the presence of chloramphenicol *after* the first hour of incubation. These results are comparable to the "transplantation" experiments, in which it was found that decreasing the enrichment level after the first hour of incubation on high enrichment levels was not effective in reducing the mutation frequency.

The Effect of Incubation in Buffer. It has been shown that, when the rate of protein synthesis is decreased by limiting the concentration of exogenous amino acids, or by the presence of chloramphenicol, in a medium that is otherwise growth-supporting, the yield of induced prototrophs is irreversibly reduced within one hour after irradiation. It seemed important to determine whether the mutation yield would respond with the same timing to the inhibition of protein synthesis in a medium also suppressing other biosynthetic activities. Table 15 shows the results of an experiment in which irradiated cells were incubated at 37°C in buffer, and plated after various periods of time on optimally enriched medium. It is evident that the ability to produce induced prototrophs is

TABLE 13. THE EFFECT OF POSTTREATMENT WITH CHLORAMPHENICOL FOR VARIOUS PERIODS OF TIME ON THE YIELD OF INDUCED PROTOTROPHS OBTAINED FROM IRRADIATED WP2

Time on Chloramphenicol	No. Viable Cells per Plate after Chloramphenicol Treatment-	No. Induced Prototrophs per Plate (after Replating)
minutes		
0	9.5×10^6	110, 131
30	1.1×10^7	76, 92
60	1.2×10^7	34, 30
90	9.9×10^6	14, 12
120	9.9×10^6	16, 10

TABLE 14. THE EFFECT OF POSTTREATMENT WITH CHLORAMPHENICOL AFTER ONE HOUR OF INCUBATION ON CHLORAMPHENICOL-FREE MEDIUM ON THE YIELD OF INDUCED PROTOTROPHS OBTAINED FROM IRRADIATED WP2

Experiment No.	No. Viable Cells Plated on Final Plates		No. Induced Prototrophs per Plate	
	Chloramphenicol treated	Control	Chloramphenicol treated	Control
1	2.3×10^6	1.8×10^6	166	149
			188	155
			172	156
2	2.4×10^6	2.3×10^6	135	143
			135	134
			162	152

TABLE 15. THE EFFECT OF POSTIRRADIATION INCUBATION IN BUFFER ON THE YIELD OF INDUCED PROTOTROPHS OBTAINED FROM *try3*

Washed suspension of *try3* cells irradiated in phosphate buffer (pH 7); irradiated suspension incubated at 37°C as indicated; after each time interval, suspension assayed to determine no. viable cells per ml, and 0.1 ml aliquots plated on semienriched (2.5% nutrient broth) plates to determine yield of induced prototrophs.

Time of Incubation in Buffer at 37°C	No. Viable Cells per ml after Incubation in Buffer	No. Induced Prototrophs per Plate
minutes		
0	2.7×10^8	144, 121
30	3.1×10^8	143, 137
60	3.1×10^8	121, 137
120	3.3×10^8	158, 124
180	2.8×10^8	66, 94

preserved much longer in the absence of protein synthesis, if other metabolic activities are arrested as well. The sensitive period is not to be measured in absolute time, therefore, but in relation to the metabolic conditions under which the posttreatment is administered.

PART III. THE EFFECTS OF POSTIRRADIATION TEMPERATURE ON THE YIELD OF INDUCED PROTOTROPHS

The timing of the sensitive period during which the frequency of induced prototrophs can be influenced by the amino acid concentration of the medium and by chloramphenicol is strikingly similar to the temperature-sensitive period reported for a variety of induced mutations in *E. coli* (Witkin, 1953; Berrie, 1953), the first third of the lag phase (one hour at 37°C). A study of the effects of postirradiation temperature on the yield of ultraviolet-induced prototrophs obtained from *try3* was conducted, in the hope that the integra-

TABLE 16. EFFECT OF POSTIRRADIATION TEMPERATURE
OF INCUBATION ON THE YIELD OF INDUCED
PROTOTROPHS OBTAINED FROM *try3*

Identical aliquots of irradiated suspension plated on
minimal agar enriched with 2.5% nutrient broth; assays
to determine survival made on same medium (*try3*
colonies grow to visible size on this enrichment level
when seeded sparsely).

Temperature of Incubation	Survival	No. Induced Proto-trophs per Plate
	%	
45°C	7.1	0, 0
37°C	9.5	101, 121
24°C	10.5	256, 263
15°C	9.5	21, 25

tion of these effects and those of the nutritional
factors described above might provide a more
substantial basis for the interpretation of the
complex events leading from irradiation to stable
genetic change.

Table 16 shows the frequency of induced prototrophs obtained when irradiated cells are incubated on optimally enriched plates (2.5 per cent
nutrient broth) at various temperatures. No important differences in the number of survivors, nor
in the amount of residual division, were found, but
the number of induced prototrophs was affected
dramatically by the incubation temperature,
ranging from none at 45°C to a number two to
three times higher than the 37°C frequency at
24°C. Having established that postirradiation
temperature influences the mutation frequency,
experiments designed to determine the limits of
the temperature-sensitive period were conducted.
Plates seeded with irradiated *try3* were incubated
for various periods of time at an initial temperature, and the plates were then transferred to a
second temperature at which incubation was
continued until the prototrophs could be counted.
These "temperature-switch" experiments were
done using all possible combinations of the four
temperatures studied, two by two. In all of these

TABLE 17. THE DURATION OF THE PERIOD OF SENSI-
TIVITY TO POSTIRRADIATION TEMPERATURE OF THE
YIELD OF INDUCED PROTOTROPHS OBTAINED FROM
try3

The temperature-sensitive period is the minimum
time of incubation at the temperature indicated after
which changes in temperature of incubation have no
further influence on the yield of induced prototrophs.

Temperature	Length of Lag Phase	Duration of Tempera-ture-Sensitive Period
37°C	3 hours	1–1½ hours
24°C	9 hours	3–4 hours
15°C	30 hours	10–12 hours

experiments, it was found that, if the length of
time of incubation at the initial temperature
before switching to the second temperature was
as long as one third the length of the lag phase,
the mutation frequency was the same as that in
controls incubated throughout at the initial temperature. Changes in the temperature of incubation, as was found in the studies with *E. coli*, have
no effect upon the yield of induced mutations after
the first third of the lag period. Table 17 summarizes the results of some of these experiments,
details of which will be presented elsewhere. The
period of sensitivity to postirradiation temperature (when the initial incubation is set at 37°C)
thus has about the same duration as the periods
of sensitivity to the action of chloramphenicol and
of low concentrations of amino acids.

The temperature-switch experiments revealed
a particularly interesting phenomenon in the case
of irradiated cells incubated for short periods of
time at 37°C and then permitted to complete
their growth at a lower temperature (24° or 15°C).
The mutation yields obtained under these conditions are considerably higher than those obtained
at any single temperature of incubation, the maximum frequency (about 5 times the 37° yield)
resulting from a switch to a lower temperature
after about 30 minutes at 37°C. A similar synergistic effect is obtained when short incubations at
45°C are followed by transfer to lower temperatures.

DISCUSSION

The basis of the "delayed appearance" of induced prototrophs can now be described as a
response of the mutation frequency to increasing
concentrations of amino acids present in the medium during the first hour of postirradiation incubation (at 37°C), or, by inference, as a response
to increasing rates of protein synthesis during this
time. The insight gained in these studies,
although they appear to have general validity for
induced prototrophy, cannot be applied to the
interpretation of the expression curves for induced
bacteriophage-resistance or streptomycin-resist-
ance. In these cases, the measurement of delayed
appearance involves the use of the same medium
throughout, the control over residual growth re-
siding in the time of application of the selective
agent. The 10 to 12 generation delay described
for phage-resistance, therefore, must have its
basis elsewhere. The finding that the phenotypic
lag for induced prototrophs is no more than one
generation, however, does not exclude the possibility that other classes of mutations may exhibit
much more prolonged phenotypic lag. Thus, the
report by Jacob, Wollman and Hayes (this Symposium) that phage-resistance introduced into
sensitive cells by recombination requires about
four generations to achieve full phenotypic expression accounts, in part, for the delayed appearance of this class of mutants. Whatever additional

factors may enter to contribute to the observed delay, the timing of the period of susceptibility to postirradiation temperature, as well as the prevalence of pure clones of induced phage-resistant mutants, makes it seem quite certain that this mutation, like that to prototrophy, is genetically established before the completion of the first postirradiation division.

Considerable evidence has been offered in support of the hypothesis that the yield of induced prototrophs is proportional to the rate of protein synthesis during the first hour of postirradiation incubation, under conditions in which protein synthesis is growth-limiting.[3] In considering the possible significance of this finding for the theory of mutagenesis, the nature of the sensitive period will be discussed as a starting point. It is known that, for an impressive variety of mutational types, the period of susceptibility to the influence of postirradiation temperature is a constant fraction (about $\frac{1}{3}$) of the lag phase. It would seem likely, then, that the terminal event, the occurrence of which establishes the induced mutation yield irreversibly, is associated with the process of cell division. On the other hand, the sensitive period is *not* a constant fraction of the lag phase when growth is limited by the rate of protein synthesis rather than by temperature, but under these conditions, remains about one hour (at 37°C) regardless of the differences in growth rate imposed by the availability of exogenous amino acids. The terminal event marking the end of the sensitive period, therefore, must take place quite independently of protein synthesis. Both DNA synthesis and RNA synthesis are known to take place while protein synthesis is inhibited, as in the presence of chloramphenicol. Preliminary measurements made of the rate of DNA synthesis in irradiated *try3* cells, made by Dr. D. Kanazir, indicate that the DNA level is doubled in one hour at 37°C. It is tempting, therefore, to speculate that the modification of the mutation yield by posttreatments is possible only before the completion of DNA duplication. Whether or not the sensitive period proves to coincide with the period of DNA duplication, its termination is achieved through a process that is associated with cell division, that goes on independently of the rate of protein synthesis, and that is temperature-dependent with a Q_{10} of about 3.

In addition to the process leading to the termination of the period during which the mutation yield can be influenced, a second process, which we will in our ignorance call "X," must be in-

voked. The existence of X can be inferred from the temperature data alone, since their interpretation requires the postulation of at least two processes, having different temperature coefficients, the relative rates of which determine the yield of induced mutations. The studies involving the effects of the rate of protein synthesis also lead to the postulation of two processes, the first determining the duration of the sensitive period, which is independent of the rate of protein synthesis, and the second, most economically assumed to be the same X indicated by the temperature experiments, which is markedly affected by the rate of protein synthesis. Although much more information must be gathered before the construction of any detailed model would be fruitful, it is possible to speculate about the nature of X, and to map out some of the directions of future work that are most likely to lead to its identification.

One possibility is that X is the process of repair of genetic damage. According to this view, induced prototrophs arise primarily from a fraction of survivors that has undergone genetic damage (chromosome breakage?) as a result of irradiation. Protein synthesis favors repair of this damage (restitution of breaks?) and if repair is accomplished before the end of the sensitive period (DNA duplication?) the damaged cells survive, with a high probability of surviving as a mutant. If repair is not accomplished within the critical period, the damage is lethal. It is well known that the reunion of radiation-induced chromosome breaks is often delayed, and is influenced by postirradiation metabolism (see, for example, Wolff and Atwood, 1954; Wolff and Luippold, 1955). A more controversial question is the timing of the breakage process itself. Several investigators (Kaufmann, Hollaender and Gay, 1946; Swanson and Yost, 1951; Swanson, 1955) have suggested that breaks may occur after irradiation, and that they may or may not be realized depending upon postirradiation conditions, although the view that breakage is an immediate consequence of irradiation is still widely held. It is interesting in this connection that, within the framework of the hypothesis that X is a process of repair of genetic damage, the results of the temperature experiments can best be explained on the assumption that breakage, as well as reunion, is delayed, and is susceptible to postirradiation temperature. The synergistic effect of short exposures to high temperatures, followed by incubation at lower temperatures, is difficult to explain as an effect on reunion alone. All of the temperature-switch experiments, however, fit the assumption that a high frequency of breaks is favored by high temperatures during the first half-hour of the postirradiation growth period, while subsequent reunion is more efficient at low temperatures.

Another possibility is that X is the production or decay of an unstable mutagenic intermediate

[3] Preliminary work indicates that the failure to obtain induced prototrophs from irradiated *try3* incubated on Millipore filters (even when the latter are placed on the surface of optimally enriched plates) may be another example of the postirradiation effect of decreased rate of protein synthesis during the sensitive period. Irradiated *try3* cells have a longer lag phase on the filter membranes than on the surface of agar plates, when semi-enriched minimal medium is used.

resulting from ultraviolet irradiation. In this case, protein synthesis would favor the production of greater amounts of mutagen, or would enhance its stability. The yield of induced prototrophs would depend upon the amount of mutagen still present at the time of occurrence of the terminal event. The temperature results, including the synergistic effect of high and low temperatures in sequence, could be explained by the assumption that maximum amounts of mutagen are produced at high temperatures, and that low temperatures increase its stability. If a mutagenic intermediate is involved, it could not be the mutagenic cell poison postulated by Novick and Szilard (1949), since the survival level of the irradiated cells is not modified by the posttreatments affecting the induced mutation frequency.

A third hypothesis concerning the nature of X, the process affected by the rate of protein synthesis, is that it is the production or decay of an unstable condition within the genic material (Auerbach, 1946; McElroy and Swanson, 1951). The mutation yield would then depend upon the frequency of metastable configurations not yet dissipated at the critical time.

The evaluation of these hypotheses must await future developments. One differentiating prediction concerns the fate of potential mutants that fail to appear under antimutagenic postirradiation conditions. The breakage-reunion hypothesis leads to the prediction that such conditions result in the failure of these cells to survive, while the hypotheses concerning the decay of an extragenic mutagen or an intragenic state of metastability predict their survival as nonmutants. As yet, no experimental technique has been developed that could provide the answer.

It will be important to determine the extent to which a particular mutation responds to the posttreatments described after induction with different mutagenic agents, as well as to examine the behavior of different classes of mutations induced by the same mutagen. The changes generally grouped together under the heading of "induced mutations" may actually be the end results of very different kinds of primary events, and generalizations based on the study of one class of genetic changes is not justifiable. If, for example, it should be found that the rate of protein synthesis during the early postirradiation growth period has no influence upon the yield of induced auxotrophs, or phage-resistant mutants, but is limited in its influence to induced prototrophy, it may become necessary to seek the explanation of this effect in an entirely new direction. Since the change from auxotrophy to prototrophy appears to involve the rapid acquisition of a new enzymatically controlled synthetic capacity, the involvement of protein synthesis in the establishment of the new genotype could be related to the system of specificity transfer, mediated perhaps through other channels in the case of phenotypes more remotely dependent upon protein structure.

Other important areas for future work are the implementation of the genetic studies with direct biochemical analysis of the metabolic events in the critical period, the integration of these findings with the extensive studies of other postirradiation effects, and their application to the work on spontaneous mutation.

SUMMARY AND CONCLUSIONS

Part I. A comparative study of the pattern of "delayed appearance" of ultraviolet-induced prototrophs and that of genetically identical prototrophs arising by transduction in a tryptophane-requiring substrain of *Salmonella typhimurium* LT2 was made. It was found that the maximal yield of prototrophs arising by transduction was obtained under conditions permitting only one residual division, while the maximal yield of induced prototrophs was obtained only on plates sufficiently enriched with nutrient broth to permit about six residual divisions. It was concluded that phenotypic lag, irregularity of the growth pattern of irradiated cells, and nuclear segregation were not primarily responsible for the "delayed appearance" of induced prototrophs.

The rate of increase in the number of newly induced prototrophs in clones developing from irradiated auxotrophs was compared, by respreading experiments, with the growth rate of a previously isolated stock of the induced prototroph under comparable conditions. The results ruled out the possibility that the induced mutations to prototrophy are typically delayed in their occurrence for several generations after irradiation, as well as the possibility that newly induced prototrophs are markedly delayed in their time of onset of division.

It was concluded that none of the hypotheses previously proposed to account for the "delayed appearance" of induced prototrophs was correct.

The validity of the assumption that the induced mutation frequency and the number of residual divisions, both of which are functions of the amount of nutrient broth added to the postirradiation culture medium, are causally related was questioned. Residual division and induced mutation frequency were shown, in fact, to be independent and separable functions of the enrichment level, in a series of experiments in which irradiated cells were transferred from low to high enrichment levels, and vice versa, after various periods of postirradiation incubation. These experiments showed that the yield of induced prototrophs is determined irreversibly by the amount of nutrient broth present in the culture medium during the *first hour* of postirradiation incubation, while the number of residual divisions responds to increasing amounts of nutrient broth added at any time during the postirradiation incubation period.

Part II. The active component of nutrient

broth was found to be the amino acid fraction. A pool of amino acids, including a limiting amount of the required growth factor, has the same effect as nutrient broth in promoting the maximal yield of induced prototrophs when present in the post-irradiation culture medium during the first hour of incubation. The required growth factor alone was found to be inactive, as were pools of vitamins or purines and pyrimidines. In general, the yield of induced prototrophs increases as the number of different amino acids in the postirradiation medium increases.

The preirradiation culture medium was found to influence the degree of dependence upon post-irradiation enrichment with amino acids. While irradiated *try3* initially grown in nutrient broth can give rise to induced mutants only if exogenous amino acids are supplied during the first hour of postirradiation growth, cells initially grown in minimal medium supplemented with tryptophane are relatively independent of this requirement, producing substantial numbers of induced proto-trophs on minimal medium supplemented only with limiting amounts of tryptophane.

Studies of the growth rates of broth-grown irradiated *try3* on minimal agar supplemented with various amounts of nutrient broth, or with various concentrations of amino acids, revealed that the growth rate of the irradiated cells is proportional to the concentration of exogenous amino acids over a considerable range. The inference was made that the rate of protein synthesis is decreased, and becomes growth-limiting, as the concentration of exogenous amino acids is decreased within the critical range. It was found, for three different auxotrophic strains having very different patterns of "delayed appearance" as measured by expression curves, that the same linear relation was obtained when the percentage of the maximal yield of induced prototrophs obtained on various enrichment levels was plotted against the length of the lag phase (presumably a measure of the rate of protein synthesis) on the same enrichment levels. *It was inferred that the yield of induced proto-trophs is proportional to the rate of protein synthesis during the first hour of postirradiation incubation, when protein synthesis is growth-limiting.* Confirmatory evidence was obtained from experiments in which chloramphenicol was used as a posttreatment. It was found that incubation of irradiated auxotrophs in the presence of chloramphenicol for one hour (on an otherwise optimal medium for the production of the maximal yield of induced mutants) leads to drastic reduction of the number of induced prototrophs obtained, with no important effect upon the number of survivors. Exposure to chloramphenicol after one hour of incubation under optimal conditions without chloramphenicol has no effect upon the yield of induced prototrophs. The capacity to produce induced proto-trophs is maintained for relatively long periods of time when other metabolic activities are inhibited along with protein synthesis (as in buffer).

Part III. The temperature of incubation during postirradiation growth was found to have a profound effect upon the yield of induced prototrophs, while having little influence upon the survival level. The period of susceptibility to the influence of postirradiation temperature was found to be about one-third of the lag phase. When the initial temperature is 37°C, the temperature-sensitive period coincides approximately with the periods of susceptibility to the postirradiation influence of chloramphenicol and low amino acid concentrations.

The yield of induced prototrophs is increased five-fold over the frequency obtained at 37°C when short incubations at 37°C are followed by incubation at lower temperatures. This synergistic effect is obtained also when brief incubations at 45°C are followed by lower incubation temperatures.

The implications of the results are discussed in relation to theories of mutagenesis.

ACKNOWLEDGMENTS

The author is indebted to Miss Ann Lacy, Miss Constance Thomas and Miss Miriam Schwartz for their invaluable assistance at various stages of these studies.

REFERENCES

ANDERSON, E. H., and BILLEN, D., 1955, The effect of temperature on X ray induced mutability in *Escherichia coli*. J. Bact. *70*: 35–43.

AUERBACH, C., 1946, Chemically induced mosaicism in *Drosophila melanogaster*. Proc. Roy. Soc. (Edinburgh) B*62*: 211–222.

BERRIE, A. M. M., 1953, The effects of temperature on ultraviolet-induced mutability in *Escherichia coli*. Proc. Nat. Acad. Sci. Wash. *39*: 1125–1133.

DAVIS, B. D., 1948, Isolation of biochemically deficient mutants of bacteria by penicillin. J. Amer. Chem. Soc. *70*: 4267.

1950, Studies on nutritionally deficient bacterial mutants isolated by means of penicillin. Experientia *6*: 41–50.

DEMEREC, M., 1946, Induced mutations and possible mechanisms of the transmission of heredity in *Escherichia coli*. Proc. Nat. Acad. Sci. Wash. *32*: 36–46.

DEMEREC, M., and CAHN, E., 1953, Studies of mutability in nutritionally deficient strains of *Escherichia coli*. J. Bact. *65*: 27–36.

HAHN, F. E., WISSEMAN, C. L., JR., and HOPPS, H. E., 1954, Mode of action of chloramphenicol II. J. Bact. *67*: 674–679.

HOLLAENDER, A., and STAPLETON, G. E., 1956, Studies on protection by treatment before and after exposure to X- and gamma radiation. Proc. Intern. Conf. Peacetime Uses Atomic Energy, Geneva, *11*: 311–314, New York, United Nations.

JACOB, F., WOLLMAN, E. L., and HAYES, W., 1956, Conjugation and genetic recombination in *Escherichia coli* K-12. Cold Spring Harbor Symp. Quant. Biol. *21*: 141–162.

KAPLAN, R. W., 1952, Auslösung von Farbsektor und anderen Mutationen bei *Bacterium prodigiosum* durch monochromatisches Ultraviolett verschiedener Wellenlängen. Z. Naturf. *7b*: 291–304.

KAUFMANN, B. P., HOLLAENDER, A., and GAY, H., 1946, Modification of the frequency of chromosomal rearrangements induced by X-rays in *Drosophila*. I. Use of near infrared radiation. Genetics *31*: 349–367.

KELNER, A., 1949, Photoreactivation of ultraviolet-irradiated *Escherichia coli*, with special reference to the dose-reduction principle and to ultraviolet-induced mutation. J. Bact. *58*: 511–522.

LABRUM, E. L., 1953, A study of mutability in streptomycin-dependent strains of *Escherichia coli*. Proc. Nat. Acad. Sci. Wash. *39*: 280–288.

McELROY, W. D., and SWANSON, C. P., 1951, The theory of rate processes and gene mutation. Quart. Rev. Biol. *26*: 348–363.

NEWCOMBE, H. B., 1949, Origin of bacterial variants. Nature, Lond. *164*: 150–151.

——— 1953, The delayed appearance of radiation-induced genetic change in bacteria. Genetics *38*: 134–151.

——— 1955, The timing of induced mutations in *Streptomyces*. Brookhaven Symp. Biol. *8*: 88–102.

NEWCOMBE, H. B., and SCOTT, G. W., 1949, Factors responsible for the delayed appearance of radiation-induced mutants in *Escherichia coli*. Genetics *34*: 475–492.

NEWCOMBE, H. B., and WHITEHEAD, H. A., 1951, Photo-reversal of ultraviolet-induced mutagenic and lethal effects in *Escherichia coli*. J. Bact. *61*: 243–251.

NOVICK, A., and SZILARD, L., 1949, Experiments on light-reactivation of ultraviolet inactivated bacteria. Proc. Nat. Acad. Sci. Wash. *35*: 591–600.

RYAN, F. J., 1954, The delayed appearance of mutants in bacterial cultures. Proc. Nat. Acad. Sci. Wash. *40*: 178–186.

——— 1955, Phenotypic (phenomic) lag in bacteria. Amer. Nat. *89*: 159–162.

RYAN, F. J., FRIED, P., and SCHWARTZ, M., 1954, Nuclear segregation and the growth of clones of bacterial mutants induced by ultraviolet light. J. Gen. Microbiol. *11*: 380–393.

SWANSON, C. P., 1955, In: Radiobiology Symposium. Ed. Z. M. Bacq, and P. Alexander. London, Butterworths, pp. 254.

SWANSON, C. P., and YOST, H. T., 1951, The induction of activated, stable states in the chromosomes of *Tradescantia* by infrared and X-rays. Proc. Nat. Acad. Sci. Wash. *37*: 796–801.

WAINWRIGHT, S. D., and NEVILL, A., 1955a, Modification of the biological effects of ultraviolet irradiation by post-radiation treatment with iodoacetate and peptone. J. Gen. Microbiol. *12*: 1–12.

——— 1955b, Some effects of post-radiation treatment with metabolic inhibitors and nutrients upon ultraviolet irradiated spores of *Streptomyces* T12. Canad. J. Microbiol. *1*: 416–426.

WISSEMAN, C. L., JR., SMADEL, J. E., HAHN, F. E., and HOPPS, H. E., 1954, Mode of action of chloramphenicol I. J. Bact. *67*: 662–673.

WITKIN, E. M., 1951, Nuclear segregation and the delayed appearance of induced mutants in *Escherichia coli*. Cold Spring Harbor Symp. Quant. Biol. *16*: 357–372.

——— 1953, Effects of temperature on spontaneous and induced mutations in *Escherichia coli*. Proc. Nat. Acad. Sci. Wash. *39*: 427–433.

WITKIN, E. M., and THOMAS, C., 1955, Bacterial Genetics II, Yearb. Carnegie Instn. *54*: 234–245.

WOLFF, S., and LUIPPOLD, H. E., 1955, Metabolism and chromosome-break rejoining. Science *122*: 231–232.

WOLFF, S., and ATWOOD, K. C., 1954, Independent X-ray effects on chromosome breakage and reunion. Proc. Nat. Acad. Sci. Wash. *40*: 187–192.

ZINDER, N. D., and LEDERGERG, J., 1952, Genetic exchange in *Salmonella*. J. Bact. *64*: 679–699.

DISCUSSION

D. LEWIS: Still at the cellular level but in a higher plant, *Oenothera organensis*, the pollen grains with their gene controlling incompatibility reactions give a different, and in some respects a more direct, means of detecting induced mutations which are unstable. The mutational event can be placed with some accuracy in the previous history of the nuclear divisions that gave rise to the pollen; and the phenotypic change produced by the mutation can be detected when as little as one nuclear division has occurred after the event. Apart from stable mutations of the type of S_1 to S_f, unstable mutations S_1 to S_{f1} and reversion to S_1 occur both spontaneously and with X rays (U.V. cannot be used effectively with this material). A higher frequency of unstable mutations of this type would have the effect of lowering the observed frequency of mutation in Dr. Witkin's experiments with *E. coli*.

There may also be a parallel in the pollen mutations with Dr. Witkin's findings on the effect of growth phase and nutrition. The number of unstable mutations depends upon the state of the nucleus at the time of the mutational event: in early prophase stable mutations are common but are much rarer or absent in the late stages of division.

An explanation advanced for the unstable mutations in pollen is similar to Dr. Witkin's repair hypothesis.

Only a fraction and not all of the strands of the chromosome could be damaged at the locus, and this fraction might be the outer strands which were the ones to become active in producing the immediate phenotype while the inner strands, which will not become phenotypically active for some time, are undamaged. A loss of the outer strands and a preservation of the inner ones during subsequent chromosomal duplication would then be an unstable mutation.

WITKIN: It is possible, undoubtedly, that some mutations induced in bacteria may be of the unstable type described by Dr. Lewis as occurring in *Oenothera*. If this were the case in our material, however, except as a rare exception, the occurrence of mutations to prototrophy after many cell divisions could be detected in the respreading experiments. These experiments, as well as the evidence based upon the duration of the period of susceptibility to modification by posttreatment, seem to me to establish beyond doubt that most of the mutations with which we are dealing occur before the completion of the first postirradiation cell division. Not only do these mutations occur early, but there is a striking fact that must be considered in any theory of mutagenesis: In the cases analyzed (including induced phage resistance, lactose nonfermentation and prototrophy) the colonies in which the induced mutants arise do not usually contain any cells of the nonmutated parent type. The irradiated cell that gives rise to an induced mutation typically produces *only* mutants, although in a small proportion of colonies some admixture of the original type is found. By way of contrast, colonies in which prototrophs arise by transduction invariably contain also cells of the unchanged parental genotype. Any theory of mutagenesis, therefore, must incorporate the fact that the induced mutations usually affect the original locus in all its replicas, if such exist at the time of treatment. These facts would not support a copy-error concept of induced mutation, nor would they be easily reconciled with the hypothesis of Dr. Lewis involving damage to a fraction of multiple strands. This does not rule out the possibility that some bacterial mutations may be of the unstable variety, nor that a small fraction of the changes occurring in our material may be of this type. In the cases described, however, it seems to be most often true that the total population descended from a "promutant" exhibits the new genotype.

ALPER: The mechanisms by which ultraviolet light and ionizing radiation act on biological material are very different in many respects; Dr. Witkin's conclusions are therefore of great interest because it would appear that, for the genetic effects she describes, there are close parallels in the effects of the two types of radiation. There is evidence from several lines of investigation that the extent to which many types of X-ray damage are expressed greatly depends on the rate at which synthetic processes occur, immediately after irradiation. For example, Dr. Kimball has shown that in *Paramecium* lethal mutations are reduced in frequency if, after radiation, the animals are exposed to agents which slow their growth, such as cold, or high concentrations of hydrogen peroxide. On the other hand there is apparently a great difference in the lethal effects of U.V. and X rays on bacteria. Stapleton and his coworkers showed that bacteria "recovered" if they were held at temperatures below 37°, after they had been X-irradiated, and constructed curves which gave the optimal holding temperatures for recovery, for several strains of *E. coli*. Dr. Witkin has pointed out that after U.V. irradiation, prolonging the lag period reduces the number of biochemical mutants which appear, but not the number of lethal injuries. These results suggest that it may be more nearly correct to regard the X-ray injury as a lethal mutation than the U.V. effect which causes failure to multiply.

Dr. Witkin has told us that millipore membranes cannot be used in these studies, as they prolong the lag period and therefore interfere with the results. I have developed a technique for studying microcolonies and long forms after X-irradiation, and for this purpose have been using small pieces of cellophane laid over the surface of agar plates. From observations made on fixed and stained colonies, from periods of three quarters of an hour to four hours after seeding, it appears that lag period and generation time match those observed in liquid culture if the same nutrient medium is used. It seems possible therefore that

cellophane might be useful where millipore membrane cannot be used.

WITKIN: Systematic studies comparing the responses to postirradiation metabolic conditions of a particular mutation induced by a variety of mutagenic agents would be of great value in interpreting the nature of these effects. Present indications are that the responses to particular posttreatments are not mutagen-specific, as, for example, the finding by Demerec and Cahn that the "pattern of delay," which in reality is a measure of the response to amino acid concentration in the postirradiation culture medium, is the same for a given mutation induced by either ultraviolet light or manganous chloride. Postirradiation temperature effects on mutation frequency, similar to those obtained with ultraviolet light, have been observed for X-ray induced prototrophs by Anderson and Billen, the maximum yield of mutants appearing with incubation at 24°, as was found for prototrophs induced with ultraviolet light in *try3*. If these indications are borne out, it seems to me that they tend to weaken the hypothesis of mutagenic intermediates, which might be expected to show some specificity related to the agent used. The breakage-repair hypothesis, and that of intragenic metastability, on the other hand, would predict a greater degree of uniformity of results with different mutagenic agents.

With regard to the effects of postirradiation temperature on the lethal action of X rays and ultraviolet light, I do not think that the comparison of our results with those of Dr. Kimball can be usefully made. Many kinds of posttreatments do affect the survival of ultraviolet-treated bacteria, and in some strains, such as the B strain of *E. coli*, there is marked heat-reactivation. The comparison of X rays and ultraviolet in this regard should be made with the same material.

GREER: I have evidence which supports the idea that increased protein synthesis favors repair of genetic damage. In experiments with *E. coli* it has been demonstrated that certain amino acid combinations depress the rate of mutation to purine independence and streptomycin resistance induced by 5 OH,7NO$_2$ benzimidazole. While the amino acids have no effect on the spontaneous mutant frequency, they depress the chemically induced mutant frequency twenty-fold.

LIEB: Several years ago I studied the delay in the appearance of U.V.-induced prototrophs in a histidine-requiring (*h*−) culture of *E. coli* (Genetics *36*: 460–477). The bacteria were grown in synthetic medium with an optimal concentration of histidine, and after irradiation were allowed to grow for various lengths of time in the same medium. Growth for a period of time allowing one to two cell divisions was adequate for the expression of all *h*+ mutants. It was also shown that growth of irradiated bacteria on plates with limited histidine enrichment did not result in the expression of mutants.

Mutation from prototrophy to auxotrophy was studied under similar conditions. There was no growth-dependent delay in the expression of h^- mutants. This seems to favor Dr. Witkin's hypothesis of gene repair, if I understand it correctly. A process involving protein synthesis would appear to be necessary to restore a gene to its functional state, but would not be required in the case of mutation involving a loss of gene activity.

WITKIN: While the rate of postirradiation protein synthesis has a decisive influence on the yield of induced prototrophs, we have preliminary evidence that the frequency of certain other classes of induced mutations (phage resistance, for example) may be unaffected by the concentration of amino acids and by chloramphenicol posttreatment. It appears possible that protein synthesis in the early postirradiation period may be a critical factor only in the case of mutations involving the acquisition of new synthetic capacities, as Dr. Lieb suggests. If this should prove to be true, however, I do not see that it would support the repair hypothesis, at least without important revisions. This hypothesis, as well as those invoking the decay of unstable mutagenic intermediates, or of intragenic metastable configurations, presupposes a unitary mechanism of induced mutation, which, indeed, is supported by the qualitative uniformity of the postirradiation temperature effects. If protein synthesis is necessary for the fixation of genetic changes leading to new enzymatic activity, but not for other kinds of mutations, it seems to me that new parameters will have to be considered within the framework of any hypothesis. For example, if the effect of mutagenic treatment is considered to be the production of unstable configurations in genic DNA, it may be that proteins synthesized immediately after irradiation "capture" the transient configuration in stable form, and pass it back to the DNA at the time of gene duplication. In the absence of protein synthesis, the altered specificity is lost. Mutations in which postirradiation protein synthesis has no effect may utilize other routes of specificity transfer, via RNA perhaps. While it is certainly possible that the dichotomy, if it is proved to exist, between mutations that are affected by postirradiation protein synthesis and those that are not, may reflect entirely different pathways of mutagenesis, it seems more economical at first to seek the basis of the difference within one primary framework.

LIEB: The fact that several types of ultraviolet-induced mutations do not seem to require protein synthesis suggests that the basic mechanism, if there is only one, does not involve protein. However, some genes, while able to replicate, may not become functional in metabolism until certain intermediates or "primers" are synthesized. This synthesis may involve protein. Such intermediates might be closely associated with the genes, and might even be transduced. The destruction of such intermediates would account for non-hereditary growth factor requirements often observed in irradiated microorganisms.

MAALØE: Dr. Witkin's elegant analysis of the physiological conditions which favor the development of U.V.-induced mutants throws new light on experiments recently carried out in our laboratory. Exponentially growing cultures of *E. coli* and *S. typhimurium* were irradiated with moderate doses of U.V., and after various post-irradiation treatments the fractions of cells surviving to form colonies on broth plates were determined. It was found that *maximum killing* was obtained when the conditions maintained during the first 15 to 30 minutes after irradiation were such as, according to Witkin, will produce the *maximum number of mutants*. This parallelism extends to nearly all the different growth conditions, including the various combinations of nutrients and growth factors, described by Witkin.

This strongly suggests that the killing of bacteria by U.V. results from processes secondary to the absorption of radiation energy *and* that the same, or closely related processes may lead to the formation of non-lethal mutants. (A paper by Victor G. Bonce and myself, containing some of our observations on the effects of postirradiation treatment has been accepted for publication in Biochim. Biophys. Acta.)

WITKIN: In our experience, too, the survival of bacteria irradiated in the exponential phase of growth is exceedingly sensitive to postirradiation nutritional factors, and it is interesting to hear that these effects parallel those we have obtained for induced prototrophy. In our studies, we avoided the use of growing cultures, as well as the use of liquid culture media in the postirradiation growth period, specifically because of the fact that, under these conditions, survival is so greatly affected by altered conditions that the effects on induced mutation become very difficult to follow. In the strains used in this study, survival after ultraviolet treatment is remarkably uniform under the whole spectrum of posttreatments used, if stationary phase cultures and solid media are employed. While this facilitates the study of induced mutations independently of lethal effects, I do not wish to imply that the modifications of survival level are unimportant. The fact that effects on mutation and on survival are separable, however, supports the already well-documented idea that the postirradiation metabolic sequence is branched, as well as multi-step.

Conjugation and Genetic Recombination in *Escherichia coli* K-12

E.-L. Wollman, F. Jacob and W. Hayes

Institut Pasteur, Paris, France and The Postgraduate Medical School of London, London, England

". . . it is also a good rule not to put overmuch confidence in the observational results that are put forward *until they have been confirmed by theory.*"

—Sir Arthur Eddington, "New Pathways in Science."

It is just ten years since the first report of genetic recombination in *Escherichia coli* K-12 was made to this Symposium by Lederberg and Tatum. Since then a great deal of work has been devoted to study of the genetics of recombination but, in general, such studies have tended to stress the complexity of the genetic process by bringing to light the anomalies inherent in it rather than to elucidate its mechanism. We do not intend to summarise all this work here since it has already been covered by recent reviews (Lederberg, Lederberg, Zinder and Lively, 1951; Hayes, 1953b; Lederberg, 1955; Cavalli and Jinks, 1956) but only to recall such facts as are strictly relevant to our present purpose. The object of this paper is to define the different steps involved in the processes of conjugation and recombination in *E. coli* K-12, to offer a systematic analysis of what we know about these steps, based primarily on work done in the authors' laboratories in Paris and London, and from this analysis to construct a simple model of the mating process. While we are very conscious that many gaps remain in our knowledge of this subject and that alternative hypotheses may be advanced to explain some of the experimental results, we propose to adopt a rather didactic approach in order to clarify the presentation of this work.

I. The Nature of the System

Since Lederberg and Tatum's discovery, most of the work on genetic recombination in *E. coli* has involved crosses in which the observed frequency of appearance of recombinants was only 10^{-5} to 10^{-6} that of the parental population. This necessitated the use of the original experimental design of Lederberg and Tatum in which a mixture of two doubly auxotrophic mutants of the K-12 strain of *E. coli* was plated on a minimal medium on which only prototrophs, that is, bacteria in which the nutritional deficiencies of both parents had been eliminated by recombination, could grow. Under such conditions it is impossible directly to investigate events occurring at the cellular level, while interpretation of genetic results is difficult since selection permits the recovery of only one class of the progeny of numerous mating events.

When the auxotrophic parental strains were further marked by a series of differential characters which were not selected by the minimal medium used for prototroph detection, these unselected markers were found to have undergone reassortment among the prototrophic progeny of the cross. Analysis of such reassortments revealed linkage of many of the unselected markers to one another as well as to the nutritional selective markers, and four groups of clearly linked genes were revealed. However, although all the characters studied appeared to show some degree of interdependence in their inheritance, they could not be mapped on a single chromosome. Difficulties were even encountered in the analysis of recombination data between clearly linked genes, while the results of back-crosses between recombinants and parental strains frequently diverged grossly from those anticipated by genetical theory. It seemed likely that pure genetic analysis would lead only to increasing complication, rather than to clarification, of the picture and that further progress awaited the discovery of some fundamental aspect of the mating process which had not hitherto been taken into account.

A. One-Way Genetic Transfer and F Polarity

It was first demonstrated that the two parental strains of a fertile cross played different roles in mating. Although both strains were equally sensitive to streptomycin, treatment of one of them with this drug invariably resulted in sterility of the cross, whereas treatment of the other did not have this effect although the fertility of the cross was often greatly reduced. It therefore appeared that while the role of one parent was transient and independent of the capacity for further multiplication, the continued viability of the other parent was vital. The function of the first parent or gene donor was simply to fertilise the other parent or gene recipient, which thus became the zygote cell (Hayes, 1952a). In the light of subsequent work it is now believed that this differential effect was revealed because the bactericidal action of streptomycin was sufficiently slow to allow the donor population, or a moiety of it, to initiate and complete its fertilising function although further cell division was suppressed.

Another difference between the two strains is that irradiation of donor strains with small doses of ultraviolet light markedly enhances the fertility of crosses while similar irradiation of recipient strains does not (Hayes, 1952b).

This functional distinction between the two strains was independently confirmed, at the same time, by the observation that crosses between recipient strains were always sterile. Donor strains were called F$^+$ (for fertility) and recipient strains F$^-$ (Lederberg, Cavalli and Lederberg, 1952). It was further shown that F$^-$ cells could be converted to F$^+$ by contact with F$^+$ cells, with an efficiency about 10^5 times higher than that of recombination. The F$^+$ character acquired in this way by an F$^-$ cell is inheritable and very stable in cultures, but a chromosomal locus for it could not be determined (Lederberg et al., 1952; Cavalli, Lederberg and Lederberg, 1953; Hayes, 1953a, b).

B. Partial Transfer of Genetic Material

Comparison of the results of crosses of reciprocal F polarity between the same parental strains showed that the majority of the unselected markers present among recombinants were those of the F$^-$ (recipient) bacteria, irrespective of the cross or of the selection employed. The hypothesis was therefore made (Hayes, 1953a) that only a part of the donor chromosome was transferred to the recipient cell to form an incomplete zygote. An alternative hypothesis, based on results obtained with diploid heterozygotes (Lederberg, 1949), was that a complete zygote was formed but that part of the genetic material, usually contributed by the donor cell, was subsequently eliminated after crossing-over (see Lederberg, 1955). Evidence strongly favouring the hypothesis of partial transfer will be presented later.

C. Hfr Systems

The usual frequency of recombinants arising from F$^+$ × F$^-$ crosses is about 10^{-5} to 10^{-6} of the parental population. Two mutant strains of the same F$^+$ strain were independently isolated which showed a very much higher frequency of recombination in crosses with F$^-$ strains. Such strains were called Hfr (high frequency of recombination). One of these strains (HfrC) was isolated after treatment of the parent F$^+$ culture with nitrogen mustard (Cavalli, 1950); the other (HfrH) arose spontaneously (Hayes, 1953b). It is this latter strain, HfrH, or Hfr derivatives from it, which has predominantly been employed in the work to be described.

Hfr strains behave as typical donor strains but differ strikingly from F$^+$ strains in several important respects:

1. When crossed with F$^-$ strains under the conditions generally used throughout this work, the frequency of recombinants is about 2 × 10^4 times higher than in the equivalent F$^+$ × F$^-$ cross (Hayes, 1957).

2. Hfr behaviour is only manifest when selection is made for inheritance of an Hfr marker or markers (T$^+$L$^+$ or Lac$^+$) situated on a particular linkage group. Selection for markers on other linkage groups (M, B$_1$ or S, Mal) yields only a low frequency of recombinants (Lfr) comparable to that found in F$^+$ × F$^-$ crosses (Hayes, 1953b). Since only a single group of linked characters is therefore transmitted at high frequency to the recombinants, this system offers more dramatic evidence for the hypothesis, suggested by the results of F$^+$ × F$^-$ crosses, that only this group of characters is usually transferred from the Hfr to the F$^-$ cell to form a partial zygote. The Hfr chromosome can thus provisionally be visualised (Fig. 1) as having a preferential region of rupture, such that only characters located on region A will be transferred at high frequency. It is evident that the terms "high" or "low" frequency of recombination have meaning only when the selective conditions of the cross are defined. As will be seen later, there are other conditions which can profoundly influence the productivity of a cross.

3. Hfr strains, unlike F$^+$, do not convert F$^-$ strains to either F$^+$ or Hfr at high frequency, nor is the F$^+$ character inherited by recombinants from Hfr × F$^-$ crosses. Recombinants from such crosses are F$^-$ when markers on region A (Fig. 1) are selected, but when markers on region B are selected they are either F$^-$ or Hfr depending on the particular selection employed. Nevertheless Hfr strains can revert at a low rate to an F$^+$ state indistinguishable from that of the parent F$^+$ strain.

4. Irradiation of Hfr strains, unlike that of F$^+$ strains, does not increase the frequency of recombinants when markers on region A are selected, but markedly enhances Hfr fertility at low frequency when selection is made for markers on region B.

The use of Hfr strains has provided proof of one-way transfer in this system. For example when exconjugants from visually observed pairs of Hfr and F$^-$ cells are isolated with a micromanipulator and cultured, only the F$^-$ partners yield recombinants (Lederberg, 1955). Furthermore, the discovery of zygotic induction, now to be recounted, offers not only independent proof of one-way transfer but also strong evidence in support of partial transfer as well.

$$\overbrace{\text{T \quad L \quad Az \quad T}_1 \quad \text{Lac}_1 \quad \text{T}_6 \quad \text{Gal}}^{\text{A}} : \overbrace{\text{S \quad Mal \quad Xyl}_1 \quad \text{Mtl} \quad \text{M \quad B}_1}^{\text{B}}$$

FIGURE 1. The E. coli K-12 linkage group (after Cavalli and Jinks, 1956). Symbols refer to threonine (T), leucine (L), methionine (M) and thiamine (B$_1$) synthesis; resistance to sodium azide (Az), bacteriophage T1, bacteriophage T6, streptomycin (S); fermentation of lactose (Lac), galactose (Gal), maltose (Mal), xylose (Xyl) and mannitol (Mtl).

D. Zygotic Induction

The wild-type strain of *E. coli* K-12 and most of its derivatives are lysogenic for the temperate phage λ, but non-lysogenic strains have been isolated from it (E. Lederberg, 1951) and can be obtained at will. In crosses between lysogenic and non-lysogenic strains, lysogeny segregates and is linked to certain galactose markers (Lederberg and Lederberg, 1953; Wollman, 1953). Reciprocal crosses between lysogenic (*ly*⁺) and non-lysogenic (*ly*⁻) bacteria do not give symmetrical results, however, so far as inheritance of lysogeny is concerned (Wollman, 1953; Appleyard, 1954). In a cross between non-lysogenic HfrH and a lysogenic F⁻ strain, lysogeny segregates among the recombinants and can thus be shown to occupy a genetic locus on the chromosome near to the *Gal* locus. Similarly when HfrH and F⁻ parental strains, each of which is lysogenic for a different mutant of λ phage, are crossed, the two prophages segregate among recombinants in precisely the same way as did lysogeny and non-lysogeny in the previous cross, thus demonstrating that it is the prophage which is the genetic determinant of lysogeny (Wollman and Jacob, 1954, 1957).

On the other hand when the Hfr parent is characterised by lysogeny and the F⁻ parent by non-lysogeny, the outcome of the cross is quite different, for lysogeny is no longer found to be inherited by any recombinant. Instead, the transfer of λ prophage is invariably followed by the *immediate* induction of its development within the fertilised F⁻ cells with consequent lysis of the zygotes and liberation of λ phage. When the F⁻ strain used is one which imposes a phenotypic modification on λ phage, this modification is found to characterise the liberated phage (Jacob and Wollman, 1954, 1956b). This is a clear example of the one-way transfer of genetic characters in Hfr × F⁻ crosses.

Lambda prophage is therefore a genetic character whose *transfer to the F⁻ cell is immediately expressed* by zygotic induction, before genetic recombination has taken place. The fact that some recombinants are formed in HfrH(*ly*)⁺ × F⁻(*ly*)⁻ crosses but that these recombinants do not contain λ prophage, indicates that in these cases λ prophage has not been transferred to the F⁻ recipient cells. This demonstrates that the genetic locus, λ prophage, at least, is not transferred to many zygotes which yield recombinants, that is that these zygotes are not complete. This method of approach to the problem of whether the partial inheritance of Hfr characters among recombinants is entirely due to partial transfer from donor to recipient cells will be amplified later in this paper.

E. The Presumptive Stages of Mating

Despite the restriction that only a limited group of Hfr genetic characters are inherited, the proportion of recombinants issuing from Hfr × F⁻ crosses is sufficiently high to allow a quantitative study of the mating process. When Hfr and F⁻ cells are mixed one can, *a priori*, distinguish the following presumptive stages of mating:

1. Conjugation. This stage is synonymous with that of zygote formation and includes the entire sequence of events from the first encounter between donor and recipient cells to the completion of genetic transfer. It can be divided into the following substages:

(*a*) *Collision.* This is obviously the essential first step and is a process determined by chance.

(*b*) *Effective contact.* This step follows collision and involves a specific attachment between a donor and a recipient cell which probably depends on the surface properties of the two cells.

(*c*) *Genetic transfer.* The genome, or part of the genome, of the donor cell is transferred to the recipient cell which thus becomes the zygote. When transfer is accomplished the donor cell has discharged its function and is no longer necessary.

2. Formation of recombinants. This process comprises two important steps:

(*a*) *Integration.* The process at the genetic level whereby the chromosome of the recombinant cell is evolved in the zygote from the chromosomal contributions of the two parents.

(*b*) *Expression of the recombinants.* This stage comprises *segregation* of the haploid recombinant cell from the zygote cell and the *phenotypic expression* of the new recombinant chromosome in the cell which inherits it.

Before presenting an experimental analysis of these stages by means of Hfr × F⁻ crosses, we must first examine the methodology of such crosses and the kind of information which can be derived from them.

F. Methods of Approach to Hfr × F⁻ Crosses

Until recently the occurrence of mating could be measured only by the formation of recombinants. Since recombinants are the end-products of the reaction between mating cells, so that their number and constitution can potentially be modified at any stage of the process, the analytical information which they can yield is limited. What is needed in analysis is to measure the different available expressions of recombination so that information concerning different stages of the process is obtained which can then be evaluated and equated. The phenomenon of zygotic induction answers this need by giving a direct indication of the extent of genetic transfer from the Hfr cells to the zygotes, since ultraviolet-inducible prophages, located on the chromosome segment transferred at high frequency by HfrH, are expressed immediately upon transfer to the recipient cell, *before* the formation of recombinants, by the liberation of phage. Thus comparison of the results of zygotic induction and of recombination from the same cross has yielded valuable information about the nature of both transfer and integration (Jacob and Wollman, 1955a; Wollman and Jacob, 1957).

Conditions of mating: For comparative quantitative studies, crosses are made under the following basic conditions. Exponentially growing cultures of the Hfr and F⁻ strains are mixed in liquid medium and aerated, the population density of one of the strains, usually the F⁻ recipient, generally being in 20-fold excess in order to increase the efficiency of specific collisions. The frequency of the effect to be measured is then expressed as a percentage of the number of minority parental cells initially present. Samples of the mixture are removed at suitable times, diluted to prevent further contacts, and plated either on a selective minimal medium if recombination is being studied or, in the case of zygotic induction, with a phage-sensitive indicator strain on nutrient agar. It is clear that lysogenic Hfr parental cells, if present, will interfere with results by themselves producing infectious centres if they are permitted to grow on the latter medium. Moreover, in many recombination experiments a prototrophic Hfr strain, capable of growth on minimal agar, was used. It is therefore necessary either to prevent further growth of the Hfr parent after plating, or to eliminate it from the mixture, once genetic transfer has been effected and it is no longer required. When the Hfr parent is streptomycin-sensitive and the F⁻ parent resistant, the simplest and most efficient way of inhibiting Hfr growth is to incorporate streptomycin in the agar on which the mixture is plated. As one might expect from the fact that streptomycin sensitivity from strain HfrH is never inherited among recombinants formed at high frequency, the use of streptomycin in this way has no effect on the outcome of the cross (Hayes, 1953b).

Elimination of Hfr cells is achieved by treating the undiluted mixture with a high-titre preparation of virulent phage T6 to which only the Hfr parent is susceptible. After subsequent dilution, the concentration of phage on the plate is not such as to affect the frequency of appearance of recombinants inheriting sensitivity to the phage from the Hfr parent: the use of anti-phage serum is, therefore, unnecessary. In most of the recombination experiments in which the phage technique was used, the Hfr strain was auxotrophic and streptomycin-resistant so that streptomycin was not added to the minimal agar (Hayes, 1957).

Expressions of mating. 1. Formation of recombinants. Selection of recombinants from an Hfr × F⁻ cross means that selection is made for inheritance by the F⁻ cells of characters derived from the Hfr donor cells (Hayes, 1953b). Accordingly, Hfr and F⁻ strains are chosen which differ in as many as possible of those markers which are inherited at high frequency by the F⁻ cells (Fig. 1). The F⁻ recipient strain is marked by the minus alleles of those characters which can be used for selection, for example threonine⁻, leucine⁻, lactose⁻, galactose⁻ ($T^-L^-Lac^-Gal^-$), and is resistant to streptomycin (S^r). The Hfr strain has the wild alleles of these characters and is sensitive to streptomycin ($T^+L^+Lac^+Gal^+S^s$). In addition, the two strains can be made to differ in markers such as resistance or sensitivity to sodium azide (Az^r, Az^s) or to virulent phages ($T1^r$, $T1^s$) which are not usually used for selection. Thus by the use of suitable selective media one can select for different recombinant classes issuing from the same cross. For instance in a cross between Hfr·$T^+L^+Az^sT1^sLac_1^+Gal_b^+S^s$ and F⁻·$T^-L^-Az^r$-$T1^rLac_1^-Gal_b^-S^r$, $T^+L^+S^r$ or Gal^+S^r recombinants can be specifically selected and the inheritance of the other, unselected, markers among them studied. Two kinds of information can be obtained from such crosses:

(a) *The frequency of recombination:* the number of recombinants of any type (*e.g.*, $T^+L^+S^r$ or Gal^+S^r) per 100 initial Hfr cells.

(b) *The genetic constitution* of these recombinants, that is, the distribution among them of unselected Hfr markers.

2. Formation of infectious centres. What is looked for here is the proportion of lysogenic Hfr cells which, on mating with non-lysogenic F⁻ cells, transfer their prophage to the recipient F⁻ cells which thereby liberate phage as a result of zygotic induction. The cross is therefore made between Hfr$(ly)^+S^s$ and F⁻$(ly)^-S^r$ parental strains and the mixture plated for infectious centres with a streptomycin-resistant, phage-sensitive indicator strain, on streptomycin-agar. Results are expressed as the *frequency of induction* which is the number of infectious centres (plaques) per 100 initial Hfr cells.

In the following two sections the various stages of mating in Hfr × F⁻ crosses will be discussed in detail against the background of our present knowledge. Our immediate aim is not to offer a definitive answer to the many questions which can be posed about the problem but rather to report the facts as we know them in the light of our own experience. These facts relate mainly to the experimental definition of each stage and substage, and to the analysis of some of them in kinetic terms by means of the methods we have already outlined.

II. CONJUGATION IN Hfr × F⁻ CROSSES

Conjugation connotes the sequence of events from the initial collision to the completion of fertilisation of the F⁻ cell, that is up to the time at which further participation of the Hfr donor cell is no longer necessary.

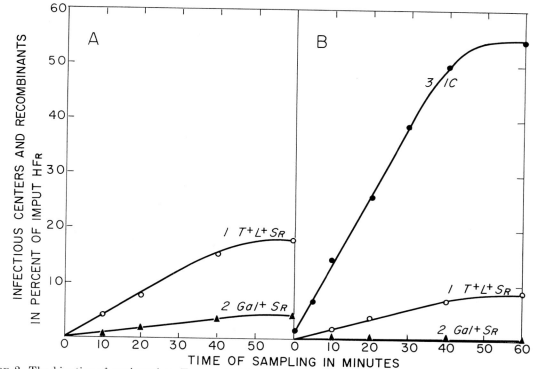

FIGURE 2. The kinetics of conjugation. Exponential broth cultures of HfrH S^s and P678 F$^-S^r$ are mixed at time 0 (1 to 2.10^7 Hfr/ml and 2 to 5.10^8 F$^-$/ml) and aerated in broth. The differential characters of the two strains are: HfrH $S^sT^+L^+Az^sT1^sLac_1{}^+Gal_b{}^+$ (for symbols see Fig. 1) and: P678 F$^-S^rT^-L^-Az^rT1^rLac_1{}^-Gal_b{}^-$. At different intervals of time samples are immediately plated, either for recombinants on glucose minimal medium + streptomycin ($T^+L^+S^r$ recombinants, curves 1) and on galactose minimal medium + threonine (T), leucine (L), and streptomycin (Gal^+S^r recombinants, curves 2), or for infectious centers on nutrient agar + streptomycin resistant indicator bacteria for phage λ (curve 3). The numbers of recombinants or of infectious centers obtained are expressed as a percentage of the number of initial Hfr cells. 2 A, cross between HfrH S^s (λ)$^+$ and P678 F$^-S^r$ (λ)$^+$, both lysogenic (λ)$^+$ for phage λ. 2 B cross between HfrH S^s (λ)$^+$ and P678 F$^-S^r$(λ)$^-$. (From Wollman and Jacob, 1957).

A. *The Kinetics of Conjugation*

1. Effective contacts. A standard cross is made between an Hfr·S^s and an F$^-$·S^r strain, both strains being either lysogenic or non-lysogenic. At intervals after mixing in broth, samples are removed, diluted and plated for recombinants. Selection is made for inheritance of either T^+L^+ or of Gal^+ from the Hfr parent, these being the most widely separated of the known selective markers on that part of the Hfr chromosome which is inherited at high frequency (Wollman and Jacob, 1955, 1957; Jacob and Wollman, 1954, 1956b). The results of such an experiment are shown in Figure 2A.

Figure 2B shows the results obtained under the same conditions when the Hfr strain is lysogenic for λ prophage and the F$^-$ strain is non-lysogenic, so that zygotic induction occurs, the samples being plated for infectious centres as well as for $T^+L^+S^r$ and Gal^+S^r recombinants.

Inspection of Figures 2A and 2B shows: 1. In all cases the curves start from the origin (*i.e.* from the time of mixing) and then continue to rise until a plateau is reached, irrespective of whether the curves express the formation of recombinants or of infectious centres. 2. All the curves reach their plateaux at about the same time although the maximum levels represented by the plateaux vary from 58 per cent for frequency of induction (Fig. 2B) to 5 per cent for frequency of Gal^+S^r recombination (Fig. 2A). Since the slope of each curve, from its inception to its maximum, represents the same rate of increase (about 2.5 % per minute), all must be an expression of the same phenomenon, the conjugation of Hfr and F$^-$ cells. The fact that all the plateaux are attained at about the same time indicates that at this time the maximum frequency of conjugation has been achieved.

2. Zygote formation. Crosses are made in the same manner as before but the samples, instead of being plated directly, are treated with a high titre preparation of phage T6, to which only the Hfr cells are susceptible, before dilution and plating (Hayes, 1957). The results of such an experiment are shown in Figure 6A (first curve).

The striking difference between curve 1 of Figure 2A and the first curve of Figure 6A is that whereas, in the first case, the number of T^+L^+ recombinants begins to rise from the time of mixing, when the samples are treated with phage there is a lag of eight minutes before recombinants begin to appear. This difference is explained in the following way. The curves constructed from untreated samples represent the kinetics of those contacts between Hfr and F⁻ cells which survive dilution and plating and can therefore continue through the succeeding steps leading to formation of recombinants or infectious centres on the plate; they thus express the *kinetics of the formation of effective contacts*. On the other hand, the curves constructed from samples treated with phage indicate the rate of development of mating pairs in which the markers T^+L^+ have already been transferred from donor to recipient cell at the time of treatment, so that the Hfr cell is no longer needed to form T^+L^+ recombinants: that is, the *kinetics of zygote formation*. From this two inferences can be drawn:

1. Effective contacts are formed very quickly, since the kinetic curve arises from the zero point of the time axis.

2. Transfer of the markers T^+L^+ from the Hfr to the F⁻ parent occupies about eight minutes from the time of contact.

B. *Genetic Transfer*

1. The kinetics of transfer. In an attempt to distinguish actual genetic transfer from conjugation as a whole, samples removed at intervals after mixing the Hfr and F⁻ cells were either plated directly as before, or subjected to violent agitation in a Waring blendor before dilution and plating in order to separate bacteria in the act of conjugation (Wollman and Jacob, 1955, 1957). Treatment in a blendor affects neither the viability of bacterial cells (Anderson, 1949) or recombinants, nor the ability of phage-infected cells

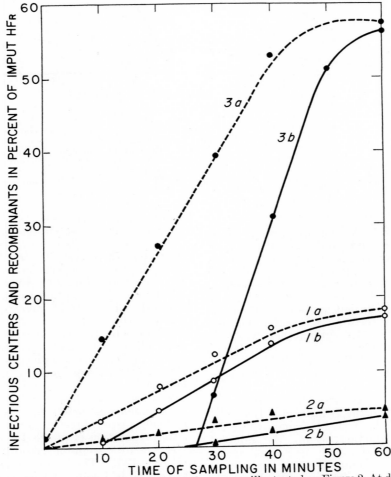

FIGURE 3. The kinetics of transfer. The experiments are the same as illustrated on Figure 2. At different time intervals samples of the mating mixtures are either plated directly on indicator media (dotted lines) or treated for 2 minutes in a Waring blendor and then immediately plated (solid lines). Curves 1 and 2 refer to the kinetics of formation of $T^+L^+S^r$ recombinants (curves 1 a and 1 b) and of Gal^+S^r recombinants (curves 2 a and 2 b) in a cross between Hfr(λ)⁺ × F⁻(λ)⁺. Curves 3 a and 3 b represent the kinetics of formation of infectious centers in a cross between Hfr(λ)⁺ × F⁻(λ)⁻. (From Wollman and Jacob, 1957).

to form plaques (Hershey and Chase, 1952). The results of two experiments of this kind are given in Figure 3. Curves 1a and 2a represent the kinetics of the formation of T^+L^+ and Gal^+ recombinants respectively in an Hfr $\times$ F$^-$ cross in which both parents are lysogenic for λ phage, samples being diluted and plated without treatment. Curves 1b and 2b are derived from equivalent samples after treatment in the blendor. Similarly, curves 3a and 3b express the formation of infectious centres, without treatment and after treatment respectively, in an Hfr $\times$ F$^-$ cross in which the Hfr parent is lysogenic for λ phage and the F$^-$ parent non-lysogenic.

It will be seen that while the curves obtained from the untreated samples all arise from the origin and reach a plateau at about 50 minutes, as in Figure 2A and 2B, the corresponding curves obtained after treatment do *not* pass through the origin but nevertheless reach the same plateaux at about the same time. Moreover the times at which the various genetic markers appear to enter the zygote vary widely. For instance, T^+L^+ recombinants begin to appear at about nine minutes, as after phage treatment, while the appearance of Gal^+ recombinants and λ infectious centres

is delayed until 25 minutes. Since the time of appearance of markers widely separated on the chromosome, such as T^+L^+ on the one hand and Gal_b^+ on the other, is very different whereas closely linked markers like Gal_b and λ prophage appear at the same time despite the great disparity in their mode of expression, the conclusion is inescapable that *there exists a definite relationship between the time at which a given marker is transferred from the Hfr to the F$^-$ cell and the location of that marker on the Hfr chromosome.*

2. Transfer as an oriented process. If this point of view is correct, then the frequency distribution among T^+L^+ recombinants of markers situated between TL and Gal_b on the Hfr chromosome should vary widely according to the time after mixing at which samples are treated in the blendor. T^+L^+ recombinants from untreated samples (Figure 3, curve 1a) and from treated samples (Figure 3, curve 1b) were therefore analysed for inheritance of unselected markers as a function of the time of sampling. The genetic constitution of T^+L^+ recombinants derived from untreated samples is constant irrespective of the time of sampling and, therefore, of the proportion of the population that have formed effective contacts.

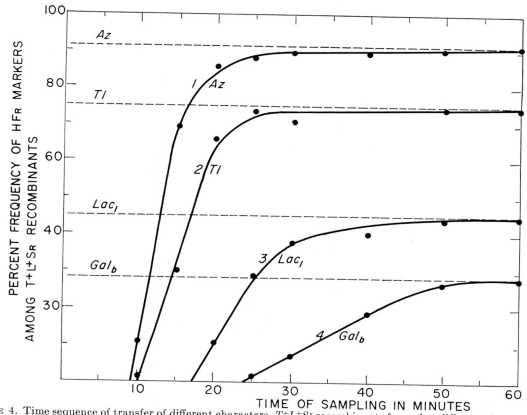

FIGURE 4. Time sequence of transfer of different characters. $T^+L^+S^r$ recombinants formed at different times on curves 1 a and 1 b, Figure 3, have been analysed as to their genetic constitution as a function of time. The distribution among $T^+L^+S^r$ recombinants of characters originating from the Hfr donor is represented as a percentage of the $T^+L^+S^r$ recombinants arising from the same sample. In dotted lines: from untreated samples. In solid lines: from treated samples. (From Wollman and Jacob, 1954 and 1957).

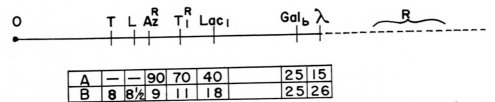

FIGURE 5. Genetic map of the OR chromosomal segment of Hfr H. The location of the different characters as measured in HfrH × P678 F⁻ crosses by A: the percentage of $T^+L^+S^r$ recombinants which have inherited the different Hfr alleles; B: the time at which individual Hfr characters start penetrating into the F⁻ recipient cells in a Waring blendor experiment. (From Wollman and Jacob, 1957).

As can be seen from the table and Figure 4, the percentage of various Hfr markers found among $T^+L^+S^r$ recombinants is approximately: Az^s 90 per cent, $T1^s$ 75 per cent, Lac^+ 45 per cent and Gal_b^+ 28 per cent. On the contrary, the frequency of inheritance of these same markers among $T^+L^+S^r$ recombinants stemming from the *treated* samples varies in a striking way according to the time of sampling, as the curves in Figure 4 show. The time at which any given character begins to appear among T^+L^+ recombinants is directly related to its distance from TL on the chromosome map (Fig. 5), the further the distance the greater being the delay in its appearance. Once a character begins to be found among T^+L^+ recombinants, the frequency of its inheritance increases rapidly as a function of time until its normal level is attained. Thus Az first appears at about nine minutes, $T1$ at ten minutes, Lac at 18 minutes and Gal at 25 minutes. At 50 minutes after mixing, all the markers transferred from the Hfr to the F⁻ cell have reached their normal frequency of inheritance. It is therefore clear that the Hfr chromosome penetrates the F⁻ cell in a specifically orientated way. The extremity, O (for "origin") enters first, to be followed by T^+L^+ eight to nine minutes later, and then by the other markers in the order of their arrangement on the chromosome and at intervals of time proportional to the distance between them until, at about 35 minutes after contact, the whole segment $O—R$ has been transferred (Fig. 5). The effect of treatment in the blendor thus seems to cut this chromosome segment during transfer and thus to determine the length of segment which enters the zygote and the markers which will be available for subsequent incorporation into recombinants (Wollman and Jacob, 1955, 1957).

Two kinds of evidence indicate that the agitation intervenes in *transfer* rather than in subsequent stages:

1. The very closely linked markers Gal_b and λ prophage appear at about the same time (25 minutes) after mixing despite the fact that transfer of prophage to the zygote is expressed immediately after transfer while the Gal_b marker is involved in the process of recombination.

2. Results similar to those obtained with the blendor are given by treatment of samples from a mating mixture with virulent phage to which

only the Hfr cells are susceptible (see Fig. 6). Destruction of the Hfr parent in this way allows an analysis of events occurring solely within the F⁻ cells which are unaffected by the phage (Hayes, 1957).

C. Physiology of Conjugation

1. *Nutritional requirements*. Zygote formation does not occur at a significant rate if parental cultures grown aerobically in broth are washed and mixed in buffer. This is especially the case if the parental suspensions are starved by aeration in buffer before mixing. Addition to the buffer of both glucose and sodium aspartate, but neither alone, allows zygote formation to proceed at a rate comparable to that found in broth. Krebs cycle dicarboxylic acids and glutamic acid, but no other dicarboxylic or amino acids, can replace aspartic acid in promoting the formation of zygotes while such metabolic inhibitors as fluoracetic acid, malonic acid, and cyanide, as well as 2:4 dinitrophenol (DNP), inhibit the process. Zygote formation does not occur in buffer + glucose + sodium aspartate under anaerobic conditions. It thus appears that energy liberated by the Krebs cycle is required (Fisher, 1957a). Moreover, differential starvation experiments show that only the Hfr parent requires energy, the F⁻ cells playing an entirely passive part until the completion of genetic transfer.

For what purposes do the Hfr cells require their energy? If a series of identical mixtures of Hfr and F⁻ cells, previously grown aerobically in broth, are made under anaerobic conditions and, at different intervals after mixing, oxygen is then admitted to each mixture in turn, it is found that, in each case, zygote formation (*i.e.*, transfer of T^+L^+ from the Hfr to the F⁻ cells) begins at eight minutes after the commencement of oxygenation and then progresses at precisely the same rate *irrespective of the duration of the preceding anaerobiosis*. This shows that, under anaerobic conditions, nothing happens which affects the efficiency of subsequent conjugation although the probability of chance contacts is the same as in the presence of oxygen. Thus the establishment of effective contacts between parental cells is an energy-requiring act performed by the donor cells (Fisher, 1957b).

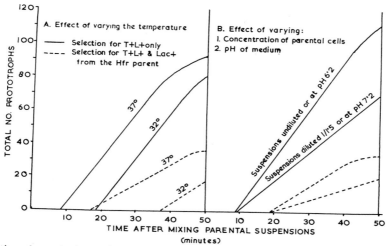

FIGURE 6. The kinetics of zygote formation, using phage T6 to eliminate the Hfr parental cells. Cultures of HfrH M⁻T6ˢ and F⁻TLB₁⁻T6ʳ were washed, resuspended in buffer + glucose + sodium aspartate at the appropriate temperature, mixed and aerated at the same temperature. At intervals samples were treated with phage T6, diluted and plated on: a. minimal agar + B₁ + glucose (selection for inheritance of *T⁺L⁺* only from the Hfr parent); b. minimal agar + B₁ + lactose (selection for inheritance of *T⁺L⁺* and *Lac⁺*). A shows the effect of the temperature at which zygote formation occurs. B shows the effect of varying the concentration of the parental cells or the pH of the medium. (From Hayes, 1957, J. Gen. Microbiol., in press).

The kinetics of genetic transfer, as demonstrated by the use of the Waring blendor, can be reproduced with great precision by arresting the transfer of the chromosome with DNP and then killing the Hfr cells with virulent phage. The use of DNP alone does not kill the parental cells so that transfer is resumed when the effective concentration of the drug is reduced by dilution. Similarly, if an Hfr × F⁻ mixture at 37°, in which chromosome transfer is proceeding, is diluted to prevent further contacts at about 20 minutes after mixing and then rapidly cooled to 4°, analysis of subsequent samples reveals no change in the inheritance of the Hfr marker *Lac⁺* among *T⁺L⁺* recombinants, showing that chromosome transfer has been arrested. When, however, the diluted mixture is warmed again to 37°, the inheritance of *Lac⁺*, which had only begun to enter at the time of cooling, immediately commences to rise again at its initial rate until its normal frequency is attained. Since the formation of new contacts was prevented by dilution, the secondary increase in *Lac⁺* inheritance among *T⁺L⁺* recombinants must have been due to subsequent entry of this locus into cells which had previously acquired *T⁺L⁺*. Such experiments not only confirm the continuity of chromosomal movement into the F⁻ cell but show that energy is required throughout the period of chromosome transfer. However, energy is not needed to hold mating cells together once effective contacts have been established (Fisher, 1957b).

2. *The effect of temperature.* As might be expected from the fact that the Hfr cells require energy for chromosomal transfer, the efficiency of zygote formation falls rapidly as the temperature diverges from the optimal at 37°. Thus at 44° the number of F⁻ cells which have received the *T⁺L⁺* markers from the Hfr parent in a given time is only 25 per cent, and at 25° only 6 per cent that at 37° (Hayes, 1956). Figure 6A shows what happens when the kinetics of chromosome transfer are studied in identical Hfr × F⁻ crosses in buffer + glucose + sodium aspartate, at 37° and at 32°. The reduction of temperature will lower the overall capacity of the Hfr cells to produce energy by carbohydrate oxidation. At 37° the *T⁺L⁺* markers (continuous line) begin to enter the F⁻ cells at eight minutes and the marker *Lac⁺* (interrupted line) at 17 minutes after mixing, so that transfer from *TL* to *Lac* occupies nine minutes at this temperature. At 32°, on the other hand, *T⁺L⁺* enters at 18 minutes and *Lac⁺* at 38 minutes so that transfer of the same piece of chromosome takes 20 minutes, that is about twice as long, at the lower temperature. It has been mentioned that since the curve expressing the kinetics of formation of effective contacts commences at zero time, effective contacts must be made very quickly so that it may be assumed that transfer of the O——*TL* segment occupies virtually the whole of the lag period preceding entry of *T⁺L⁺* into the F⁻ cell. Thus at 37°, transfer of O——*TL* takes eight minutes and of O——*TL*——*Lac* 17 minutes, while at 32° transfer of these same segments takes 18 and 38 minutes respectively. The proportionality between these times strongly suggests that that part of the chromosome from *O* to *Lac*, at least, enters the F⁻ cell at a uniform rate which depends upon the available energy, so that measurement of the relative distances between chromosomal markers

in terms of time is a valid procedure (Hayes, 1957).

The fact that the curves shown in Figure 6A are parallel, although displaced on the time axis, indicates that the only effect of this degree of limitation of energy, in so far as conjugation is concerned, is to slow the rate of chromosome transfer.

3. *The effect of population density.* When the frequency with which chance contacts occur in Hfr × F⁻ mixtures is altered by mixing the same number of cells of each parent in a different volume of fluid, the relationship of the resulting curves (shown in Fig. 6B) is quite different from that characterising alterations in temperature. It will be seen that the time of entry of various markers into the F⁻ cells remains unchanged when the population density of the parental cells is reduced; the curves arise from the same point on the time axis but their slopes differ (Hayes, 1957). This same effect of population density is observed whether the manifestation studied is formation of recombinants or infectious centres. It is thus evident that the *slope* of the curves expressing the rate of zygote formation is a simple function of the frequency of chance contacts between Hfr and F⁻ cells, within a certain population range.

4. *The effect of pH.* The rate of zygote formation in buffer + glucose + sodium aspartate is doubled when the pH is reduced from 7.2 to 6.2. Since this effect is also apparent when the cross is made in unsupplemented buffer it must be unrelated to energy requirements, because, under these conditions, the Hfr cells are limited to their endogenous resources (Fisher, 1957b). The effect is not found, or is not marked, when crosses are made in broth. When the kinetics of chromosomal transfer are compared for identical Hfr × F⁻ crosses in buffer + glucose + sodium aspartate at pH 7.2 and at pH 6.2, the same result is obtained as when the population density is varied, as Figure 6B demonstrates (Hayes, 1957). The effect of lowering the pH must therefore by ascribed to physical action on the cell surfaces which facilitates the intimacy of chance contacts so that a higher proportion of such contacts can become effective in a given time. This is in keeping with the surface differences, probably attributable to differences of charge, between F⁺ and F⁻ cells which have previously been described (Maccacaro, 1955).

A difference between the surface antigenic properties of donor and recipient strains is suggested by the results of preliminary experiments by L. and S. Le Minor at the Pasteur Institute.

D. *The Frequency of Conjugation*

When Hfr cells are mixed in broth at 37° with an excess of F⁻ cells, what proportion of the Hfr cells have conjugated at about 50 minutes after mixing, when the curves defining the kinetics of effective contact formation have reached their plateaux (Fig. 2)? If one were to examine only one expression of conjugation, such as the frequency of T^+L^+ recombinants, no absolute answer could be given to this question since the proportion of zygotes which do not yield recombinants of this class is not known. Since the frequency of T^+L^+ recombinants in Hfr (λ)⁺ × F⁻ (λ)⁺ crosses is about 20 per cent of the Hfr cells initially present, it could only be asserted that not less than 20 per cent of the Hfr cells must have conjugated. By correlating the frequency of recombination with that of zygotic induction, however, it can be estimated that approximately 100 per cent of the Hfr population conjugate (Jacob and Wollman, 1955a; Wollman and Jacob, 1957).

As has been said, in the cross Hfr (λ)⁺ × F⁻ (λ)⁺, 20 per cent of the Hfr cells form zygotes which yield T^+L^+ recombinants (Fig. 2A). When the same Hfr (λ)⁺ strain is crossed under the same conditions with F⁻ (λ)⁻, about 50 per cent of the Hfr cells transmit λ prophage to the F⁻ cells with the result that about 50 per cent of the maximum number of possible zygotes is destroyed by zygotic induction. But, as reference to Figure 2B will show, this destruction of zygotes only reduces the frequency of T^+L^+ recombinants by a factor of 2, from 20 per cent to 10 per cent. If it is assumed that those zygotes which yield T^+L^+ recombinants in Hfr (λ)⁺ × F⁻ (λ)⁻ crosses did not inherit λ prophage, then since only half of the potential T^+L^+ recombinants are removed when 50 per cent of the total possible zygotes are destroyed, the total number of zygotes formed must account for 100 per cent of the Hfr cells present.

When Hfr × F⁻ cells are mixed together and the mixture examined at intervals under a light microscope, an increasing number of pairs is observed which remain in contact for long periods. Such pairs are particularly noticeable when the two parental strains differ morphologically as in the case of HfrH and F⁻ *E. coli* strain C (Lieb, Weigle and Kellenberger, 1955). Electron microphotographs obtained by Dr. T. F. Anderson (Anderson, Wollman and Jacob, 1957) are presented in Figure 7. The top picture shows conjugation between HfrH and the F⁻ strain P678 which has been used in most of our studies. HfrH has long flagella whereas P678 is covered with bristles. As an additional distinguishing feature, HfrH has had ultraviolet-killed λc phage adsorbed to its surface: P678 is resistant to this phage. The middle picture demonstrates conjugation between HfrH and *E. coli* C. In this case the two strains are so different in their morphology that additional labelling is not required. In both crosses the conjugating bacteria appear to be united by a cellular bridge.

E. *The Evidence for Partial Genetic Transfer*

The experiments reported above demonstrate that, by use of the blendor or the phage technique, it is possible to regulate at will the length of chromosome segment transferred from the Hfr to the F⁻ cell. The partial zygote thus formed is perfectly operative and recombinants will be formed in exactly the same fashion as when transfer is allowed to proceed normally. Interruption of the mating process at about 50 minutes after mixing when Gal_b, the last known biochemical marker on the O——R segment, has been transferred (Fig. 5), has no effect either on the number or on the genetic constitution of the recombinants formed.

It can be shown that in a normal cross, where only those characters situated on the O——R segment *appear* to be transferred from donor to recipient cells, the whole of this segment is not, in fact, transferred to every zygote (Jacob and Wollman, 1955a; Wollman and Jacob, 1957). As the leading locus, O, followed in order by the other loci, penetrates the F⁻ cell, spontaneous breakages may occur in certain cases. The occurrence of zygotic induction in certain crosses makes it possible to estimate some of these breakages. Penetration of λ prophage into a non-lysogenic recipient cell leads to destruction of the zygote. If λ prophage entered every zygote no recombinants would ever be formed: an Hfr (λ)⁺ × F⁻ (λ)⁻ cross would be sterile. This, however, is not the case since half the usual number of T^+L^+ recombinants (10% instead of 20%) is recovered while only about one half the number of possible zygotes are scored as infectious centres (see *The Frequency of Conjugation*, above). These results are readily interpretable in the light of the mechanism of transfer which has been described. About half the zygotes inherit the Hfr segment O——Gal——λ and are thus destroyed by zygotic induction. The other half receives a segment *shorter* than O——Gal and will not be destroyed, so that about 20 per cent of them will yield T^+L^+ recombinants. These T^+L^+ recombinants constitute a special group in so far as they are derived from zygotes which have been selected by acquiring a shorter normal piece of Hfr chromosome. Thus, if the theory is right, they should show a lower frequency of inheritance of those unselected markers least linked to TL than does the *whole* group of T^+L^+ recombinants from a cross in which zygotic induction does not occur (Wollman and Jacob, 1954, 1957). That this is indeed so can be seen by comparing the results of crosses 3 and 4 in the table.

In the case of zygotic induction (cross 4) the frequency among T^+L^+ recombinants of those markers located close to λ prophage is greatly reduced, the closer the linkage to λ the greater being the reduction. In particular, the marker Gal_b, which is most closely linked to λ, is almost absent as can also be inferred from the $T^+L^+:Gal^+$ ratios in the table. On the other hand there is no significant difference in the inheritance of unselected markers between crosses 3 and 4 (table) when Gal^+ is selected instead of T^+L^+, showing that if Gal^+ enters the zygote and the zygote

survives, the outcome of the cross is the same irrespective of the lysogenic relationships. As a matter of fact the orientated nature of chromosomal transfer from the Hfr to the F⁻ cell can be deduced directly from comparison of the data of Figures 2A and 2B and of the table. The blendor experiment is only a direct demonstration of its reality.

It can also be shown by the study of a series of inducible prophages (Jacob and Wollman, 1955a, 1956b) that the probability of chromosomal rupture increases rapidly as R is approached. All these prophages are located on the O——R segment between Gal_b and R. The frequency of zygotic induction which they evoke is a measure of the frequency of their transfer from Hfr$(ly)^+$ to F⁻$(ly)^-$. For the seven different prophages studied, this ranges from 65 per cent to 5 per cent. When this information is correlated with the order of arrangement of these prophages on the chromosome, established by genetic analysis of Hfr$(ly)^-$ × F⁻$(ly)^+$ crosses in which there is no zygotic induction, it is found that the further a prophage is located from Gal_b the lower is the frequency of prophage transfer. The relative positions of these prophages can also be assessed by the blender technique, their times of entry ranging from 25 to 33 minutes.

The point of rupture, R, beyond which no markers enter the F⁻ cell can formally be considered as genetically equivalent, although conceptually opposed, to the elimination locus, E, which Cavalli and Jinks (1956), working with F⁺ × F⁻ systems, have located at, or very close to, the λ locus.

III. THE FORMATION OF RECOMBINANTS

As a result of conjugation a zygote is formed. The experiments recounted in the previous sections indicate unambiguously that the mechanisms involved in bacterial conjugation are quite different from what is found in other organisms. The two main differences are the following:

1. Bacterial conjugation involves a one-way transfer of genetic material from a donor to a recipient strain.

2. This transfer is partial since only a piece of the Hfr chromosome of variable size is injected into the recipient cell. The resulting zygote is therefore a rather peculiar one for which the term *merozygote* has been proposed (Wollman and Jacob, 1957).

Once the merozygote is formed, a series of processes is initiated which ultimately result in the appearance of a recombinant bacterium. It is unlikely that these processes differ fundamentally from those which mediate the expression of other kinds of partial genetic transfer among bacteria, such as transformation and transduction. In all three cases a recombinant chromosome is evolved which is essentially that of the recipient parent

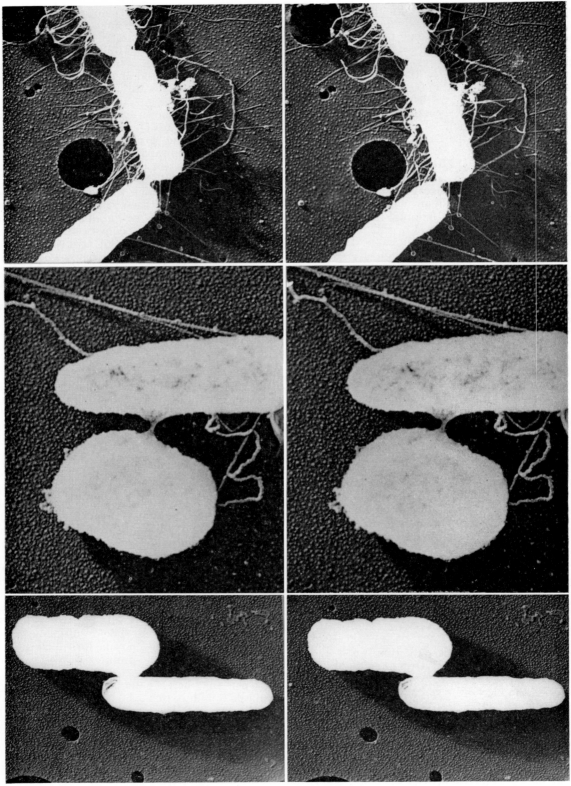

FIGURE 7.

TABLE 1. GENETIC ANALYSIS OF $T^+L^+S^r$ AND Gal^+Sr RECOMBINANTS OBTAINED IN VARIOUS CROSSES BETWEEN HfrH·S^s AND P678 F$^-$·S^r

The strains used are, as in Figure 2, HfrH·$S^sT^+L^+Az^sT_1{}^s$ $Lac_1{}^+Gal_b{}^+$ and P678 F$^-S^rT^-L^-Az^rT1^rLac^-Gal_b{}^-$ (for symbols see Figure 1).

In column 1 are the different crosses reported (for details see text).

In column 2 the ratio of the numbers of $T^+L^+S^r$ to Gal^+S^r recombinants obtained.

In column 3 the distribution of the different alleles contributed by the Hfr donor to $T^+L^+S^r$ recombinants on one side, to Gal^+S^r recombinants on the other side, as a percentage of recombinants having inherited those characters. (From Wollman and Jacob, 1957.)

No.	Crosses	Ratio $T^+L^+S^r$/ Gal^+S^r	Genetic constitution of recombinants									
			$T^+L^+S^r$					Gal^+S^r				
			Az	$T1$	Lac	Gal_b	(λ)	TL	Az	$T1$	Lac	(λ)
1	Hfr$(\lambda)^- \times$ F$^-(\lambda)^-$	4.2	91	72	48	27	—	83	78	79	81	—
2	Hfr$(\lambda)^- \times$ F$^-(\lambda)^+$	3.7	92	73	49	31	15	75	75	74	74	84
3	Hfr$(\lambda)^+ \times$ F$^-(\lambda)^+$	4.2	90	70	47	29	14	80	78	78	82	82
4	Hfr$(\lambda)^+ \times$ F$^-(\lambda)^-$	54	86	60	21	2.5	<0.1	82	79	78	74	1
5	Hfr$(\lambda)^-$U.V. $\times$ F$^-(\lambda)^-$	4.5	50	32	9	1	—	17	24	29	41	—

save that a segment or segments of variable size have been replaced by homologous fragments of the donor genome. Once this integration has been achieved, the recombinant cell will emerge through segregation and phenotypic expression of the character or characters contributed by the donor parent.

We will now discuss in turn the available information relating to each of these steps.

A. Chromosomal Integration

There is at present little understanding of the processes which lead to the formation of a recombinant chromosome from the two parental constituents of a merozygote. Since there is insufficient evidence on which to base a definite hypothesis we will simply examine briefly the facts that are known to us.

1. Genetic patterns of integration. The segment of Hfr chromosome which enters the zygote may or may not be incorporated into a new recombinant chromosome. When, however, integration does occur, the asymmetry of the chromosomal contributions from the two parents may be expected to impose certain patterns of recombination.

(a) Efficiency of integration. It is possible to calculate the probability that a character derived from the donor parent will appear in recombinants, and this probability is found to be very constant for any given cross. It has already been shown, by comparison of the frequency of recombination with that of zygotic induction, that whereas the Hfr markers T^+L^+ are transferred to about 100 per cent of zygotes, only some 20 per cent of these zygotes yield T^+L^+ recombinants. Thus the efficiency of integration of these markers together is about $\frac{1}{5}$. Similarly we know that the Gal_b marker is transferred to about 60 per cent of zygotes but is only found among recombinants issuing from five per cent of the total zygotes, so that it is integrated with an efficiency of about $\frac{1}{12}$. There is thus rather a small probability of integration for an Hfr gene which has entered the zygote, and this probability varies with the location of the gene on the chromosome (Jacob and Wollman, 1955a; Wollman and Jacob, 1957).

(b) Polarity of integration. From the example

FIGURE 7. Stereoscopic electron micrographs showing connections between cells of opposite mating type. Top. Mixture of *E. coli* K-12 Hfr and K-12 F$^-$/λ. Bacteriophage λc (which had previously been killed with ultraviolet light) was adsorbed on the Hfr cells to identify them. The F$^-$/λ which failed to adsorb the phage could also be recognized by their numerous "bristles." In this view, a bridge 1500 Å wide can be seen connecting the end of a dividing F$^-$ bacterium with the end of a Hfr bacterium to which bacteriophage particles are attached. EMG 5.IV.56 Bl, 2. × 21,000. Middle. Mixture of *E. coli* K-12 Hfr and *E. coli* CF$^-$. At the top is a typically long and narrow K-12 Hfr cell connected by a 500 A bridge to a typically short and plump CF$^-$ cell. EMG 20.IV.56 C 3, 4. × 40,000. Bottom. Mixture of *E. coli* F$^+$ and *E. coli* CF$^-$. At the top is a typically long and narrow K-12 Hfr cell connected by a 500 Å bridge to a typically short and plump CF$^-$ cell. EMG 20.IV.56 C 3, 4. × 40,000. Bottom. Mixture of *E. coli* K-12 F$^+$ and *E. coli* CF$^-$. Here the plump CF$^-$ cell at the top is in intimate contact with the narrow K-12 F$^+$ cell in the lower part of the picture. EMG 3.V.56 D, 4, 5. ×20,000.

It seems probable that during conjugation the genetic material from Hfr or F$^+$ donor cells passes to F$^-$ recipient cells through connections like the ones shown here.

Twenty minutes after mixing, specimens were fixed in the vapor over 2% OsO$_4$ and then dried by the critical point method to conserve the three dimensional structure of the specimen. Specimens were lightly shadowed with a An-Pd mixture and coated with 10 Å of carbon to reduce charging effects in the electron microscope. (From Anderson, Wollman and Jacob, 1957).

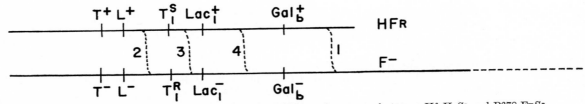

FIGURE 8. Patterns of integration among Gal^+S^r recombinants in a cross between HfrH S^s and P678 F$^-S^r$. Different classes observed, expressed as a percentage of total Gal^+S^r recombinants

Percent	Alleles from Hfr donor					Crossing over in region
	T	L	T1	Lac	Gal	
68	T	L	T1	Lac	Gal	1
5			T1	Lac	Gal	1 and 2
1.7				Lac	Gal	1 and 3
11.6					Gal	1 and 4
7.5	TL			Lac	Gal	1, 2 and 3
2.5	TL		T1		Gal	1, 3 and 4
1.7	TL				Gal	1, 2 and 4
2			T1		Gal	1, 2, 3 and 4

just given it would appear that the closer a gene is situated to O the greater is its chance of integration. The O——R segment therefore seems to be characterized by an integration gradient as well as by a gradient of transfer. These two gradients are exemplified by comparison of the genetic constitution of $T^+L^+S^r$ and Gal^+S^r recombinants from crosses 1, 2 and 3 in the table. While the frequency of inheritance of markers among T^+L^+ recombinants is strongly dependent on their distances from O, in the Gal^+ recombinants all the unselected markers on the O——R region appear with the same high frequency (Jacob and Wollman, 1955a; Wollman and Jacob, 1957). Figure 8 illustrates the types of recombinants observed in the Gal^+S^r class, which have issued from zygotes which certainly received the whole of the O——Gal_b segment from the Hfr parent. It will be seen that almost 70 per cent have inherited the TL——Gal_b segment as a whole. If O represents the extremity of the chromosome, as seems reasonable, these recombinants would result from a single crossover in position 1. The other recombinants would be the result of two or more crossings-over. A certain amount of negative interference is therefore apparent.

The table clearly shows that the combined effect of a gradient of integration as well as of transfer is to facilitate mapping of the *order* of unselected markers when characters close to O (such as T^+L^+) are selected but to render this mapping almost impossible when selection is made for characters (such as Gal_b) situated close to R since, in this latter case, all the unselected markers appear with the same high frequency among the recombinants. The possibility of simple genetic mapping is precluded even following T^+L^+ selection, since the genetic outcome also depends in part on variations in transfer. Thus the only reliable way of mapping the *distances* between genes as well as their order is to measure their relative times of appearance in the F$^-$ cell by means of the blendor or some equivalent technique. The only assumption which must be made

to establish the validity of this mode of measurement is that injection of the Hfr chromosome into the F$^-$ cell proceeds at a constant speed, and evidence has been provided that this is so as long as the available energy is kept constant. The value of the blendor technique is well shown by attempts to map some of the inducible prophages located on the Gal——R segment. Whereas some of the phages situated farthest from Gal can scarcely be located by analysis of a cross between lysogenic and non-lysogenic cells, the blendor technique allows an accurate determination of the time at which the prophage enters the F$^-$ cell (Wollman and Jacob, 1957).

2. The process of integration. The following experiments may throw some light on how integration is accomplished.

(a) The effect of ultraviolet light on integration. If, in a non-lysogenic system, the Hfr parent is exposed to small doses of ultraviolet light prior to mating, the genetic constitution of recombinants is drastically modified although their total number is only slightly decreased, irrespective of whether T^+L^+ or Gal^+ is selected (Jacob and Wollman, 1955a and unpub.). The table (cross 5) reveals that the frequency with which unselected markers are found among both $T^+L^+S^r$ and Gal^+S^r recombinants is strikingly reduced by ultraviolet treatment. This means that radiation results in a loosening of the linkage observed among the markers lying between TL and Gal or, to put it another way, that the probability of a crossover occurring between two markers is increased. Since the frequency of recombination is decreased proportionately for both classes, it seems likely that radiation affects the processes of integration within the merozygote rather than genetic transfer from Hfr to F$^-$ cell.

If a mating mixture is diluted in nutrient broth at 37° 15 minutes after mixing, in order to prevent further collisions, and samples are thereafter irradiated with ultraviolet at intervals, it is observed that irradiation affects the genetic constitution of recombinants up to 70 minutes after

irradiation
whether the
s are treated.
After 70 minutes ———— shes until, at
120 minutes, it is no longer found. This suggests
that the processes involved in the formation of
the recombinant chromosome begin to be completed at about 70 minutes and are complete by
120 minutes.

This action of ultraviolet light on bacterial
recombination recalls the similar effect which the
same ultraviolet doses exert on recombination in
λ phage (Jacob and Wollman, 1955b) which was
thought to be best interpreted according to

rate of inactivation decreases between 40 and 80
minutes after mixing and is no longer measurable
after 100 minutes. Whatever the mechanism of
this stabilisation may be, it implies that after 100
minutes the genetic information of the Hfr fragment has been transmitted to material which is
not susceptible to P^{32} decay.

B. Expression of Recombinants

This is the final stage in the sequence of events
which follows fertilisation of the F^- cell. The
recombinant chromosome has been formed within
the zygote. The process whereby it attains an
autonomous position within a haploid cell is

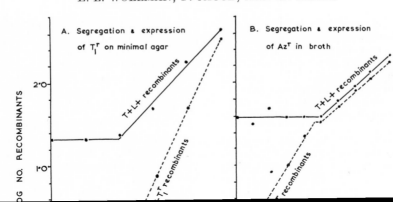

herited from the Hfr parent are quite different. Expression of the character Az^r commences at the time of dilution (or of plating) of the zygotes and then rises exponentially to become complete just before the segregants which inherit it start to divide (Figure 9B). In contrast, the character T1^r does not begin to be expressed until *after* segregation while full expression (i.e. in 75% of all T^+L^+ recombinants) is delayed until the fourth generation (Figure 9A).

The gene *T1^r* has been reported, from work on *E. coli* diploids, to be recessive to *T1^s* (Lederberg, 1949) so that its expression is not to be expected until after segregation; the further extension of its phenotypic lag is a natural consequence of the dependence of the development of phage resistance on structural alterations of the cell wall. Since expression of the character Az^r rises rapidly during a period when both alleles must be present together in the diploid merozygote, it follows that Az^r is dominant to Az^s; this is an exception to the rule that wild type alleles are dominant to their mutant alleles in *E. coli*.

Knowledge of the kinetics of phenotypic expression following recombination in bacteria has a two-fold importance. Firstly it offers a normal control against which the results of mutation kinetics can be studied. Secondly it is necessary for the rational design of recombination experiments, whether in *E. coli* or in other bacterial species. For example, the choice of selective markers which are recessive, or whose expression is normally delayed, is unlikely to yield recombinants from an otherwise fertile cross unless application of the selective agent is withheld until expression has occurred. This is well exemplified by the fact that virtually no Az^r recombinants appear if recently formed zygotes which have inherited the gene Az^r from the donor parent are plated directly on medium containing sodium azide, despite the fact that Az^r appears to be dominant and is rapidly expressed.

IV. THE RELATIONSHIP BETWEEN F$^+$ AND Hfr SYSTEMS

The discussion so far has dealt exclusively with the features of crosses involving an Hfr donor (HfrH) and F$^-$ recipient strains. In this section we propose to examine the properties of the equivalent F$^+$ × F$^-$ cross and hope to show that a comparative analysis of the two systems may lead to a unified interpretation of the mating process in *E. coli*. The principal points of difference between F$^+$ and Hfr strains have already been summarized and will not be reiterated here. The main aim of this analysis is to attempt to equate the two systems. It will be found that some of the paradoxes which seem to exist are resolved as the analysis proceeds: others remain and will be discussed in their proper context.

In the light of the results of analysis of the Hfr system, it may be asked whether the low fre-quency of recombination found in F$^+$ × F$^-$ crosses is due to low frequency of conjugation, of transfer, or of integration. The evidence relevant to this question will now be presented.

A. Analysis of F$^+$ × F$^-$ Crosses

1. Conjugation. There is one character of F$^+$ cells which is transferred to F$^-$ cells at high frequency. This is the F$^+$ character itself, and its transfer requires cellular contact (Cavalli *et al.*, 1953; Hayes, 1953a). The kinetics of F$^+$ transfer can be studied by the same methods as those used for the analysis of Hfr systems. A mixture of F$^+$ and F$^-$ cells is made in broth, the F$^+$ cells being in excess. Samples are removed at intervals and plated, both directly and after treatment in a Waring blendor, on a medium on which only the F$^-$ recipient cells can grow. The resulting F$^-$ clones are then scored for inheritance of F$^+$ as a function of time after mixing. In the case of the untreated samples it is found that the curve expressing the proportion of F$^-$ cells which have inherited the character F$^+$ arises from the origin and increases linearly until a plateau is reached about 50 minutes after mixing, when some 75 per cent of the F$^-$ cells have been converted. In the case of the treated samples, the F$^+$ character begins to appear at about five minutes after mixing (Jacob and Wollman, 1955a). It thus turns out that transfer of F$^+$ from F$^+$ donor to F$^-$ recipient cells is very similar to the transfer of such characters as T^+L^+ from Hfr to F$^-$ cells (Fig. 3) except that F$^+$ transfer occurs several minutes earlier than any of the hitherto known markers on the O——R segment of HfrH. It therefore seems probable that F$^+$ is located on the F$^+$ chromosome within a region $0'$——R' which is transferred at high frequency to the F$^-$ cell. Another kind of character which appears to be transferred at high frequency from F$^+$ to F$^-$ cells is the ability to synthesise certain colicines such as colicine E, originally a character of *E. coli* strain K-30 (Frédéricq and Betz-Bareau, 1953). Kinetic analysis of the transfer of this ability shows that production of colicine E is transferred from a K-12 F$^+$ strain to an F$^-$ recipient strain at about two and a half minutes after mixing. The ability to produce colicine E would therefore seem to be controlled by a locus situated between $0'$ and F$^+$ on the F$^+$ chromosome (Jacob and Wollman, unpub.).

One can thus conclude that conjugation between F$^+$ and F$^-$ bacteria is no different from Hfr × F$^-$ conjugation and occurs with a frequency of the order of 100 per cent. In substantiation of this, conjoint pairs of cells, and cellular bridges uniting them, similar to those observed in Hfr × F$^-$ crosses, can also be seen in F$^+$ × F$^-$ crosses by means of phase contrast and electron microscopy (Fig. 7, bottom picture) (Anderson, Wollman and Jacob, 1957).

2. Transfer and integration. Since the frequency of conjugation, and of transfer of certain markers, is found to be high in F⁺ × F⁻ crosses, the question arises whether those F⁺ markers which are not inherited at high frequency are absent because they are not transferred, or because they are transferred but not integrated. The most significant evidence is derived from zygotic induction. Whereas this phenomenon can be directly demonstrated in the cross HfrH $(\lambda)^+ \times F^- (\lambda)^-$, it is hardly detectable in the equivalent $F^+ (\lambda)^+ \times F^- (\lambda)^-$ cross (Jacob and Wollman, 1956b). Since the transfer of λ prophage is immediately expressed it must be concluded that prophage is not *transferred* at high frequency from an F⁺ lysogenic donor to an F⁻ non-lysogenic recipient cell. It must therefore be assumed that the failure of at least the *Gal*—λ region of the F⁺ chromosome to be inherited at high frequency is due to lack of transfer. The hypothesis can therefore be made that the two systems are similar in every respect save one; that the location of the region of preferential rupture is different. Accordingly, the chromosome of F⁺ bacteria also comprises two segments separated by a new region of rupture, R', such that the segment O'——R', carrying the markers colicine E and F⁺, is transferred at high frequency. The other known genetic markers are all located on the other segment which is not transferred at high frequency.

B. The Mechanism of Low Frequency of Recombination

HfrH cells can only transfer, at high frequency, markers located on the O——R segment of the chromosome. In the case of the equivalent F⁺ cells, only markers on the chromosome segment O'——R' can similarly be transferred to F⁻ cells. Let us consider how, in either case, a marker situated on neither of these segments may be transferred at low frequency. There are two possible hypotheses; either each Hfr or F⁺ cell has a small but equal probability of transferring a chromosome segment on which the marker is located, or else there exists in each Hfr or F⁺ population a small fraction of mutant cells which can transfer the marker with high efficiency. In this latter event the number of recombinants formed by independent cultures of the same F⁺ strain should be extremely variable as compared with those formed by samples of the same culture. The results of such fluctuation tests (Luria and Delbrück, 1943) in which the F⁺ population was standardised so as to contain only a few presumptive mutant clones in each independent culture, are in agreement with this prediction (Jacob and Wollman, 1956a). Genetic analysis of recombinants isolated from fluctuation tests of this kind affords striking confirmation of the mutation hypothesis. When the genetic patterns of the progeny of different independent cultures are compared they are found to vary widely between cultures, both in the characters of the F⁺ parent

which are transferred and the proportion of these characters found among recombinants. On the other hand, the genetic constitution of recombinants arising from different samples of the same culture is very homogeneous.

It is therefore probable that most, if not all, of the recombinants formed in an F⁺ × F⁻ cross must be due to preexisting Hfr mutants in the F⁺ population. By means of the method of indirect selection known as "replica plating" (Lederberg and Lederberg, 1952), it is in fact possible to isolate different types of Hfr strains from F⁺ cultures. When the means of selection are adequate, the efficiency of isolation of Hfr mutants responsible for particular recombinant colonies is close to 100 per cent. By selecting for recombinants which have inherited different markers from the F⁺ parent it is possible, by the replica plating method, to isolate a variety of different Hfr strains capable of transmitting the selected marker to recombinants at high frequency. These Hfr strains differ from one another not only in the characters they can transfer to the zygote but also in the *sequence* in which these characters are transferred (Jacob and Wollman, 1956a). Each of the known markers of *E. coli* K-12 can be transferred at high frequency by one or another Hfr strain but no single Hfr strain has so far been isolated which alone can transfer all these markers. That low frequency of appearance of a given character among recombinants is indeed due to the fact that the locus determining it is not situated on the chromosome segment transferred at high frequency, is demonstrated by the fact that zygotic induction is not observed in crosses between strains of Hfr(λ)⁺ which do not transmit the Gal_b character, and non-lysogenic F⁻ strains. This situation is found in crosses involving HfrC. This strain has been otherwise shown by Skaar and Garen (personal communication) to transfer the TL——Lac segment in a sequence which is the reverse of that exhibited by HfrH.

The hypothesis therefore appears well substantiated that characters transmitted to recombinants at low frequency, either in F⁺ × F⁻ or in Hfr × F⁻ crosses, are transferred by spontaneous Hfr mutants. Among the Hfr strains isolated there seem to exist certain preferential patterns of transfer but the possibility has not yet been excluded that this is due to a bias introduced by the use of streptomycin as a contra-selective agent. The properties of these different Hfr strains is still under investigation.

Despite the low frequency with which recombinants are found, F⁺ × F⁻ mixtures in broth can be analysed kinetically by the use of virulent phage to eliminate the F⁺ parent, in the same way as the Waring blendor has been used for analysis of Hfr × F⁻ crosses (Hayes, 1957). In comparative experiments of this kind the cross HfrH × F⁻ is found to be about 2×10^4 times more productive of T^+L^+ recombinants than the equivalent F⁺ ×

F⁻ cross. When selection is made for the T^+L^+, $T^+L^+Lac^+$ or $T^+L^+B_1^+$ markers of the F⁺ parent (see Fig. 1), it is found that the transfer of T^+L^+ starts at about eight minutes and of Lac^+ at 18 minutes after mixing, exactly as in the equivalent Hfr × F⁻ cross. Unlike the Hfr × F⁻ cross, however, the F⁺ marker B_1^+ is transferred at about 45 minutes after mixing. No recombinants inheriting the xylose, maltose or streptomycin markers of the F⁺ parent are found up to 90 minutes after mixing when selection is made for them. This implies that among those Hfr mutants which can transfer T^+L^+ at high frequency, the most common types are broadly similar to HfrH. The late transfer of the F⁺ marker B_1^+, and its appearance among T^+L^+ recombinants with a frequency of five per cent, indicates, however, that at least five per cent of these Hfr mutants can transfer at high frequency a different chromosome segment.

V. DISCUSSION

A. Sexual Differentiation

Sexual conjugation in *E. coli* takes place between cells of opposite mating type which can, for convenience, be referred to as *donor* and *recipient* since, after cellular contact, genetic material is transferred from the former to the latter. At the present time these two mating types can only be defined in terms of the properties expressed by the donor. These properties comprise a surface configuration which enables effective contact with the recipient cell's surface to be established, the ability to inject a chromosomal segment, O——R, which differs from donor to donor and finally, the capacity to mutate from one donor type to another. Upon high frequency transfer of a small chromosome segment from an F⁺ donor to an F⁻ recipient, the recipient is thereby converted into an F⁺ donor in which these three properties are simultaneously expressed. It is not known, however, whether these properties are all expressions of the same genetic factor or whether they may exist independently.

The distinction between F⁺ and Hfr donor strains is more artificial than real since the frequency of recombination observed in practice will depend only upon whether the selective markers used happen to lie on the O——R segment or beyond it. Since the low frequency of recombination found in the latter case appears to be mediated by different Hfr mutants preexisting in the donor culture, use of the terms "Hfr" and "F⁺" to denote a fundamental distinction in the capacity of the two strains to yield recombinants loses its validity. The term "F⁺ strain" has also been used to imply the ability of the strain to transmit the donor state to F⁺ cells at high frequency. In contrast, neither of the Hfr strains hitherto isolated could transmit either the F⁺ or Hfr donor state at high frequency. However, when selection is made for certain markers of either HfrH or HfrC, the Hfr donor state is inherited by a high proportion of recombinants and, in the case of HfrC at least, appears to be controlled by a specific locus closely linked to one of the *Gal* loci (Hayes, 1953b; Cavalli and Jinks, 1956).

In its transmissibility and inheritance, F⁺ displays the properties of a gene. In strain HfrH, F⁺ is no longer found as such but appears to be replaced by a new locus determining the donor state, situated distal to a new region of rupture. Since this strain can revert to the original F⁺ donor state, the most likely hypothesis is that the *position* of F⁺ determines the region of preferential rupture and that mutation to Hfr is a function of the shift of F⁺ to a new position on the chromosome. If, in a Hfr strain, F⁺ happened to be located on the O——R segment proximal to the region of rupture it determined, then the donor state would be transferred at high frequency to F⁻ cells as in the case of F⁺ strains. The range of Hfr strains which have now been isolated has not yet been investigated from this point of view. It should be pointed out, however, that in F⁺ × F⁻ crosses all, or nearly all, the recombinants may be F⁺ even when the cross is made in broth and the F⁺ parent is eliminated by phage to prevent secondary transfer of the F⁺ character to the recombinant cells after plating. If, as is supposed, these recombinants result from Hfr mutants one would expect them to inherit either the Hfr or the F⁻ character, not the F⁺ (Hayes, 1957).

Different donor strains differ in the chromosomal location of the region of rupture, R, which determines the length of chromosome they are able to transfer. Any donor type apparently possesses the potentiality to mutate to other donor types, with a consequent shift in the position of R (F⁺ $\rightleftharpoons$ Hfr₁ $\rightleftharpoons$ Hfr₂ etc.), as well as to the recipient type (Lederberg *et al.*, 1952; Hayes, 1953a). When a recipient F⁻ cell inherits that region of a donor chromosome controlling the donor properties of the cell (F⁺ or Hfr) it also inherits the capacity to mutate to other donor types. Thus it has been possible to obtain F⁺ and various Hfr derivatives of *E. coli* strain C which was originally F⁻ (Jacob and Wollman, unpub.). The occurrence of mutation from the recipient to the donor state has not yet been reported.

A population of donor cells is therefore heterogeneous and contains, in addition to a majority of the original type which, on conjugation, can transfer a particular chromosomal segment, a variety of other donor types which are responsible for the recombinants formed at low frequency. Recombinants obtained by crossing an F⁺ population of this kind with an F⁻ population would be formed by different Hfr mutants transferring a different range of characters. Their number and genetic make-up would depend on the relative frequencies of the different Hfr types present in the donor population. Moreover it may be expected that the results of crosses involving the same F⁻ strain but F⁺ strains of different origin will not be the same but will differ according to the "Hfr mutability pattern" of the F⁺ strain employed. The difficulties encountered in the genetic analysis of F⁺ × F⁻ crosses are readily understandable in such a model (Jacob and Wollman, 1956a).

The mechanism of the mutation from one donor type to another is still a matter for speculation. It may be an example of chromosomal mutation since it seems to involve breakage and rearrangement within the chromosome which can only be expressed when the donor character is present. Such mutation appears to be associated with a change in the location of the donor character although it is not known whether the alterations in position are the cause or the effect of the rearrangements. This behaviour is reminiscent of the phenomena found in maize by McClintock (1956). The "donor character" could be conceived as being a "controlling element" whose location commands, in an unknown fashion, the region of chromosome breakage, R, as well as the pattern of chromosome rearrangements. Whether or not the "donor character" will be transferred on conjugation will depend on whether it is located between O and R or distal to R.

B. Meromixis

Once the genetic contribution of the donor cell has been transferred to the recipient cell a partial zygote or *merozygote* is formed which comprises the entire genome of the recipient cell together with a chromosomal segment of variable size from the donor cell. Thus a comparable situation is attained in transformation, transduction and conjugation, the three varieties of genetic transfer found among bacteria, for in each only a fragment of the genome of a donor cell is transferred to a recipient cell. The difference between them lies in the method whereby genetic transfer is accomplished, transformation being effected by the DNA extracts of donor cells, transduction by a phage vector and conjugation by direct injection of a chromosomal segment into the recipient cell by the donor cell. In some strains like *E. coli* K-12 transfer of genetic material can be performed by either conjugation or transduction (Lennox, 1955; Jacob, 1955). We therefore propose to unite, under the name of *meromixis*, these three known processes which are characterised by partial genetic transfer.

As to the mechanisms whereby characters transferred from the donor cell are integrated into a recombinant chromosome, the same problems are clearly raised by the three types of meromixis, and have already been considered in the case of transformation (Ephrussi-Taylor, 1955; Hotchkiss, 1955) and transduction (Demerec and Demerec, 1955; Lederberg, 1955). In conjugation it is evident that a segment of donor chromosome, although present in a merozygote, does not always participate in the formation of a recombinant chromosome and, when it does, that it is not necessarily incorporated as a whole. A mechanism analogous to crossing over must therefore be assumed although its physical basis is likely to differ from one of simple breakage and reunion in view of the asymmetry of the parental components, one of which may be very small. The question therefore arises whether the transferred fragment itself enters into the constitution of the recombinant chromosome, or whether some mechanism in which replication and recombination are combined, such as that proposed by Levinthal for recombination in phage, is not more likely. The experiments briefly reported here on the effects of ultraviolet light on recombination, as well as those involving the transfer of a radioactive chromosome segment to the merozygote, favour such an hypothesis although their interpretation cannot yet be regarded as unequivocal.

Recombination of genetic characters in bacteria is thus accomplished by means of mechanisms very different from those known in other organisms, since chromosomal fragments of variable size are transferred from one bacterium to another. Of the three known processes by which this transfer is accomplished, that of conjugation in *E. coli* is the most highly developed and most closely resembles a sexual mechanism with sex differentiation, the donor's chromosome segment playing the role of an incomplete male gamete while the recipient cell is analogous to a female gamete which contributes both its intact genome and its cytoplasm to the zygote.

Summary

1. When Hfr and F⁻ bacteria are mixed, effective pairing between donor and recipient cells follows chance collisions. The efficiency of this pairing is modifiable by environmental influences such as pH, and is an energy requiring process. An actual bridge of cellular material can be seen to join the paired cells in electron microphotographs. Under optimal conditions, 100 per cent of Hfr cells conjugate.

2. Effective contact is immediately followed by the orientated transfer of a segment of Hfr chromosome, O——R, to the F⁻ cell which thus becomes a partial zygote. Loci situated on this segment always penetrate the F⁻ cell in the same order as their arrangement on the chromosome. Transfer of the whole O——R segment takes about 35 minutes in broth at 37°. Markers located beyond R do not enter the F⁻ cell at all and are therefore not inherited among recombinants.

3. During chromosome transfer spontaneous breaks occur and the probability of breaking increases towards its distal end. This distal end, R, is therefore thought to be a region of increasing fragility rather than a well defined locus.

4. Chromosome transfer is an energy-requiring process carried out solely by the Hfr cell. The

speed at which the chromosome proceeds appears to be constant at any given temperature but can be modified by changes in the energy supply.

5. The O——R segment of chromosome can be ruptured at will during transfer, either by mechanical separation of the mating bacteria or by selectively killing the donor parent with phage. Only those Hfr markers which have already entered the F⁻ cell at the time of treatment will participate in recombination.

6. Hfr markers which have entered the zygote have a probability of being integrated into the recombinant chromosome which becomes less the further the marker is situated from O on the O——R segment, as might be deduced from the partial nature of the zygote if it is assumed that O is an extremity of the donor chromosome.

7. The time at which a marker inherited from the donor cell is phenotypically expressed in the recombinant segregant cell or its progeny depends on whether it is dominant or recessive, as well as on its manner of expression. Expression of the Hfr gene determining resistance to sodium azide commences in the zygote and is complete before the segregants begin to divide: resistance to phage T1 is not expressed until after segregation and requires four generations for completion.

8. F⁺ × F⁻ crosses show a high frequency of conjugation and of F⁺ transfer. The kinetics of F⁺ transfer are compatible with the view that F⁺ donor cells transfer a segment of chromosome O'——R', on which F⁺ is located, to F⁻ cells. F⁺ markers situated distal to R' are not transferred.

9. Transfer of any particular marker situated distal to R on the Hfr chromosome, or to R' on the F⁺ chromosome, is mediated by Hfr mutants in the donor population which can transfer the marker to F⁻ cells at high frequency. These Hfr mutants are very heterogeneous both in the range of markers they can transfer and in the order of transference.

10. The mechanisms by which donor strains may mutate from one type to another are discussed.

REFERENCES

ANDERSON, T. F., 1949, The reactions of bacterial viruses with their host cells. Bot. Rev. *15:* 477.

ANDERSON, T. F., WOLLMAN, E. L., and JACOB, F., 1957, Sur les processus de conjugaison et de recombinaison génétique chez *E. coli*. III. Aspects morphologiques en microscopie électronique. Ann. Inst. Pasteur (in press).

APPLEYARD, R. K., 1954, Segregation of λ lysogenicity during bacterial recombination in *Escherichia coli* K-12. Genetics *39:* 429–439.

CAVALLI, L. L., 1950, La sessualita nei batteri. Boll. Ist. sierotera. Milano *29:* 1–9.

CAVALLI-SFORZA, L. L., and JINKS, J. L., 1956, Studies on the genetic system of *Escherichia coli* K-12. J. Genet. *54:* 87–112.

CAVALLI, L. L., LEDERBERG, J., and LEDERBERG, E. M., 1953, An infective factor controlling sex compatibility in *Bacterium coli*. J. Gen. Microbiol. *8:* 89–103.

DEMEREC, M., and DEMEREC, Z. E., 1955, Analysis of linkage relationships in *Salmonella* by transduction techniques. Brookhaven Symp. Biol. *8:* 75–87.

EDDINGTON, A., 1935, New Pathways in Science. Cambridge, England, Cambridge Univ. Press.

EPHRUSSI-TAYLOR, H., 1955, Current status of bacterial transformations. Adv. Virus Res. 275–307.

FISHER, K., 1957a, The role of the Krebs cycle in conjugation in *Escherichia coli* K-12. J. Gen. Microbiol. *16:* No. 1 (in press).

1957b, The nature of the endergonic processes in conjugation in *Escherichia coli* K-12. J. Gen. Microbiol. *16:* No. 1 (in press).

FREDERICQ, P., and BETZ-BAREAU, M., 1953, Transfert génétique de la propriété colicinogène en rapport avec la polarité F des parents. C. R. Soc. Biol. *147:* 2043–2045.

FUERST, C. R., and STENT, G. S., 1956, Inactivation of bacteria by decay of incorporated radioactive phosphorus. J. Gen. Physiol. *40:* 73–90.

FUERST, C. R., JACOB, F., and WOLLMAN, E. L. 1957, Sur les processus de conjugaison et de recombinaison génétique chez *E. coli*. Etude de la recombinaison à l'aide du phosphore radioactif (in preparation).

HAYES, W., 1952a, Recombination in *Bact. coli* K-12: unidirectional transfer of genetic material. Nature, Lond. *169:* 118–119.

1952b, Genetic recombination in *Bact. coli* K-12: analysis of the stimulating effect of ultraviolet light. Nature, Lond. *169:* 1017–1018.

1953a, Observations on a transmissible agent determining sexual differentiation in *Bact. coli*. J. Gen. Microbiol. *8:* 72–88.

1953b, The mechanism of genetic recombination in *Escherichia coli*. Cold Spring Harb. Symp. Quant. Biol. *18:* 75–93.

1957, The kinetics of the mating process in *Escherichia coli*. J. Gen. Microb. *16:* No. 1 (in press).

HERSHEY, A. D., and CHASE, M., 1952, Independent functions of viral protein and nucleic acid in growth of bacteriophage. J. Gen. Physiol. *36:* 39–56.

HOTCHKISS, R. D., 1955, Bacterial transformation. J. Cell. Comp. Physiol. *45,* suppl. 2: 1–22.

JACOB, F., 1955, Transduction of lysogeny in *Escherichia coli*. Virology *1:* 207–220.

JACOB, F., and WOLLMAN, E. L., 1954, Induction spontanée du développement du bactériophage λ au cours de la recombinaison génétique chez *E. coli* K-12. C. R. Acad. Sci. *239:* 317–319.

1955a, Etapes de la recombinaison génétique chez *E. coli* K12. C. R. Acad. Sci. *240:* 2566–2568.

1955b, Etude génétique d'un bactériophage tempéré d'*E. coli*. III Effet du rayonnement ultraviolet sur la recombinaison génétique. Ann. Inst. Pasteur *88:* 724–749.

1956a, Recombinaison génétique et mutants de fertilité. C. R. Acad. Sci.,*242:* 303–306.

1956b, Sur les processus de conjugaison et de recombinaison génétique chez *E. coli*. I. L'induction par conjugaison ou induction zygotique. Ann. Inst. Pasteur *91:* 486–510.

LEDERBERG, E. M., 1951, Lysogenicity in *E. coli* K-12. Genetics *36:* 560.

LEDERBERG, E. M., and LEDERBERG, J., 1953, Genetic studies of lysogenicity in *E. coli*. Genetics *38:* 51–64.

LEDERBERG, J., 1947, Gene recombination and linked segregations in *E. coli*. Genetics *32:* 505–525.

1949, Aberrant heterozygotes in *Escherichia coli*. Proc. Nat. Acad. Sci. Wash. *35:* 178–184.

1955, Recombination mechanisms in bacteria. J. Cell. Comp. Physiol. *45,* suppl. 2: 75–107.

LEDERBERG, J., and LEDERBERG, E. M., 1952, Replica plating and indirect selection of bacterial mutants. J. Bact. *63:* 399–406.

LEDERBERG, J., LEDERBERG, E. M., ZINDER, N. D., and LIVELY, E. R., 1951, Recombination analysis of bacterial heredity. Cold Spring Harb. Symp. Quant. Biol. *16:* 413–441.

LEDERBERG, J., and TATUM, E. L., 1946, Novel genotypes in mixed cultures of biochemical mutants of bacteria. Cold Spring Harb. Symp. Quant. Biol. *11:* 113–114.

LENNOX, E. S., 1955, Transduction of linked genetic characters of the host by bacteriophage P_1. Virology *1:* 190–206.

LEVINTHAL, C., 1954, Recombination in phage T2: its relationship to heterozygosis and growth. Genetics *39:* 169–184.

LIEB, M., WEIGLE, J. J. and KELLENBERGER, E., 1955, A study of hybrids between two strains of *E. coli*. J. Bact. *69:* 468–471.

MACCACARO, G. A., 1955, Cell surface and fertility in *E. coli*. Nature, Lond. *176:* 125–126.

McCLINTOCK, B., 1956, Controlling elements and the gene. Cold Spring Harb. Symp. Quant. Biol. *21:* 197–216.

NEWCOMBE, M. B., and NYHOLM, M. H., 1950, Anomalous segregation in crosses of *E. coli*. Amer. Nat. *84:* 457–465.

ROTHFELS, K. H., 1952, Gene linearity and negative interference in crosses of *E. coli*. Genetics *37:* 297–311.

WOLLMAN, E. L., 1953, Sur le determinisme génétique de la lysogénie. Ann. Inst. Pasteur *84:* 281–293.

WOLLMAN, E. L., and JACOB, F., 1954, Lysogénie et recombinaison génétique chez *E. coli* K-12. C. R. Acad. Sci. *239:* 455–456.

1955, Sur le mécanisme du transfert de matériel génétique au cours de la recombinaison chez *E. coli* K-12. C. R. Acad. Sci. *240:* 2449–2451.

1957, Sur les processus de conjugaison et de recombinaison génétique chez *E. coli*. II. Polarité du transfert et de la recombinaison génétique. Ann. Inst. Pasteur (in press).

The Genetic Unit[1]

Dedicated to the memory of Professor Lewis J. Stadler

DAVID M. BONNER

Yale University, New Haven, Connecticut

The nature of a genetic unit is a problem which has long held the fascination of scientists in all walks of science. It is a problem, however, which has not proven amenable to an easy and clear-cut answer. The late Professor Stadler devoted a large measure of his experimental career to this problem, and it is to him that I owe much of my own interest in the problem, as well as some understanding of the difficulties that confront one when tackling a problem of this sort.

In 1950 it was our good fortune to have the late Professor Stadler spend a semester with us at Yale. During this semester he delivered a series of lectures concerned with his concept of the genetic unit. During these lectures he repeatedly emphasized the fact that our concept of the gene must necessarily reflect the limitations of the basic tool of genetics, the inheritance test. As the science of genetics is largely based on the use of the inheritance test, questions concerning the nature of the genetic unit can thus be asked only in a restricted way and answers must be limited. Preconceptions could thus loom large in considerations of a phenomenon as elusive as the genetic unit.

As Professor Stadler many times emphasized, conclusions concerning the discrete nature of the gene and the comparison of the genetic structure of an organism to a series of beads threaded along a string could well reflect the experimental bias of the inheritance test. Stadler's own investigations of the *r* locus of maize suggested that this particular genetic unit might be compound (Stadler, 1951). Many investigations during the past 15 years have similarly emphasized the complexity of the genetic unit and have in fact suggested the possibility that the genetic unit as described in physiological terms may well be comprised of specific genetically separable subunits (Stadler, 1954). Such investigations thus stress the complex nature of a genetic unit and lead to the supposition that a chromosome represents a genetic continuum in which a given physiological action is associated with certain specific subunits arranged in a specific fashion. Most of these investigations have been concerned with morphological traits, such as pigment formation in corn and certain body or eye color characteristics in *Drosophila*, and with certain nutritional requirements of fungi. In all of these cases, however, relatively little has been known about the biochemical action of the locus under investigation. In view of current speculation concerning the nature of the genetic unit, it is obviously of interest to look into the nature of a genetic unit in instances where the biochemical action associated with a locus is known.

THE NATURE OF A GENETIC UNIT JUDGED BY MUTATIONAL CHANGES

For a number of years we have had in progress genetic and biochemical studies concerning the formation of the amino acid tryptophan and the vitamin niacin. This work has been a collaborative effort, and the part which I wish to summarize has been largely carried out by my colleagues, Drs. Charles Yanofsky, Sigmund Suskind, and Patricia St. Lawrence.

In *Neurospora* tryptophan has been shown to be formed from indole by condensation with serine (Tatum and Bonner, 1944). This reaction requires the participation of a specific enzyme, tryptophan synthetase (Umbreit *et al.*, 1946). This enzyme can be readily obtained in cell-free extracts and has been well purified and characterized (Yanofsky, 1955). In *Neurospora* there are mutations which affect the synthesis of tryptophan. One genetic class has been shown to interfere specifically with the ability to carry out the terminal step in tryptophan formation, the coupling of indole and serine (Mitchell and Lein, 1948), and such strains are found altered in tryptophan synthetase formation. In the past few years 35 independent recurrences of such mutations have been isolated and all of them are found to be biochemically similar in that they require exogenous tryptophan for growth and cannot use indole.

Twenty-five of the phenotypically similar mutants have been studied extensively, both genetically and biochemically. With the exception of a temperature sensitive strain all of these strains were found similar in lacking detectable tryptophan synthetase activity (Yanofsky and Bonner, 1955). The independent mutations characteristic of all of these strains have thus lead to similar alterations judged in terms of mutational requirements as well as in ability to form a specific enzyme. Genetic investigations of these strains have shown that all 25 represent mutations of a

[1] The work reported in this paper was supported in part by the Atomic Energy Commission, contract AT-(30-1)-1017 and in part by the American Cancer Society on recommendation of the National Research Council, Committee on Growth.

restricted region of a chromosome; interallele crosses of these strains yield few if any tryptophan independent progeny. This locus has been termed the *td* locus. Thus one is permitted the tentative conclusion that in *Neurospora* there appears to be a single genetic area in which mutations have a pronounced effect on the ability of the organism to form the enzyme tryptophan synthetase.

Of the 25 strains, one does differ from the other 24 in temperature sensitivity. At temperatures of 30° or more it will grow in the absence of exogenous tryptophan, while at lower temperatures it requires tryptophan for growth. We do know, therefore, that not all of the mutational changes of these 25 alleles are identical. Are the mutational changes of the other 24 alleles identical? In the absence of detectable tryptophan synthetase activity one needs additional criteria with which to examine possible differences between alleles. All of these allelic strains have lost their ability to form a protein which is enzymatically active in catalyzing the conversion of indole to tryptophan. It might be possible, however, to detect differences between these alleles by examining them immunochemically, since an immunochemical study could determine whether any of these strains can form a compound which is serologically related to the parental tryptophan synthetase.

A partially purified preparation of parental tryptophan synthetase was found to elicit the formation of antibodies when injected into rabbits (Suskind *et al.*, 1955). Tryptophan synthetase antiserum was found to neutralize the enzymatic activity of tryptophan synthetase, and thus by appropriate methods it was possible to use the neutralizing property of tryptophan synthetase antiserum in detecting the presence of material serologically related to the parental tryptophan synthetase (Suskind *et al.*, 1955).

On testing the various *td* alleles for the presence of serologically related material we were fortunate to find that one strain (*td-1*) contains no cross-reacting material. Thus our initial experiments strongly suggested that in *Neurospora* there are no other proteins serologically related to the enzyme tryptophan synthetase. Extracts of a second strain, (*td-2*) were found to contain generous amounts of a material which reacts with and removes antitryptophan synthetase. *Td-2* then, unlike *td-1*, forms a material which is serologically related to the tryptophan synthetase of the parental strain. Obviously the nature of the serologically related material formed by *td-2* is of considerable interest. Investigations concerning the nature of the materials formed by strain *td-2* have been carried out by Dr. Suskind in collaboration with Dr. A. M. Pappenheimer of New York University, who have kindly permitted me to discuss their work. Perhaps the most significant observation from their investigation is the fact that parental tryptophan synthetase and the material of *td-2* are serologically almost indistinguishable.

The serologically related material of *td-2* is found to be antigenic in rabbits and antiserum induced with this material appears indistinguishable from the antiserum induced against tryptophan synthetase. While tryptophan synthetase and the *td-2* material are similar in many respects, they do differ with respect to their serological inactivation by prolonged dialysis, and it has thus been possible to examine the parental strain for the presence of serologically related material. Dr. Suskind has found that the parental strain does contain some material which is certainly similar to that of *td-2*, and so at present it does not appear that the presence of serologically related material need be a unique property of *td-2*. Additional *td-* alleles have been scanned for the presence of cross reacting material and all which have been tested to date with the exception of *td-1* have been found to form material which will react with and remove antitryptophan synthetase (Suskind *et al.*, 1955). Whether the serologically related material of each of these strains is identical with that formed by *td-2* is not known. Even in the absence of more detailed knowledge concerning the origin and nature of such materials formed by *td-2* and other *td* alleles certain conclusions concerning the mutations affecting the formation of tryptophan synthetase can be reached. The mutational change characteristic of *td-1* must differ from that characteristic of *td-2*, despite the fact that both of these mutations have resulted in the loss of ability to form tryptophan synthetase. These experiments thus clearly demonstrate that the genetic material controlling the formation of tryptophan synthetase is complex in that mutational events can lead to similar phenotypic expressions which represent different functions with respect to the formation of a given enzyme.

Further evidence for the complexity of the genetic material controlling the formation of tryptophan synthetase can also be demonstrated with quite different criteria of comparison. Evidence of differences between these alleles can be obtained by observation of suppressor mutations. The use of suppressor mutations in this connection can perhaps be best illustrated by considering a single allele. Strain *td-2* undergoes reversion with the formation of strains which are tryptophan independent, that is, strains which are able to grow in the absence of an exogenous supply of tryptophan. A large proportion of such apparent reversions are found to be reversions of the *td* locus itself. However, not all of the tryptophan independent strains derived from *td-2* are of this type. Certain revertants upon crossing with wild type give asci showing a 6:2 segregation with respect to tryptophan independence (Yanofsky, 1952), six of the spores giving rise to cultures which will grow in the absence of exogenous tryptophan, two giving rise to cultures which require added tryptophan for growth.

This type of segregation tells us that the restoration of ability to grow in the absence of added tryptophan is due not to a reverse mutation of the *td* locus itself but to a mutation at a second locus, a suppressor locus.

An obvious explanation for strains of this type might be that the second mutational event has led to a duplication of the *td* locus. This possibility seems entirely reasonable since upon analysis of suppressed strains, that is, mutant strains carrying effective suppressor genes, one finds that an enzyme is formed and appears to be indistinguishable from the tryptophan synthetase formed by the parental strain (Yanofsky, 1952). If suppressor mutations were duplications of the *td* locus, then on crossing a suppressor gene effective for one allele into other *td* alleles one might expect tryptophan synthetase formation to be restored in all of them. However, the suppressor gene which restores the ability of strain *td-2* to form tryptophan synthetase on *td-1* is without effect (Yanofsky and Bonner, 1955). Strain *td-1* carrying a *td-2* suppressor gene shows no alleviation of its tryptophan requirement for growth nor does it form detectable amounts of the enzyme tryptophan synthetase. In fact a *td-2* suppressor gene will not restore the ability of any of 24 other *td* alleles to form tryptophan synthetase (Yanofsky and Bonner, 1955). This suppressor gene is, therefore, not a duplication of the *td* locus, and thus tryptophan synthetase formation in suppressed mutants requires the interaction of both the *td* allele and the suppressor gene. More important to this discussion, however, is the fact that the *td-2* allele must in some way differ from the other 24 *td* alleles tested. In a similar way one can make use of other suppressor mutations for detecting still further differences between the *td* alleles. In this way it can be shown that *td-1*, *td-2*, *td-3*, *td-6*, and *td-24* must differ from each other (Yanofsky and Bonner, 1955).

In considering the nature of these differences it might be well to consider briefly the action of suppressor genes in tryptophan synthetase formation. One finds in a suppressed mutant that enzyme formation can be restored by the concerted action of a mutant *td* allele and a specific suppressor gene. These two genes need not show genetic linkage to prove effective in restoring tryptophan synthetase formation. One characteristic of such suppressor genes, however, is that they show great allele specificity. In fact, from a study of suppressor genes affecting the *td* locus it appears that in general a given suppressor gene has a pronounced effect on only one allele (Yanofsky and Bonner, 1955). The fact that tryptophan synthetase formation in suppressed strains requires both the *td* allele and the suppressor gene might indicate that tryptophan synthetase formation in such strains is in part mediated by the *td* allele and in part by the suppressor gene. The additional fact that the suppressor gene

shows *td*-allele specificity indicates that the action of the suppressor gene is highly specific. One might expect, therefore, that only one gene, or at least a very few genes, should be active in the restoration of tryptophan synthetase formation for a given *td* allele. Several independent recurrences of suppressor mutations affecting *td-2* have been isolated. The suppressor genes so isolated have been tested for their genetic identity. Five independent recurrences of suppressed *td-2* strains have been analyzed and surprisingly enough all of the five were found to have different suppressor mutations (Yanofsky and Bonner, 1955a). Thus, this type of experiment suggests that any one of a very large number of genes will have a similar effect with respect to restoration of tryptophan synthetase formation for a given *td* allele. This poses an enigma. Investigations concerning the relationship between genes and biochemical reactions in *Neurospora* of course have long suggested that single genes affect single biochemical events. In view of this fact one is forced to the conclusion that whatever the action of a suppressor gene is, it either mediates the synthesis of a relatively minor portion of the tryptophan synthetase molecule or it acts in a quantitative rather than a qualitative manner. This conclusion would appear to be further substantiated from immunochemical studies. Strain *td-2* is suppressable and is known to form a material serologically related to tryptophan synthetase. Strain *td-1* is not suppressable and does not form a cross reacting material. In fact all suppressable strains have been found to form serologically related material (Suskind *et al.*, 1955). This fact might again suggest that the suppressor gene if directly involved in tryptophan synthetase formation mediates the formation of a relatively minor portion of the tryptophan synthetase molecule. Thus it appears that even in suppressed mutants tryptophan synthetase formation is primarily mediated by the *td* locus. Suppressor genes do, however, aid in the detection of functional differences between alleles.

A study of suppressor mutations affecting tryptophan synthetase formation leads to the conclusion that the genetic area controlling the formation of this enzyme is complex and perhaps subject to an almost infinite array of functional alterations. Immunochemical and suppressor studies together suggest that the genetic area controlling the formation of tryptophan synthetase is sufficiently large to permit a variety of functional alterations, and one could suppose that the *td* locus is composed of discrete independently mutable areas. This then poses the problem of whether such a genetic area which is known to control the formation of a single enzyme and which shows a high degree of mutational complexity is also complex genetically. Can crossovers occur in this region? Interallele crosses involving the *td* strains have been carried out and, in fact, crosses between td-1 and td-2 yield infrequent tryptophan independent progeny. However, our analysis of this particular locus in terms of its genetic complexity is inadequate at the present time since analysis of interallele crosses of the td mutants has been severely handicapped by sterility of many of the interallele crosses. In order to consider the question just posed, therefore, we must turn to a second, but similar locus.

THE NATURE OF A GENETIC UNIT JUDGED IN CROSSOVER TERMS

The locus which I wish to discuss is that termed the q locus of *Neurospora* (Bonner, 1951). Mutations at this locus give rise to strains which require niacin for growth. A number of independent occurrences of mutations at this locus have been obtained. All of them are phenotypically similar in that they all require niacin for growth, and this requirement cannot be replaced by known niacin precursors. All of these strains accumulate quinolinic acid. They appear physiologically similar in that they do not form niacin independent heterocaryons with each other.

When each of these q locus alleles is crossed by itself no niacin independent progeny are found even when large populations of ascospores are scanned. Interallele crosses however do result in the formation of prototrophic progeny, and the frequency with which such prototrophs are found is dependent on the parental strains that are used (Bonner, 1951). The origin of such niacin independent progeny found in interallele crosses has been studied in detail by St. Lawrence (1956).

To avoid complications which might arise if these mutants were to represent translocations or other chromosomal aberrations the linkage relationship of each q allele with other linked markers was initially studied. Two of these mutants, q1 and q2, were found to have normal linkage relationship in comparison with a standard strain and thus might be considered as point mutations. Two other strains, q3 and q4, were found to have reduced crossing over in a short region between the two linked markers, albino and lysine. In these two mutants it has not been possible to secure strains with entirely normal crossover relationship within that region (St. Lawrence, 1956). In these studies ascospores isolated at random were used and it was observed that recovery of niacin independent progeny was unaffected by the presence of additional biochemical markers. Thus selection does not appear to be a complicating factor under the conditions used. Using genetic markers on both sides of the q locus one would expect a high frequency of one class of markers if prototrophic progeny resulted from a crossover within the q region. It was found, however, that in crosses of q1 by q2 the crossover and non-crossover classes were equal (St. Lawrence, 1956). One might also expect if the prototrophic progeny result from a crossover within the q region that there would be an excess of one crossover class in the prototrophs, which should reverse in reverse crosses. Yet in both crosses the recombinant classes were found to be equal (St. Lawrence, 1956). The q locus is closely linked to the genetic marker lysine and again if niacin independent progeny were to result from a crossover in the restricted q area one would expect an excess of either lysine dependent or lysine independent strains. However, it was found that the ratio of lysine independent to lysine dependent strains was one in the niacin independent progeny (St. Lawrence, 1956). Without presenting the data in greater detail one can summarize these experiments by stating that the formation of niacin independent progeny in interallele crosses of the q alleles does not appear to be related to a crossover event within the q region. This conclusion suggests that prototrophic progeny can arise in interallele crosses by a mechanism other than a crossover mechanism. This conclusion further suggests that the occurrence of prototrophic progeny in interallele crosses need not in itself suggest that a physiological locus is comprised of elements which are separable by a crossover event. Such conclusions obviously have a pronounced bearing on our concepts of the fine structure of a physiological locus.

DISCUSSION

What can one conclude from these observations? We might initially consider the phenomenon just discussed, namely the formation of prototrophic progeny in interallele crosses. The conclusion reached in the case of the q mutants is similar to that reached earlier by Mitchell (1955) in her beautiful study of interallele crosses of pyridoxineless mutants of *Neurospora*. In her investigations she found that interallele crosses of pyridoxineless strains yielded prototrophic progeny. Using serial isolation of asci she found that asci containing two pyridoxine independent ascospores lacked the recombinant class of markers. Thus she concluded that the pyridoxineless independent progeny must have arisen by a mechanism which did not involve a crossover within the pyridoxine region. These observations concerning the pyridoxineless mutants and the q mutants in turn are similar to observations by Lindegren (1955) and Roman (1956) making use of interallele crosses in yeast. Thus there can be little doubt at the present time that prototrophic progeny can arise in the absence of a crossover.

The term gene conversion, (Winkler, 1932), has in general been applied to phenomena of this sort. The interpretation of this term has differed with various investigators and while I shall refer to this phenomenon as gene conversion for descriptive purposes I do not wish to have the use of this term signify a particular mechanism. The chief characteristic of gene conversion is that rare genetic changes associated with meiosis or somatic synapsis occur. Such genetic changes obviously could be explained in a variety of ways. They could simply reflect the physical characteristics of mutation and synapsis. One might assume that mutations often reflect the distortion of an area of the genetic material resulting from the formation of additional bonding. During synapsis bonds which might have been formed during the mutational process, and which in turn give rise to the distortion of a specific area, could be broken by the forces involved in pairing. Such forces might occasionally break bonds formed as a consequence of a mutational event and result in the formation of a normal strand. Thus the formation of a normal locus might simply represent a physical change, and prototrophs might arise from a single strand without material contribution from sister strands.

Still other mechanisms can obviously account for gene conversion. The demonstration by McClintock (1951) that the insertion of chromosomal material at or near a given locus can result in the appearance of a mutant allele of the locus and reversion or recovery of normal function which accompanies removal of the inserted material, as pointed out by St. Lawrence (1956), suggests a possible model for observations such as those reported for the q locus. One might consider that the requirement for niacin in the q mutants is occasioned by the insertion of material which inactivates or alters normal functioning of the locus and that the removal of this substance allows a return to normal activity. The appearance of niacin-independent progeny in crosses between the q mutants could then be considered to represent a mutational event but of a nature somewhat different than that initially discussed. Still other interpretations of gene conversion such as those advanced by Mitchell (1955) and by Lindegren (1955) have been given. At the present time, however, experimental data do not permit a definite conclusion with respect to the actual mechanism involved in cases of gene conversion. The fact, however, that gene conversion has been observed does have a pronounced bearing on our concept of the genetic unit even in the absence of a precise knowledge of the mechanism of gene conversion itself. Let us review briefly the present state of our knowledge concerning a physiological genetic unit.

Investigations of the td locus of Neurospora suggest that in the genetic material of this organism there is a single region which has a profound influence on the ability of the organism to form the enzyme tryptophan synthetase. Diverse comparisons of alleles suggest that this physiological locus represents a region sufficiently large to enable it to undergo a varied array of functional changes. The genetic information available concerning the q locus and the pyridoxineless locus suggests that the physiological genetic unit is indivisible. By this I mean that within this physiological unit crossovers appear not to occur or if they do occur within such a restricted region they apparently lack precision. The chromosomes of Neurospora might therefore be considered as showing differentiation along their length, with areas where crossovers can effectively occur and other areas where crossovers cannot effectively occur. The strand also appears functionally differentiated and it seems possible that specific functional areas are areas which do not show effective crossovers. Such considerations are of course reminiscent of the analogy of the gene to a bead on a string, and it may well be that such considerations have more substance than has been supposed in recent years. Our data suggest that the genetic material controlling the formation of a specific enzyme may represent a discrete and physiologically indivisible unit. Such a concept of a genetic unit which controls the formation of a specific enzyme differs sharply from the concept of a physiological genetic unit which is comprised of functionally related genetic material separable by crossovers. This latter concept of genetic material has come from a detailed study of the behavior of alleles in interallele crosses in a number of different organisms. In Drosophila in particular there are many instances in which pseudoallelic relationships can be clearly demonstrated (Green and Green, 1949; Green, 1956; Lewis, 1951). In a similar way pseudoallelic relationships have also been observed in corn (Laughman, 1955) and Aspergillus nidulans, (Pontecorvo, 1953), though the evidence in these cases is not so clear cut as it is in the cases studied in Drosophila. The lack of clarity concerning pseudoallelic relationships in Aspergillus may be due to an excess of multiple crossovers. Pritchard (1955) finds that crossover relationships in Aspergillus are normal between physiological units, yet within a restricted region, a crossover event seems to insure a second crossover within that restricted region, and Dr. Pontecorvo feels that many of the anomalies that have been observed in interallele crosses may be due to this fact. All of these cases, however, have one feature in common, that the biochemical function of the locus under investigation is not known. Interpretation of these cases could thus be difficult because of a lack of detailed knowledge concerning the function of the locus, and it may well be that this lack of biochemical knowledge is the basis for much of our present apparent confusion. To illustrate how detailed knowledge of the action of the locus could have a profound influence on our concept of the gene, let us turn to some slightly different work.

Demerec and his collaborators (1956) have recently shown in a series of elegant studies involving transduction in Salmonella that the genes controlling sequential steps in the biosynthesis of substrate molecules such as vitamins, amino acids, and purines are linked. Yanofsky and Lennox (unpub.) have shown that the genes controlling the formation of tryptophan in *E. coli* are closely linked and in fact are so closely linked that the ability to convert anthranilic acid to tryptophan, a conversion which probably requires on the order of six independent enzymatic events, can be entirely lost by a segmental elimination. This elimination which results in the loss of ability to form tryptophan does not lead to other detectable metabolic disturbances.

In *Neurospora* similar linkage of sequential biosynthetic steps has not been noted and it is probably fair to state that the major genetic areas controlling biosynthetic events in this organism are relatively more spread out in the genetic material than they are in the genetic material of the Enterobacteriaceae. However, no cases are really well known in *Neurospora* in which each unique enzymatic event in the complete synthesis of a given substrate molecule is known. In fact, in the past we have often considered as single-step-events some which may turn out to require the participation of a number of enzymes. For instance, in the case of tryptophan we have considered that the conversion of anthranilic acid to tryptophan must involve four unique events since four specific genes affecting tryptophan formation are known. These genes are randomly scattered throughout the genomes of the organism. Yet more recent evidence concerning the series of biochemical events necessary in the conversion of anthranilic acid to tryptophan suggests some six or seven reaction steps (Yanofsky, in press). Thus, it could well be that linkage of sequential steps in *Neurospora* could occur and perhaps be more common than has been supposed in the past. Our lack of recognition of such linkage might simply reflect the inadequacy of our biochemical knowledge. In this connection, let us again consider the available immunochemical data concerning the *td* locus. As I mentioned earlier, *td-2* forms a material serologically related to tryptophan synthetase while *td-1* does not. What does this material represent? One obvious possibility, of course, is that the material represents an altered tryptophan synthetase. This would be of great interest if it could be proved, and the fact that *td-1* entirely lacks both tryptophan synthetase and the serologically related material favors this possibility. However, the serologically related material might also represent a related enzyme. Arguments favoring this view can also be advanced. As I mentioned it has recently been shown by Dr. Suskind that the serologically related material characteristic of *td-2* may be present in the parental strain, and as I mentioned, it has also been found in all of the tested alleles except *td-1*. Yanofsky (in press) has recently shown that the conversion of anthranilic acid to tryptophan in *E. coli* involves the condensation of anthranilic acid with phosphoribosyl-

pyrophosphate, giving rise to indole glycerol phosphate. This compound is in turn hydrolyzed to indole which is then converted to tryptophan. Lerner and Yanofsky, (unpub.), have found in mutant strains of *E. coli* that those strains which lack tryptophan synthetase, and which also accumulate indole, form in *E. coli* crossreacting material. Those strains which do not accumulate free indole and which lack both the indole triosphosphate hydrolase and the tryptophan synthetase do not form a crossreacting material. Indole triosphosphate hydrolase and tryptophan synthetase in *E. coli* have certain physical similarities and it could be that the crossreacting material in *E. coli* is not an altered tryptophan synthetase but is rather a structurally and functionally related enzyme such as the indole triosphosphate hydrolase. Thus the genetic material controlling the formation of each of these enzymes might be not only closely linked but also structurally closely related. These same possibilities also hold true for the serologically related materials characteristic of the *td* alleles of *Neurospora*. In *Neurospora*, *td-1* is unique in showing little indole accumulation and thus differs in this respect from the other *td* alleles. *Td-1*, of course, is also the allele which forms no crossreacting material. For a number of reasons it appears doubtful that the cross reacting material is the *Neurospora* hydrolase but certainly the possibility that cross reacting material could be a structurally and functionally related enzyme appears real. If this were true, the genetic material controlling the formation of the cross reacting material would be known to be closely linked to the area controlling the formation of tryptophan synthetase and structurally these two areas would have to be remarkably similar. An additional possibility of course is that the enzyme involved in the conversion of indole triosphosphate to tryptophan is a poly-functional exchange enzyme. What I want to point out here, however, is that the possibility of closely linked and functionally similar genetic material is, I feel, an entirely reasonable supposition. Other lines of evidence, I feel, also point towards this possibility.

De Serres (1955, see Giles, 1955) has studied in detail a number of phenotypically similar adenineless mutants. He found that these strains could be divided into two physiological classes, on the basis of their behavior in heterocaryon tests. Crosses between strains which formed adenine-independent heterocaryons were found to give rare adenine-independent progeny which arise by a crossover mechanism. Thus, these two genes having a related function in adenine formation are closely linked (less than a tenth of a unit apart) and are genetically separable. Interestingly enough crosses formed between those strains which did not form adenine-independent heterocaryons; adenine independent progeny were formed but in these instances the origin of these progeny did not clearly involve a crossover mechanism (de Serres, 1956). These data suggest linkage of functionally similar genetic material. Giles and his collaborators (personal communication) have recently found in still other allelic series instances in which heterocaryons can be established between presumed alleles. Thus, these data again suggest the close linkage of functionally related genetic material.

It would seem from de Serres' (1955) and Giles' (1955) work that functionally related physiologically complementary genetic material, while closely linked, is genetically divisible. However, this need not be true in all instances. The pyridoxineless mutants which Mitchell (1955) studied are complementary in a heterocaryon test yet appear genetically indivisible. Thus it would seem possible that various types of linkage of functionally related material can occur.

In viewing the literature concerned with interallele crosses one is struck by the fact that all gradations with respect to formation of prototrophic progeny by a crossover mechanism appear to exist. In many instances interallele crosses are found to yield prototrophic progeny solely by a crossover mechanism, while in other cases prototrophic progeny arise solely by gene conversion. Still other cases are confusing and might represent in part a crossover mechanism and in part a gene conversion mechanism. I wonder whether this gradation of type might not reflect the interplay of a variety of different phenomena. It could reflect the fact that a chromosome strand is differentiated with respect to functional and effective crossover areas, that functionally related material may de linked in higher organisms, and that during heterozygotic synapsis gene conversion can occur. The various events which could thus occur in crosses of closely related strains might well make it difficult to arrive at a reasonable concept of the nature of the genetic unit. To assess also the size of a genetic unit in terms of nucleotide units, using data based on the inheritance test, would also seem difficult as again preconceptions loom large and, in fact, we do not as yet have convincing proof that crossovers can occur in the DNA of higher organisms. In this connection it might be well to point out that what is measured as a crossover during recombination in bacterial viruses and in transduction in the Enterobacteriaceae might be quite different from the event measured in the inheritance test in higher organisms.

In conclusion I might simply say that in the case of *Neurospora* I feel that our knowledge of what constitutes a genetic unit is as yet fragmentary. We have an increasing number of facts with which to work and from these facts each one of us enjoys a certain number of fantasies. At present, however, neither the facts nor fantasies give rigorous proof of the nature of the genetic unit nor its action.

The facts at the present time at least seem to me to suggest the possibility that the genetic material controlling the formation of a specific enzyme represents a genetically indivisible unit. Whether this conclusion is fact or fantasy cannot be judged at present. However, the experimental means with which to tackle questions of this sort are rapidly improving. Thus, five years from now when we again consider this problem, I trust that we will be able to enjoy the use of additional facts which may in turn permit the formulation of a still more precise and exciting concept of the genetic unit.

REFERENCES

BONNER, D. M., 1951, Gene-enzyme relationships in *Neurospora*. Cold Spring Harbor Symp. Quant. Biol. 16: 143–157.

DEMEREC, M., 1956, A comparative study of certain gene loci in *Salmonella*. Cold Spring Harbor Symp. Quant. Biol. 21: 113–121.

DE SERRES, F. J., 1955, Thesis, Yale University.

GILES, N. H., 1955, Forward and back mutation at specific loci in *Neurospora*. Brookhaven Symp. Biol. 8: 103–125.

GREEN, M. M., 1955, Pseudo-allelism and the gene concept. Amer. Nat. 89: 65–71.

GREEN, M. M. and GREEN, K. C., 1949, Crossing over between alleles at the lozenge-locus in *Drosophila melanogaster*. Proc. Nat. Acad. Sci. Wash. 35: 586–591.

LAUGHNAN, T. R., 1955, Structural and functional basis for the action of the *A* alleles in maize. Amer. Nat. 89: 91–104.

LEWIS, E. B., 1951, Pseudoallelism and gene evolution. Cold Spring Harbor Symp. Quant. Biol. 16: 159–174.

LINDEGREN, C. C., 1955, Non-mendelian segregation in a single tetrad of *Saccharomyces* ascribed to gene conversion. Science 121: 605–607.

McCLINTOCK, B., 1951, Chromosome organization and genic expression. Cold Spring Harbor Symp. Quant. Biol. 16: 13–47.

MITCHELL, H. K., and LEIN, J., 1948, A *Neurospora* mutant deficient in the enzymatic synthesis of tryptophan. J. Biol. Chem. 175: 481–482.

MITCHELL. M, B., 1955, Aberrant recombination of pyridoxine mutants of *Neurospora*. Proc. Nat. Acad. Sci. Wash. 41: 215–219.

PRITCHARD, R. H., 1955, The linear arrangement of a series of alleles of *Aspergillus nidulans*. Heredity 9: 343–372.

PONTECORVO, G., 1953, The genetics of *Aspergillus nidulans*. Adv. Genetics 5: 141–238.

ROMAN, H., 1956, Studies of gene mutations in *Saccharomyces*. Cold Spring Harbor Symp. Quant. Biol. 21: 175–185.

STADLER, L. J., 1951, Spontaneous mutation in maize. Cold Spring Harbor Symp. Quant. Biol. 16: 49–63. 1954, The gene. Science 120: 811–819.

ST. LAWRENCE, P., 1956, The *Q* locus of *Neurospora*. Proc. Nat. Acad. Sci. Wash. 42: 189.

SUSKIND, S. R., YANOFSKY, C., and BONNER, D. M., 1955, Allelic strains of *Neurospora* lacking tryptophan synthetase: A preliminary immunochemical characterization. Proc. Nat. Acad. Sci. Wash. 41: 577–582.

TATUM, E. L., and BONNER, D. M., 1944, Indole and serine in the biosynthesis and breakdown of tryptophan. Proc. Nat. Acad. Sci. Wash. 30: 30–37.

UMBREIT, W. W., WOOD, W. A., and GUNSALUS, I. C., 1946, The activity of pyridoxal phosphate in tryptophan formation by cell-free enzyme preparations. J. Biol. Chem. *165*: 731–732.

WINKLER, H., 1932, Konversions-theorie und Austausch-theorie. Biol. Zbl. *52*: 163–189.

YANOFSKY, C., 1952, The effects of gene change on tryptophan desmolase formation. Proc Nat. Acad. Sci. Wash. *38*: 215–226.

  1955, Tryptophan synthetase from *Neurospora*. Methods in Enzymology, Vol. II: 233–238.

YANOFSKY, C., and BONNER, D. M., 1955 Gene interaction in tryptophan synthetase formation. Genetics *40*: 761–769.

  1955a, Non-allelic suppressor genes affecting a single *td* allele. Genet. Soc. Rec. *24*: 602.

DISCUSSION

DE SERRES: Heterokaryon tests on a series of phenotypically similar purple adenine mutants of *Neurospora crassa* have shown that these mutants comprise two functionally different groups located in the *ad-3* region on the right arm of linkage group I. All mutants within a group give negative heterokaryon tests with each other, but positive heterokaryon tests with all mutants in the other group. The characteristic frequency with which adenine-independent isolates arise in various inter- and intragroup crosses has been used to find the positions of various mutants on the chromosome map of this region. Utilizing closely linked markers located on both sides of the *ad-3* region, it has been shown that in intergroup crosses between mutants located about 0.5 to 1.3 units apart, that adenine independent progeny are entirely of one of the crossover genotypes, indicating that the origin of such progeny is associated with an exchange of closely linked markers. In a serial ascospore analysis in one such cross, performed in collaboration with Prof. Giles, the presence of the complementary crossover product, the double adenine mutant, has been demonstrated in six asci containing an adenine independent pair of ascospores.

In an intergroup cross between more closely linked mutants (about 0.1 unit) adenine independent progeny are predominantly of one crossover type, but adenine independent progeny of both parental genotypes are recovered with a frequency that suggests intense negative interference.

Quite different results have been obtained from intragroup crosses between closely linked mutants (about 0.001 unit). Adenine independent progeny from these crosses are distributed about equally between the crossover and noncrossover classes, indicating that some phenomenon other than crossing over, as we generally visualize it, is operative in these crosses.

Allelism

G. Pontecorvo

The University, Glasgow, Scotland

A radical reappraisal of the ideas on the divisibility of the genetic material and, more generally, of the relations between organization and function of the chromosomes started with the work of Serebrovsky and Dubinin (1929). The writings of Goldschmidt (review, 1956) over many years have had this as their central theme, and 16 years ago Muller (Raffel and Muller, 1940) stated the problems facing us with unsurpassed clarity. Referring to a tacit assumption, still current, he wrote, "... there is as yet no empiric evidence, and only doubtful theoretical ground, for assuming that the lines of demarcation between genes, as defined, on any one of these systems (*crossing over, chromosome breakage, mutation* and *self reproduction*, [my italics]) would coincide with those of any of the others ... it is not far fetched to imagine that the 'gene for scute,' as recognized by test of allelism of its mutations, may nevertheless consist of an undetermined number of parts ... these parts, then, might themselves be denoted 'genes' and the whole a 'gene-complex,' or the parts may be called 'sub-genes' and the whole a 'gene' depending upon the taste of the writer and upon the criterion which he prefers (that of 'allelism' or that of breakage) for defining the limits of a gene." In the case of "scute" in *Drosophila*, Muller could only consider then the alternative definitions based on allelism or chromosome breakage. In the many more cases now known in *Drosophila* (*bx, lz, w, v, sn, f*), in *Aspergillus* (*ad8, pro1, pro4, ad9, bi, paba*), in maize (*A* and *R*), etc. Muller's argument applies also to the other alternatives based on crossing-over and on mutation.

The discussions in this symposium have shown that in spite of Muller's old and perfectly clear statement, terminology is still emotionally loaded. My theme will keep clear of it. It will be that whatever our criteria—functional, structural, or both—for resolving the genetic material we have a continuous series of examples which bridge the gap from clear-cut resolution to no resolution. "Allelism" is a relation between elements of the genetic material which is approached asymptotically as we consider elements located nearer and nearer along the chromosome, or more and more similar in phenotypic effects. To approach this asymptote is the best that we can do at present because we have no basis for predicting from first principles where the actual ultimate functional or structural unit of resolution will lie. A good deal of present-day confusion arises precisely from preconceived—and very firm—ideas on what these ultimate units *ought* to be.

KINDS OF RELATIONSHIP BETWEEN MUTANTS

Let us take, from the work in our laboratory on *Aspergillus nidulans*, a series of examples of the kinds of relationship encountered between pairs of mutant chromosome segments. The maps of the two best marked chromosomes are in Figure 1.

In the first place, we can consider pairs of linked mutants such as *w* (white conidia) and *putr* (putrescine requirement) or *ribo* (riboflavin requirement) and *pro4* (proline requirement), etc. The positions of the members of each pair are far apart on the linkage maps and the mutants determine changes from the wild type which presumably have very little in common. These are examples of clear-cut resolution, both in position and function, between two sections of the chromosomes.

In the second place, we can consider *ad14, ad9* and *ad8*. These three markers are located far apart on one chromosome and all determine a nutritional requirement for adenine in the haploid or homozygous diploid. They are all recessive because the heterozygote for any one of them is wild-type (nonrequirer). From the growth response to the few presumed intermediates in purine synthesis which are known, haploid strains carrying any one of these mutants are indistinguishable from those carrying any one of the others. They all respond to adenosine, adenine, hypoxanthine and 4 amino-5 imidazole carboxamidine, growth-response spectrum common to all six *ad* markers shown on the maps (Fig. 1). Tests of complementarity of the three mutants taken two by two, however, show that they are all three functionally different. The heterokaryon with two different mutants in each kind of nucleus and the heterozygote, either in *trans* or *cis* arrangement, show the dominant, nonrequirer, phenotype. This is, therefore, an example of chromosome sections easily resolvable by crossing over as to their positions but not so by comparison of phenotypes. To detect a difference in function we need the test of complementarity, that is, mutant *a* and mutant *b* are considered as functionally different because in the heterokaryon $(a+)$ + $(+b)$ and in the heterozygote $\frac{a\ +}{+\ b}$ each carries a nonmutant section capable of compensating for the damage in the other.

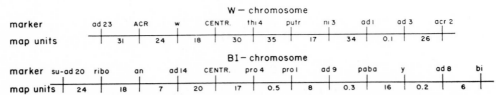

FIGURE 1. Maps (May, 1956) of two out of the seven linkage groups in *Aspergillus nidulans*. The symbols of the mutant markers indicate nutritional requirements (adenine, *ribo*flavine, *an*eurin, *pro*line, *p-a*minobenzoate, *bi*otin, *thi*azole, *putr*escine, *ni*trite); resistance to poisons (*acr*iflavine); suppressors (*su-ad20*); and conidial colours (*w* = colourless, *y* = yellow, the wild-type is green *WY*). CENTR.; = centromere, located by tetrad analysis and mitotic crossing-over.

In the third place, we can consider three more recessive adenine-requiring mutants, *ad23*, *ad1* and *ad3*, all in the *W*-chromosome. Again the qualitative tests of growth-response do neither differentiate between them, nor between any of them and any of the three previously mentioned. The tests of complementarity are again positive in all combinations among these three and among these and the others. Thus all six adenine-requiring mutants are functionally different; four of the six are also far apart or on different chromosomes from each other and from the remaining two, *ad1* and *ad3*. The interesting point is that *ad1* and *ad3* are very closely linked, recombining only at a rate of the order of 10^{-3}. This pair is, thus, an example of mutants the locations of which are so close that they can be resolved only by analyzing 10^4 products of meiosis, and the effects of which are so similar that they can be resolved only by a test as sensitive as that of complementarity. Two cases of this kind are known so far in the two chromosomes of *Aspergillus nidulans* shown in Figure 1: *ad1* and *ad3*, just mentioned, and *pro1* and *pro4* (Forbes, 1956). In both cases the recombination fractions are $^5/_{1000}$ or less.

In the fourth place, we can consider a number of recurrences of mutation in any one of the *ad* sections mentioned before: in particular let us consider the *ad8* series of mutants investigated by Pritchard (1955 and unpub.). Five mutants of independent origin (*ad20*, *ad16*, *ad11*, *ad8*, and *ad10*) have been tested extensively. They are all located very close to *y* and about 5 units from *bi*. The strains carrying them are qualitatively indistinguishable; *ad20* and *ad16* permit a certain amount of growth even in the absence of adenine. The former is also distinguishable by means of a series of specific "suppressors," located in different positions, which "suppress" completely *ad20* but none of the other mutants of this or of other series. The five mutants are also all functionally allelic in the sense that the heterokaryons carrying one mutant in one kind of nucleus and another one in another kind of nucleus are mutant, and so are the heterozygotes carrying two mutants in *trans*. By tests of recombination both at meiosis and at mitosis, Pritchard (1955 and unpub.) has been able to work out a tolerably linear order for the five alleles within a segment of total length of about 0.3 unit. The recombination fraction

between the two mutants (*ad20* and *ad16*) which show the lowest, is of the order of 10^{-6}.

That crossing-over is the mechanism underlying this recombination was shown in certain cases by Pritchard (1955) and by Roper and Pritchard (1955) by recovering the double heterozygote in *cis* (that is, having two mutants in one chromosome and the wild type constitution in the homolog) by means of mitotic crossing over from the heterozygote in *trans*. In certain cases it has also been verified that the wild type originates by a reciprocal exchange the other product of which is the double mutant. This does not mean that reciprocal exchange is necessarily always involved in the origin of the wild type. I am mentioning these details because there has been a tendency to generalize from the example of the pyridoxineless (*pdx*) mutants in *Neurospora* analyzed by M. Mitchell (1955). In the examples in *Aspergillus* there is no doubt that one (mitotic) crossing over event *can* give origin to a strand carrying two mutant alleles and one of wild-type constitution. We do not know whether this accounts for all or even most of the cases of recovery of the wild-type strand either in mitotic analysis or in single-strand meiotic analysis. Conversely, the *Neurospora* experiments of M. Mitchell (1955) do not exclude that the double mutant strand may actually be produced in her material, and if it does, that it may do so as the reciprocal product of a single event. What they do exclude is that this should always be so.

The main interest of examples like those of *pdx* in *Neurospora* lies in the possibility that they may bridge the gap between reciprocal crossing over, as known in higher organisms, and non-reciprocal recombination as known in bacteriophage and, perhaps, in bacteria. But it would be unwise, because of this interest, to ignore the more general situation based on six allelic series in *Aspergillus* and at least four in *Drosophila* (*lz*, *w*, *bx*, and *v*) in which reciprocal crossing over between alleles is known to occur.

This fact—first revealed by the pioneer work of Roper (1950) on the *bi* series in *Aspergillus*—led me to suggest a model of gene structure (Pontecorvo, 1952) which, paradoxically, is now being supported by the results of workers with organisms like phage and bacteria where the process underlying recombination may be basically different from that in the organisms for which the model was proposed. The support comes from the remarkable work of Benzer (1955) on bacteriophage and Demerec (this Symposium) on *Salmonella*, while workers with *Drosophila* and *Neurospora* hold different views. This model pictures a minute chromosome section as made up of a series of linearly arranged (but not necessarily continuous) "mutational sites" capable of mutation, either by individual change or loss or by change in relative arrangement, and capable of undergoing crossing over with one another. A number of these sites integrated in function we may call a "gene," or a "set" if the term "gene" should be reserved for the cruder levels of analysis at which it was, and still is, so useful. Whether the integration of sites is at the level of determining the surface specificity of a single protein, or the arrangement of aminoacid residues into a protein, or the surface necessary for two proteins to work together, etc. it is not profitable to speculate at present.

Calculations of the (minimum) number of sites in certain genes in *Aspergillus* and *Drosophila* (Pontecorvo and Roper, 1956) leads to high figures, of the order of tens or hundreds. One of the methods for these calculations, admittedly full of pitfalls, is based on the fact that in *Aspergillus* none of the pairs of alleles of independent origin of any one gene so far tested against each other have failed to recombine in experiments with resolving power of 10^{-7}. The sample in *Aspergillus* includes seven genes and a total of 19 alleles originated by independent mutational events. Such results would be extremely improbable if the number of mutational sites of each of these genes were less than eight.

Another method for calculating the minimum number of mutational sites in one gene is applicable also to *Drosophila*. It assumes uniform distribution of crossing over between mutational sites of one gene and estimates their (minimum) number from the ratio of the recombination fraction between the two sites furthest apart and that of the two closest together. This method gives, for example, 62 sites for *w* in *Drosophila* and 150 for *ad8* in *Aspergillus*.

In all the preceding discussion, two sites have been considered as integrated in function, that is, as parts of one gene or set rather than of two different ones, on the basis of noncomplementarity, which usually also goes with the *cis-trans* or "Lewis effect" (Pontecorvo, 1955). Could we then use this criterion as absolute for identifying discontinuity in the genetic material? Another group of adenineless mutants in *Aspergillus* tells us that the answer is, no.

The *ad9* series, studied by Calef (1956) provides an example of a situation intermediate between complementarity and noncomplementarity. Three recessive phenotypically indistinguishable mutants (*ad13*, *ad17*, and *ad15*), located between *pro1* and *paba* 0.3 unit from the latter, re-

combine with one another at very low rates (10^{-5} to 10^{-6}). The order is *ad17*, *ad15*, *paba*; the position of the third mutant, *ad13*, is not yet certain but probably *not* in the middle. The interest of this series lies in the phenotypes of the *trans* heterozygotes: $\dfrac{ad13 \ +}{+ \ ad17}$ and $\dfrac{ad13 \ +}{+ \ ad15}$ are extreme mutants indistinguishable from the three haploids *ad13*, *ad15* or *ad17*. The *trans* heterozygote $\dfrac{ad17 \ +}{+ \ ad15}$ is intermediate between mutant and wild type. The *cis* heterozygotes $\dfrac{ad13 \ ad17}{+ \ +}$ and $\dfrac{ad13 \ ad15}{+ \ +}$ are wild type, as expected in similar cases. Unfortunately the *cis* heterozygote $\dfrac{ad17 \ ad15}{+ \ +}$ is not yet available because of the difficulty in selecting it from the *trans*; it would be, presumably, wild type.

This example shows that even in the case of completely recessive mutants the test of noncomplementarity is not always decisive. This raises anew, and very critically, the problem of which systems of integration may be operating between sites unquestionably involved in one such system. It seems quite possible that at least in some cases the transition between the sites of one system of integration, that is, one gene, and the next may be gradual and with overlaps just as Muller and Goldschmidt suggest.

DISTRIBUTION OF MUTANTS

The total identified map length of the *W* and *B1* chromosomes of *Aspergillus* is 330 units, within which 20 markers are known (Fig. 1). They include four pairs of very closely linked markers in which the linked mutants are complementary to each other (Table 1). In two pairs, already mentioned, the mutants in each pair have related effects (*ad1* and *ad3*; *pro4* and *pro1*); in the two others (*ad9* and *paba*; *y* and *ad8*) they have not. We may ask whether these four cases suggest any trend.

If the 20 markers were distributed at random along the two chromosomes, the probability of

TABLE 1. CLOSELY LINKED MUTANTS WITH
COMPLEMENTARY ACTION IN TWO
CHROMOSOMES OF *A. nidulans*

(Total length of these chromosomes: 330 units; total number of markers located in them: 20)

	Recombination	Phenotypes
	%	
ad1 and *ad3*	0.1	similar
pro1 and *pro4*	0.5	similar
ad9 and *paba*	0.3	different
y and *ad8*	0.2	different

finding a marker within 0.5 units either side of a particular other one would be $2 \times \dfrac{0.5}{330} \times 19 =$ 0.063. The probability of finding, as we have found, four such examples would be considerably less than $0.633 \times 0.509 \times 0.399 \times 0.303 =$ 0.039. We can conclude that the distribution of the 20 markers is not likely to be random; there is an excess of close linkages.

The next question is: to what extent is this departure from randomness accounted for by the two pairs of mutants related in action (as judged from similarity of phenotypes)? This is the sort of question which prompted the working hypothesis (Pontecorvo, 1950) of close linkage between genes acting on successive steps of reactions involving limited, unstable or undiffusible substrates. We know now that in this form the working hypothesis is untenable.

The 20 markers grouped according to phenotypes fall into 13 classes of clearly dissimilar phenotypes. There are (Table 1) two cases of close linkage between classes: *ad9* and *paba* and *y* and *ad8*. Calculations similar to the preceding ones give a probability of 0.055 for two such cases in a sample like ours if the distribution of phenotypically unrelated markers were random.

This analysis only suggests that there is a tendency for close linkages to be more frequent than would be expected if the distribution of crossing over were uniform. This tendency is perhaps more marked for genes with similar or related action. A survey of the distribution of genes with related action in various higher organisms (Pontecorvo, 1956) also points the same way. Thus the examples in *Salmonella* of close linkage between genes concerned with successive steps in biosynthetic reactions (Demerec, this Symposium) may be a striking particular instance of this general tendency. That it is no more than a tendency is shown even in *Salmonella* by the prevalence of cases in which such linkage does not occur.

In retrospect it is interesting to ask in which way the working hypothesis of close linkage between genes controlling successive steps in reactions involving effectively limited substrates was wrong. It was probably wrong in assuming the juxtaposition of genetic elements controlling the synthesis of *different* enzymes. The above examples, including those of *Salmonella*, show that this sort of linkage is likely to be the exception rather than the rule; though possibly less of an exception in organisms like bacteria in which the delegation of metabolic functions from the nucleus to cytoplasmic structures is presumably not as advanced as in more complex organisms. What has emerged from the *Aspergillus* and *Drosophila* work since 1950 is that the level at which juxtaposition of chromosomal elements is essential for their proper functioning is usually a level lower than the one conjectured then. Perhaps it is the level of assemblage of submolecular components, such as aminoacid residues into a protein.

Thus the search for structural organization at the "intergenic" level has resulted in a clearer appreciation of the complexities at lower levels. At present, most promising situations seem to be those—like that of *ad13*, *ad17* and *ad15*—which represent a transition from complete localized integration to lack of such integration, that is, transition from noncomplementarity to complementarity of recessive mutants.

REFERENCES

BENZER, S., 1955, Fine structure of a genetic region in bacteriophage. Proc. Nat. Acad. Sci. Wash. *41:* 344–354.

CALEF, E., 1956, Functional relationships between three adenineless mutants in *Aspergillus nidulans*. Heredity *178:* 83–84.

DEMEREC, M., 1956, A comparative study of certain gene loci in *Salmonella*. Cold Spring Harbor Symp. Quant. Biol. *21:* 113–121.

FORBES, E., 1956, Recombination in the *pro* region in *Aspergillus nidulans*. Microbial Genetics Bulletin No. *13:* 9–11.

GOLDSCHMIDT, R., 1956, Theoretical Genetics. Berkeley, University of California Press.

MITCHELL, M., 1955, Further evidence of aberrant recombination in *Neurospora*. Proc. Nat. Acad. Sci. Wash. *41:* 935–937.

PONTECORVO, G., 1950, New fields in the biochemical genetics of microorganisms. Biochem. Soc. Symp. *4:* 40–50.

    1952, Genetic formulation of gene structure and action. Advances Enzymol. *13:* 121–149.

    1955, Gene structure and action in relation to heterosis. Proc. Roy. Soc. B. *144:* 171–177.

    1956, Trends in genetic analysis. New York, Columbia University Press (in preparation).

PONTECORVO, G., and ROPER, J. A., 1956, The resolving power of genetic analysis. Nature, Lond. (in press).

PRITCHARD, R. H., 1955, The linear arrangement of a series of alleles of *Aspergillus nidulans*. Heredity *9:* 343–371.

RAFFEL, D., and MULLER, H. J., 1940, Position effect and gene divisibility considered in connection with three strikingly similar scute mutations. Genetics *25:* 541–583.

ROPER, J. A., 1950, A search for linkage between genes determining vitamin requirements. Nature, Lond. *166:* 956.

ROPER, J. A., and PRITCHARD, R. H., 1955, The recovery of the complementary products of mitotic crossing-over. Nature, Lond. *175:* 639.

SEREBROVSKY, A. S., and DUBININ, N. P., 1929, Artificial obtaining of mutations and the problem of the gene. Prog. Exp. Biol. *8:* 235–247. (In Russian).

Studies of Gene Mutation in *Saccharomyces*

University of Washington, Seattle, Washington

It can be argued that when two recessive mutant genes in combination produce the mutant phenotype, they are either variants of a locus (Pontecorvo, 1952), that is, they are alleles, or they are variants of neighboring loci and are exhibiting position pseudoallelism in combination (Lewis, 1955; Green, 1956). A principal criterion for pseudoallelism is the demonstration that the two loci are separable by crossing over. Thus the hybrid Ab/aB, in which a and b are pseudoalleles, yields both AB and ab from the same recombinational event. The genes a and b are regarded as functionally and spatially separate.

The study of gene mutation is therefore complicated by the problem of distinguishing between mutation at a single locus and mutation at a series of adjacent loci. Since the validity of the criterion of crossing over as a general indication of separate loci is open to question (Pritchard, 1955) and since the failure to obtain crossing over may mean only that it occurs with a relatively low frequency, the criterion itself has limited usefulness. The value of the criterion of functional identity to indicate variants of the same locus is also limited, at the present time, by the difficulty of proving identity. Stadler (1954) has discussed these aspects and others inherent in the study of gene mutation, and has emphasized the need for additional criteria.

Two types of evidence have been accumulating in the past year or so which hold the promise of providing such criteria. One of these arises from the fractionation of genetic material, as in bacteriophage (Benzer, 1955; Streisinger and Franklin, this Symposium), in bacteria (Demerec, this Symposium), in *Neurospora* (Giles, 1955; St. Lawrence, 1956), in *Aspergillus* (Pritchard, 1955), and in yeast (Leupold, 1955; Roman, 1955), and leads to a view of the gene as a complex structure separable by mutation into individual elements. The second type of evidence is that of a mechanism of recombination which does not yield reciprocal products from the same recombinational event (Mitchell, 1955) and which could turn out to be a specific mechanism for recombination between the elements of the gene.

In this report I will describe the evidence for genic complexity and for non-reciprocal recombination in yeast (*Saccharomyces*).

The Mutant Genes

We have been working with a number of mutations affecting the synthesis of adenine. The mutations are distributed among seven loci. At two of the loci the mutant gene is recognized by the effect that the block in the synthesis of adenine leads to the production of a red pigment. One of the two types of red strains carries the recessive gene *ad1* (Reaume and Tatum, 1949). The other is recessive for *ad2* (Ephrussi, Hottinguer, and Tavlitzki, 1949). We have received 19 additional red strains from Dr. Caroline Raut, these having arisen in the course of U.V. and X-ray treatment experiments. Fourteen of the 19 were found to carry *ad2*; the other five carried *ad1*. However, only three of each type of the Raut collection are known to be of separate mutational origin.

The remaining mutants were obtained by a technique which has been described elsewhere (Roman, 1956). The technique depends on the fact that when haploid red strains are grown aerobically in yeast extract-peptone medium, there is a strong selection for cells carrying a second recessive mutation affecting the synthesis of adenine and preventing or inhibiting the production of the red pigment. The strains which are now doubly recessive are of two phenotypes: they are white if the block in the production of pigment is complete, or they are pink if the block is incomplete.

The new mutant gene is isolated in haploid segregants by crossing the doubly recessive strain with an adenine-independent haploid of opposite mating type. The resulting diploid is sporulated and the desired segregants are found in two of the three ascus types which are obtained. Figure 1 illustrates the scheme for isolating the mutant gene, in this case *ad5*, from the double mutant (*ad2 ad5*) in which it occurred. The desired +*ad5* genotype segregates in the tetratype and the nonparental ditype asci.

In this way five new loci have been identified as being concerned with the synthesis. These are numbered *Ad3*, *Ad4*, *Ad5*, *Ad6*, and *Ad7*. Eighty independently-occurring mutations, all of spontaneous origin, have been obtained at these loci. The *ad3* mutant gene also affects the synthesis of histidine. A schematic representation of the seven adenine loci in relation to the production of adenine and histidine is given in Figure 2.

Our working material consists therefore of the 80 mutations at the five new loci and of eight mutations at the *Ad1* and *Ad2* loci (Table 1). It should be noted that mutation frequently affects the *Ad5* and *Ad7* loci simultaneously to give the *ad5–ad7* mutation. The crosses *ad5–ad7* × *ad5*

175

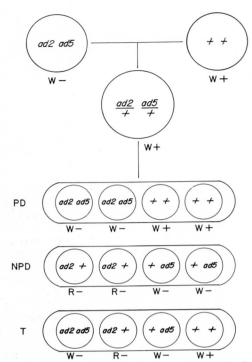

PD

NPD

T

FIGURE 1. Scheme to illustrate the method of isolation of new adenine mutants arising in a red haploid culture (*ad2*). W = white, R = red, + = adenine independent, − = adenine dependent. The asci are parental ditype (PD), nonparental ditype (NPD), and tetratype (T).

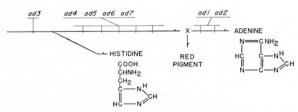

FIGURE 2. A schematic representation of the seven adenine loci in relation to the synthesis of adenine and histidine and the red pigment characteristic of *ad1* and *ad2* strains.

TABLE 1. THE DISTRIBUTION OF THE MUTANT ALLELES AMONG THE SEVEN ADENINE LOCI

The numbers in parentheses indicate the alleles which do not completely block the synthesis of adenine.

ad1	4
ad2	4
ad3	9 (1)
ad4	17 (3)
ad5	8 (2)
ad6	29 (3)
ad7	6
ad5-ad7	11
	88

and *ad5–ad7* × *ad7* yield adenine-requiring diploids. However, the cross *ad5* × *ad7* results in an adenine-independent diploid and for this reason the two mutant genes are regarded as nonallelic. The two loci are tightly linked and have been inseparable in 163 meiotic segregations.

There is no other indication of meiotic linkage among the adenine loci. The evidence from mitotic recombination (Roman, 1956) and from trisomic studies (unpub.) indicates that the seven loci are distributed among at least four chromosomes. *Ad1*, *Ad3*, *Ad4*, and *Ad5–Ad7* are on different chromosomes; the location of *Ad2* in relation to these others is unknown. It will be shown later, however, that *Ad3* and *Ad6* are linked in mitotic recombination and are therefore on the same chromosome.

THE EVIDENCE FOR DIFFERENCES AMONG THE ALLELES OF A LOCUS

The haploid strains obtained as indicated above were intercrossed to provide diploids with various combinations of the alleles of a locus. The crosses were usually made by the prototroph-selection technique, according to a schedule which is illustrated by the following example: A strain carrying the allele *ad5-1* and requiring uracil for growth was mixed in yeast extract-peptone medium with a strain of opposite mating type carrying *ad5-2*, of different mutational origin from that of *ad5-1*, and requiring histidine for growth. After 24 hours the mixture of the two strains was plated on synthetic medium (Roman, 1956) lacking both uracil and histidine. The colonies which arose on this plate came from zygotic cells produced in the mixture.

A portion of one or more of the diploid colonies arising from each cross was inoculated into five cc yeast extract-peptone medium (1% yeast extract, 2% bactopeptone, 2% glucose) and the culture was shaken for 48 hours. About 10^6 cells of each culture were then plated on synthetic medium lacking adenine, for the purpose of detecting reversions to adenine independence.

Two strikingly different results were obtained. Among those cultures in which the two alleles were of different mutational origin, the large majority produced from about 100 to several thousand adenine-independent colonies per plate. These are designated heteroallelic combinations. By contrast, the cultures which carried the same allele at both loci, the homoallelic combinations, produced no revertant colonies, or only very few. The effect can be seen in Figure 3, which summarizes the results of tests of the nine *ad3* alleles in all combinations. The nine homoallelic combinations produced few if any revertant colonies. Of the 36 combinations of alleles of different mutational origin, 35 were heteroallelic and gave a substantial number of revertant colonies. The combination *ad3-1/ad3-2* gave no revertants. This may mean that *ad3-1* and *ad3-2* are identical mutations. Or it could mean that the combination has a low frequency of reversion and that a more sensitive test would reveal that the combination is heteroallelic. In any case, the results of these tests indicate that eight of the nine *ad3* alleles are different in some way which is detectable by the enhanced rate of reversion when these are in combination.

The results of applying the above test to combinations of alleles at the other loci are given in Table 2. It will be seen that the four *ad1* alleles are different, as are the four *ad2* alleles, eight of the nine *ad3* alleles, eleven of the thirteen *ad4* alleles which were tested, five of the seven *ad5* alleles which were tested, 26 of the 29 *ad6* alleles, four of the six *ad7* alleles, and all of the eleven *ad5-ad7* mutations. The combinations of seven of the *ad5* alleles and the six *ad7* alleles with the eleven *ad5-ad7* mutations were all found to be heteroallelic. In total, 73 of the 83 mutations which were tested were found to be different by the reversion test.

THE EVIDENCE FOR NON-RECIPROCAL RECOMBINATION

In the technique described above, the event which occurs in heteroallelic combinations and results in reversion to adenine-independence has its origin in diploid cells dividing mitotically. The observations which follow were made in experiments designed for the purpose of placing some limits on speculations concerning the mechanism responsible for reversion.

It is obvious that crossing over could account for the reversional event. If the alleles of the heteroallelic diploid are defective at different points, a crossover between these points would restore the non-mutant allele for adenine-independence. Recombination does occur in mitotically-dividing diploids (James and Lee-Whiting, 1955; Roman, 1956); additional evidence will be given below.

The results to be expected from crossing over are given for a specific example in Figure 4. The chromosomes are presented in four-strand condition as in meiosis. A crossover as indicated would produce a ++ chromatid for adenine-independence. The diagram illustrates the types of adenine-independent diploids which could arise in the division following the crossover event, and the ascus types which would identify the diploids. The asci are therefore expected to exhibit 2:2 segregation for adenine-independence *versus* adenine-dependence. The segregants which are dependent should be identifiable by the reversion test, as follows: If the segregant carries the allele *ad5-1*, its combination with an *ad5-2* strain should produce revertants and its combination with an *ad5-1* strain should not. If *ad5-2* is present, its combination with *ad5-1* should yield revertants whereas its combination with *ad5-2* should not.

ad3-1	2	3	4	5	6	7	8	9
ad3-1 O	O	+	+	±	+	+	+	+
2	O	+	+	±	+	+	+	+
3		O	+	+	+	+	+	+
4			O	+	+	+	+	+
5				O	+	+	+	+
6					O	+	+	+
7						O	+	+
8							O	+
9								O

FIGURE 3. The results of the tests for reversion of the nine *ad3* alleles in all of the possible combinations. + indicates that several hundred revertants were obtained from the test, ± indicates about a hundred revertants, and 0 indicates either very few or no revertants.

If, however, the segregant carries the doubly-defective allele, *ad5-1,2*, as the reciprocal product of crossing over, the combination with either *ad5-1* or *ad5-2* should not yield revertants since either combination would be homoallelic for one or the other defect.

One hundred and nineteen individual cases of reversion to adenine-independence have been investigated. These have arisen from heteroallelic diploids involving *ad3*, *ad5*, *ad5-ad7*, *ad6*, and *ad7*. One hundred and thirteen of the revertant diploids produced asci in which two of the segregants were adenine-independent and two were dependent. The remaining six produced asci in which all four segregants were adenine-independent. The diploids were heterozygous at from three to eight other loci concerned with mating type, the ability to ferment galactose, sucrose, or maltose, and the requirements for methionine, histidine, tryptophane, and uracil (see Roman, 1956, for the

TABLE 2. THE NUMBERS OF ALLELES AT EACH OF THE SEVEN LOCI WHICH WERE FOUND TO DIFFER FROM EACH OTHER BY THE REVERSIONAL TEST

Locus	No. of Alleles Under Test	No. Found to Be Different
Ad1	4	4
Ad2	4	4
Ad3	9	8
Ad4	13	11
Ad5	7	5
Ad6	29	26
Ad7	6	4
Ad5-Ad7	11	11
	83	73

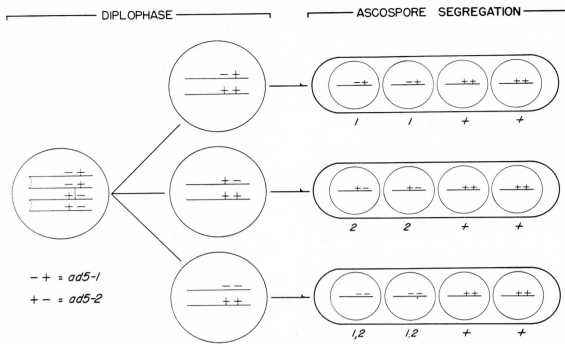

FIGURE 4. The diploids and asci expected if crossing over is responsible for the reversional event.

sources of the marker genes). The regular segregation of the auxiliary markers indicated (1) that the heteroallelic diploid in which the reversional event had occurred was the hybrid expected from the cross from which it came, and (2) that the asci from the revertant diploid came from a normal meiosis.

The reversional test was next applied to the

adenine-dependent segregants of 88 of the revertant diploids to identify the allele which was present in the segregant. In every case, the test revealed that the allele which was present was one of the two alleles carried by the heteroallelic diploid prior to the reversional event. Thus not a single case was found in which was present the doubly-defective allele expected as the reciprocal of a crossover between adjacent elements.

It could be argued that the doubly-defective chromosome is not recovered because of a preferential disjunction of the chromatids following chromatid exchange. Suppose, for example, that the ++ chromatid regularly disjoins with its sister. If this were so, separately-occurring revertants from the same heteroallelic combination should carry the same mutant allele in heterozygous condition; referring to Figure 4, the revertants from the ad5-1/ad5-2 combination should regularly contain the ad5-2 allele. A number of independent revertants from each of several heteroallelic combinations have been analyzed to test this point. It turns out (Table 3) that both of the alleles are recovered although not always in equal numbers. It will be shown later that segregation is regular for a marker proximal to the locus under investigation and this would not be expected if preferential disjunction occurred. The data, taken together, indicate that chromosomal distribution following the reversional event is that expected of a normal mitosis.

It could also be argued that it is an error to regard the − − condition as being doubly defec-

TABLE 3. THE MUTANT ALLELES RECOVERED IN
SEPARATE REVERTANTS FROM SPECIFIC
HETEROALLELIC COMBINATIONS

Heteroallelic Combination Allele a/Allele b	Allele Recovered	
	a	b
ad3-1/4	6	4
ad3-2/9	2	4
ad6-2/3	3	4
ad6-2/7	1	10
ad6-2/12	7	15

TABLE 4. MEIOTIC LINKAGE DATA FOR
ad3, ad6, AND Ma
The segregations are given as PD:NPD:T. See text.

	ad6	ad3
ad3	29:24:138	
Ma	14:22:76	32:8:87
tr1	65:53:99	16:19:76

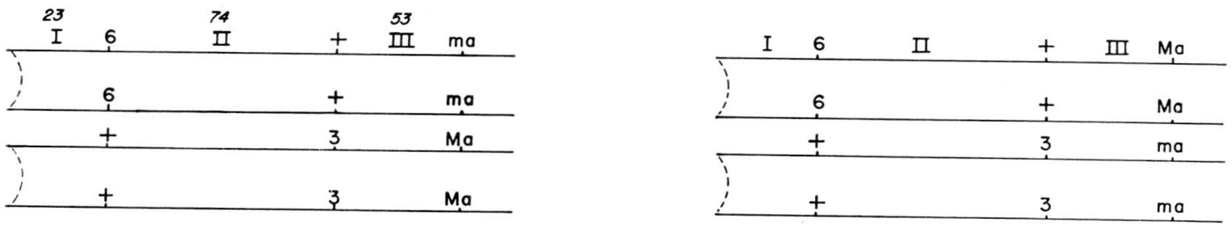

CROSSOVER EXPECTATIONS

REGION I

66 + + ma ma   8   66 + + Ma Ma   II

++ 33 Ma Ma   I   ++ 33 ma ma   2

REGION II

6+ 33 Ma Ma   8   6+ 33 ma ma   9

REGION I & II

66 3+ Ma ma   3   66 3+ Ma ma   5

REGION II & III

6+ 33 Ma ma   2   6+ 33 Ma ma   0

22   27

FIGURE 5. The types of diploids which are expected and are obtained following mitotic crossing over in regions I, II, and III of the *ad6-ad3-Ma* linkage group. The numbers above the roman numerals indicate the estimated amount of meiotic crossing over in the corresponding regions.

tive, that it may (1) simulate the effect of one or the other of the two mutant alleles from which it arose or (2) be wild-type in its effect. The fact that some of the revertants gave only adenine-independent segregants might support the second possibility except that revertants of this kind occur so infrequently. There is the third possibility that the − − chromosome exerts a deleterious effect even in combination with a ++ chromosome and is selected against for this reason. Because of these objections, plausible or not, it was important to find an independent technique which would provide information on the relation between crossing over and the reversional event.

We were fortunate to find that the loci of *ad3*, *ad6*, and *Ma* (for maltose fermentation) are in the same chromosomal arm, the probable order being centromere—*ad6*—*ad3*—*Ma*. The evidence from meiotic segregation indicated that *ad6* is about 23 crossover units from its centromere whereas *ad3* and *Ma* are not centromere-linked. This is shown in Table 4, in which are given the segregational data for *ad3* and *ad6* in combination with *tr1*, the locus of which is about two units from another centromere (Hawthorne, 1955). The proportion of parental ditypes: nonparental ditypes: tetratypes is expected to be 1:1:4 if the locus in question is not centromere linked (Lindegren, 1949a). If the locus is centromere-linked and on a chromosome different from that which contains *tr1*, the PD:NPD proportion should be

1:1 and the sum of the ditypes should exceed half the tetratypes. *Ma* and *ad3* are linked, as is shown by the excess of parental ditypes in relation to nonparental ditypes. Neither *ad3* nor *Ma* exhibit linkage with *ad6*; thus there was no basis, from meiotic segregation alone, to place the three loci in the same linkage group.

The evidence that *ad3* and *ad6* are on the same chromosome comes from a study of mitotic segregation (Roman, 1956). Additional data have since been obtained from diploids in which *Ma* was also segregating. These diploids were homozygous for *ad2* and were heterozygous for *ad3*, *ad6*, and *Ma* in the following two dispositions: *ad6 Ad3 Ma/Ad6 ad3 ma* and *ad6 Ad3 ma/Ad6 ad3 Ma*. Both diploids were therefore red and adenine-requiring. White diploids were obtained from these by the technique described above for the procurement of the adenine mutations in haploid strains. Three types of whites were obtained: Those which were *Ad2 ad2 Ad6 ad6 Ad3 ad3 Ma ma*, due to mutation of *ad2* to *Ad2* and therefore adenine-independent; those which were *ad6* homozygotes and could grow on histidineless medium but not on adenineless medium; and those which were *ad3* homozygotes and could not grow on either histidineless or adenineless medium. The *ad3 ad3* diploids occurred with a frequency of eight to ten times the frequency of the *ad6 ad6* diploids. Twenty-seven *ad6 ad6* diploids and 22 *ad3 ad3* diploids were sporulated

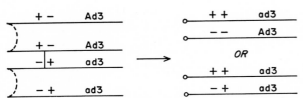

FIGURE 6. The distribution of a distal marker following the reversional event if crossing over is the recombinational mechanism.

for evidence of segregation at the other loci; the segregations are recorded in Figure 5.

It will be seen that 19 of the 27 *ad6 ad6* diploids were homozygous for the markers distal to *ad6*; these are interpreted to be the result of a crossover in the centromere to *ad6* region (region I, Fig. 5). The remaining eight are heterozygous for the distal loci, as would be expected from crossing over in both regions I and II (from *ad6* to *ad3*). Among the *ad3 ad3* diploids, three were the complementary product of the crossover in region I; 17 were due to crossing over in region II and were heterozygous for *ad6* and homozygous for the distal marker at the *Ma* locus; two were the result of crossing over in both regions II and III (between *ad3* and *Ma*) and were heterozygous at both the proximal and distal loci. Thus homozygosity at the *ad3* locus serves as an indicator of crossing over in the centromere to *ad6* region in about two-thirds of the cases and homozygosity at the *Ma* locus is an even better indicator of crossing over in the *ad6-ad3* region.

These correlations can be made use of to see if crossing over will account for the reversional event in heteroallelic combinations. The consequences of a crossover between the + and − elements of two dissimilar *ad6* alleles are shown in Figure 6. It is assumed that the new ++ chromatid may assort with either of the chromatids of the

homologous chromosome. Homozygosity at the *ad3* locus would therefore be expected to follow from only half of the instances of such a crossover and from only about one-third if a second crossover also occurred in the *ad6-ad3* region with a frequency as indicated from the data on mitotic crossing over. Yet in 40 separate revertants from heteroallelic combinations of *ad6* in which *ad3* was heterozygous, there was only one dubious indication that crossing over had taken place. In this exception, in one of the two asci which were dissected from the revertant diploid, the segregation for *ad3* was 2:2, whereas in the other ascus the segregation was 4 *Ad3*:0 *ad3*. Homozygosity could have been achieved secondarily and not in relation to the reversional event. Furthermore, in six separate revertants from heteroallelic combinations of *ad3*, in which *ad6* and *Ma* were both in heterozygous condition, segregations of 2:2 were obtained for both *ad6* and *Ma* whereas homozygosity for either *Ma* or *ma* would have been expected in half the cases if crossing over had been the reason for reversion.

In summary, there are three types of evidence to indicate that crossing over is not responsible for the reversional event. These are: (1) the failure to recover the double mutant from the revertant diploids, (2) the recovery of each of the two alleles from revertants of a specific heteroallelic combination, and (3) the failure to correlate reversion with the occurrence of mitotic crossing over. The evidence points to a mechanism which produces a recombinant allele without at the same time producing a reciprocal product.

THE EFFECT OF SPORULATION ON THE RATE OF REVERSION

If crossing over is not responsible for the revertant diploid, is contact between the homologous chromosomes carrying the mutant alleles

TABLE 5. THE EFFECT OF SPORULATION ON THE RATE OF REVERSION IN HETEROALLELIC AND HOMOALLELIC COMBINATIONS

Note that the frequencies of revertants before sporulation (BS) and after sporulation (AS) are given per 10^6 cells whereas the frequency of new revertants is given per 100 asci.

Strain	Combination of Alleles	Hemacytometer Counts after Sporulation						Frequency of Revertants/10^6		New Revertants per 100 Asci
		Spores per ascus				Total count	% asci	BS	AS	
		1	2	3	4					
86	*ad6*-8/9	9	88	111	14	347	64	1695	7340	0.9
87G1	*ad6*-8/10	8	9	10	0	253	11	198	650	0.4
89	*ad6*-8/12	2	11	30	7	217	23	319	3680	1.5
94G	*ad6*-9/10	8	6	2	0	304	5	49	170	0.2
96	*ad6*-9/12	7	9	4	0	240	8	114	500	0.5
102G1	*ad6*-10/12	3	1	2	1	199	4	46	80	0.1
94P1	*ad6*-9/10	0	0	0	0	988	0	16	18	—
85G1	*ad6*-8/8	12	18	54	19	281	37	—	0/10^7	—
100G1	*ad6*-10/10	12	66	90	21	366	52	18	25	0.001

necessary for its occurrence? For information on this point, the frequency of revertant cells was determined in heteroallelic diploids before and after sporulation, on the assumption that meiotic pairing during sporulation should result in a higher frequency of revertants if contact is required.

It should be explained that the frequency of reversion during vegetative division is low, of the order of about 10^{-4} to about 10^{-6} or 10^{-7}, depending on the heteroallelic combination. This may seem to be in contradiction with the results of the reversional test cited earlier but it is not, for the following reason: The reversional test made use of an unsupplemented yeast extract-peptone medium in which there is a strong selection for the revertant diploid when it arises. If this medium is supplemented with adenine, 40 mg per liter, the effect of selection is suppressed and the true reversion rates may be determined.

The cultures were sporulated on a non-nutrient medium containing 0.3 per cent sodium acetate, 0.02 per cent raffinose, 1.5 per cent agar, and 40 mg/l of adenine (to avoid differential endogenous growth of revertant and nonrevertant cells). A thick suspension of cells was placed on this medium and a sample of the suspension was taken three days later for cell counts and for plating on adenineless medium for the frequency of revertants. It should be noted that the yeast ascus remains intact during plating and thus each diploid cell which undergoes reversion during sporulation will produce only one adenine-independent colony. The results, given in Table 5, indicate a strong enhancement of the frequency of revertant cells as a consequence of meiosis. The dependence of enhancement on the heteroallelic condition is shown in the comparison with homoallelic diploids which did not show a significant increase in frequency of revertant cells when handled in the same way. Its dependence on sporulation is shown further in the fact that culture 94P, a cytochrome-deficient (petite) derivative of 94G which did not sporulate on the raffinose-acetate medium, also did not produce a significantly higher frequency of revertants.

The low frequency of reversion during vegetative growth therefore increases to as much as one per cent or so after meiosis has intervened. Although this enhancement may be dependent on some other property of meiosis it is reasonable to assume that contact or nearness of the mutant alleles in the cell is a requirement for the occurrence of reversion.

The Number of Alleles at a Locus

The data at hand may be used as a rough estimate of the minimal number of ways in which a locus may be altered to produce a mutant allele. I am indebted to Dr. James F. Crow for supplying me with the following equation for this purpose: n = N/I, n being the number of alleles at the locus, N the number of allelic combinations which were tested for heteroallelism, and I the number of allelic combinations which were not heteroallelic by the reversional test. For example, the nine *ad3* alleles may be combined in 36 ways; since one of the combinations was not heteroallelic the estimated number of alleles is 36. Similarly, there are an estimated 39 alleles of *ad4*, 77 alleles of *ad5*, 135 alleles of *ad6*, and 64 alleles of *ad7*. (The *ad5-ad7* mutation is regarded here as a mutation to *ad5* and to *ad7*; on this basis 16 of 18 *ad5* alleles were different and 15 of 17 *ad7* alleles were different.) In making these estimates, it is assumed that the alleles at hand are a fair sample of the alleles at the locus and also that the allelic combinations which do not appear to be heteroallelic do in fact carry identical alleles. If either of these assumptions is in error, the estimates will be too low.

The interpretation of the complexity which is thus found at a locus is different for different models of the locus. If a locus consists of a linear array of mutational sites (see Benzer, 1955; Demerec, 1956; Streisinger and Franklin, 1956), the number of alleles at a locus should correspond to the number of mutational sites. If, however, mutation is due to some kind of spatial reorganization of a certain number of elements, this number could be much smaller. For example, five elements could produce 120 spatial permutations. It may be possible to decide between these broad alternatives from information on the reversion frequencies of different heteroallelic combinations if valid inferences of order can be drawn from a comparison of these frequencies.

On the Mechanism of Non-Reciprocal Recombination

Various mechanisms have been suggested to achieve recombination without crossing over. There is the gene conversion (mutation) hypothesis of Winkler (1930), which was modified by Lindegren (1949b) to include exchange of genic material between alleles (see also Winge, 1955). Lederberg (1955) has proposed a model of alternative replication in which the new chromatid can copy from either its sister or from a non-sister fragment. A similar mechanism has been suggested by Mitchell (1955) to account for nonreciprocal recombination in *Neurospora*. St. Lawrence (1956) has dealt with nonreciprocal recombination in terms of controlling elements (see McClintock, 1956).

The data obtained with yeast are not specific enough to define clearly the mechanism of reversion in the heteroallelic combinations. The mechanism should account for (1) non-reciprocal recombination without concurrent recombination of outside markers, (2) the enhancement of the rate of reversion during meiosis, (3) the recovery of each of the two alleles in revertants from specific heteroallelic combinations, and (4) the occasional occurrence of revertants which are homozygous for adenine independence as indicated by

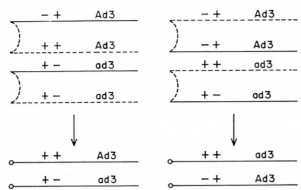

FIGURE 7. A scheme for alternative replication to account for non-reciprocal recombination without distal recombination. The dotted lines represent the newly-formed chromatids.

the fact that asci from these exhibit 4:0 segregation for independence.

The model which is illustrated in Figure 7 is chosen as a matter of simple convenience to bring together the observations in yeast. It depends on alternative replication (the dotted line represents the newly-formed chromatids) and will account for non-reciprocal recombination, for the recovery of both alleles, and for the 2:2 segregation of distal markers. The revertants which are homozygous for adenine independence can be obtained without too much difficulty if it is assumed that the two chromatids do not form at the same time; the first ++ chromatid could therefore serve as a partial template for the second or the second could repeat the replicating "error" of the first. The enhanced rate of reversion in meiosis is to be expected since alternative replication requires nearness of the homologous chromosomes.

Alternatively, it could be supposed that the mechanism involves migratory genic elements. If the + element of one chromatid should produce more than one replica in a division, the extra element could replace the corresponding − element in the homologous chromosome. The requirements of the evidence would thereby be fulfilled.

In *Neurospora*, nonreciprocal recombination is accompanied by extensive recombination between nearby outside markers. It may be that the condition for non-reciprocal recombination is an intimate contact between the participating chromosomes which leads to a higher frequency of crossing over than would be obtained in an unselected sample. If so, it is surprising that coincidental crossing over was not found as a common occurrence in the cases studied in yeast. It is important to emphasize that non-reciprocal recombination was investigated in mitotic division in yeast and meiotic division in *Neurospora*. Nevertheless, the results in yeast suggest the possibility that the event leading to non-reciprocal recombination may be separable in time or type of contact from that of crossing over and that this difference may be accentuated in mitosis.

ADDENDUM: IRREGULAR SEGREGATION IN YEAST

The asci from a diploid of genotype $+/-$ are expected to exhibit a phenotypic segregation of $2+:2-$; occasionally, however, segregations of $4+:0-$, $3+:1-$, $1+:3-$, and $0+:4-$ are obtained. These irregular segregations have been emphasized by Lindegren (1949b, 1953) as the basis for his gene conversion hypothesis. It has been shown that the irregular asci may in specific cases be attributed to unsuspected chromosomal duplication, to mutation at the mating-type locus, to a supernumerary mitosis within the developing ascus, etc. (see Winge and Roberts, 1954; Roman, Phillips, and Sands, 1955), but after allowances are made for the known genetic mechanisms which will account for an apparent irregular segregation, there remain cases which do not easily fit into a conventional scheme. An indication of the frequency with which these occur is given in Table 6, in which are listed the segregations obtained for six of the seven adenine loci in a series of crosses of genetically homogenous material.

It will be seen that some loci segregate irregularly more frequently than others. In those segregations other than *ad2*, about one in 20 asci exhibit an irregular segregation, usually 3:1 or 1:3. These ratios could be due to mutation in the four-strand stage of meiosis or later, of *Ad* to *ad* for the 1:3 ratio or of *ad* to *Ad* for the 3:1 ratio. It has to be specified however that there is something about the heterozygous condition which remarkably enhances the mutation rate of these loci. In Lindegren's view, the 1:3 ratio is evidence that, in the four-strand condition, one of the dominant genes has lost some of its essential substance to the two recessives, thereby "degrading the dominant to recessive status."

It now becomes possible to test the hypothesis of mutation. It was shown above that of 83 mutations from the dominant to the recessive condition at the adenine loci, 73 differed from each other. Thus there is a high probability that one of the three recessives in the 1:3 ascus will differ from

TABLE 6. IRREGULAR SEGREGATIONS FOR ADENINE ALLELES IN ASCI FROM DIPLOIDS OF GENOTYPE *Ad/ad*

Segregating Marker	Number of Segregations	Irregular Segregations			
		0:4	1:3	3:1	4:0
ad2	262	0	0	0	0
ad3	27	0	1	0	0
ad4	44	0	1	1	0
ad5 (also *ad5-ad7*)	65	0	2	1	1
ad6	80	0	2	2	0
ad7	19	0	0	1	0
	497	0	6	5	1

the other two if it arises by mutation. Eight 1:3 asci were selected and the three recessives of each were placed in combination with the specific recessive known to have been present in the hybrid which produced the 1:3 ascus. For example, the three *ad3* segregants of an *Ad3/ad3-1* hybrid were crossed with strains carrying *ad3-1*. If one of the *ad3* segregants had been a new mutation, *ad3*-x, it would be expected in most instances that the combination *ad3*-x/*ad3-1* would revert with the frequency of a heteroallelic combination. However, none of the eight cases gave evidence of heteroallelism. It is therefore highly improbable that mutation is responsible for the irregular asci, and if gene conversion in the Lindegren sense is to be invoked, it must be specified that the process by which it occurs is directed in such a way as to produce a mutant locus indistinguishable by the reversional test from the recessive allele originally present. Alternatively, the 1:3 and 3:1 segregations can be accounted for in terms of alternative replication or of migratory elements, as mentioned above.

ACKNOWLEDGMENTS

The investigation was supported by a research grant (E-328) from the National Institutes of Health, Public Health Service, and by a grant from the Biological and Medical Fund of the State of Washington. I am indebted to Mrs. Alcetta Campbell and Mr. S. M. Sands for excellent technical assistance.

REFERENCES

BENZER, S., 1955, Fine structure of a genetic region in bacteriophage. Proc. Nat. Acad. Sci. Wash. *41:* 344–354.

DEMEREC, M., 1956, A comparative study of certain gene loci in *Salmonella*. Cold Spring Harbor Symp. Quant. Biol. *21:* 113–121.

EPHRUSSI, B., HOTTINGUER, H., and TAVLITZKI, J., 1949, Action de l'acriflavine sur les levures. II. Etude génétique du mutant "petite colonie." Ann. Inst. Pasteur *76:* 419–450.

GILES, N. H., 1955, Forward and back mutation at specific loci in *Neurospora*. Brookhaven Symp. Biol. *8:* 103–123.

GREEN, M. M., 1956, A further analysis of the forked locus in *Drosophila melanogaster*. Proc. Nat. Acad. Sci. Wash. *42:* 73–77.

HAWTHORNE, D. C., 1955, The use of linear asci for chromosome mapping in *Saccharomyces*. Genetics *40:* 511–518.

JAMES, A. P., and LEE-WHITING, B., 1955, Radiation-induced genetic segregations in vegetative cells of diploid yeast. Genetics *40:* 826–831.

LEDERBERG, J., 1955, Recombination mechanisms in bacteria. J. Cell. Comp. Physiol. 45 (Suppl. 2): 75–107.

LEUPOLD, U., 1955, Versuche zur genetischen Klassifizierung adenin-abhängiger Mutanten von *Schizosaccharomyces pombe*. Arch. Jul. Klaus-Stiftung Zürich *30:* 506–516.

LEWIS, E. B., 1955, Some aspects of position pseudoallelism. Amer. Nat. *89:* 73–89.

LINDEGREN, C. C., 1949a, Chromosome maps of *Saccharomyces*. Proc. 8th Intern. Congr. Genet. (Hereditas Suppl. Vol.) 338–355.
    1949b, The yeast cell, its genetics and cytology. St. Louis, Educational Publishers, Inc.

    1953, Gene conversion in *Saccharomyces*. J. Genetics *51:* 625–637.

McCLINTOCK, B., 1956, Controlling elements and the gene. Cold Spr. Harb. Symp. Quant. Biol. *21:* 197–216.

MITCHELL, M. B., 1955, Aberrant recombination of pyridoxine mutants of *Neurospora*. Proc. Nat. Acad. Sci. Wash. *41:* 215–220.

PONTECORVO, G., 1952, Genetical analysis of cell organization. Symposia Soc. Exp. Biol. *6:* 218–229.

PRITCHARD, R. H., 1955, The linear arrangement of a series of alleles of *Aspergillus nidulans*. Heredity *9:* 343–371.

REAUME, S. E., and TATUM, E. L., 1949, Spontaneous and nitrogen mustard induced nutritional deficiencies in *Saccharomyces cerevisiae*. Arch. Biochem. *22:* 331–338.

ROMAN, H., 1955, Mutation studies in yeast. Genetics *40:* 592.
    1956, A system selective for mutations affecting the synthesis of adenine in yeast. Compt. Rend. Lab. Carlsberg, Sér. Physiol. *26:* 299–314.

ROMAN, H., PHILLIPS, M. M., and SANDS, S. M., 1955, Studies of polyploid *Saccharomyces*. I. Tetraploid segregation. Genetics *40:* 546–561.

ST. LAWRENCE, P., 1956, The *q* locus of *Neurospora crassa*. Proc. Nat. Acad. Sci. Wash. *42:* 189–194.

STADLER, L. J., 1954, The gene. Science *120:* 811–819.

STREISINGER, G., and FRANKLIN, N., 1956, Mutation and recombination in bacteriophage. Cold Spr. Harb. Symp. Quant. Biol. *21:* 103–111.

WINGE, Ö., 1955, On interallelic crossing over. Compt. Rend. Lab. Carlsberg, Sér. Physiol. *25:* 341–354.

WINGE, Ö., and ROBERTS, C., 1954, Causes of deviations from 2:2 segregations in the tetrads of monohybrid yeasts. Compt. Rend. Lab. Carlsberg, Sér. Physiol. *25:* 285–329.

WINKLER, H., 1930, Die Konversion der Gene. Jena, Verlag Gustav Fischer.

DISCUSSION

LINDEGREN: There are both legal and psychological aspects involved in assigning the proper name to the phenomenon which I have called "gene conversion." Priority to the name is clearly vested in Winkler. Winkler based his views partly on irregular segregations obtained from tetrad analysis and stated that they could explain, as they most certainly do, recombinations produced without crossing over. His mistake was in assuming that this proved that crossing over did not occur, just as Stern assumed the converse, namely, that the demonstration of crossing over disproved the possibility of gene change independent of crossing over; these are independent phenomena, however, and the demonstration of one has no bearing on the occurrence of the other. It is quite irrelevant whether conversion, as the name implies, involves the transformation of one gene into another. We speak of atoms although we know these particles are further divisible; we retain the name for oxygen although we know that the element is not an "acid former"; suppressors do not "suppress" but restore enzyme synthesis, etc. Misappropriation of scientific prestige is an illegal process but it can be achieved by intimidation or adroit manipulation. I also toyed with the idea of assigning another name to the phenomenon in the hope that poor old Winkler might be forgotten. I salved my conscience with the arguments that his proofs were not adequate, that his concept was principally theoretical, etc. etc., but finally faced the cold hard fact of his priority and gave in.

Dr. Roman may have overlooked these legal difficulties since the psychological problems which he faces loom so largely. He has insisted for the past five years that "gene conversion" does not exist and he would certainly find it easier to adjust to the "Mary Mitchell phenomenon" since it relieves him from facing the fact that he has lived for the past five years "in error." His difficulties arose from his fixed ideas (1) that the gene is a stable entity and (2) that genic variation can only arise from longitudinal discontinuity along the chromosome. These ideas are rapidly disappearing, and we are forced now to reevaluate all influences involving mitotic crossing over, pseudoallelism and single strand analysis based on these assumptions.

STERN: In the present stage of knowledge concerning genetic elements uniformity of nomenclature is hard to attain. It seems fully permissible for different workers to use the same terms in different ways so long as each individual defines clearly the meaning he attaches to the term.

Concerning the term "conversion" it may be pointed out that Winkler was primarily interested in a theory of recombination which would represent an alternative to that of crossing over. He conceived of a mutation-like process, occurring only in heterozygotes which would transform an A allele to a and a to A. This conversion he assumed to be possible in two ways which he termed monogenic and digenic. The former involves one of the two alleles only, the latter both. The former leads from Aa to AA or aa, the latter to aA. Both types of conversion produce recombination of linked genes. Thus, a double heterozygote AB/ab would be converted into aB/ab or AB/Ab by monogenic, into aB/Ab by digenic conversion of the Aa pair. To explain the actually observed types of recombinations of linked genes Winkler had further to postulate group conversions of blocks of genes, interference of conversions, etc. He regarded both monogenic and digenic conversion as possible mechanisms though he inclined to believe particularly in the former which, as he pointed out, would account for abnormal segregation ratios in tetrads. In my discussion, in 1930, of Winkler's theory, I did not assume, as Dr. Lindegren maintains, "that the demonstration of crossing over disproved the possibility of gene change independent of crossing over." On the contrary, I then stated that detailed studies of tetrads in *Funaria* and *Coprinus* were desirable in order to test for the possible existence of conversion. Abnormal segregation ratios in tetrads even if independent of ploidy and other "orthodox" mechanisms are not proofs of conversion in the sense of instability of genes since this is only one of several possible interpretations.

ROMAN: When Winkler proposed his conversion hypothesis, he took as his only supporting evidence the scattered observations of irregular segregations in tetrads which were then beginning to be reported. When Dr. Lindegren found irregular segregations in yeast, he accepted the Winkler concept and modified it. It soon became apparent, however, that irregular segregation in yeast has a variety of causes (see Addendum, this paper) and it should have become just as apparent that evidence of irregular segregation was not necessarily evidence for conversion. The problem became one of finding irregular segregation which could not be explained by any of the known mechanisms. When such segregations are found, the need which supersedes the quarrel over nomenclature is that of finding a mechanism for the event. Those who find the term "conversion" useful should use it, but not for reasons of priority. Winkler was specific in defining conversion to this extent: The mechanism occurred in the heterozygote only, not in the homozygote, and it involved a change of an existing gene into an allelic form. We may perhaps find that such a mechanism exists. In the meantime, it may be more appropriate to speak in noncommittal terms, such as the Lindegren effect, the Mitchell effect, the Benzer effect, etc., until we know more about mechanisms and can either homologize the various observations or distinquish between them.

KRIEG: In the cases of irregular tetraspore segregations which you have observed, has it been possible to observe also segregation of markers on either side? It would be interesting to see if the correlation of "gene conversion" with crossing over as found by Mary Mitchell is found here also.

ROMAN: We do not yet have markers which are closely enough linked for the purpose which you suggest.

GILES: I would like to describe briefly some recent studies with a group of adenine-requiring mutants in *Neurospora* which are related in certain respects to the results obtained by Dr. Roman. In particular, they point up a further difficulty in using biochemical complementation as a criterion of non-allelism. This discussion will be concerned with a series of adenine-specific mutants (responding to hypoxanthine, but not to adenine) obtained from concentration-filtration experiments utilizing X-irradiated and control conidia of wild type strain 74A. On the basis of heterocaryon and crossing tests, these isolates comprise two genetically distinct groups of allelic mutants—group E (10 mutants) and group F (14 mutants). (The only previously known adenine-specific mutant type in *Neurospora*, ad 4— mutant 44206, falls into group F.) Biochemical studies indicate that the two types are involved in two sequentially related terminal steps in adenine synthesis, group E mutants being blocked in the conversion of inosine monophosphate (IMP), to adenosine monophosphate succinate

(AMPS), and group F mutants being blocked in the splitting of AMPS to adenosine monophosphate (AMP) and fumaric acid. Spectrophotometric evidence indicates that activity of the AMPS splitting enzyme, adenylosuccinase, is absent in extracts of all F mutants (and also in mutant 44206), whereas highly active enzyme preparations are obtained from wild type and from E mutants. Addition of F mutant extracts to wild type extract fails to produce inhibition of activity.

Of particular interest have been the results of comparisons in which all possible combinations of E and F mutants have been tested for possible intra-group positive heterocaryon responses. Whereas all E mutant combinations are negative as expected, certain positive responses are obtained with particular F mutant combinations. Mutant F_{12} when combined with mutants F_1, F_4 or F_5 forms heterocaryons which grow in the absence of added adenine at a rate equivalent to wild type. All other combinations of F mutants are negative such that heterocaryons fail to form on minimal. Forced heterocaryons have been formed with several of these latter mutant combinations, and in all instances exogenous adenine is required for growth. Extracts of heterocaryons which grow in the absence of adenine have been shown to contain adenylosuccinase activity. In preliminary experiments, no enzyme activity has yet been detected in mixtures of extracts from mutants capable of forming heterocaryons on minimal. The present evidence strongly suggests that the restoration of specific enzymatic activity in these heterocaryons arises from some type of interaction between two genetically different types of nuclei taking place in the cytoplasm of the heterocaryon. Further studies will be required to elucidate the biochemical mechanism involved in this unexpected complementation.

Analysis of a Complex Gene in the House Mouse

L. C. DUNN

Columbia University, New York

The recent period of genetical research has been marked by an increasing diversity of methods of study and by a certain loss of focus on central problems. This is to be expected in a period of exploration when new methods tend to be developed for their inherent interest and for the sake of the variety of new facts which they disclose. We know as a result that the genetical elements may be apprehended and studied in many ways, not merely by structural or qualitative criteria, but by quantitative, metabolic and biochemical, and other functional ones as well.

As we approach what may well be the end of this period, we can already see clear signs of a return to the main highway, that which leads more directly toward an elucidation of the focal problems of genetics, the nature of the gene and of the process of self-reproduction which is the most interesting aspect of genetical units.

One of the signs of this resumption of focus is the increasing attention that is being paid to those genes of which the complexity has become clearly evident. When within one element characterized by some unity of phenotypic effects, the different forms that the element assumes are related to each other in ways formerly thought to be characteristic of different genes, some revisions of older ideas about gene structure are surely required. The old rules for simple genes have been broken one by one. Recombination between parts of the same gene has been clearly proved; and so has the ability of one part of a gene to make good—to complement—a change in another part. It seems useless to try to evade the issues raised by such facts by giving the element within which such events occur another name, for then we lose the solid ground on which the older work had placed it. I confess to some such evasion by having used the term "complex locus" which survived even in the preliminary title of this paper. But, encouraged by such recent work as that of Pontecorvo and Demerec, I propose to be bolder and to denote such elements within which the changes are related as variations on a common theme, and in which the parts can be identified individually by recombination or complementarity, as complex genes. The implication is clearly that many, perhaps most, genes, when studied by methods competent to reveal complexity, will prove to be complex. If that time comes we may drop the adjective and call them simply genes.

I propose to describe the relations between the forms assumed by one such element in the mouse. A great variety of forms of this gene has been found, some in laboratory stocks, of which 13 have been studied (8 of which were observed at or near their origin by mutation), and some in populations of wild house mice, of which 16 have been studied at least in part. I propose to call the forms identified by phenotypic effects as different *alleles*; and for purposes of discussion to associate each different allele with a different *site of mutation*, which I shall regard, following Pontecorvo's lead, as equivalent to locus.

The primary problem which we have set for ourselves is to relate the effects of the alleles, identified by the usual breeding methods of genetic analysis, to a central function of the gene. The effects of the alleles are deduced from their phenotypes in homozygotes and in compound combinations (t^n/t^n, t^x/t^x, t^n/t^x). Since most of the alleles studied are lethal, when homozygous, in early embryonic stages, their effects have been characterized by embryological study of the developmental systems involved, by the usual methods of descriptive embryology, supplemented at a few points by experimental study of the embryos.

The breeding analysis was begun by Dobrovolskaia-Zawadskaia who discovered the first mutants of this gene. It has been continued in this laboratory since 1932 with independent confirmation of some points by Kobozieff in France, and most recently by Tutikawa (1955) in Japan. The embryological study was initiated by Chesley in our laboratory, some points were studied by Ephrussi by tissue culture methods, but the bulk of the work was done by Gluecksohn-Schoenheimer (now Mrs. Waelsch) in our laboratory, with some recent important additions by Jean Smith. Most of the observations of both kinds have been published or are in course of publication, except for alleles 11–18 from wild populations which are reported here for the first time. Other recent contributors from our laboratory are Joan Suckling and Louis Levine whose papers are in press. Many assistants and students have contributed materially; of these, the help of Mary Ann Dann, Harriett Tinker, Andrew Beasley, Robert Stephenson and Malkiat Deol has not yet received public acknowledgment.

The basic method of maintaining the alleles and of discovering changes in them is the breeding of balanced lines, each containing the dominant mutation *T* and one of the other variants, known collectively as *t*-alleles. Each of the 21 lethal *t*-alleles so far analysed, when combined with *T*, forms a balanced lethal line, T/t^{lethal}, which breeds true without selection, since no recombination has ever been observed between T and any t-allele. The lethal zygotes die *in utero* and are resorbed, TT at ten and a half days, tt at various times before ten days, according to the allele. The lines containing a viable allele, t^v, are maintained similarly except that the tailless offspring T/t^v are selected for breeding, the t^v/t^v class (always normal-tailed) being discarded or used in other experiments.

Lethal alleles are judged to be different when matings between two balanced lethal lines, such as $T/t^0 \times T/t^1$, produce, in addition to tailless offspring T/t^0 and T/t^1, normal-tailed progeny which on testing prove to be t^0/t^1. The fact that many such compounds, containing two different lethal alleles, are viable and phenotypically normal (in respect to tail structure) provides us with the basic complementarity test by which new alleles can be detected and characterized as different from the t-allele in the balanced lethal stock in which they arose.

There is no such direct method for judging whether viable alleles are different, since both homozygotes t^{v1}/t^{v1} and compounds t^{v1}/t^{v2} have normal tails. Here recourse may sometimes be had to another peculiarity of the compounds since in many cases the males containing both a lethal and a viable allele (t^v/t^{lethal}) are sterile or quasi-sterile. The degree of sterility is different depending on which viable allele is involved. Representative results of breeding and testing the balanced lethal lines are shown in the tables.

MUTATION

In addition to the tailless offspring born in the balanced lethal line 1, twelve exceptions, each with a normal tail, were recorded among some 5000 births. Four of these were lost or were sterile. From each of the others a new balanced line was derived as follows:

Exception $t^1/t^x \times T/+$ (Brachy)

$$\text{F}_1 \quad T/t^1 \times T/t^x \qquad T/t^1 \times T/t^1 \quad +/t^1 \qquad +/t^x$$

tailless normal   tailless   normal tail

$\text{F}_2 = \text{F}_1 T/t^x \times \text{F}_1 T/t^x$ (new balanced line)

Whenever an exception was found it was given a number in the order of discovery and if it gave rise to a new balanced line, both the line and the t-allele in it took this number. In this way lines containing t^4, t^9 and t^{12} (lethals) and t^3, t^7, t^8, and t^{11} (viables) were isolated. T/t^{12} in turn gave rise to an exception which proved to be t^{12}/t^{13} and the new viable balanced line T/t^{13} was derived from it.

I think that methods of identifying changes in this gene will become clearer if I describe in some detail the methods used and the results obtained with one of the newer alleles found in a laboratory stock. This evidence moreover is mostly unpublished and contains points of special interest for interpretation of other alleles and for future work.

ORIGIN OF t^{12}

The balanced lethal stock t^1 (formerly known as Line 29) produced an exception in the fifth brother-sister generation after making this stock isogenic with a Brachy stock. This was a single normal tailed male among 110 offspring from one male mated to his siblings. The exception was mated for four months with fertile Brachy females but gave no offspring. Sterility is the usual condition of such male exceptions. His genotype was suspected to be t^1/t^x, that is, with an allele other than t^1. We tested all his tailless litter mates by mating to T/t^1. Two of them, a male and a female (out of 5 tested) also produced normal tailed exceptions as shown in Table 1. Since a balanced line shown to be T/t^{12} was established from these, these were diagnosed as T/t^{12}. Thus amongst the progeny of ♀ 24871 three exceptions occurred: one normal male t^1/t^{12}? and two tailless T/t^{12}, including ♀ 25641. It was assumed that either ♀ 24871 was herself T/t^{12} (derived from an undetected mutation in the previous generation) or else she gave three exceptional t^{12} gametes, indicating a mosaic gonad. All tailless progeny of ♀ 25641 were tested by matings to T/t^1. Two of these produced normal tailed progeny (2/32 and 3/37). These two were diagnosed as T/t^{12}. Further T/t^{12} animals were produced by mating ♀ 25641 (T/t^{12}) by Brachy which can introduce no t-allele. Such offspring tested by mates diagnosed as T/t^{12} produced only tailless offspring. The balanced line t^{12} was established by inbreeding their descendants (Table 2).

Once the line was established, it became evident that t^{12} is a new lethal shown by the complementarity test to be different from t^1. Crosses of $T/t^1 \times T/t^{12}$ regularly produce, in addition to tailless animals, the compound type with a normal tail. The males of this genotype are sterile, the females when tested by Brachy produce only tailless and normal, never Brachy. The latter type would be expected if a $+$ allele of the gene were present in any gametes, arising by recombination or otherwise. Its absence indicates that all gametes carry t-alleles, presumably either t^1 or t^{12} (barring further mutation). This is the evidence that t^1 and t^{12} are complementary alleles. The genotype t^1/t^{12} has low viability before birth, only 15 per cent of the expected proportion of such normal tailed animals being found in litters from $T/t^1 \times T/t^{12}$, which are nearly as small as those depleted by two lethals in the balanced lines (Table 2). Direct observations by Smith (1956) show that a large proportion of t^1/t^{12} embryos die in the period 12 to 19 days after mating. Low viability of the

TABLE 1. OCCURRENCE AND IDENTIFICATION OF t^{12}

Exp.	Parents		Offspring		Diagnosis
	Female	Male	Tailless	Normal	
1	F_5 Tailless[1]	24891 Tailless[1]	91	—	
2	F_5 24871 Tailless[1]	24891 Tailless[1]	18	1	mother T/t^{12}?
3	Brachy	Normal exception	—	—	sterile
4	Sibs of exceptions from 2	Tailless[1]			
	a) ♀ Tailless[1]	25641 Tailless	19	2	father T/t^{12}
	b) ♀ Tailless[1]	26211 Tailless	8	2	father T/t^{12}
	3 ♀ Tailless[1]	Tailless[1]	132	—	mother T/t^1
	c) Brachy	25641 Tailless[12]	—		
5	Sibs of exceptions from 4				
	Tailless[1]	26017 Tailless	30	2	father T/t^{12}
		26220 Tailless	34	3	father T/t^{12}
6	11 Tailless[12] (from 4c)	Tailless[1]	186	13	
7	Tailless[12] (from 4c)	26017 Tailless[12]	51	—	Tailless[12] line from these
8	Normal exceptions	Brachy	101	71	t^1/t^{12}

TABLE 2. TAILLESS LINE 12

Exp.	Phenotypes		Parent Genotypes	Normal	Brachy	Tailless	Total	Litter Size
1	Tailless[12]	Tailless[12]	$T/t^{12} \times T/t^{12}$			378		4.1
2	Tailless[12]	Tailless[1]	$T/t^{12} \times T/t^1$	10		160	170	4.6
3	Tailless[1]	Tailless[12]	$T/t^1 \times T/t^{12}$	27		289	316	4.3
4	F_1 normal*	Brachy	$t^1/t^{12} \times T/+$	101		71	178	7.0
5	Normal	Tailless[12]	$+/+ \times T/t^{12}$	291	32		323	8.1
6	Tailless[12]	Normal	$T/t^{12} \times +/+$	29	40		69	
7	F_1 normal†‡	Brachy	$+/t^{12} \times T/+$	131	71	83	285	
8	F_1 normal§	Brachy	$+/t^{12} \times T/+$	2474	1185	1095	4754	
9	Brachy	F_1 normal†‖	$T/+ \times +/t^{12}$	59	7	38	104	
10	Brachy	¶F_1 normal	$T/+ \times +/t^{12}$	1874	435	1378	3687	

* From Exp. 3.
† From Exp. 5.
‡ 29 ♀♀ tested $+/t^{12}$.

§ 265 ♀♀ tested $+/t^{12}$ (from Smith, 1956).
‖ 9 ♂♂ tested $+/t^{12}$.
¶ 29 ♂♂ tested $+/t^{12}$ (from Smith, 1956).

compounds coupled with male sterility makes detection, isolation and identification of such mutant t-alleles difficult and laborious; and we may be sure, that because of these peculiarities, the numbers of mutants found represent only a part of those that occur. The viability of t^1/t^{12} is near the limit which would permit detection; if much rarer the compounds would appear as sporadic exceptions, and if all the compounds were non-viable they could not be discovered at all except by mass dissection of pregnant females.

The manner of occurrence and the low viability of this compound are connected in a suggestive way. The first exception was produced by a female presumed to be T/t^1. It cannot be determined whether this female was herself T/t^{12} or whether she or her mate produced three identified mutant gametes. Her mate was almost certainly T/t^1 since by other females he produced 91 tailless without any exceptions. It is at any rate highly probable

that the mutation to t^{12} occurred in a T/t^1 animal either in this or in earlier generation. In the case of t^{12}, complementarity with the stock allele (t^1) is only partial, suggestive of a condition intermediate between full complementarity and the recurrence of a duplicate allele of t^1. t^1 and t^{12} are both pre-implantation lethals, t^{12}/t^{12} zygotes not developing beyond the morula stage (Smith, 1956). Both also show the extreme male segregation ratio abnormality, and in many ways are more alike than any other pair of t-alleles yet studied. Yet they have been shown to be *non-identical* alleles. This is a representative example of the complexity of this gene.

OTHER t-ALLELES

All other t-alleles detected as mutations in the laboratory arose in the same way as exceptions in one of the balanced lethal stocks. We may now list the other alleles known. They fall into two

TABLE 3. BREEDING ANALYSIS OF NEW WILD ALLELES t^{w11}—t^{w15}

Source	Parents	Tailless	Litter Size	$+/+ \times 0^t \male$ Normal	$+/+ \times 0^t \male$ Brachy	Total	Litter Size	$\dfrac{\text{Total}}{\text{Normals}}$
t^{w11} Storrs, Conn...............	$t^{w11} \times t^{w11}$	304*	3.4	518	21	539	7.7	.961
t^{w12} Oakland, Cal.............	$t^{w12} \times t^{w12}$	158*	4.3	319	17	336	6.5	.949
t^{w13} El Paso, Tex..............	$t^{w13} \times t^{w13}$	89	3.8	428	9	437	6.0	.979
t^{w14} Norwich, Vt..............	$t^{w14} \times t^{w14}$	77	3.7	392	20	412	6.9	.951
t^{w15} Lawrence, Kans...........	$t^{w15} \times t^{w15}$	92	3.7	391	40	431	6.5	.907

* + 1 normal exception.

classes, eight being lethals and five viables. All lethals of independent origin (t^{12}, t^1, t^0, t^4, t^9 and T) are different by the complementarity test and by their known effects in homozygotes. The two found in other stocks and not observed at origin (t^2 and t^6) cannot be distinguished by either of these tests from one of the distinct alleles: t^2 is either another example of t^1, a recurrence of t^1 or is lethal in compound with t^1; t^6 is indistinguishable by any test from t^0, and the same possibilities exist. The viable alleles differ as a group from the lethals but show some differences, though possibly not decisive ones, from each other. Thus t^3 and t^7 differ when compounded with t^1, t^1/t^3 males being generally sterile while t^1/t^7 males are fertile. T/t^{13} males have an extreme segregation ratio abnormality producing only two thirds of the expected (normal) proportion of t^{13} sperm. The viable alleles probably fall into at least three categories and possibly all five are different. Nine is thus the minimum number of different alleles, 13 the maximum. Of the analyzed alleles found in wild populations (to be described later) 13 are lethal (at least five of these are different by complementarity), and three are viable. The minimum number of different alleles is five, the maximum is 16 (including 4 now under study). Thus the t-alleles number between 14 and 29 so far found.

MUTATION RATE

It is difficult to compute a mutation rate from the above observations. The best we can do is to take the ratio between all viable normal exceptions observed and the total number of offspring observed at birth from balanced lethal lines. This is about 21/11164 or one in 530 gametes. The estimate is not greatly changed if we take only the cases analysed from one line (t^1). This is about 7/3500 or one in 500. It is only the order of magnitude that is important, and it is clearly higher than mutation rates estimated for other genes in the mouse which is of the order of 10^{-6}.

This leads us to ask whether these "mutations" are due to recombination within the gene or to some other form of escape from control of the balanced lethal system. Here it must be remembered that all of the lethal alleles observed at origin have been shown to be different (t^4, t^9, t^{12})

while at least three of the viables are probably different from each other (t^3, t^7, t^{13}). These would represent at least six different types of recombinants from one compound (T/t^1). Second, no instance of recovery of the expected type of recombinant, that containing a + allele, has been observed in 11,164 offspring of balanced lethal lines, nor in 2542 offspring of crosses between lines. In addition some 3000 test offspring have been observed from the cross $t^x/t^n \female \times T/+ \male$. Here recombination between two different t-alleles should yield + gametes which in combination with T should yield $T/+$, with brachy phenotype. None of this class was found. Progeny tests of 1223 normal tailed offspring of the cross $T/t^x \times +/+$ have been made. All proved to be $+/t^x$. The sum of these test instances is 15,929, but since each of the tests is competent to detect only one recombinant class (the + one) we must divide this figure by 2. Hence the present score on such recombination tests is 0/7964. This should be sufficient to make improbable a normal recombination fraction of .001 or more.

We must next consider whether t-alleles are included in structural rearrangements which prevent recombination. Three of the lethal alleles (t^0, t^1, t^{12}) do suppress recombination in the segment from T to Ki (about 5 map units away) but a fourth allele (t^3, a viable) does not. There is some cytological evidence that t^0 and t^1 are connected with a small inversion but a thorough cytological study has still to be made. Since t^3 arose from t^1, the loss of crossover suppression which accompanied the mutation led to the inferences that (1) the phenotypic effect of t-alleles on producing taillessness when combined with T is not due to a rearrangement (although the lethal effect might be); (2) the change to t^3 might be due to reinversion or may have been induced in a chromosome without the rearrangement by the presence of t^1. Our knowledge of the structural condition of these alleles is still too meagre to support further speculation. t^3 and the other viable t-mutations behave as good genetical alleles of T with no evidence of recombination.

The most striking fact about the changes to new t-alleles is that none has been observed to arise except in stocks that already contain a t-

allele. We have now tested some 10,000 gametes derived from $+/+$ and $T/+$ by matings with $T/+$. Change of $+$ or T to t would be revealed by finding T/t (tailless) progeny. A few tailless offspring have occurred in these test progenies but all such that lived to be tested proved to be $T/+$ probably with minus modifiers of Brachy. Some 4000 of these test progeny were from $+/+$ animals from wild populations. The result is sufficient to show that no such mutation rate as occurs in T/t^n stocks is apparent in animals lacking a t-allele. The instability is clearly connected with the presence of a t-allele.

This led us to devise a test for the hypothesis that one of the properties of t-alleles is the ability to induce changes to t in the homologous locus of the partner chromosome. This would perforce have to occur in an unreduced cell so that mutants arising in this way should occur in clusters. Two of the new t-alleles were in fact first found in several gametes at once, suggesting that they had arisen from a mutation in a gonial cell, leading thus to a mosaic gonad. Later on, evidence will be given showing that males T/t^0, T/t^1, T/t^{12} and males carrying t-alleles from wild populations usually produce an excess of functional t^n sperm, and that segregation of these t-alleles from T or $+$ tends to be non-random. This suggested that the same inducing properties of such t-alleles, in males, might produce both effects, that is, induction of new t-alleles, and induction or conversion of $+$ alleles to the same t-allele.

The experiment was as follows. t-alleles known to suppress recombination in the T–Ki region (t^0, t^1, t^{12}) were combined in males with Ki, a dominant marker some 5 map units away, viz. $Ki+/+t$ ♂ ♂. These were mated with $T/+$ ♀ ♀ and the tailless progeny selected for testing. Three genotypes were tested for amongst these: (1) $Ki+/+T$; (2) T/t; (3) $Ki\,t/+T$. Genotype 3 alone would confirm the hypothesis. These tailless animals were tested by $++$. Of 200 tested so far 197 proved to be T/t by giving normal ($+/t$) and Brachy ($T/+$) progeny. Three gave only Ki or Brachy progeny. These were then mated by $T/+$ to test for presence of t on the Ki chromosome. All proved to be $Ki+/+T$. This is sufficient to exclude the hypothesis that induction (or conversion) by t accounts for the excess of t sperm from $+/t$ or T/t males since such excesses amount to about 80 per cent of the sperm in the alleles tested. The data are at present insufficient to test the hypothesis of induction of new forms of t since this has a frequency of about .05 per cent. The experiments are being continued.

Summarizing the facts to date about occurrence of t-mutations observed at origin in the laboratory it can be said that these are frequent (1/500) in balanced stocks containing t-alleles, infrequent or absent, as new occurrences, in other stocks. They appear not to be due to recombination in the ordinary sense. The evidence that one t-allele induces a mutation to another is at present negative but indecisive. The most striking fact is that each allele arising by mutation is probably a new and different one.

t-ALLELES IN WILD POPULATIONS

When the mutation rate in the balanced lines in the laboratory proved to be high, we turned to examine the condition of this gene in wild house mice, captured in different regions of the United States in places remote from laboratory populations. Samples, usually from one to eight mice, from some 21 North American populations, have been tested by mating with Brachy ($T/+$). t-alleles have been found in 15 of these and 16 alleles have been isolated in balanced lines. Data on seven alleles have been published (Dunn and Suckling, 1956). Four additional ones are described in Table 3. In only one large sample of 23 tested (Great Gull Island, N. Y.) has no t-allele been found. Moreover, each of the first three Japanese populations tested by Tutikawa (1955), using our stocks and methods, contained t-alleles.

I do not propose to discuss in detail this work which is still in progress, but only to report features pertinent to the topic of this paper and to the possible relation of changes in this gene to selective forces in nature. Sixteen alleles have been studied sufficiently to yield a classification of thirteen lethals and three viables (Table 5) compared with seven lethals (of which only 5 are certainly different from each other) and five viables found in laboratory stocks. The difference is probably sufficient to indicate that lethals are favored in the wild populations. The frequency of heterozygotes in wild populations containing a t-allele is in fact quite high; it is 40 per cent or higher. Not all alleles from wild populations have been cross-tested with each other but the general pattern is clear. Many of them are different from each other and from the laboratory alleles. All of them, lethals and viables alike, show extremely high segregation ratio in males, averaging about 96 per cent of t-gametes from heterozygotes T/t^w (Table 4). This is itself sufficient to account for the high frequencies of heterozygotes found, in spite of the negative selection against the lethal homozygotes and against males homozygous for viable alleles which are sterile. A preliminary experiment indicated that wild males heterozygous for a lethal $+/t^w$ had higher net fertility than their $+/+$ siblings. This experiment is being repeated on a larger scale, and judgment is in the meantime witheld. It is significant that in one population, tested in 1952 and again in 1955, the proportion of heterozygotes rose significantly from 50 to over 60 per cent (Levine and Dunn, 1965).

These facts all indicate that t-alleles are common, perhaps usual components of the wild genotypes in this species. This does not necessarily indicate a high mutation rate since heterozygotes may be favored by selection. But we have already found five cases of mutation in t-alleles from the

TABLE 4. BALANCED TAILLESS LINES,
"WILD" ALLELES

Allele	Diagnosis	Male Ratio t^w/total
t^{w1} N. Y. 1	lethal	.89
t^{w3} Conn. 1	lethal	.99
t^{w4} Wisc.	lethal	.98
t^{w5} N. Y. 2	lethal	.94
t^{w6} Fla.	lethal	.99
t^{w11} Conn. 2	lethal	.96
t^{w12} Cal.	lethal	.95
t^{w13} Tex. 2	lethal	.98
t^{w14} Vt. 1	lethal	.96
t^{w15} Kans.	lethal	.91
t^{w16} Vt. 2	lethal	.95
t^{w17} Ariz.	lethal	
t^{w18} Conn. 2	lethal	
t^{w2} N. Y. 1	viable	.95
t^{w7} Tex. 1	viable	.92
t^{w8} Va.	viable	.94

wild; in one of these a heterozygous female from a wild population produced, among eight tested progeny, seven with one lethal allele (t^{w11}) and one with a different lethal allele (t^{w18}). This is the first instance in which a mutant allele was proved to have arisen in a female heterozygote. This case may provide the pattern by which new alleles arise in wild populations, namely by mutation in heterozygotes. This suggests that the t-alleles of wild populations are connected in a chain-wise relation, one arising from the other as in the laboratory populations. In fact the t-alleles originally found by Dobrovolskaia in laboratory stocks of Brachy may very well trace to origins in the wild, since Kobozieff reports that each of the first three tailless stocks arose from outcrosses of Brachy to other stocks, at least one of which was wild. Our example also suggests that the T/t constitution, the genotype from which all the laboratory mutants were detected, is not a necessary condition for the observed instability of t-alleles.

But the most important suggestion from this work for our present purposes is that the polymorphism of t and $+$ alleles, which is characteristic of wild populations, indicates an important contribution of this gene to fitness. The high value of the segregation ratio of wild male heterozygotes is characteristic of all wild alleles and not peculiar to certain ones as in the laboratory alleles which have not been exposed to selection in nature. The segregation ratio advantage may thus itself be a product of selection. If selection is responsible for the maintenance of a variety of t-alleles in nature, even when lethal, we may be sure that the gene, in many of its forms, has an important positive effect on development.

DEVELOPMENTAL EFFECTS

I turn now to the last aspect of this gene to be considered here, its relation to developmental processes. I shall not review the embryological evidence which has been published and reviewed by Waelsch (1954), but shall discuss only the general conclusion drawn from it, namely that the basic effects of the t-alleles so far studied are on organization processes centering in those leading to or dependent upon the organization of the chorda-mesoderm. In t^0/t^0 no mesoderm is formed and death occurs at a stage equivalent to gastrulation (5–6 days); in t^4/t^4, dying at seven to eight days, the development of the archenteron which in mouse embryos is involved in the development of the mesoderm-notochord, is abnormal; in t^9/t^9, dying at nine days or later, duplications of the embryonic axis and of other structures and escape of some parts from inductive control indicate profound effects on a main inductor system; while in T/T, dying in the eleventh day, the chief abnormalities are in the notochord which is entirely absent at this stage, in the neural tube, and in the somites, and these are probably interdependent. Smith (1956) has now added important information on t^{12}/t^{12}, the lethal with earliest detectable effects in the mouse, or in any mammal. These zygotes never progress beyond the morula stage, dying at three and a half to four days, with clear indications of ribose-nucleic acid deficiency and failure of the organization of the cells to form a blastocyst. The first effect may be a consequence of the second, or may be the result of an earlier metabolic disturbance such as the production of an anti-metabolite. If the failure of ribose nucleic acid synthesis is a sign of deficiency in protein synthesis, then it is tempting to speculate that the earliest sign of organization failure is a metabolic one which may be related to the later evidences of defects in mesenchyme formation and function associated with other t-alleles. Possibly this supplies a needed clue to the essential function which gives unity to the whole gene, of which the mutations in different sites express different degrees of defect according to the stage at which the defective process becomes the limiting factor.

Another aspect of unity in the effects of this gene as seen in the failure of the posterior notochord resulting in taillessness in all compounds of T with different t-alleles, is in part a reflection of the criteria by which t-alleles are recognized, since we diagnose t-alleles by this interaction effect. The frequent, perhaps usual association between t-alleles and abnormal segregation ratios in the heterozygous males, and sterility in male compounds is a later and less constant consequence of earlier developmental alterations, probably influenced also by other factors. It does, however, like the other agreements in effect, suggest something in common amongst the different alleles.

It is obvious that in vertebrate development, the elements in an analysis of genic effects cannot be single reactions, but parts of processes in the interconnected network of dependencies which constitute epigenesis. It seems to me rather surprising that the evidence of connectedness between the processes controlled by the parts of this gene is as good as it is. I suppose it means that these must be processes of a fundamental nature in vertebrate development, and the changes in them drastic ones, otherwise they would not have been identified at all by the rather crude methods of embryological observation used. It may mean also that the simple methods of genetic analysis may be, in comparison, rather delicate and the differences which they distinguish quite sharp and discontinuous ones.

DISCUSSION AND SUMMARY

What can be said now about the relation within the gene of the parts identified by allelism? We have no secure evidence that any of the alleles of independent origin are identical (the two cases of apparent identity, t^0—t^6, t^1—t^2, may not be of independent origin), nor is there conclusive evidence of identity amongst any of the wild alleles; although two cases have not proved themselves to be different either (t^{w1}—t^{w3} and t^{w5}—t^{w6}). Let us make the assumption that all have occurred at different sites of mutation. How may these be arranged with reference to each other? If we use earliness of effect in homozygotes, the order is t^{12}, $t^1 = t^2$, $t^0 = t^6$, t^4, t^9, T, followed by all the viables in which the order cannot be specified. If we proceed from lethality through increasing degrees of complementarity in compounds the order is t^{12}, t^1, t^0, (t^4—t^9?), T, followed by the viables as a group; male sterility in compounds may follow the same order but the evidence is insufficient. In descending order of abnormality in the male segregation ratio the arrangement would be t^{12}, t^1, t^0, t^9, T, t^4, t^3, $t^7 = t^8 = t^{11}$, t^{13}; but we may be warned by the equivalence, in this effect, of all alleles both lethal and viable in wild populations, that this property may not be determined entirely by individual t-alleles but influenced as well by other factors. There are a few signs of correspondence in the orders derived from the different criteria: the earliest lethals are at one end, the viables at the other, except amongst the alleles just taken from wild populations; T is usually in the middle between the lethals and the viables. Amongst the lethals, the most suggestive correspondence is that between onset of lethal effect and complementarity although adequate data on this are available for only four lethal alleles. There is a suggestion of similar correspondence between stage of lethality, complementarity and ratio abnormality in males, but this will remain insecure until isogenic stocks are compared. Work with the wild alleles, now in progress, will provide good material for testing these correspondences.

It is too early to guess what these rather rough but suggestive correspondences mean. One may however set up some hypotheses for testing. One of these is that different sites of mutation are concerned with different parts of a chain of processes concerned with inductive relations between parts of the early embryo. Mesenchyme and its derivatives seem to be most frequently implicated as the channel through which these effects flow. Are these cells, which form a kind of matrix in vertebrate development, merely the most responsive to modifications in general metabolic state, or do they have more specific functions with respect to synthesis of particular metabolites? Methods different and more refined than those used hitherto in this study will be needed to test such an hypothesis.

Are the similarities and differences amongst the sites of mutation related to their spatial orientation? It is tempting to think that they are, but as long as we have only the complementarity test and stage of lethality as criteria, the evidence will remain indirect. Larger populations may yield evidence of rare recombination, but this does not seem likely. Bracketing this gene with nearby easily followed markers on both sides may throw some light on conditions in this region during mutation (the H2-histocompatibility-gene, also a complex gene according to Allen, 1955) lies on the same side of T as Ki, but farther away. A properly marked chromosome is also essential for testing another hypothesis about the structural arrangement, namely that mitotic recombination in gonial cells may be involved in the mutations and the segregation ratio abnormality, leading to gonadal mosaicism for t-alleles, which show non-random segregation in males, a point which is under analysis. The genetical extent of the gene appears now to be so great—already between 16 and 29 sites of mutation—that some definition of its boundaries may be obtained by cytogenetic methods which have not been systematically employed.

The essential question here is the relation of the whole region to inductive or organizing processes in early development, since according to Waelsch (1954) a neighboring gene, Ki, shares some of the effects (on organ duplication) of at least one of the t-alleles. The existence of a region concerned with such processes has been suspected ever since similarities in effect of three neighboring genes T, Ki, and Fu were noted eleven years ago (Dunn and Caspari, 1945). Some evidence of allelism of Ki and Fu has since been obtained, but as Allen (1955) has pointed out, this is not conclusive. I once thought of this region as one in which, perhaps because it might contain much heterochromatin, any change should result in disturbance of basic developmental processes, but there is no direct evidence of this. What we know is that changes identified by a common effect—reversal of differentiation processes in the posterior part of the axial system, leading to taillessness—have in many cases, individual and more specific effects connected with mutations which act as "good" alleles, some of which are certainly able to complement each other.

The discovery that a variety of mutant forms of this gene are common in wild populations, and may have adaptive significance, puts the problem on a new footing. The plasticity of such a gene suggests that its complexity is itself the quality which has been selected for; and the increasing frequency with which such cases are encountered gives us some confidence that the new view now taking form—that genes in general are complex organizations of mutational sites— will prove more fruitful than the simpler, but more static, model of discrete beads on a string which served so well, and still serves, as a guide to formal genetics.

REFERENCES

References to work published prior to 1952 are given in full in Grüneberg (1952), below.

ALLEN, SALLY LYMAN, 1955, Linkage relations of the genes histocompatibility-2 and fused tail, Brachyury and Kinky-tail in the mouse, as determined by tumor transplantation. Genetics *40*: 627–650.

DUNN, L. C., 1955, Widespread distribution of mutant alleles (t-alleles) in populations of wild house mice. Nature *176*, Lond.: 1275–1276.

DUNN, L. C., and SUCKLING, J., 1956, Studies of genetic variation in wild populations of house mice. I. Analysis of seven alleles at locus *T*. Genetics *41*: 344–352.

GRÜNEBERG, H., 1952, The genetics of the mouse. The Hague, Nijhoff. pp. 650.

LEVINE, L., and DUNN, L. C., 1956, The frequency of t^w alleles in a confined population of wild house mice. Proc. Soc. Exp. Biol. N. Y. *92*: 308–310.

SMITH, J., 1956, Studies of a pre-implantation lethal, t^{12}, in the house mouse. J. Exp. Zool. *132*: 51–84.

TUTIKAWA, K., 1954, Further studies of *T* locus in the Japanese wild mouse, *Mus musculus molossinus*. Ann. Rpt. 5, Nat. Inst. Genetics (Japan): 13–15.

WAELSCH, S., 1954, Some genetic aspects of development. Cold Spr. Harb. Symposium Quant. Biol. *19*: 41–49.

DISCUSSION

RIZKI: Is it possible to subject *T* recovered from various *t*-series stocks to analysis similar to that by which *t*-alleles were studied? It would be interesting to see whether dominant *T* would seriate into recessive *t*-phenotypes.

DUNN: The *T*-allele in all of the T/t^n stocks studied by us was the original allele from Zawadskaia. No differences in $T/+$ stocks extracted from these have been noted. Two additional examples of *T* from laboratory stocks have been sent to us, T^E (from T. C. Catter, Edinburgh) and T^s (from G. D. Snell, Bar Harbor). Interactions of these with *t* (few tests made) were similar to those given by *T*; Dr. Waelsch examined T^E/T and T^s/T embryos and noted no differences from T/T.

E. B. LEWIS: Does t^3 (the viable allele which did not suppress recombination between *T* and *Ki*) show recombination with *T*?

DUNN: This was examined only in matings of T/t^3 by T/t^3 in which half of the recombinants should be $T/+$. None was found in 500 offspring. Similar results have been obtained with other viable alleles.

M. C. GREEN: Do you have any information on the cause of the abnormal segregation ratio or any good guesses about it?

DUNN: We do not know the cause of the aberrant ratios produced by most T/t^n males. Our guesses so far have been wrong. Evidence against extra mitotic divisions of t^n pro-gametes in males, while not conclusive were not suggestive that this played an important role. We may probably also eliminate on the evidence presented in this report, the hypothesis that t^n induces conversion of the normal or *T* allele to t^n. Mitotic crossing over or somatic segregation in T/t^n or $+/t^n$ males, as in gonial cells producing a mosaic gonad, consisting of a majority of t^n/t^n tissue has not been eliminated. We cannot seriously test such hypotheses until we have nearby markers on both sides of *t*. The possible inactivation of + or T sperm by t^n sperm has also not been tested. For this serological methods would have to be developed.

M. C. GREEN: Since the abnormal segregation ratio is confined to males, I should like to inquire whether the mutations which you have observed are also known to have occurred only in males.

DUNN: This is not known. Since such mutants are detected in matings of T/t^n by T/t^n it is usually not possible to know from which parent the *t*-mutant came. In one case (t^3), a T/t^1 male probably produced several t^3 sperm (three detected); in another case (t^{w18}) it was certainly the mother, a $+/t^{w11}$ female, which produced at least one mutant (t^{w18}) egg. The father in this case was $T/+$ in which both alleles appear to be stable. Prior to this case, we had suspected, as the question implies, that the mutations arose in males.

WAELSCH: A question of fact. The viability of t^0/t^1, given in your table as .8, seems high in comparison with values previously obtained for the compound. Did you take into account the altered segregation ratios of T/t^0 and T/t^1 males?

DUNN: The segregation ratios were taken into account, but the viability of this compound is an estimate from a relatively small amount of new data and may well be too high. We hope soon to get a more reliable estimate.

HADORN: Do other genes in the mouse show abnormal segregation ratios such as you find in T/t^n and $+/t^n$ males?

DUNN: A large number of segregation ratios of alleles at other loci, and of sex, were examined statistically by Grüneberg and Haldane several years ago. None showed significant deviations from normal, nor do any of our data for other loci suggest such an effect. So far as I know, the *t*-ratios are unique in mammals, altho they have not been the subject of special study except in the mouse.

HADORN: To return to the effects of these alleles in wild populations: Do you regard your evidence as suggesting that heterozygotes for *t* are superior in vigor or fitness?

Dunn: The high frequency of lethal *t*-alleles in wild populations would of course suggest this; but we have first to work out the effect of the segregation ratio advantage of the *t*-alleles in wild populations. We already know that high values of this ratio are sufficient to bring the frequency of a lethal as near to fixation as a lethal can get. Before expected equilibrium values can be computed, we shall also have to allow for the effect of inbreeding in the wild populations which are probably quite small. Only then will we be able to evaluate the third parameter which is the selection coefficient. This work is in progress. In the meantime, I can say that one direct preliminary comparison of the fertilities of $+/+$ and $+/t^w$ wild males seemed to favor the heterozygote. This is being repeated on a larger scale.

The heterosis of T/t^n (where both T and t^n are lethal) is of course very striking, as is the viability of a fraction of the compounds t^1/t^{12} in which both alleles, when homozygous, act as preimplantation lethals.

Controlling Elements and the Gene

Barbara McClintock

Department of Genetics, Carnegie Institution of Washington, Cold Spring Harbor, New York

In a recent brief review (McClintock, 1956), a description was given of types of elements carried in the maize chromosomes that serve to control gene action and to induce, at the site of the gene, heritable modifications affecting this action. These elements were initially discovered because they do not remain at one position in the chromosome complement. They can appear at new locations and disappear from previously determined locations. The presence of one such element at or near the locus of a known gene may affect the action of this gene. In so doing, it need not alter the action potentials of the genic substances at the locus. Therefore, these elements were called controlling elements. It was also shown that controlling elements fall into groups, the members of each operating as an integrated system in the control of gene action.

In this report, some aspects of controlling elements will be considered that could not be discussed in the above-mentioned review. This will necessitate mention of some of the well known gene loci in maize, and symbols for them will be used in the discussion. So that a ready reference may be available, the pertinent information about each of these loci is given in the following list.

Chromosome 1: P, pericarp and cob color. A large number of alleles are known, including P^{vv}, which gives variegated pericarp and cob color.

Chromosome 3: A_1, anthocyanin pigment produced in kernel and plant; a_1, standard recessive allele, no anthocyanin in kernel or plant.

Sh_2, normal development of endosperm tissues; sh_2, recessive allele, shrunken endosperm. Very closely linked with A_1; less than a quarter of a crossover unit distal to it.

Chromosome 5: Pr, purple aleurone color; pr, recessive allele, red aleurone color. Located in long arm of chromosome 5.

A_2, anthocyanin pigment developed in kernel and plant; a_2, standard recessive allele, no anthocyanin developed in kernel or plant. Located in short arm of chromosome 5. Gives approximately 28 per cent recombination with Pr.

Chromosome 6: Y, yellow starch in endosperm; y, recessive allele, white starch.

Chromosome 9: I, dominant inhibitor of aleurone color in kernel.

C, allele of I, pigment produced in aleurone layer of kernel; c, recessive allele, no pigment in aleurone layer.

Sh_1, normal development of endosperm of kernel; sh_1, recessive allele, shrunken endosperm. Located approximately four crossover units proximal to I.

Bz, purple anthocyanin pigment in plant and aleurone layer of kernel; bz, standard recessive allele, bronze color in both plant and kernel. Located approximately two crossover units proximal to Sh_1.

Wx, amylose starch produced in pollen and endosperm, stains blue with solutions of I-KI; wx, recessive allele, starch is amylopectin, stains red-brown with I-KI solutions. Located approximately 15 crossover units proximal to Bz.

Distinctions Between Controlling Elements and Gene Elements

In maize, as in other organisms, a change at a particular locus in a chromosome is made evident by modification of a particular phenotype. Independently occurring alterations (mutations) at the same locus give rise to change in expression of this one particular phenotype, be it recognized by change in a particular enzymatic reaction or by means of some less well defined but identifiable modification of phenotypic expression. Because it is possible to predict which phenotypic character will be altered after modification at a particular known locus in a chromosome, it is inferred that some component is present there whose mode of action may be recognized within certain limits. These components appear to reside at fixed positions in the standard chromosome complement of maize, and they will be referred to in this discussion as the genes. Modification of action of a known gene component can result from insertion of a controlling element at or near the locus of the gene; and, in general, the types of change in phenotypic expression induced by its presence there are those that could be anticipated from previously acquired knowledge of mutant expressions that have resulted from modifications at this locus. Controlling elements, on the other hand, need not occupy fixed positions in the chromosome complement, and detection of the presence of one such element depends upon characteristics it exhibits that are independent of its position.

It is realized that our present knowledge of the gene does not allow formulation of a definition of it based on structural organization, dimension, or primary type of activity. However, all the so-called gene loci with which we will be concerned are recognized because a change at the locus effects a change of some component that normally appears in the cytoplasmic region of the cell and therefore the alteration at the gene locus is reflected in this region. All the controlling elements so far identified, on the other hand, may have their area of activity confined within the nucleus itself, for they are known to serve as modifiers, suppressors, or inhibitors of gene action as well as mutators. They behave as if they were modulators of the genome. Each controlling element or system of interacting elements has its own mode of modulation, and this is expressed in an individualistic manner that is quite independent of the recognized type of action of the gene which it may be modulating. Our present knowledge would suggest that gene elements and controlling elements represent two different classes of primary components of the chromosome and that a close relationship exists between them.

The largest amount of evidence concerning the mode of behavior of controlling elements has been derived from study of the element called Activator (Ac), which by itself may control gene action at the locus where it resides, and also of another controlling element that responds to it. When this latter element is inserted at a known gene locus, changes in gene action may occur either immediately after its insertion or subsequent to it. Both the insertion of this element at the gene locus and the subsequent modifications in gene action it induces depend on the presence of the Ac element somewhere in the chromosome complement. In the absence of Ac no changes affecting gene action occur, and stability of gene expression will be exhibited as long as it is absent. Return of Ac to the nucleus through appropriate crosses will again effect activation of the second element of the system, and this will be expressed in a series of mutation-type changes at the locus of the gene where this element resides.

The second element of the system outlined above was originally given the designation Dissociation (Ds) because, in the presence of Ac, breaks appeared to be formed at the locus where it resided. It was later determined that the apparent "breaks" were produced because at this locus a dicentric chromatid and a corresponding acentric chromatid were formed. The acentric chromatid, composed of the segment of the chromosome from Ds to the end of the arm, was eliminated from the nucleus during a mitotic anaphase whenever such an event occurred. These dicentric-acentric chromatids were formed both in somatic and sporogenous cells, and the time during the development of a tissue when this took place was found to be a function of the dose of Ac: the higher the dose, the later the time of these

occurrences. In the absence of Ac, however, no dicentric-acentric chromatids were produced nor was there any evidence that would suggest the presence of this Ds element at the locus. Return of Ac again initiated these dicentric-acentric chromatid formations. It is evident, therefore, that tests of the presence or absence of Ac in a plant may be made by crossing it with one that is homozygous for Ds but does not have Ac. These are the so-called Ac tester stocks, and descriptions of their usefulness for detecting the presence of Ac have been given elsewhere (McClintock, 1951, 1953; Barclay and Brink, 1954). If these Ac tester stocks carry recessive alleles of other known genetic markers, and if the plant carrying Ac is heterozygous for them, it is possible to determine the location of Ac and changes in location that may occur. By this means, various different positions of Ac have been detected. Evidence of its transposition from one known location to another has also been obtained.

In the presence of Ac, the Ds element undergoes transposition, and its insertion at various locations were detected. Sometimes Ds was inserted at or close to a known gene locus, and the effects of its presence on gene action were thereby discovered. In some cases both dicentric chromatid formations and changes in gene action were noted to occur at this gene locus, but only when Ac was also present in the complement; and the time of the occurrences in the development of a tissue reflected the dose of the Ac element that was present in the nucleus. In examining these cases, it was soon learned that the Ds element itself could undergo modifications that altered its mode of response to Ac. Some of them resulted in a reduced frequency of occurrence of dicentric chromatid formations, often correlated with an increased frequency of occurrence of change in gene action; and these latter were unaccompanied by gross change in chromosome morphology. Still other modifications of this Ds element resulted in almost complete elimination of dicentric chromatid formations, although mutations continued to occur at the locus of the gene where the Ds element resided. Thus, in such cases, the designation of "Dissociation" (Ds) for the element responsible for these mutations no longer appeared to be applicable. Nevertheless, this original designation has been retained because in the early studies it was possible to follow sequentially the changes in the Ds element that altered its type of response to Ac: from a high rate of dicentric chromatid formation to a low rate—and also the reverse, from a low rate to a high rate. Therefore, the designation "Ds" will be applied to any element at a known gene locus that responds to Ac in the following manner: in the absence of Ac, it undergoes no alterations that affect gene action; but in the presence of Ac such alterations occur, and the time of their occurrence during the development of a tissue, and cells of the tissue in which they occur, are a function of Ac, particularly of its dose. The designation "Ds" for an element responding to Ac should not be construed to mean that this element will produce dicentric chromatids wherever it may be located. It may produce none. Nevertheless, its responses to Ac, as described above, are readily detected. It is also probable that there are different kinds of "Ds" elements, but all of them respond to Ac in this quite predictable manner.

It is clear that both the Ac and the Ds elements retain their characteristic modes of expression when located at various different positions in the chromosome complement, and that methods of detecting their presence in these different locations have been developed. The study of Ac and of the integrated Ds-Ac two-element system has been of considerable help in investigating other unrelated control systems. This applies particularly to the well known Dt (Dotted)-a_1 system originally discovered by Rhoades (1936, 1938, 1941, 1945). The standard recessive, a_1, is very stable in the absence of Dt. In its presence, however, mutations occur to the higher alleles of A_1 or to stable recessives that no longer mutate in the presence of Dt. The pattern of response to Dt is quite predictable. Dots of deep anthocyanin pigment appear in a nonpigmented background in the kernel, and streaks of anthocyanin appear in a nonpigmented background in the plant. The number of dots (mutations) that appear in the kernel is an expression of the dose of Dt: the higher the dose, the more frequent the mutations. The Dt element was located by Rhoades in the short arm of chromosome 9. Subsequently, Nuffer (1955) discovered the presence of Dt in two South American strains of maize. In one strain, it was located in chromosome 6 and in the other strain it was located in chromosome 7. The response of the standard a_1 allele to each of these newly detected Dt elements is the same as that expressed when the original Dt element, discovered by Rhoades, is present. Recently, Nuffer (personal communication) obtained evidence of transposition of the Dt element located in chromosome 7 to a new location in the chromosome complement. Thus, in this respect, also, Dt resembles Ac; both may undergo transposition without loss of identity.

The response of the standard a_1 allele to Dt is similar in many essential respects to that of Ds to Ac when the former is present at the locus of a known gene. It could be inferred, then, that a controlling element, responding to Dt, is also present at the standard a_1 locus and that it is this element which is responsible for the observed mutations and for their pattern of appearance in the plant and kernel tissues. Evidence of this is now available from studies aimed at analyzing the composition of the A_1 locus made by Laughnan (1952, 1955) and also by Nuffer (personal communication). When plants carrying an A_1 allele in one chromosome 3 and the standard a_1 allele in the homologue are crossed by plants homozygous for the latter recessive, some kernels exhibiting a mutant phenotype appear on the resulting ear. These express a lower level of intensity of pigmentation than that given by the A_1 allele. It has been shown that the majority of these mutants arise as a consequence of crossing over within a compound A_1 locus. When plants grown from these pale-colored kernels were crossed by plants carrying Dt, it was discovered that in about 5 to 10 per cent of them the mutant expression was unstable. Mutations to higher alleles of A_1 occurred, and the pattern of response (dots of deep pigmentation) was the same as that given by the standard a_1 allele. In these cases, however, the mutations were registered in a pale-colored background rather than in a colorless one. Plants that were homozygous for the A_1 allele also gave rise to pale mutants. It could be shown that many of these arose from crossing over within the compound A_1 locus. None of them, however, were unstable in the presence of Dt. From this it might be inferred that an element responding to Dt is not present at this A_1 locus. Because the pale mutants derived from crossing over in the heterozygote with a_1 do carry this element, it may be inferred that those crossovers that occur within a restricted region of the compound locus will introduce it. In the presence of Dt, it will respond in this new organization of the locus in the very same manner that it was responding before the crossover occurred.

On the self-pollinated ear of a plant that was A_1/a_1, Dt/Dt in constitution, a single kernel appeared that showed a striking change in pattern of mutation (Nuffer, 1951). A very large number of pigmented dots appeared in a colorless background, and the intensity of pigmentation in these dots varied from light to very dark. A plant was grown from this kernel, and an investigation of the nature of the change responsible for this altered mutation pattern was commenced. It proved to be a new allele of a_1 that responds to the presence of Dt by giving this strikingly different pattern of mutation: a high frequency of occurrence of mutation in plant and kernel in the presence of Dt, some of which gives rise to large sectors of mutant tissue and others to small areas. In the absence of Dt, however, no mutations occur and the mutant behaves as a stable recessive. By appropriate tests Nuffer (personal communication) was able to learn that the controlling element responsible for the dotted pattern of mutation and that responsible for this new pattern occupy different sites in the compound locus and that they can be separated by crossing over. It is now evident that the basic mechanism of control of gene action in the Dt-a_1 system is essentially the same as that in the Ds-Ac system. Interactions between the members of these two systems do not occur, however, for

Dt will not substitute for *Ac* in control of *Ds* (Nuffer, unpublished) nor will *Ac* substitute for *Dt* in control of gene action at a_1 (McClintock, 1953).

Recognition of other types of controlling elements is made possible by procedures that are essentially similar to those outlined above. This applies to the Suppressor-mutator system associated with control of gene action at a modified A_1 locus ($a_1{}^{m-1}$, McClintock, 1955, 1956), to a similar system operating to control gene action at A_2 (McClintock, unpublished), to several systems investigated by Dollinger (1955 and unpub.), and to still other systems now under investigation in several different laboratories. The presence of controlling elements in the maize chromosome complement is now well established. It is for the future to determine the extent to which such elements, and systems of interacting elements, operate in the over-all control of activity of the genome during development. The ever-increasing recognition of these elements and their modes of action suggest that they may perform a major function in this respect, and an understanding of the manner by which it is accomplished may be gained from examination of the modes of behavior of particular elements or systems of interrelated elements that are now known.

DETECTION OF TRANSPOSITIONS OF CONTROLLING ELEMENTS

As stated earlier, the presence of elements, independent of the genes but controlling their action, was initially detected because they undergo transposition from one location to another within the chromosome complement, and the effects they produce when inserted at known gene loci are thereby made evident. Therefore, a description of some of the methods that have been used to detect such transpositions is of considerable importance for an appreciation of the nature of the behavior of controlling elements. A number of different methods have been used and they fall into two general categories, selective and nonselective. The nonselective method is more laborious than the selective method but its use may be required in the initial study of a controlling element. For example, in a cross of a plant having a single *Ac* element, whose location is unknown, to plants having no *Ac*, half the progeny can be expected to carry an *Ac* element as a result of meiotic segregations in the parent plant. If the individuals in this progeny are tested for the presence of *Ac* by the method described earlier, the expected ratio of presence and absence of *Ac* will usually be found. However, an occasional plant may be present in the progeny that has two *Ac* elements instead of the expected one. Again, if genetic markers have been introduced into the cross, and if the *Ac* element has shown no linkage with them in the parent plant, the progeny may include an occasional plant which has one *Ac*, as

expected, but in which the *Ac* element now shows linkage with one of the markers (for an example, see Table 1, McClintock, 1951). If the progeny of this plant, in turn, is tested for the location of the *Ac* element, the majority of *Ac*-carrying individuals will show the same linkages of *Ac* with the given markers as exhibited by the parent plant. An individual may be found, however, in which this linkage is not expressed, and no linkage with the given markers will be exhibited in its progeny. In this manner, successive changes in location of the *Ac* element may be detected, but the method is quite unselective and it requires tests of a number of individuals in successive generations. Once the location of a controlling element has been determined, however, selective methods of detecting subsequent changes in its location may be applied, and these will be considered shortly.

A number of different selective methods of detecting transposition of controlling elements have been applied, and some of them take advantage of the particular mode of action of the controlling element under investigation. For example, the dose effects produced by the *Ac* element may be useful in this respect, for it is known that the higher the dose the later the time of occurrence of modifications affecting *Ac* itself or affecting *Ds* or *Ds*-type elements wherever the latter may be located. Changes in location of *Ac* usually occur rather late in the development of the somatic and sporogenous tissues, but occasionally they occur in a cell early in plant development and this can result in the appearance of sectors in which the *Ac* constitutions differ. If such a sector enters the ear, the altered *Ac* constitution in its cells is made apparent by the distinctive phenotypes of the kernels that develop within it after pollen from an *Ac* tester stock has been placed on the silks of the ear. They indicate either that *Ac* is absent in the cells that formed the sector or that it is increased in number. By selecting kernels from such a sector and by making test crosses with the plants derived from them, it is possible to verify the change in *Ac* constitution that has occurred in a somatic cell of the parent plant. Some sectors are twinned, in that the *Ac* element appears to be absent from one sector and increased in number in the twin; and verification of this is readily obtained from examination of the plants derived from the kernels in each component of the twinned sector.

The dose effects produced by *Ac* have also allowed detection of some of the changes in *Ac* location that occur late in the development of sporogenous cells and consequently are exhibited only in individual kernels on an ear. Their usefulness in this respect was described earlier (McClintock, 1951) in connection with tests devised to detect such changes in location of *Ac* that occur in plants carrying this element at allelic positions in a pair of homologous chromosomes. They also allow detection of gametes carrying two *Ac* elements, produced by plants having only one. When such a plant is used in a test cross, the functioning of a gamete having two *Ac* elements gives rise to a kernel that exhibits a much delayed time of occurrence of the dicentric-acentric formations at *Ds* in chromosome 9 or of mutation at those gene loci where the *Ds-Ac* system is operating. Verification of the presence of more than one *Ac* element in these kernels may be obtained by testing the *Ac* constitution in the plants derived from them, provided, of course, that the change in *Ac* constitution occurred in a cell of the parent plant before gamete formation and thus provided for an endosperm and embryo that were alike in *Ac* constitution.

During studies of transposition of *Ds* and also of mutation occurring at those gene loci in which the *Ds-Ac* system of control of this operates, it has been noted that change in location of *Ac* often accompanies the event that affects the *Ds* element of the system. Such coincidences are so numerous that selection of individual kernels exhibiting modification of the *Ds* element is also useful as a method of selection for changes in location of *Ac*.

One of the most effective methods of selection for transposition of *Ac* utilizes those cases in which the *Ac* element resides at the locus of the gene whose action it is directly controlling: that is, the case of *Ac* (called Modulator and symbolized as *Mp*) at the *P* locus in chromosome 1, described by Brink and his collaborators (Brink and Nilan, 1952; Brink, 1954; Barclay and Brink, 1955; Fradkin and Brink, 1956), and that of *Ac* at the bronze locus in chromosome 9 (McClintock, 1956). Mutations at these loci are associated with events occurring to and instigated by the *Ac* element itself, and many of them are accompanied by removal of *Ac* from the affected gene locus and its insertion elsewhere. Therefore, if those kernels on an ear that exhibit germinal mutations are selected, and the plants grown from them are tested for *Ac*, it will be found that in a number of these plants *Ac* no longer resides at the mutant locus. However, *Ac* may still be present in the chromosome complement but located elsewhere. Tests of this type were made by Brink and his collaborators with regard to the *P* locus and by me with regard to the bronze locus. As an example of the type of result obtained from such tests, those conducted by me with the bronze locus will be given here.

The phenotypic expression produced when *Ac* is present at the bronze locus resembles that given by the standard recessive, *bz*. This latter recessive is completely stable in the presence of *Ac*, but mutations occur at the bronze locus where *Ac* resides. Some of these give the dominant *Bz* expression, and the majority of such mutants are thereafter stable in the presence of *Ac*. A larger fraction of the mutants express the recessive, *bz*,

and this expression is thereafter stable in the presence of *Ac*. Some mutations, however, give rise to unstable dominants or to other types of change that will be considered later. Here we will consider only those changes that give rise to mutants that are stable in the presence of *Ac*. Kernels exhibiting mutant phenotypes were selected from ears produced by plants carrying only one *Ac*, and it was present at the unstable bronze locus in one chromosome 9. The homologous chromosome 9 in these plants carried the standard, stable recessive, *bz*. The short arm of each chromosome 9 carried other distinguishing genetic markers, to make it possible to ascertain that the observed mutations had occurred at the bronze locus where *Ac* resides. The ears from which the mutant-carrying kernels were selected were produced by these plants when they were crossed by plants having no *Ac* and homozygous for the recessive alleles of the selected genetic markers. On these ears, those kernels that were homozygous for the standard recessive, *bz*, were completely bronze; no *Bz* spots appeared in them. On the other hand, the majority of those kernels that received the chromosome carrying the bronze locus with *Ac* showed a number of deep purple (*Bz*) spots in a bronze (*bz*) background. A few kernels having this locus, however, showed an altered phenotypic expression and some of these, in turn, were either totally *Bz* or totally *bz*. Because of the constitution of these kernels with respect to the other genetic markers carried in chromosome 9, it was possible to refer the changed expression in each case to an event that had occurred, in a cell of the heterozygous parent plant, at the bronze locus where *Ac* resides. Some of these kernels were selected from the ears and plants were grown from them. These plants, in turn, were tested for presence or absence of *Ac*, for location of *Ac* if present, and for stability of the mutant expression. Among 16 *Bz* mutants selected, 14 proved to be stable. In six of the plants derived from these 14 *Bz* kernels, no *Ac* was present. In five plants, one *Ac* was present, but its position was altered. In four of these five plants, it was no longer linked with genetic markers carried in the short arm of chromosome 9, and in the fifth plant it was very closely linked with *Wx*. In the remaining three plants, *Ac* was present and its position was close to the locus of *Bz* but probably a short distance to the right of it. Thus, in at least 11 of these 14 cases of mutation to stable *Bz*, the association of mutation with removal of *Ac* from the bronze locus could be established with certainty, and in five of these cases the event could be related to transposition of *Ac* to a new location in the chromosome complement. It is probable that transposition of *Ac* to a new location was also associated with the mutation-inducing event in the six cases where *Ac* was absent in the plant derived from a *Bz* kernel. If this event occurred in a sporogenous cell before meiosis, segregation of the chromosome carrying the Ac element in its new location at the following meiotic divisions could have resulted in the production of a gamete in which the Bz mutant was present but Ac was absent.

Twenty-four independent cases of mutation to a stable recessive were also examined. In nine of them, no Ac was present in the gamete that carried the stable recessive. In five cases, one Ac was present but it showed no linkage with markers in the short arm of chromosome 9. In nine cases, one Ac was present and showed linkage with these markers. In two of these nine cases, Ac was located close to Wx, and in one case it was located very close to Sh. In the remaining six of these nine cases, its exact location was not determined; it was linked with Wx and showed from 20 to 30 per cent recombination with it. In the remaining case of the 24 examined, two Ac elements were present, one located close to bz, and the other showing no linkage with markers in the short arm of chromosome 9. Thus, again, in this test, mutation could be associated with a change occurring to the Ac element at the bronze locus; for its removal from this locus was established with certainty in 17 of the 24 cases, and in eight of them the transposition of Ac to a new location could be determined.

It is obvious from the accounts given above that by selection of mutants one can also select for transpositions of Ac, and that this method is highly efficient. Somewhat similar results were obtained in tests of Ds in the case of c^{m-1} (Ds at the C locus). The majority of mutations to C were found to be associated with removal of Ds from the C locus, although its insertion at new locations could not be detected in most of the cases. Appropriate genetic markers that would have allowed detection of such insertion were not present in the tested plants.

Another useful selective method for detecting transpositions of controlling elements takes advantage of crossover techniques. For instance, a case was found in which Ac was inserted close to but to the left of Wx. Various tests were conducted to determine its location by means of crossover techniques. Recombinants appeared in about 10 per cent of the gametes of the plants tested; but this figure did not represent the true crossover value, as the example below will illustrate. In one test, the plants having Ac had the constitution $C\ Ac\ Wx$ in one chromosome 9 and $C\ wx$ and no Ac in the homologue; no other Ac element was present in these plants. When they were crossed with plants homozygous for I, wx, and Ds (located just to right of wx), and having no Ac, the majority of the Wx class of kernels on the resulting ear showed variegation for C areas in a colorless background. These kernels carried Ac. The C areas were produced by responses of Ds in the $I\ wx$-carrying chromosome to Ac, which resulted in dicentric-acentric formations at the locus of Ds. I, carried in the acentric fragment, was eliminated

from daughter nuclei in the mitotic division which followed this event. The majority of the wx class of kernels, on the other hand, were totally colorless, since no dicentric-acentric chromatid formations occurred at Ds because no Ac was present in the nuclei of the endosperm. However, a few of the Wx kernels were nonvariegated (no Ac) and a few of the wx kernels showed C areas (Ac present). These last two classes of kernels represented the recombinants. When the plants grown from the variegated kernels in the wx class were tested for Ac location, its position, in about half of them, was no longer just to the left of wx, as might be expected from a crossover event. Instead it occupied a new location in the chromosome complement. In the other half of these plants, its location was that expected from crossing over. In other words, in this test, about half of the "recombinants" arose not from crossing over but rather from a transposition of Ac; and this probably occurred before the meiotic divisions and as a consequence allowed the Ac in the new location to be segregated at meiosis with a wx-carrying chromosome. Other examples illustrating this type of selective method will be considered in the following discussion of modes of detection of transpositions of the controlling element Spm (Suppressor-mutator) in the Spm-a_1^{m-1} system of gene control.

A series of studies has been made of transposition of the Spm element in the Spm-a_1^{m-1} system of control of gene action at the A_1 locus in chromosome 3, and it indicates that transposition of this element occurs with a high frequency. In this respect, it resembles the Ds and Ac elements, which also may undergo frequent transposition. The action of the Spm-a_1^{m-1} system was outlined in previous reports (McClintock, 1955, 1956), but its origin and mode of operation will be reviewed here. A modification at the standard A_1 locus in a sporogenous cell of a plant in a maize culture under investigation resulted in change in action of the genic materials at that locus. The change was discovered in a single kernel on an ear produced by the plant when it had been crossed by a plant homozygous for the standard recessive, a_1. Instead of being fully colored, as expected, this kernel was variegated for colored areas in a colorless background. The plant arising from this kernel also exhibited variegation for anthocyanin pigmentation. Subsequent tests indicated the mode of control of gene action at this modified A_1 locus. The basic mechanism involves two controlling elements: one resides at the modified A_1 locus (designated a_1^{m-1}) and directly controls gene action and the types of change in this action that may subsequently occur; and the other is an independently located element, designated Suppressor-mutator (Spm), which can modify this action in two distinctly different ways. When the Spm element is present, no anthocyanin pigment is formed. All action of the genic materials at the $a_1{}^{m-1}$ locus is inhibited by its presence until, in some cells, a mutation occurs at $a_1{}^{m-1}$ that allows the genic materials to be active, the type of activity being a reflection of the type of modification produced by the controlling element at $a_1{}^{m-1}$. The expression of the gene induced by this modification is thereafter stable in the presence of *Spm* and a stable mutation is thereby effected. In the absence of *Spm*, on the other hand, the genic materials at the $a_1{}^{m-1}$ locus are capable of some degree of activity and the kernels and plants are uniformly pigmented. This type of gene action at $a_1{}^{m-1}$ is quite stable in the absence of *Spm*, and will be expressed without change in successive plant generations. When, however, *Spm* is again introduced into the endosperm and zygote nuclei having $a_1{}^{m-1}$, suppression of gene action is again made evident and the capacity of the *Spm* element to initiate stable mutation-type changes at $a_1{}^{m-1}$ is also made evident. Unlike *Ac*, *Spm* does not show dosage effects, and the number of *Spm* elements present in a plant is indicated only by progeny tests. At least three and probably more independently located *Spm* elements were present in the initial plant having $a_1{}^{m-1}$, and because of this the majority of gametes produced by this plant, and by many of its progeny plants, carried *Spm*. Its detection was therefore obscured in the initial tests of $a_1{}^{m-1}$. Only after several generations of crosses to tester plants having no *Spm* was it possible to recognize this element, for individuals were then isolated that had only one or two *Spm* elements, and the part this element plays in the control of gene action and mutation at $a_1{}^{m-1}$ was then clearly revealed. Clarification of the behavior of this system of control of gene action was thereafter readily accomplished.

When plants homozygous for $a_1{}^{m-1}$ and having one *Spm* element are crossed by plants having no *Spm* but homozygous for the standard recessive, a_1, which is stable in its presence, the ratio of kernel types on the ears produced will usually approximate one uniformly colored (no *Spm*) to one variegated for deep colored spots in a colorless background (*Spm* present). If two independently located *Spm* elements are present, the ratio of kernel types approximates one uniformly colored (no *Spm*) to three variegated (*Spm* present); and if more *Spm* elements are present, the ratio of kernel types deviates in the expected manner. Again, tests of *Spm* constitutions may be made with plants that are homozygous for the standard a_1 allele (and therefore do not directly reveal the presence or absence of *Spm*) if these plants are crossed by ones homozygous for $a_1{}^{m-1}$ but carrying no *Spm*. The ratios of uniformly colored to variegated kernels on the resulting ears reflect the *Spm* constitutions in the plants. Thus, plants homozygous for $a_1{}^{m-1}$ and carrying no *Spm* can serve as tester parents in crosses made for the purpose of determining the presence or absence of *Spm* in individual plants and its num-

bers when present. If the plants being tested are heterozygous for other genetic markers, and if the tester stock carries the recessive alleles, linkage of an *Spm* element with one such marker may be detected after it has been inserted into the chromosome that carries this marker. By this means it was possible to detect linkages of *Spm* with genetic markers carried in chromosome 5, in chromosome 6, and in chromosome 9.

In plants that are $a_1{}^{m-1}/a_1{}^{m-1}$ or $a_1{}^{m-1}/a_1$ in constitution and that have a single *Spm* element, large sectors may appear, some of which exhibit the pigmented phenotype that is characteristically produced in the absence of *Spm*. It can be shown that these sectors arise through loss of the *Spm* element from a cell early in development of the plant. The progeny of such a cell may contribute to the development of the ear, producing either all of it or only a part of it. When the ear is used in a cross with a plant that is homozygous for $a_1{}^{m-1}$ but carries no *Spm*, in the former case all the kernels on the ear will be uniformly colored (no *Spm*), and in the latter case all the kernels within a well-defined sector will be uniformly colored (no *Spm*). If the plants derived from these uniformly colored kernels are again tested for *Spm* constitution, its absence in them may be verified. That they carry an $a_1{}^{m-1}$ locus capable of responding to *Spm* may be shown by crossing them to plants that are homozygous for the standard a_1 allele and have one or more *Spm* elements. The typical variegated pattern of deeply pigmented areas in a nonpigmented background will appear in all kernels that have received $a_1{}^{m-1}$ from one parent and *Spm* from the other.

In order to detect some of the changes in *Spm* constitution that may occur early in development of a plant, tests were conducted to determine its constitution in the cells that gave rise to an ear on the main stalk of the plant and also in those that produced an ear on one or more of its tillers (side branches). Tests of two ears per plant were obtained from 101 plants. In 95 of them, the number of *Spm* elements was the same in the cells that produced each ear (63 with one *Spm*; 26 with two *Spm*; 6 with three *Spm*). In six plants, the *Spm* constitution was not the same in the cells that gave rise to each ear (one case of one *Spm* in one ear and no *Spm* in the other; three cases of one *Spm* in one ear and two *Spm* in the second; two cases of one *Spm* in one ear, the second ear having a sector with no *Spm*). From twelve other plants, tests of three ears per plant were obtained; and correspondence in number of *Spm* elements was evident in each of the three ears of eleven of them (6 with one *Spm*; 4 with two *Spm*; 1 with three *Spm*). In one plant, the cells that gave rise to two ears carried one *Spm* element but the cells that gave rise to the third ear had two *Spm*.

Tests were also conducted to determine *Spm* constitutions in progeny of plants in which one, two, or three *Spm* elements were known to be present. Those conducted with 249 individuals in the progeny of plants having one *Spm* will illustrate the type of result obtained. The parent plants carrying *Spm* had been crossed by plants that were homozygous for a_1^{m-1} but had no *Spm*. A ratio on the resulting ears of one uniformly pale-colored kernel (no *Spm* present) to one that showed spots of deep color in a colorless background (*Spm* present) indicated the presence of one *Spm* element in the cells that gave rise to the ears. Variegated kernels were selected from these ears, and the plants grown from them were again crossed by plants homozygous for a_1^{m-1} but having no *Spm*. From this test it was learned that one *Spm* element was present in the cells that gave rise to the ear in 215 of these plants. In 20 plants two *Spm* elements were present, and in six plants three *Spm* elements were present. In the remaining eight plants, no *Spm* was present in any part of the plant. It appears from these tests that many of the modifications affecting *Spm* constitution occur in individual cells relatively late in development and may occur even in the gametophytic cells of the plants.

In order to examine more precisely these changes in *Spm* constitution, tests were made of the progeny produced by plants having one *Spm* element at a known location in the chromosome complement. *Spm* may be located at various positions, and several different positions in chromosome 5, chromosome 6, and chromosome 9 have been identified. Tests of the progeny of plants having *Spm* at these different locations were conducted. Several examples will illustrate the kinds of information such tests can give.

One plant that carried a single *Spm* element was Y/y in constitution. The test cross made with it indicated that this *Spm* element was linked with y. On the ear produced by the test cross, one of the two recombinant classes of kernels was Y and exhibited the variegated phenotype (*Spm* present). Plants were grown from some of the kernels in this recombinant class, and these, in turn, were tested for *Spm* constitution and location. The

results obtained from one such plant are given in Table 1. This plant, $a_1^{m-1} Sh_2/a_1sh_2$, Y/y in constitution, was used as a female parent in a cross with a plant whose constitution was $a_1^{m-1} sh_2/a_1sh_2$, y/y and which had no *Spm* element. Linkage of *Spm* with Y was clearly expressed in those kernels carrying a_1^{m-1} in both the Sh_2 and the sh_2 classes. As expected, kernels homozygous for the standard a_1 allele were completely colorless, for this allele is stable in the presence of *Spm*. Plants were grown from 22 of the variegated kernels in the $Sh_2 Y$ class, and these in turn were crossed by plants homozygous for a_1^{m-1}, Sh_2, and y, and having no *Spm*. This test cross was made in order to determine whether or not *Spm* would continue to show linkage with Y and, if so, the number of individuals that would show it. In 19 of these 22 plants, one *Spm* element was found to be present, and it was linked with Y in each of them. The percentages of recombinant classes of kernels were similar on the ears produced by all of these plants. Among a total of 7569 kernels produced by these ears, there were 3847 uniformly pale-colored kernels (no *Spm*), of which 683 were Y and 3164 y. Among the 3717 variegated kernels (*Spm* present) on these ears, 3033 were Y and 684 were y. In addition, there were five deeply colored kernels, which may be attributed to germinal mutation at a_1^{m-1}, for a few such mutations are to be expected. The recombinants were 18.0 per cent of the total, and this percentage compares well with that of the parent ear (see Table 1) which was 16.3. In two of the 22 tested plants, two *Spm* elements were present and one of them was linked with Y (39 pale colored, Y: 118 pale colored, y: 315 variegated, Y: 181 variegated, y). The remaining plant had one *Spm*, but it showed no linkage with Y (117 pale colored, Y: 112 pale colored, y: 101 variegated, Y: 100 variegated, y; and in addition 2 deeply colored kernels attributable to germinal mutation).

A much more extended series of tests of the type just outlined was conducted with progenies of plants carrying *Spm* in chromosome 6 but at another location in the chromosome, and these tests were extended into the fourth generation. A description would require more space than is justified here; it need only be stated that, in general, the results obtained were similar to those described above. In the interest of further clarification of the behavior of *Spm*, however, we should present an example of this kind of test made with plants carrying the *Spm* element in a different chromosome of the complement. In the following case, it was located in chromosome 5.

The silks of one ear of a plant that was $a_1^{m-1} Sh_2/a_1sh_2$, Pr/pr in constitution and carried *Spm*, received pollen from a plant that was homozygous for a_1, sh_2, and pr and had no *Spm* (cross 1). Another ear of this plant was used in a cross with a plant of similar constitution except that it was

TABLE 1. TEST CROSS INDICATING LINKAGE OF *Spm* WITH Y IN CHROMOSOME 6

♀ $a_1^{m-1}Sh_2/a_1sh_2$; $Y Spm/y$ × ♂ $a_1^{m-1}sh_2/a_1sh_2$; y/y; No *Spm*

	Phenotypes of Kernels						
	Pale aleurone (No *Spm*)		Colorless aleurone with spots of deep color (*Spm*)		Colorless aleurone		Totals
	Y	y	Y	y	Y	y	
Sh_2 class......	20	113	111	30	0	0	274
sh_2 class......	10	65	59	8	77	72	291
Totals......	30	178	170	38	77	72	565

homozygous for Pr (cross 2). The kernel types appearing on the ear produced by cross 1 indicated linkage of Spm with Pr. Plants were then grown from some of the variegated kernels in the Sh_2, Pr class on each of these ears, and these plants, in turn, were tested for Spm constitution. Examples of the results of tests of several of these plants are given in Table 2 (plant 6684D-1 and some of its progeny from cross 1, plant 6685F-2 and some of its progeny from cross 2, and also progeny of plant 6685G-2 from cross 2). Plant 6684D-1 proved to be $a_1{}^{m-1} Sh_2/a_1sh_2$, Pr/pr in constitution, and it had one Spm that was located in the chromosome 5 carrying Pr. Its linkage with Pr was evident in all the test crosses (rows 1 to 3 under A of Table 2). Plant 6685F-3 was also Pr/pr in constitution, but the Spm element was linked with pr (B, Table 2). The location of Spm in the pr-carrying chromosome may be attributed to a crossover in the parent plant carrying Spm, which introduced it into a pr-carrying chromosome. Most of the variegated plants in culture 6685 (derived from cross 2) were Pr/Pr in constitution. The Spm element in most of them could be expected to be located in one of the two Pr-carrying chromosomes. The results of tests of one plant of the culture, 6685G-2, which was $a_1{}^{m-1} Sh_2/a_1sh_2$, Pr/Pr in constitution, were as follows. This plant was crossed by one that was homozygous for $a_1{}^{m-1}$, Sh_2, and also for the recessive, pr, and had no Spm. The kernel types on the ear produced by this cross (132 pale-colored kernels: 137 kernels that had deep-colored spots in a colorless background) indicated that plant 6685G-2 had one Spm. All the kernels, however, were Pr in phenotype. Twenty plants were grown from the variegated kernels on this ear, and each was tested for Spm constitution and for the linkage of Spm with Pr. Spm was found to be present in 17 of the 20 plants but absent in three of them. Fifteen of these 17 plants carried a single Spm element; in 14 of them it was linked with Pr (rows 1 and 2 under C of Table 2), and in one it gave no evidence of linkage with Pr (row 3, C, Table 2). The remaining two of the 17 Spm-carrying plants had two Spm elements, one of which was linked with Pr (rows 4 and 5, C, Table 2).

The kernel types produced by the crosses shown in A of Table 2 indicated that Spm in plant 6684D-1 was located in the chromosome 5 that carried Pr. In order to determine whether or not this linkage would be expressed in the following generation, plants derived from the Pr class of variegated kernels produced by the crosses entered in lines 2 and 3 of A of Table 2 were examined for Spm constitution and location. Among the eleven tested plants in the progeny of the cross given in line 3, one did not have Spm. Each of the remaining ten plants had one Spm, and its linkage with Pr was clearly expressed in nine of them. The phenotypes of the kernels on the ears produced by these plants, after the given test

cross, are entered in row 1 under D of Table 2. The Spm element in one plant did not show linkage with Pr (row 2, D, Table 2). In the second test, all ten of the examined plants derived from the variegated kernels in the Pr class on the ear produced by the cross given in line 2 of A, Table 2, carried Spm. In nine of them, one Spm was present, and in eight of these it was obviously linked with Pr (row 3, D, Table 2); in the ninth plant no linkage with Pr was observed (row 4, D, Table 2). In the remaining plant, three Spm elements were present, as the ratio of kernel types entered in row 5, D, Table 2 will indicate.

In plant 6685F-3, which was Pr/pr in constitution, Spm was found to be linked with pr (B, Table 2). Most probably, it was introduced into the pr-carrying chromosome as a consequence of crossing over. The variegated kernels in the Pr class on the ear produced by the cross given in B, Table 2, represent recombinants, and plants derived from ten of them were examined for Spm constitution and location. Spm was found to be present in nine of these ten plants, and absent in one of them. One Spm was present in eight of the nine plants, but in only four of them was it linked with Pr. The combined ratios of kernel types on the ears produced by these four plants are entered in row 1 of E, Table 2. In the remaining four plants having one Spm, no linkage with Pr was exhibted (rows 2 and 3, E, Table 2). In one plant, three or four Spm elements probably were present, as the ratio of kernel types on two tested ears of this plant indicates (row 4, E, Table 2). It was mentioned earlier, in connection with transposition of Ac, that selection of recombinants is an effective method of detecting transposition of this controlling element. The example given above illustrates the usefulness of this method for detecting transpositions of Spm. Another illustration of the effectiveness of this selection method will be outlined below.

A variegated plant that was $a_1{}^{m-1}/a_1{}^{m-1}$, Wx/wx in constitution was crossed by a plant homozygous for $a_1{}^{m-1}$ and for wx but carrying no Spm. On the ear produced as the result of this cross, there were 365 kernels; 196 of them were uniformly pale colored (no Spm), and 169 had deep-colored spots in a colorless background (Spm present). It may be concluded that one Spm element was present in the plant that produced this ear. Among the pale-colored kernels, 156 were Wx and 40 were wx, whereas the ratio in the variegated class of kernels was 29 Wx to 140 wx (A, Table 3). Linkage of Spm with the wx allele carried in one chromosome 9 is obvious. Nine plants derived from the variegated kernels in the Wx class (the recombinant class) were examined for Spm and for its location. All of them carried Spm, and in seven of them one element was present. In none of the nine ears obtained from test crosses of these seven plants, however, was there any evidence of linkage of Spm with Wx. The com-

See text for origin of plants in A to E below, for the constitutions of plants entered in B to E, and for test crosses made with them.

Crosses		Phenotypes of Kernels						
		Pale Sh_2 (No *Spm*)		Colorless with spots of deep color; Sh_2 (*Spm* present)		Colorless sh_2	Germinal mutant; Sh_2	Totals
♀	♂	*Pr*	*pr*	*Pr*	*pr*			

A. Types of kernels on ears produced by test crosses of plant 6684D-1 which was $a_1^{m-1}Sh_2/a_1sh_2$, $Pr\ Spm/pr$ in constitution

Crosses		Pale Sh_2 (No *Spm*) Pr	pr	Colorless w/ spots; Sh_2 (*Spm* present) Pr	pr	Colorless sh_2	Germinal mutant; Sh_2	Totals
6684D-1	a_1sh_2/a_1sh_2 ; *pr/pr*; No *Spm*	50	90	91	48	321	2	602
a_1sh_2/a_1sh_2 ; *pr/pr*; No *Spm*	6684D-1	120	223	214	114	622	5	1298
$a_1^{m-1}Sh_2/a_1^{m-1}Sh_2$; *pr/pr*; No *Spm*	6684D-1	80	188	114	46	—	1	429

Spm Constitution of Plants	No. of Plants	Phenotypes of Kernels					
		Pale (No *Spm*)		Colorless with spots of deep color (*Spm* present)		Germinal mutant	Totals
		Pr	*pr*	*Pr*	*pr*		
B.							
1 *Spm*	1	275	91	67	214	4	651
C.							
1 *Spm*	6	434	1646	1512	415	9	4016
1 *Spm*	8	1798 (*Pr* and *pr*)*		1429	341	2	3570
1 *Spm*	1	281 (*Pr* and *pr*)*		114	132	0	527
2 *Spm*	1	49	105	209	148	1	512
2 *Spm*	1	128 (*Pr* and *pr*)*		132	87	1	348
D.							
1 *Spm*	9	429	1174	1133	366	3	3105
1 *Spm*	1	67	73	71	77	0	288
1 *Spm*	8	1089 (*Pr* and *pr*)*		616	251	1	1957
1 *Spm*	1	234 (*Pr* and *pr*)*		98	99	1	432
3 *Spm*	1	31	36	167	176	0	410
E.							
1 *Spm*	4	149	550	510	113	1	1323
1 *Spm*	3	321	290	248	254	1	1114
1 *Spm*	1	185	171	134	152	1	643
3 or 4 *Spm*	1	15	14	235	246	2	512

* In some crosses, difficulty was encountered in discriminating between *Pr* and *pr* kernels because of segregation of another factor that modifies pigment color in *pr/pr* kernels but only, however, in the pale class.

bined ratio of kernel types on these ears is given in row 1 under B of Table 3. One plant had two Spm elements, but linkage with Wx was not indicated in either of the two tested ears of this plant (line 2, B, Table 3). The ratio of kernel types on two ears produced by the remaining plant indicated the presence in it of three Spm elements, as shown in row 3, B, Table 3. When such a high number of Spm elements is present in a plant, evidence of linkage of one of them with a given marker is obscured. Thus it cannot be stated whether or not in this plant one of the elements was linked with Wx. It is clear, however, that there is no evidence among these recombinants of linkage of Spm with Wx. It may be concluded that the Spm element in the parent plant was located very close to wx and that the recombinants appearing on the ear of this plant arose mainly from a premeiotic transposition of the Spm element to a new location, which allowed it to be segregated at meiosis with the chromosome carrying the Wx allele.

In Table 2, the results of tests of 47 variegated plants are entered. The variegated plant was used as female parent in test crosses of 46 of them. In eight of these 46 plants, two ears per plant were used for such tests, and agreement with regard to Spm number and location was shown by the two ears in seven of the eight plants. In one plant, the kernel types on the ear produced by the main stalk indicated the presence of two Spm elements, one of which was linked with Pr, and these are entered in line 5 under C of Table 2. Tests of the tiller ear of this plant indicated the presence of only one Spm in the cells that gave rise to it, and this Spm was linked with Pr (9 pale colored, Pr: 84 pale colored, pr: 69 variegated, Pr: 11 variegated, pr). In two additional plants, three ears were used for the test cross, and agreement with regard to Spm number and location was shown in all three ears produced by each plant. The nine plants that gave the kernel types entered in B of Table 3 were all used as female parents in the test cross, and in four of them two ears per plant were so tested. Agreement with regard to Spm number was shown by both ears produced by each of the four plants.

Before we leave the subject of methods of detection of transposition of controlling elements, one other fact should be emphasized. If, in any one test, the controlling element is found to be linked to a known marker, and if other known markers are present in the same chromosome, linkage with them will also be exhibited, and in the expected manner. If genetic markers on other chromosomes are also present, and are followed in the tests, no linkage with them will be exhibited. In other words, the basic mode of inheritance is like that of other known genetic markers, because the controlling element resides at a particular locus until some event causes it to be transposed elsewhere, where its position may again be

TABLE 3

Spm Constitution of Plants	No. of Plants	Phenotypes of Kernels					Totals
		Pale (No Spm)		Colorless with spots of deep color (Spm present)		Germinal mutants	
		Wx	wx	Wx	wx		

A. Test cross indicating linkage of Spm with wx in chromosome 9

♀ $a_1{}^{m-1}/a_1{}^{m-1}$; Wx/wx Spm × ♂ $a_1{}^{m-1}/a_1{}^{m-1}$; wx/wx; No Spm

	1	156	40	29	140	0	365

B. Tests of Spm constitution in 9 plants derived from variegated kernels in the Wx class of A, above. All plants were used as females in crosses with plants that were $a_1{}^{m-1}/a_1{}^{m-1}$, wx/wx, and that had no Spm

1 Spm	7	860	953	801	824	1	3439
2 Spm	1	52	66	197	208	0	523
3 Spm	1	46	36	402	377	0	861

identified. The time of occurrence of these changes in location, during development of a tissue, and the frequency of their occurrence, depend on several factors: dose (the Ac element and the control it exerts on transpositions of Ds), environmental conditions such as temperature and nutrition (Eyster, 1926; Rhoades, 1941; van Schaik, 1954), the genetic background (Brink, personal communication), and the location of the element in the chromosome complement (see account of nontransposing controlling elements in McClintock, 1956).

THE STRUCTURE OF CONTROLLING ELEMENTS

Controlling elements and gene elements are alike in one important aspect, and this is related to the replication of their structural organization during chromosome reduplication. With respect to both types of elements, the newly constituted chromosome is a replica of the parent chromosome, provided no event occurs to alter the structure of the controlling elements or that of the locus where it may rseide; and in most division cycles such events do not occur. The most effective demonstration of maintenance of organization of a controlling element through successive mitotic cycles is provided by that element of a two-element system which undergoes modification only when the second element of the system is also present, such as Ds in the Ds-Ac system, or the element at the A_1 locus in the a_1-Dt system and the $a_1{}^{m-1}$-Spm system. In the absence of Ac, Dt, or Spm, in each of these systems the organization at the locus where the complementary controlling element resides must be replicated without altera-

TABLE 4. EXAMPLES OF TYPES OF ALLELES OF A_1 PRODUCED BY THE OPERATION OF THE Ds-Ac SYSTEM, THE a_1-Dt SYSTEM, AND THE $a_1{}^{m-1}$-Spm SYSTEM OF CONTROL OF GENE ACTION AT THE A_1 LOCUS IN CHROMOSOME 3

A. The Ds-Ac System   Example: $a_1{}^{m-3}$

Phenotype produced in absence of Ac	Phenotype produced when 1 Ac is present
Allele 1 Colorless kernel. No anthocyanin pigment in plant. No mutations.	Allele 1 Dots of the full A_1-type expression in restricted regions of kernel. Few streaks of A_1 pigment in plant. Few germinal mutations to higher alleles of A_1. Some chromosome "breaks" at $a_1{}^{m-3}$ locus.
Allele 2 Uniformly light pale-colored kernel and lightly pigmented plant. No mutations.	Allele 2 Numerous spots of various sizes showing deep pigmentation in pale-colored background in kernel. Sectors of deep pigmentation in pale-colored background in plant. Many germinal mutations to higher alleles of A_1. Few if any "breaks" at $a_1{}^{m-3}$ locus.
Allele 3 Uniformly pigmented kernel and plant. Intensity of pigment much darker than that given by allele 2. No mutations.	Allele 3 Similar to allele 2 above except that mutant spots in kernels and sectors in plants appear in background coloration of medium intensity.

B. The a_1-Dt System

Phenotype produced in absence of Dt	Phenotype produced when 1 Dt is present
Allele 1 (standard a_1) Colorless kernel. No anthocyanin in plant. No mutations.	Allele 1 Few dots of deep A_1-type in pigmentation in colorless background in kernel. Fine streaks of A_1-type pigmentation in plant. Few germinal mutations to higher alleles of A_1 and to stable recessives. Most germinal mutants are stable in presence of Dt.
Allele 2 Colorless kernel. No anthocyanin in plant. No mutations.	Allele 2 Large number of pigmented spots or dots in colorless background in kernel. These show various grades of intensity of pigmentation from light to deep. Plant shows many sectors of mutant tissue in nonpigmented background. Many germinal mutations to alleles giving various grades of intensity of pigmentation, the majority of which are stable in the presence of Dt; a few, however, are unstable.

C. The $a_1{}^{m-1}$-Spm System

Phenotype produced in absence of Spm	Phenotype produced in presence of Spm
Allele 1 Colorless kernel. No anthocyanin pigment in plant. No mutations.	Allele 1 Many areas of different sizes showing various low levels of intensity of pigmentation in colorless background in kernel and in nonpigmented background in plant. Many germinal mutations to give alleles producing these low levels of pigment intensity. Mutants so obtained are stable in presence of Spm.
Allele 2 Very pale color in kernel. Intense anthocyanin pigmentation in plant. No mutations.	Allele 2 Small dots of full A_1-type pigmentation in colorless background in kernel. Fine streaks of $A1$-type pigmentation in nonpigmented background in plant. Very few germinal mutations. These are stable in presence of Spm.
Allele 3 Intense pigmentation in both kernel and plant. No mutations.	Allele 3 Many medium-sized dots showing full A_1-type pigmentation in colorless background in kernel, and many fine streaks of A_1-type pigmentation in nonpigmented background in plant. Few germinal mutations to higher alleles of A_1. These are stable in presence of Spm.
Allele 4 Pale color in kernel. Intense pigmentation in plant. No mutations.	Allele 4 Many spots and large areas of full A_1-type pigmentation in nonpigmented background in kernel, and numerous sectors and streaks of A_1-type pigmentation in nonpigmented background in plant. Many germinal mutations to higher alleles of A_1 that are stable in presence of Spm.

tion in each mitosis in the germ line, and because of this it is maintained through successive plant generations. Only when, by appropriate crosses, the second element of the system is introduced, will alterations occur, and then only in some cells of the plant. Illustrations of the type of evidence that has revealed this are given below.

When *Ds* was first discovered, many dicentric-acentric chromatid-forming events were observed at the locus of *Ds* when *Ac* was also present in the nuclei of a plant. The frequency of their occurrence was high and they could be observed readily in both the plant and the endosperm tissues. Gametes having no *Ac* were produced by such plants, and in the next generation those plants having *Ds* but no *Ac* showed no dicentric-acentric chromatid formations at the locus of *Ds*, nor any other type of change that would reveal its presence. When, however, *Ac* was reintroduced in a subsequent generation by an appropriate cross, the presence of *Ds* was revealed, because dicentric-acentric chromatids were now formed at the previously determined position of *Ds*, and the frequency of their occurrence was the same, with the same dose of *Ac*, as that observed before *Ac* had been removed. Besides dicentric-acentric chromatid formation at the locus of *Ds*, other types of change in the presence of *Ac* were also noted, and some of them effected transposition of *Ds* to a new location. Occasionally, another type of modification occurred at the locus of *Ds*, but again only when *Ac* was also present, and this was recognized by a decided change in the relative frequency of occurrence of the above-mentioned types of response of *Ds* to *Ac*. The location of *Ds*, however, was not altered by the event that was responsible for this. If, by meiotic segregation, *Ac* was removed from the chromosome complement that carried such an altered *Ds*, the particular modification responsible for it was maintained without further change through successive plant generations. This was made evident because return of *Ac* in a later generation elicited from it the very same pattern of response that it had given before *Ac* was removed. Through selections based upon such clear-cut changes in the particular types of response of *Ds* to *Ac*, it was possible to isolate several different alleles of *Ds*, and to maintain them unaltered in successive generations in plants that did not have *Ac*. The behavior of each of them, when *Ac* was returned to the nucleus, could be predicted in advance if its behavior before the removal of *Ac* was known. Such predictions are possible only if the particular organization at the locus of *Ds* in each such case is replicated in each successive mitotic cycle in the germ line. It is difficult in the face of such evidence to avoid the conclusion that these alleles of *Ds* reflect organizational and thus structural differences either of the *Ds* element itself or of other components at the locus where it resides, even though the type and dimension of such differences are not yet known.

In all examined cases where a two-element system of control of gene action is known to operate, changes have been noted in the type of response of the element at the affected gene locus, and isolates showing different types of change have been made. The different isolates so far tested have behaved in inheritance as alleles of one another; and the type and pattern of response shown by each, when the second element of the system is present, is predictable. Table 4 was constructed in order to illustrate some of the kinds of differences these isolates may exhibit. Each of the alleles listed in this table demonstrates the presence of a particular type of organization at the gene locus where the controlling element resides. This organization is reproduced in each successive mitosis, and this is maintained through successive plant generations, provided the complementary element of the system concerned is absent.

It might be considered that a controlling element represents some kind of extrachromosomal substance that can attach itself or impress its influence in some manner at various positions in the chromosome complement and so affect the action of the genic substances at these positions. The modes of operation of controlling elements do not suggest this, however. Rather, they suggest that controlling elements are integral components of the chromosomes themselves, and that they have specific activities and modes of accomplishing them, much as the genes are presumed to have. Any proposed view of the structure and organization of controlling elements must consider not only the origin and maintenance of distinct alleles, as described above, and the modes of interaction exhibited by two-element systems, but also the nature of the change responsible for alteration in gene action that appears after either insertion or removal of a controlling element at a known gene locus. Insertion need not effect mere inhibition of gene action, as the analysis of the $Spm-a_1^{m-1}$ system illustrates. Also, removal of the identifiable controlling element is not usually accompanied by exact restoration of the type of action shown by the genic substances before the controlling element appeared there, although sometimes it may give rise to a similar type of action. In many cases there is a clearly expressed difference, ranging from slight to marked. Thus, the presence of a controlling element at a gene locus need not effect mere inhibition of gene action, and its removal from the locus need not effect mere release of such inhibition. Other types of modification occur. Some form of organizational or structural change in chromosome materials must occur, both when a controlling element is present at a locus and also as a consequence of its removal. The available evidence suggests that the disappearance of an identifiable controlling element from a known location in a chromosome is associated with its appearance at a new location. The mechanism of transposition, then, is significant in any consideration of the structures concerned, and our knowledge of this mechanism, inadequate as it is, should be evaluated.

THE MECHANISM OF TRANSPOSITION

Transposition of *Ds* from its first known position in the short arm of chromosome 9 to another position within that arm was detected very early in the study of the *Ds-Ac* system, and attempts were made to obtain information about the manner by which transposition is accomplished. Besides dicentric-active chromatid formation at the locus of *Ds*, other types of chromosomal aberration were noted in these early studies; they were made evident by the appearance of translocations, inversions, duplications, ring chromosomes, and deficiencies, but only when *Ac* was also present in the nucleus. In all such cases it was found that one of the two positions in the chromosome or chromosomes involved in the origin of the rearrangement was always at the previously identified locus of *Ds*. It was obvious, therefore, that the *Ds* element was primarily responsible for them. It was then decided to determine whether or not transposition of *Ds* accompanied such events, and for this purpose those cases that produced a duplication of a segment of the short arm of chromosome 9 were examined. They were chosen because the genetic markers located in this arm would allow the most precise analyses to be made. Three such cases were examined in detail, and from all three it was learned that transposition of *Ds* had accompanied the event that accomplished the duplication. A description of the origin and constitution of the chromosome having the duplication, in two of these three cases, was given in an earlier publication (McClintock, 1951) and need not be repeated here. It could be determined from a study of the three cases, however, that the *Ds* element that was inserted into the new location came from only one of two sister chromatids 9. It was also learned that the insertion of *Ds* at the new location was accompanied by its removal from its previous location. In each of the three examined cases, the involvement of sister chromatids in the origin of the duplication, the orientation of the duplicated segment, and the location of the two *Ds* elements suggested that contact of the locus of *Ds* with another locus in this chromosome preceded the event that produced the duplication and the transposition of *Ds*; and that the transposition could be associated with the mechanism of the subsequent chromosome reduplication itself. It was also learned from these cases that insertions of *Ds* into new locations could take place without effecting gross chromosomal rearrangements (see positions of *Ds* in diagrams given in McClintock, 1951).

The allele of *Ds* that gives rise to the types of chromosomal aberrations mentioned above is one that produces many dicentric-acentric chromatid formations at the locus of *Ds* itself, but only, of course, when *Ac* is also present in the nucleus. It might be considered that such configurations could arise either from lack of reduplication of the components at the locus where *Ds* resides, or from "stickiness" of these materials. The cases mentioned above indicate, however, that the *Ds* element is reduplicated when chromosomal aberrations occur, for the two *Ds* elements produced by the reduplication process can be accounted for even though one of them occupies a new location. This suggests that the dicentric-acentric chromatid formations might arise not from lack of reduplication at the locus but rather as a consequence of the reduplication mechanism itself. Some component of this particular allele of *Ds* may be so ordered that it will allow a reverse bonding between linearly arranged components during the reduplication process; this, in turn, would lead to the dicentric-acentric chromatid formations that are so clearly expressed in some cells of the somatic and sporogenous tissues of plants having the allele.

It should be emphasized, in this discussion of transposition, that the *Ds* element undergoes alterations which modify its type of action. These were mentioned earlier. Some of them give rise to an allele of *Ds* that no longer produces dicentric chromatids (or only a few of them) or other types of chromosomal rearrangement. Transpositions continue to occur, however. The controlling elements *Ac* and *Spm* also undergo frequent transpositions and these are not usually accompanied by chromosomal translocations. Thus it appears that transposition is not the consequence of "stickiness" at the locus where these elements reside; for, if it were, many cases of chromosomal aberration should have been detected in association with their transposition. The absence or infrequence of such cases is conspicuous.

One can conclude, then, that transpositions of controlling elements either arise from some yet-unknown mechanism or occur during the chromosome reduplication process itself and are a consequence of it. At present, the latter interpretation is favored, for it will account for many of the observations of change in number and location of controlling elements. If, in a plant having one such element at a known location, the element is transposed from one of two sister chromatids of one chromosome to a new location in one of two sister chromatids of another chromosome, segregation at the following mitotic anaphase could result in several different types of change in constitution of the element in the sister nuclei. Either one nucleus would have this element at the previous known location and the sister nucleus would have it at a new location, or one nucleus would have no element and the sister nucleus would have two, one at the previous known location and one at a new location. As a consequence of such segregations, cells could be formed having no such element, or one that was unchanged in its location, or one at a new location, or two elements, one at the previously known location and one at a new location. In the gametes produced by plants having a transposable element, just such types of change in location and number of elements have been found; examples were given earlier. Changes in constitution of *Ac* occurring in somatic cells give rise to sectors that exhibit these changes, and in some of them it is clear that the dose of *Ac* has been increased. It is possible to observe that subsequent changes in *Ac* constitution may also occur, for subsectors showing them may appear within the larger sectors. If sequential transpositions of a controlling element occur in the cells of the germ line in the manner outlined above, gametes carrying more than two elements may be produced by plants whose zygote nuclei had but one; and examples of this have been found (see examples under D and E of Table 2).

If transposition occurs during the chromosome reduplication process, then the means by which it is accomplished is of considerable importance. It is conceivable that it is brought about by some mechanism similar to that proposed to account for transduction in bacteria (Demerec, Blomstrand, and Demerec, 1955; Demerec and Demerec, 1956) —a form of exchange or "crossing over" between the component contributed by the phage and that present in the bacterium, which requires a reduplication of both components. If such an event accounts for transposition, then reciprocal substitutions of components at the loci concerned should be produced as a consequence. There is evidence to suggest that such substitutions may occur. In the study of *Ac* at the bronze locus, described earlier, three cases of change in mode of control of mutation at this locus were noted. Each was associated with removal of *Ac* from the bronze locus, and in two of the three cases it could be established with certainty that *Ac* had been transposed to a new location. In two of the three cases, a recessive, bronze, phenotype appeared as a consequence of the removal of *Ac*; but instead of being stable in its presence, as in most such cases, this phenotype was stable only in its absence. In its presence, mutations to the higher alleles of *Bz* occurred, and the type of response was the same as that exhibited in other cases in which the *Ds-Ac* system of control of gene action operates. The mode of control in the third case was similar. In this case, however, removal of *Ac* was associated with partial expression of the genic substance at the bronze locus, for some *Bz*-type pigment appeared both in the plants and in the kernels having it. This expression was quite stable in the absence of *Ac*, but in its presence mutations occurred to give alleles that are associated with the appearance of higher or lower levels of intensity of the pigment. The origin of these three cases could be explained if a *Ds*-type element (one respond-

ing to *Ac*) had been substituted for *Ac* during the transposition process.

There is other evidence that should be mentioned in considering the possibility that substitution may accompany transposition, and this is related to the types of mutation that are produced when a known controlling element is removed from a locus. As stated earlier, the mutations so produced need not be alike; in some cases, wide differences in their mode of expression can be observed. It is possible that some of the differences they exhibit are the consequence of substitution of one type of controlling element for another. Only through further investigation, however, woult it be possible to verify this; and except in the three above-mentioned cases evidence is not yet available, although in several other cases there is evidence suggestive of it.

POSITIONS IN THE CHROMOSOME COMPLEMENT AT WHICH CONTROLLING ELEMENTS MAY BE INSERTED

It is known that controlling elements may be inserted at various locations within the chromosome complement. In order to learn whether these positions are randomly distributed or selectively located, a large number of independent transpositions of a particular element from a known location to new locations needs to be determined. Even though many sequential transpositions of the elements *Ds*, *Ac*, and *Spm* have been detected, the evidence obtained from any one of these elements is insufficient to allow definite conclusions to be drawn. The evidence does suggest a degree of nonrandomness, which, however, may merely reflect degrees of viability following upon insertions at particular positions rather than selectivity of positions at which the elements may be inserted. Such inviabilities were discovered in studies aimed at detecting the positions within the short arm of chromosome 9 into which *Ds* may enter. This arm carries genetic markers that allow easy detection in kernels of insertion of *Ds* between any two of them. Plants having *Ds* at a known location in this arm produce some gametes having *Ds* at new locations, some of which are also in the same arm. When plants carrying *Ds* and also dominant alleles of some of the known genetic markers in this arm were crossed to plants that were homozygous for the recessive alleles, kernels that arose from functioning of a pollen grain in which *Ds* occupied a new position in the arm were readily detected. The endosperm and embryo of a number of such kernels were quite normal in appearance, but other kernels were abnormal in various ways. Some of them were smaller than normal, others were germless or had defective embryos, and still others exhibited distorted growth in the endosperm tissues. Most of these kernels did not germinate. Some of the normal-appearing kernels also did not germinate. In other words, dominant lethality was exhibited among a number of kernels having Ds at new positions within the short arm of chromosome 9. The new position of Ds could be verified only in plants derived from the kernels that did germinate. The positions occupied by Ds in these plants seemed not to be randomly distributed but to be clustered about certain locations within the arm. It is suspected that they represented only some of the positions into which Ds may enter, and that the insertion of Ds at other positions results in dominant lethality. This inference is supported by the results of examinations of cases that exhibited semidominant lethality of the following type. In endosperms with two normal chromosomes 9 not carrying Ds and a chromosome 9 with Ds at the new location, growth was so distorted that many kernels failed to mature. Only a few reached maturity but all of them were obviously aberrant in morphology. Plants could be obtained from some of the latter, however. Four independent cases of this type were examined, and in all four the semilethal effect was associated with a modification induced by Ds in a chromosome component located to the right of Bz. In these plants, the chromosome 9 carrying Ds was quite normal in morphology. The semidominant lethality was not due, primarily, to inhibition of gene action, for it is known that endosperms that are deficient for all of the short arm of one chromosome 9 develop normally. Some change in gene action other than localized inhibition was induced in these cases.

Because dominant lethality may be expressed when controlling elements are inserted at some positions in the chromosome complement, as described above, difficulties are encountered in attempts to determine whether a particular element can enter any site in the chromosome complement or is restricted to certain sites. At present, no definite statement can be made regarding this. It is known, however, that controlling elements may be inserted at a number of different positions. Those that seem to be preferred, on the basis of present knowledge, may represent only a selected number of possible sites at which the presence of the element does not induce inviability at some stage in development.

INFLUENCE OF CONTROLLING ELEMENTS IN MODIFYING GENE ACTION

It is now known that controlling elements may modify gene action in a number of different ways. They may influence the time of gene action in the development of a tissue, and also determine the cells in which it will occur. Again, they may influence the type of action, with regard to either degree (quantitative aspects) or kind (qualitative) aspects). They may also act as inhibitors, suppressors, and modifiers, as well as inducers of types of change at a gene locus that resemble those often referred to in the past as point or gene mutation.

When a particular controlling element is inserted at a gene locus, its presence there may be detected by the changes in phenotypic expression that appear. Tests may then be conducted to determine the position in a chromosome at which the responsible changes are occurring, and thus the locus involved may be identified. Subsequent tests may be made to examine the mode of operation of the particular controlling system concerned with these changes and to determine its components. From such procedures it was learned that one system can operate at a number of different gene loci, and that the action at one gene locus may be controlled by different systems; the evidence has been presented in previous publications (McClintock, 1953, 1955, 1956).

When a controlling element is inserted at the locus of a known gene, a recognizable change in phenotypic expression may be observed as an immediate consequence, or no immediate change may result. In the latter case, the presence of a controlling element at the locus is detected subsequently, for it will initiate recognizable changes in gene action. The origins of a_1^{m-3} and a_1^{m-4} will illustrate this fact. Both arose from insertion of a Ds-type element (one responding to Ac) at the standard A_1 locus in chromosome 3, and the Ds-Ac two-element system controls gene action in both cases. In the case of a_1^{m-4}, inhibition of gene action probably occurred as an immediate consequence of insertion of a Ds element at the standard A_1 locus, as its presence there was made evident a few cell generations after that event occurred. In the case of a_1^{m-3}, on the other hand, insertion of the Ds element at the A_1 locus did not produce an immediate change in gene action. Its presence was revealed later, however, by altered expressions of the gene substance at the locus, which were recognized in some of the progeny of one particular plant of a culture. At least a full plant generation intervened between insertion of the Ds element at A_1 and recognition of its presence there. Had Ac been removed from the nucleus shortly after this insertion, the presence of the Ds element at the locus would not have been detected, for in the absence of Ac the phenotypic expression would have remained unaltered. Only by some fortuitous cross that again introduced Ac into a plant carrying this original state of a_1^{m-3} would the presence of Ds have been revealed, for only then would frequent change in gene action occur. Thus, the presence of a controlling element at a particular locus is revealed by the types of change that occur under given conditions, and if these conditions do not prevail its presence at the locus may not be recognized.

That the presence of a controlling element at a locus need not effect inhibition of gene action is also shown by studies of those cases in which Ac resides at the bronze locus in chromosome 9 and at the P locus in chromosome 1. The phenotype produced when these cases were initially recognized was that of the recessive, or null, expression. In both cases, mutations occurred, and the part that Ac plays in these was reviewed earlier. It was found that removal of Ac from the locus concerned was associated in some cases with a change in gene action from one that gives the null expression to one that gives a high degree of activity, and also that the mutant so formed was subsequently stable in the presence of Ac when the latter was located elsewhere. Some of the mutants were not stable, however, and subsequent mutations occurred. In the case of Ac at the bronze locus, two of the 16 Bz mutants examined were of this type. From studies of both of them it was learned that the event that gave rise to the Bz expression did not result in removal of Ac from the immediate vicinity of the Bz locus and that Ac was responsible for the subsequent mutations that occurred. Some of these later mutations resulted in stability of the Bz expression, and in the three examined cases it was learned that Ac had been removed from the locus of Bz. Other changes were detected by the reappearance of the unstable recessive, and in the several examined cases it was learned that Ac was still present at the bronze locus. Still other types of mutant expression were noted, but these need not be discussed here. It is desired only to emphasize that the presence of a controlling element at a gene locus need not effect inhibition of action but may instead condition a mode of control of gene action in subsequent cell and plant generations, which will follow in a predictable manner. The ability to predict depends, of course, upon the extent of knowledge of the controlling system in operation in any one case.

The presence of a particular controlling element at a known gene locus can influence gene expression in different ways, which may range from complete suppression to various degrees of action. Moreover, the types of action may differ not only quantitatively but also qualitatively. There is evidence to suggest that in some cases these various types of mutation are reflections of modifications affecting different components of a compound locus, and that each component of the locus is concerned in its own way with development of one particular phenotype. Extensive evidence based on crossover studies of the compound nature of the A_1 locus in chromosome 3 has been presented by Laughnan (1949, 1952, 1955a, b) and evidence regarding the R locus in chromosome 10 has been obtained by Stadler and colleagues (Stadler and Nuffer, 1953; Stadler and Emmerling, 1954, 1956). Instability of expression of A_1 has appeared rather frequently, and cases of this have been examined by several maize geneticists (Rhoades, 1936, 1938, 1941, 1945; McClintock, 1951, 1953, 1956; Nuffer, 1955, 1956; Laughnan, 1956; Peterson, 1956; Richardson, 1956). On the basis of our present knowledge of the origin and behavior of such "unstable loci" it is inferred, when not determined with certainty, that a controlling element resides at the A_1 locus in each such case. The modifications in gene action it induces

there can affect the action of one or another of the known components of this locus, or it may affect all of them simultaneously. Other gene loci, such as that of C in chromosome 9, also appear to be compound. Evidence of this was obtained by study of several distinguishable types of mutation that occur in the case of c^{m-2}. (For origin of this case and the controlling system involved, see McClintock, 1951.) These are associated with the production of at least two different diffusible substances, both of which are required for pigment formation. It was also noted that the dose expression given by the C allele commonly used in genetic studies is related to the limited production of one of these substances by this allele: the more C alleles present, the greater the amount of this substance formed, and, consequently, the denser the pigmentation. It is conceivable, then, that some of the qualitative differences in expression of mutants of a given locus reflect alterations in action of different components of a compound locus, and that a controlling element as the consequence of one event, may affect the action of only one component or of more than one; or the modification induced by any one event may affect the action of all of them.

It is now known that the presence of a controlling element at a known locus can effect change in gene action not only of the genic components located close to it, but also of other genic components located some distance to either side of it. A number of examples of this kind affecting gene action in a particular segment within the short arm of chromosome 9, extending over a region 5 or more crossover units in length have been examined; and these have been reviewed in previous publications (McClintock, 1953, 1954, 1955, 1956). Recently, Richardson (1956) found a case of "spreading effect" that appeared to be induced by a controlling element located at A_1 in chromosome 3. The nature of the changes responsible for such spread of mutation along the chromosome is of considerable importance for an understanding of the manner by which controlling elements can induce their effects, and those involving the segment of chromosome 9 that includes the loci of I, Sh, and Bz are particularly useful for this purpose. The "spreading effect" in these cases is known to be induced by the presence of a Ds element that is located just to the left of Sh; and it is also known that the mutation-inducing process is not accompanied by change in location of Ds. One might consider that the "spreading effect" is merely the expression of a deficiency for the loci involved, even though most such cases give viable homozygotes, or, barring this, that the organization of the chromosome segment concerned or the structure or organization of components within it is altered in some particular manner by the Ds element. Therefore, tests of some of these cases are being conducted in order to determine whether or not crossing over occurs within the affected segment. It has been learned, in several of these cases, that either crossing over does not occur or its frequency of occurrence is very low. In others, however, crossing over takes place within the affected segment and the frequency of occurrence differs among the several examined cases. Plants derived from reciprocal crossovers are now under investigation in order to determine if mutant expressions of genic components within the affected segment will appear in their progeny, and if so, the types each may give. That separation by crossing over can occur between the individual genic components whose modification is responsible for the compound mutant expression has already been shown by Richardson in the case of the "spreading effect," mentioned above.

Examination of the mode of operation of two-element controlling systems has revealed the breadth of influence of such systems in modifying gene action. The study has concerned not only the number of different genes that such systems control, but also the manner of this control, which is of greater significance. It has been possible to examine the mode of operation of the Ds-Ac system at seven different gene loci (for references, see McClintock, 1953, 1956), and to learn that the system operates in essentially the same way in each case. The mode of control of gene action resides in the system itself. It is the Ds-type element at the locus of the gene that is directly responsible for control of gene action and for the changes that occur in gene action; and it is the Ac element of the system that is responsible for initiating these modifications where the Ds element resides, and also for the time of their occurrence. In some of the cases examined, the change in gene action is usually associated with removal of Ds from the gene locus, and stability of mutant expression in the presence of Ac is thereby effected (c^{m-1}, bz^{m-1} are examples). In other cases, the Ds element is not usually removed when a change in gene action is initiated, and, in the presence of Ac, subsequent changes may occur (c^{m-2}, wx^{m-1}, a_1^{m-3} are examples). Any one of the mutants so produced, however, will be stable in the absence of Ac. Thus, by removing Ac from the nucleus, it is possible to isolate a number of alleles that are distinguishable from each other by different modes of gene expression (see Table 4 for examples). Extensive examination of the operation of this Ds-Ac system as well as other systems has thus provided a large body of knowledge, from which it is possible to conclude that controlling systems are composed of distinct and well-defined entities in the nucleus, that these are independent of the gene elements as defined earlier, that they need not reside at fixed sites in the chromosome complement, that they retain their identities when transposed from one location to another, and that they operate in much the same general manner wherever they may be located.

The mode of operation of the Spm-a_1^{m-1} two-element system, which was considered in some detail earlier in this discussion, is impressive because one aspect of control of gene action expressed by the Spm element of the system is suggestive of the mode of operation of suppressors, inhibitors, and modifiers that have been identified in other organisms. In its presence, all action at the a_1^{m-1} locus is suppressed, but in its absence all but one of the alleles of a_1^m are active to some degree, and some of them produce kernels and plants that exhibit intense pigmentation (see Table 4). The Spm element undergoes many transpositions without suffering loss of identity, for its mode of control of gene action at a_1^{m-1} has been found to be the same when variously located. In contrast to Ac in the Ds-Ac system, increments of Spm do not effect modification in time of mutation at a_1^{m-1}. The same phenotypes appear when either one or more Spm elements are present in the nuclei of a plant.

Another two-element system has been examined in which the mode of control of the independently located element resembles, in certain respects, those of both Spm and Ac. The element in this system that is comparable to Ac, Spm, or Dt, exhibits a suppressor-mutator type of control of gene action and mutation at a modified A_2 locus, designated a_2^{m-1}, and in a manner that is similar to that of the Spm element of the a_1^{m-1} system. For example, in its absence, gene action at the a_2^{m-1} locus in one of the isolates (one of the alleles of a_2^{m-1}) resembles that given by the standard A_2, for the plants and kernels are intensely and uniformly pigmented and no mutations occur. In its presence, however, all gene activity at a_2^{m-1} is suppressed until the occurrence there of a mutation-inducing event that allows pigment to be produced; and the time of occurrence of such events during the development of a tissue depends on the dose of this suppressor-mutator-type element that is present in the nucleus: the higher the dose, the later the time of occurrence. In this respect, it very much resembles Ac.

Differences in phenotype produced by increments of Ac or of the Spm-type element just described are sharply defined. However, the effects of additions of elements that exhibit this type of dosage expression need not be so contrasting. It is known from other evidence that these effects may be expressed in a somewhat different manner, and an example will be given here. It involves two elements, one of which resides at the A_2 locus in chromosome 5; the other element is independently located. A low dose of the independently located element of this system effects early-occurring mutations at the locus of A_2, from a nonactive allele to one that gives an apparently standard A_2-type expression. Added increments of this element effect step-wise delays in time of occurrence of these mutations, until mere specks of pigment appear in a nonpigmented background in the kernel and only very fine streaks of anthocyanin pigment appear in a nonpigmented background in the plant. Increments of the element above that which gives this speckled pattern result in a striking change in phenotypic expression. Now, pigment is produced in both plant and kernel. Although the intensity of color is low, the pigment is uniformly distributed and no mutations occur. This change in gene action is not the consequence of mutation at the modified A_2 locus, but rather the expression of a high dose of the independently located element of the system. This may be shown by crossing the pale-colored plants to standard a_2 tester stocks in which the element is absent. Doses of it are thereby reduced in some of the progeny, and this reduction is evidenced by the reappearance in kernels and plants of the variegated phenotype: a nonpigmented background in which pigmented spots or areas appear. It has also been determined that this element undergoes transposition. This may sometimes be exhibited in sectors in the plant or kernel, which express the change in number of the element that occurred in the ancestor cell giving rise to the sector.

It was stated earlier that the presence of a controlling element at a particular gene locus may not be recognized unless favorable conditions for revealing it are also present; and examples were given. The origin of a number of mutants might well be traced to effects produced by controlling elements, but this might be as difficult as it initially appeared to be for the standard a_1 mutant in maize. This mutant responds to Dt by producing higher alleles of A_1, but in the absence of Dt the recessive mutant expression is most stable. The mutant was used in genetic studies long before Dt was discovered or its control over the element at the a_1 locus recognized. Had Dt not been discovered, the a_1 mutant would still be considered an example of stable gene change, just as many of the other known mutants are now considered. In order to identify readily the presence of controlling elements and to be able to examine their different modes of behavior, only those cases were selected, originally, that gave clear-cut evidence of their presence by modification of gene action in both somatic and sporogenous cells. These are the so-called "mutable genes" or "mutable loci." It is quite evident, however, that the standard a_1 mutant is as good a member of the "mutable gene" class as any other that has been described in this or previous reports. How many other known mutants, whose behavior appears to be stable in the existing experimental cultures, also belong to this class? Can conditions be altered so as to expose the presence of a controlling element? Efforts in this direction have not yet been made, except with the standard a_1 mutant itself (McClintock, 1951a, b). The method used gave positive results in that case; and this suggests that positive results might also be obtained if similar experiments were conducted with other known mutants which appear to be stable in the genetic stocks now being used.

Controlling elements appear to reflect the presence in the nucleus of highly integrated systems operating to control gene action. The modes of operation of the known two-element systems bring into sharp relief one level of this integration. Other levels are now under investigation, and these are related to the effects produced by modifiers of particular systems that have appeared within the cultures under examination or been introduced by strain crosses. For example, in the Spm-carrying cultures, a certain type of modifier arises with rather constant frequencies. In its action it resembles, in certain respects, the Spm element itself, and it may be derived from this element in some manner. It differs from the original Spm, however, in quite recognizable ways. In the absence of Spm, this modifier effects suppression of gene action at a_1^{m-1}, but only in the aleurone layer of the kernel. The kernels may be totally colorless or they may show one or several small dots of deep color. The plants, on the other hand, show the pigmented phenotype that is exhibited in the absence of Spm. In the presence of Spm, the modifier behaves as a recessive, and in test crosses of plants carrying both of them typical segregation ratios for both elements are exhibited. The modifier probably undergoes transposition just as Spm does, for it has been located at several different positions in the chromosome complement. It is a controlling element and also it is a component of this system. Still other types of modifiers of this system have appeared, each expressing a characteristic type of modification of the system, or, in other words, a characteristic type of integrative action within the system as a whole. Recognition of the presence and operation of a so-called two-element system, then, represents only recognition of the lowest integrative level of those elements in the chromosome complement that are directly concerned with modification of the genome as a whole.

Mendelizing units associated with phenotypic expressions that are similar in many essential respects to those produced by known controlling elements in maize, such as modifiers, suppressors, and some types of inhibitors, have been described in a number of organisms. Are many of their effects also attributable to the activities of controlling elements; and what kinds of criteria may be used to discriminate between the proposed two classes of genetic elements, that is, gene elements and controlling elements? Transposability, which made possible the recognition of controlling elements in the chromosome complement of maize, may not serve in all cases as a reliable criterion for discrimination between the two classes of elements, because the frequency of its occurrence may be so low, under certain conditions, that detection may be difficult (McClintock, 1956). Nevertheless, as far as my knowledge goes, little if any effort has been made to detect transposition of mutators, modifiers, suppressors, or some types of inhibitors in other organisms, and the degree to which it may occur is not yet known. It would be surprising, indeed, if controlling elements were not found in other organisms, for their prevalence in maize is now well established.

REFERENCES

BARCLAY, P. C., and BRINK, R. A., 1954, The relation between Modulator and Activator in maize. Proc. Nat. Acad. Sci. Wash. 40: 1118–1126.

BRINK, R. A., 1954, Very light variegated pericarp in maize. Genetics 39: 724–740.

BRINK, R. A., and NILAN, R. A., 1952, The relation between light variegated and medium variegated pericarp in maize. Genetics 37: 519–544.

DEMEREC, M., BLOOMSTRAND, I., and DEMEREC, Z. E., 1955, Evidence of complex loci in Salmonella. Proc. Nat. Acad. Sci. Wash. 41: 359–364.

DEMEREC, M., and DEMEREC, Z. E., 1956, Analysis of linkage relationships in Salmonella by transduction techniques. Brookhaven Symp. Biol. 8: 75–87.

DOLLINGER, E. J., 1955, Analysis of a mutable system in maize. (Abstract.) Genetics 40: 570.

EYSTER, W. H., 1926, The effect of environment on variegated patterns in maize pericarp. Genetics 11: 372–386.

FRADKIN, C. W., and BRINK, R. A., 1956, Effect of Modulator on the frequency of endosperm mosaics in maize. Amer. J. Bot. 43: 267–273.

LAUGHNAN, J. R., 1948, The action of allelic forms of the gene A in maize. I. Studies of variability, dosage and dominance relations. The divergent character of the series. Genetics 33: 488–517.

1949, The action of allelic forms of the gene A in maize. II. The relation of crossing over to mutation of A^b. Proc. Nat. Acad. Sci. Wash. 35: 167–178.

1952, The action of allelic forms of the gene A in maize. IV. On the compound nature of A^b and the occurrence and action of its A^D derivatives. Genetics 37: 375–395.

1955, Structural and functional aspects of the A^b complexes in maize. I. Evidence for structural and functional variability among complexes of different geographic origins. Proc. Nat. Acad. Sci. Wash. 41: 78–84.

1955, Structural and functional bases for the action of the A alleles in maize. Amer. Nat. 89: 91–103.

1955, Intrachromosomal association between members of an adjacent serial duplication as a possible basis for the presumed gene mutations from A^b complexes. (Abstract.) Genetics 40: 580.

1956, A possible clue to the nature of Dt action. Maize Genetics Cooperation News Letter 30: 67–68.

McCLINTOCK, B., 1951, Chromosome organization and genic expression. Cold Spring Harbor Symp. Quant. Biol. 16: 13–47.

1953, Induction of instability at selected loci in maize. Genetics 38: 579–599.

1953, Mutation in maize. Carnegie Inst. Wash. Year Book 52: 227–237.

1954, Mutations in maize. Carnegie Inst. Wash. Year Book 53: 254–260.

1955, Controlled mutation in maize. Carnegie Inst. Wash. Year Book 54: 245–255.

1956, Intranuclear systems controlling gene action and mutation. Brookhaven Symp. Biol. 8: 58–74.

NUFFER, M. G., 1951, A highly mutable allele of A_1. Maize Genetics Cooperation News Letter 25: 38–39.

1955, Dosage effect of multiple Dt loci on mutation of a in the maize endosperm. Science 121: 399–400.

1956, Instability of the alpha and beta components of the A_1 locus. Maize Genetics Cooperation News Letter 30: 101.

PETERSON, P. A., 1956, An a_1 mutable arising in pg^m stocks. Maize Genetics Cooperation News Letter 30: 82.

RICHARDSON, D. L., 1956, An unstable compound locus, $a_1{}^{pm}$. Maize Genetics Cooperation News Letter 30: 111–118.

RHOADES, M. M., 1936, The effect of varying gene dosage on aleurone color in maize. J. Genet. 33: 347–354.

1938, Effect of the Dt gene on mutability of the a_1 allele in maize. Genetics 23: 377–397.

1941, The genetic control of mutability in maize. Cold Spring Harbor Symp. Quant. Biol. 9: 138–144.

1945, On the genetic control of mutability in maize. Proc. Nat. Acad. Sci. Wash. 31: 91–95.

VAN SCHAIK, T., 1954, Effect of plant vigor on variegation of pericarp. Maize Genetics Cooperation News Letter 28: 81–82.

STADLER, L. J., and EMMERLING, M., 1954, Problems of gene structure. III. Relation of unequal crossing over to the interdependence of R^r elements (S) and (P). (Abstract.) Science 119: 585.

1956, Relation of unequal crossing over to the interdependence of R^r elements (P) and (S). Genetics 41: 124–137.

STADLER, L. J., and NUFFER, M. G., 1953, Problems of gene structure. II. Separation of R^r elements (S) and (P) by unequal crossing over. Science 117: 471–472.

DISCUSSION

CATCHESIDE: I would like to suggest that Dr. McClintock has in the transposition of controlling elements the explanation of the phenomenon which has been referred to by several speakers as negative interference. It would follow that evidence for controlling elements in organisms other than maize should be sought in those cases which show apparent negative interference.

Nuclear Differentiation and Functional Morphology of Chromosomes

Wolfgang Beermann

Zoologisches Institut, Universität Marburg, Germany

Introduction

The classical concept of cellular differentiation, as formulated by Boveri (1904) more than 50 years ago, may be stated in modern terms as follows: 1) All cells of an individual or, in Protozoa of a clone, obtain two or some other number of complete sets of chromosomes and genes by means of mitosis, a process especially evolved to this end. 2) Differentiation is primarily cytoplasmic. It does not normally involve irreversible, that is, mutational changes of chromosome or gene structure and number (other than polyploidy), but may cause reversible changes in gene activity.

There is scarcely any doubt that these statements are correct with respect to early somatic development. However, they have not yet been shown to be equally true for ultimate differentiation of tissues and cells in higher animals and plants. One instance of differentiation, that of primordial germ cell formation, may even be characterized by visibly unequal distribution or loss of chromosome material. The first part of this report will serve to illustrate problems involved in germ-line differentiation, with special reference to the conditions recently discovered in Chironomids and Tipulids. The second and greater part of the present review is concerned with cytological lines of attack on the general question of differential gene activation, reversible or irreversible, in differentiated cells subsequent to embryogenesis, based on investigations of the giant chromosomes of Chironomids and Sciarids. Most of the work reported here has been conducted in Dr. Bauer's laboratory at Wilhelmshaven. It has been, or will be, published in extenso elsewhere. Therefore, details will be omitted unless they are of special interest to the point under discussion.

Germ-Line Chromosomes in Orthocladiinae

Elimination of chromosomes or of parts of chromosomes has previously been reported for various animals, for example, members of the nematode genus *Ascaris*, or of the Dipteran families of Sciaridae and Cecidomyidae. Though differing in detail these cases have one thing in common: During early development certain chromosomes or chromosomal constituents are regularly lost from all but the primordial germ cells of the segmenting egg. As compared to the soma, the germ line of these animals is thus characterized by supernumerary chromosomes or extra chromatin.

A new case of this sort has recently been studied in detail (Bauer and Beermann, 1952b). An entire subfamily of Chironomids, the Orthocladiinae, have been found to possess supernumerary germline chromosomes. The number of these elements varies according to the species studied. The highest number found as yet is about 80, in a member of the genus *Cardiocladius*, as against a haploid set of two somatic chromosomes in this species (Fig. 1). Other Orthocladiine species normally average numbers between two and 20 supernumeraries in their germ line.

A highly aberrant chromosome cycle has evolved in conjunction with chromosomal germline differentiation in the Orthocladiinae. It is characterized by three different mitotic events. One of these occurs during early somatic development, at about the fifth to seventh division of the segmenting egg, and results in elimination of all germ line chromosomes from the soma. Elimination, as in other similar cases, is due to incomplete splitting of daughter chromatids when anaphase begins.

The other two aberrant events take place in the germ line itself. One of them occurs after hatching of the larva, when the primordial germ cells begin to divide again. It has the effect of reducing the number of supernumeraries to about half their zygotic number, by partial elimination during anaphase. This numerical reduction compensates for a peculiar duplication process taking place later at the time of differentiation of spermatocytes and oocytes, when all spermatogonia and oogonia undergo one differential division. Though reduplicated in prophase, the germ-line chromosomes fail to divide in this division. Instead, they congregate around one of the spindle poles, while mitosis of the somatic set proceeds as usual. Eventually, two cells arise, one of which contains all the reduplicated germ line chromosomes plus one diploid set of somatic ones, while the other shows the diploid somatic set only. In the female, the latter cell regularly develops into a nurse cell; in the male it gives rise to a degenerating spermatocyte, being unable to carry out normal meiosis. Thus, functional spermatocytes and oocytes both contain two sets of supernumerary chromosomes. Each pair of sister elements then forms a bivalent during meiosis. It follows that both sperm and egg contribute a numerically unreduced set of germ line chromosomes to the germ line of the zygote. Partial germ line elimination, the other

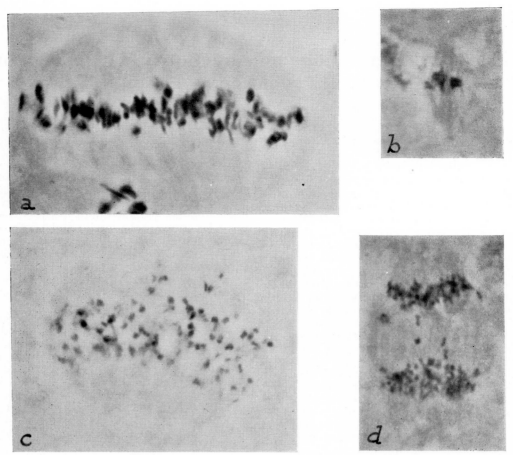

FIGURE 1. *Cardiocladius* spec.: (a) metaphase I of spermatocyte with about 80 bivalents, only 2 of which are "somatic" ones, all others being formed by germ-line supernumeraries. (b) aberrant spermatocyte in metaphase I, with 4 somatic chromosomes as univalents (one is out of focus). (c) anaphase I, (d) anaphase II, both with about 80 supernumeraries. × 2000.

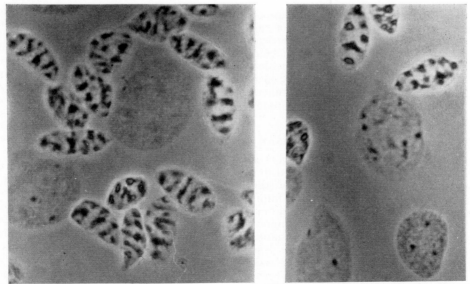

FIGURE 2. Squash preparations (aceto-orcein) of the retina of a 10-day old kitten. Retinal rod nuclei with heteropycnotic blocks arranged transversely to the long axis of the nucleus. Nuclei belonging to other cells of the retina are also shown. × 1500.

218

aberrant event mentioned above, is therefore necessary to keep the number of supernumeraries down at the normal level.

This sequence of events raises several questions. The purely genetical, cytochemical and evolutionary ones will be disregarded for the moment in favor of the point of view of differentiation. One should like to know, for instance, the effect of germ-line chromosomes when present in somatic tissues, and conversely, whether and how far somatic nuclei would function when transferred to the early germ-line. There is no evidence on this point as yet. Likewise it is not known just why and how half of the supernumeraries become eliminated in early germ-line reduction. Those supernumeraries which are to be eliminated can be seen to turn heteropycnotic in the resting stage during embryonic development. Further questions concentrate around the differential division step preceding meiosis. Considering the extreme inequality of chromosomal segregation in some cases—in *Cardiocladius* more than 80 chromosomes go to one pole, and only four to the other—one is tempted to ascribe the different fate of the daughter cells to the act of differential chromosome distribution itself, an idea on Weismann's lines. Even if the polarity of the division were determined by a cytoplasmic gradient, the subsequent behavior of the daughter cells would thus depend on their nuclear constitution. This assumption, however, appears unlikely in view of recent observations: Males of a *Trichocladius* species (*T. triannulatus*) have been found which had no supernumeraries at all in their testes. Yet, the premeiotic gonial division is clearly differential, not with respect to chromosomes this time, but still with respect to the potencies of the daughter cells. Only one of them carries out normal spermatogenesis; the other regularly degenerates just as in other Orthocladiine males. Thus, differential distribution of germ line chromosomes can neither be the cause nor the necessary condition of differentiation in this case. To be sure, this does not exclude that supernumerary chromosomes may fulfil important functions where they occur. This problem will be considered later.

Nurse Cell Differentiation in Tipulids

Another case of differential mitosis was recently described by Bayreuther (1952, 1956). In the growing larval ovaries of Tipulids (crane-flies) a period of mere proliferation is followed by one where each oogonium gives rise, in four division steps, to a group of 16 cells, the "Eianlage." Only one of these becomes a functional oocyte later, all others differentiate into nurse cells. That differentiation takes place during the four divisions is directly demonstrated by the appearance and differential distribution of peculiar nuclear elements, called "nucleine bodies" (Nukleinkörper) by Bayreuther, on account of their intensive Feulgen reaction. In *Tipula lateralis*, for instance,

such bodies appear during prophase of the second division in either daughter cell of the first division. A Feulgen positive substance, enclosing the nucleolus, accumulates in close contact with the heterochromatic X-chromosomes. This material gradually condenses and grows in size as the nucleolus disappears. In metaphase, both cells show a round, slightly vacuolated, Feulgen positive body attached to the long arm of one or both X-chromosomes. This body never divides during anaphase; instead it is included into only one of the two daughter chromosome groups at late anaphase. Thus, four cells arise, only two of which contain a nucleine body. During interphase the bodies disintegrate, but as soon as prophase of the next division begins new lumps of chromatic material begin to accumulate in two of the four nuclei then present, again in contact with the X-chromosomes. The process of differential distribution is repeated during the third as well as the fourth division so that only two of the 16 cells formed eventually receive a nucleine body. It seems natural to assume that nucleine bodies are built up in the same two nuclei which had received them in the preceding division. On this assumption, the Feulgen positive material would be passed along in two lines of cells. Only those two cells of a group of 16 enter pachytene whose nucleus contains a nucleine body. These two, therefore, ought to be considered as potential oocytes; all others invariably retain the reticular type of nuclear structure and develop into nurse cells later. Of course, one of the two potential oocytes ultimately must turn into a nurse cell, too.

In embryological terms determination of potential oocytes and nurse cells in the ovary of *Tipula lateralis* might provisionally be described as a process involving loss of the potency to enter pachytene by all those cells that do not receive a nucleine body in telophase. It is tempting to identify loss of potency with loss of nuclear elements in this case, especially since conditions in other crane-fly species seem to confirm this view: In *Pales crocata*, for instance, from one to four cell lines may show a nucleine body during ovarial differentiation and, correspondingly, from one to four cells in a group of 16 may enter pachytene. Hence, considered separately, the potency to enter pachytene may actually depend on the presence of DNA-containing nuclear elements which have irrevocably been lost from the chromosomes of the future nurse cells during synthesis of the nucleine bodies. A strict relation of this sort cannot, however, exist: In *Tipula oleracea*, for instance, small secondary nucleine bodies appear in other than the original two cell lines, though never more than two cells in a group of 16 enter pachytene. On the other hand, in *Tipula paludosa*, nucleine bodies may be present in some cells, in spite of the fact that invariably all 16 cells enter pachytene in this species. Thus, the situation is not entirely clear; final proof or disproof can only come from experimental work.

Other Cases of Differential Mitosis

The conditions encountered in different Tipulid species are of evolutionary interest not only by themselves but also in view of the long known case of *Dytiscus* (*e.g.* Günthert, 1910). In *Dytiscus* and other related species of water beetles differentiation of oocytes and nurse cells is still more conspicuous than in *Tipula lateralis*. As is well known the four divisions of the secondary oogonia in *Dytiscus* are differential with respect to nuclear as well as cytoplasmic constitution. The ring of extra-chromatin (Feulgen-positive, according to Bauer) which forms around the metaphase plate in each differential division of the future oocyte appears to be homologous to the nucleine bodies of Tipulids. It is reincorporated into the nucleus of the future oocyte in every division and persists during interphase. In *Dytiscus*, ovarial differentiation is clearly cytoplasmic in the first place. On the other hand, the potency to enter pachytene might still depend on the presence of extra chromatin.

Differential divisions in the germ-line such as those discussed probably are more frequent than was hitherto assumed. Thus, Bayreuther (personal communication) has seen nucleine bodies in the ovarial development of fleas, for instance. Furthermore, inconspicuous elimination processes may often have been overlooked wherever early segregation of germ-line and soma occurs in embryonic development. It may also be recalled that differential divisions of the teloblastic type regularly occur in somatic development. Though cytological evidence on this subject is not yet available, differential distribution or loss of chromosomal constituents might play a role in such divisions.

Significance and Nature of Extra Chromosomes or Extra Chromatin in the Germ-line

The occurrence of supernumerary genetic material in the germ-line seems far too frequent to be dismissed as exceptional. On the contrary, selective conditions in the germ-line are such that accumulation of extra chromosomes or extra chromatin might easily take place as soon as an elimination mechanism is provided for in early somatic development. Somatic cell-lineages end with the death of the individual, while the germ-line is continuous over the generations. Chance alone could lead to the accumulation of supernumerary elements; actually, however, selection is seen to be at work in controlling and maintaining different typical numbers of germ-line chromosomes in different species. Selection in the germ-line may have various physiological bases. Boveri

(1904) pointed to a possible correlation between the occurrence of diminution in nematodes and structural features of eggs and sperm of these animals. Extra germ-line chromatin seems to occur in genera such as *Ascaris* whose eggs have thick shells and whose spermatozoa show a large acrosome. Boveri's idea finds support in a recent finding of Scholl (personal communication): Two parthenogenetic strains of the Orthocladiine species *Pseudosmittia arenaria* which are morphologically indistinguishable differ in the coloration of the chorion of their eggs. The "yellow" race has supernumerary chromosomes in the germ line, while the "brown" race has none. White (1955) thinks that elimination of supernumeraries in early somatic development contributes specific nucleoproteins to the segmenting egg. An alternative hypothesis may be based on Boveri's idea. Of all cells, those of the germ-line alone can afford the luxury of fixing general physiological functions to extra self-reduplicating elements in the nucleus. Such functions might involve synthesis of enzymes and other substances utilized in meiosis and subsequent gamete formation. Moreover, supernumerary material might keep the somatic genes from becoming involved in the metabolism of the germ line. Conversely, any functional change in the "somatic" direction, such as in nurse cells, would then require elimination of the supernumerary material as is actually observed.

The nature and origin of supernumerary germline chromatin are largely obscure. Supernumerary chromosomes are often considered as heterochromatic, but White (1947) has found that in the germ-line of *Miastor* the somatic rather than the extra chromosomes show total heteropycnosis. New evidence on this subject comes from unpublished work of Ortiz (personal communication) on the Orthocladiine species *Metriocnemus hygropetricus*. Ortiz transferred sections of germ-line chromosomes into the soma by radiation induced translocation either of the insertional type or of the reciprocal type, the breaks in the somatic chromosomes being close to the end. A few cases clearly show euchromatic, normally banded supernumerary sections which cannot be homologized to any section of the somatic set. Other sections of the supernumeraries seem to be heteropycnotic when transferred to the soma.

Concerning Bayreuthers "nucleine bodies" and the *Dytiscus* case it has been assumed that the material in question is chromosomal in origin, probably arising from atypical reduplication processes in the heterochromatin. This assumption finds support in the fact that specific morphological differences exist between nucleine bodies of different species. Formally, the material has to be treated as extrachromosomal and constitutes a probable exception to the rule of DNA-constancy, a possibility which needs photometric confirmation.

DIFFERENCES IN GROSS STRUCTURE OF THE RESTING NUCLEUS IN CELLS OF DIFFERENT FUNCTION

One of the most drastic bifurcations in early development has been recapitulated above—differentiation of germ-line and soma. Apart from differences caused by differential elimination of chromosomes this event results in differences in cytoplasmic constitution as well as appearance of the resting nucleus. In Chironomids, the nuclei of primordial germ cells, in contrast to those of the soma, do not return to the reticular type of structure as long as division is arrested. Throughout embryogenesis the primordial germ cell nuclei are seen to contain individual, contracted chromosomes, a condition which is not changed until after the onset of mitotic multiplication in early larval life. A similar situation was found in a Copepod, *Ectocyclops strenzkei*, and may be assumed to prevail in many other arthropods. Contraction of chromosomes, if it persists during the resting stage of germ-line nuclei, may indicate a state of transient inactivity on the part of the chromosomes, or might in itself be a means of decreasing reactivity in a rapidly changing embryonic milieu. It would seem interesting to study nuclear structure in such primordial germ cells which in *Drosophila*, according to Poulson (1947) become incorporated into the larval midgut.

Different somatic nuclei of a multicellular organism usually display a similarity strikingly in contrast to the wide divergence of cytoplasmic structures. Heidenhain (1901) once called the nucleus "den ruhenden Pol in der Erscheinungen Flucht." Differences in nuclear size occur, of course, parallel to the phenomenon of somatic polyploidy. However, repeated reduplication of the chromosome complement has not yet been shown to be accompanied by gradual or sudden changes in cellular character. There is no specific degree of polyploidy which would be specifically related to only one kind of cellular function. Somatic polyploidy will therefore not be considered in the present context.

Barigozzi (1950) recently pointed to changes in nuclear structure not caused by polyploidy or simple changes in dispersion and hydration. In the salamander *Amblystoma tigrinum*, differences in the appearance of chromocenters in different stages of development are apparent. In particular, the nuclei of liver and striated muscle are said to be rich in heteropycnotic elements, while in contrast, those of early embryonic stages show no chromocenters at all. Barigozzi extended his observations to arthropod tissues; these and other findings have been reviewed recently by Geitler (1953). Striking instances of differential heteropycnosis are encountered in mammals as shown by preliminary observations of Bayreuther (personal communication). In orcein squash preparations of mouse testis the Sertoli cells have finely granular nuclei with two large chromocenters, while cells of the follicular epithelium exhibit up to 15 regularly distributed chromocenters in the nucleus. A similar difference is found on comparison of heart muscle and liver.

One observation of this sort has been discussed more than 70 years ago by Flemming (1882) and other histologists. The retinal rod nuclei of some mammals contain heteropycnotic masses in two or three large blocks arranged transversely to the rod axis (Fig. 2). A reinvestigation of this peculiar phenomenon is now under way and has already shown that the structures in question are Feulgen-positive.

As pointed out by Barigozzi, differential heteropycnosis as a phenomenon again raises the question of a clearcut definition of the term "heterochromatin". Disregarding this difficulty, differential heteropycnosis might be considered as an indication of differential inactivation of the genes in different cells, or of differential reproduction of the heterochromatin, as envisaged by Schultz (1947a and b). On the other hand, the phenomenon might reflect nothing but differences in the "stickiness" of heterochromatin or differences in the degree of mitotic telophase congression of the kinetochores. It will be difficult to decide between these alternatives as long as mammalian nuclear structure is not understood in terms of interphasic chromosome morphology.

GIANT CHROMOSOMES IN CELLS OF DIFFERENT CHARACTER AND FUNCTION: CONSTANCY OF THE BANDING PATTERN

In the giant cells of Diptera, nuclear differentiation may be analyzed in detail, that is, with reference to the genetic organization of the chromosomes. Polyteny has been shown to be a special type of somatic polyploidy (Bauer, 1938; Bauer and Beermann, 1952a). From the genetic point of view the essential feature of polytene chromosomes is their banding pattern, as determined by spacing, thickness, fine structure, and staining capacity of the chromatic cross bands or discs.

The banding pattern in cells of one and the same salivary gland, for instance of *Drosophila*, has proved to be constant to such a degree that single band differences between individuals can be defined with certainty, a long known fact which, of course, does not exclude variations in the clearness of structure such as are encountered in any field of morphology. The construction of cytological chromosome maps (Bridges, 1935) would never have been attempted if pattern constancy were an illusion. In view of intra-tissue constancy the existence of the same constancy in all cells of the individual has long, and justly, been considered as self-evident. Recently, this view has been contested (Kosswig and Sengün 1947, and in a series of other papers). A detailed definition of the alleged differences with reference to chromosome maps, or to some other system of reference, was not given, however. Studies to settle this point (Slizynski, 1950; Beermann, 1950 and 1952a; Pavan and Breuer, 1952) have shown the original view to be the correct one. Homologous chromosomes of different organs and tissues display a homologous banding pattern. This statement does not exclude variations in the number of countable bands since clearness and precision of banding must be subject to specific conditions in different tissues. In *Chironomus tentans*, for instance, a study of chromosome 3 has revealed about 380 bands in both salivary gland and rectum, as against 440 in the Malpighian tubules and 480 in the anterior portion of the midgut of fourth instar larvae. Variation concerns the faintest bands only and hence must be due to variation in the clearness of banding, as stated. In *Chironomus*, the thinnest bands are definitely beyond the limit of light optical resolution as electron microscopical examination has shown, with band thickness values down to .05 μ (Beermann and Bahr, 1954). Thus, the actual number of bands cannot be established unless the electron microscope is used. Obviously, this technical difficulty has no bearing on the basic fact of pattern constancy.

Pattern constancy of homologous giant chromosomes throughout the body constitutes definite proof that mitosis normally is not differential with respect to number and arrangement of the genetic units, barring somatic exchanges. It should be kept in mind, however, that this statement is strictly valid for normally banded, "euchromatic," elements only. Heterochromatin is unsuitable to detailed study in polytene chromosomes.

DIFFERENTIAL STRUCTURAL MODIFICATION OF SINGLE LOCI, AND THE PROBLEM OF NUCLEAR DIFFERENTIATION

True morphological differences between homologous polytene chromosomes of different tissues are of three types: 1) Differences in the degree of polyteny, and structural differences conditioned by the degree of polyteny, such as coiling and cross sectional appearance; 2) general differences independent of the degree of polyteny, as determined by the arrangement of the constituent fibers of the chromosome, including differences in the precision of banding; 3) specific local modifications. The last named class of differences will be considered in detail subsequently.

Drosophila and *Sciara* workers have long been familiar with local variations in the appearance of giant chromosomes, called "puffs" (Bridges, 1938; Poulson and Metz, 1938). It was clear that these variations could not be of a genetic nature and hence the phenomenon has been largely neglected in the past. Detailed investigation of puffing in *Chironomus tentans*, a large species which permits study of polytene chromosomes in four different tissues of fourth instar larvae, has revealed a specific correlation between the development of puffed regions and the character of the cells studied within one individual (Beermann, 1952a). The nature of this correlation as well as of "puffing" itself may be illustrated by an example. A very short region in the right arm of chromosome 3 of *Chironomus tentans*, comprising about 40 bands, has been closely investigated (Beermann, 1952a, fig. 39). Six different loci each of which could be identified and precisely localised in the different tissues studied showed differential morphological expression in one individual. The same band, or interband space, which appeared sharply defined in one tissue was found to be in a more or less diffuse and swollen condition in another. Pretreatment of the larvae with low temperatures and subsequent re-warming tends to enhance the differences. Figure 3 is sufficient to demonstrate the situation encountered in the particular case under discussion. Comparative study of other chromosome sections has led to the same result with respect to the basic principle of differential puffing: Structural modification, or "puffing" at one locus is not as a rule specific for one tissue alone. Thus, tissue specificity would be attributable not to the single puff, but rather to the pattern of puffing.

Diffuse swelling, or "puffing" of the chromosomes is a phenomenon arising from single bands or interband spaces. This, along with the finding that adjacent loci may puff independently constitutes the first direct morphological demonstration of the fact that giant chromosomes consist of linearly arranged, independently reactive, genetic units of the order of magnitude of the bands, in other words that bands, or less probably interbands, are gene loci. The facts may therefore be restated in terms of genes. Puffing obviously indicates changes, most probably increases, in the activity of gene loci. Hence, nuclear differentiation in cells of different function would be characterized by different specific patterns of activation along the chromosomes. This conclusion is precisely the one which has been deduced indirectly from current and earlier work in the field of developmental genetics, ever since Boveri's time (*e.g.* Demerec, 1934; Stern, 1954; Hadorn, 1955; Waddington, 1954, etc.).

"Puffing" is not an all-or-none effect. Different degrees of diffuse swelling may be distinguishable

FIGURE 3. Tabular representation of differential puffing in region 14 of chromosome 3 of *Chironomus tentans.* "+" indicates puffing of various degrees.

	Locus					
	1	2	3	4	5	6
Salivary gland.............	−	−	+	−	−	+
Malpighian tub.............	−	−	+	+	+	+
Rectum...................	+	+	−	+	+	+
Midgut...................	−	−	−	−	−	−

at a specific locus. This observation leads to the question how far the parallel goes between "puffing" as a morphological phenomenon, and gene activation as a physiological one. It seems extremely unlikely that all non-puffed regions of a chromosome are physiologically inactive, if only because the general tendency of chromosomes to "puff" is demonstrably different in different tissues, greater, for instance, in the rectum of *Chironomus* than in the midgut cells. Puffing may be considered as a threshold phenomenon so that a certain threshold concentration of a specific substrate must be exceeded in order to change the morphological expression of a gene locus. Since a gene might act on several different substrates, only one of which might cause puffing at all, and since the threshold concentration of the latter might be rather high at some loci, it seems clear why puffing is not observed in the great majority of bands. As another logical consequence of the threshold hypothesis of puffing, equality in the structural state of two different loci would not necessarily be indicative of equal activity in terms of the rate of turnover of substrate.

THE RINGS OF BALBIANI

According to the views just stated, differential puffing should be considered as a qualitative reflection rather than direct measure of differential activation of the genes in different tissues. There are, however, instances of local modifications of chromosome structure where it is hard to escape the conclusion that highly disproportionate changes of activity must be involved. "Puffs" belonging to this category are known under the name of "rings of Balbiani" in Chironomids where they are present in the salivary glands of all species so far studied. Swollen regions of comparable dimensions may sometimes be found in salivary gland chromosomes of Sciarids (Poulson and Metz, 1938; Breuer and Pavan, 1955).

Very large puffs necessarily change the appearance of more than just the single band from which they originate. Thus, up to ten bands may be included in the structural sphere of influence of the diffusely swollen region of a Balbiani-ring and hence become indistinguishable. Comparative study of the same Balbiani-ring at different degrees of puffing leaves no doubt, however, that the phenomenon is entirely dependent on a change in the behavior of a single band. In addition, Balbiani-rings are seen to involve a progressive splitting of the chromosome cable on either side of the diffuse ring region, obviously resulting from the fact that Balbiani-rings, or the specific structural state which causes Balbiani-rings to appear, exist from the onset of larval life when polytenisation is just beginning.

Most characteristic of Balbiani-rings is the peculiar shape of the puffed region as such. Superficially, it looks like a ring of extrachromosomal material. This appearance has led to the erroneous

conclusion that Balbiani-rings are a special type of nucleoli. The ring shape, however, is easily understood on the basis of the facts of polyteny as will be shown later.

From the point of view of nuclear differentiation, Balbiani-rings exhibit several interesting features. 1) They are very large, hence easily distinguished; 2) their number is very low (1-3); 3) their appearance generally is not subject to much variation, they are either present or absent throughout larval life; 4) as yet they have been found exclusively in salivary glands of Chironomids. Taken together, these features suggest a close correlation to the function of the salivary gland. Of the few larval tissues suitable to study, the salivary glands alone produce secretion in large amounts. This secretion certainly is proteic in character. Synthesis of proteins in large amounts necessitates a high turnover-rate of specific precursors and enzymes in the cytoplasm as well as in the nucleus of the salivary gland cell. Therefore a general relation may safely be assumed to exist between puffing of the Balbiani-ring type and the secretory function of salivary gland cells in Chironomids. It should be added that in *Chironomus tentans* there is no puffing in Malpighian tubules, rectum and midgut chromosomes at those loci which form Balbiani-rings in the salivary glands.

The very low number of Balbiani-rings per nucleus suggests a relation to salivary synthesis still more specific than that postulated above. That such a relation exists, specific with respect to the special character of the salivary gland cell, has been established by cytological examination of salivary glands that consist of morphologically and functionally different regions. Glands of this type occur in different genera of Chironomids. Bauer (personal communication, see also 1953) was the first to observe differential appearance of Balbiani-rings in the salivary glands of *Cryptochironomus*. The giant chromosomes of four super-giant cells located at the proximal end of the salivary gland never showed a Balbiani-ring, though one was present in all other cells of the gland. Similar phenomena have been discovered and worked out in detail in the species *Trichocladius vitripennis* (Beermann, 1952b) and *Acricotopus lucidus* (Mechelke, 1953).

In *Trichocladius*, six special cells may be distinguished by their granular cytoplasm and by their location around the duct of the gland. General structural features such as the degree of polyteny, the precision of banding, and of course, the banding pattern itself are identical in the chromosomes of the granular cells and those of the rest of the gland (disregarding minor specific differences in the appearance of a few bands). Striking and constant differences exist, however, with respect to the Balbiani-rings (*cf.* Fig. 4). Two regions which are normally banded in the normal type of gland cells regularly appear as big

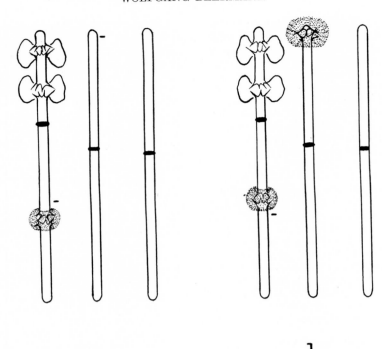

a   **b**

FIGURE 4. *Trichocladius vitripennis*: Differential development of Balbiani-rings in two functionally different sections of the larval salivary gland. (a) chromosomes in cells of the larger, normal part of the gland; (b) chromosomes of "special cells" with granular cytoplasm. 2 nucleolar organizers with constant location in chromosome 1; kinetochore regions black.

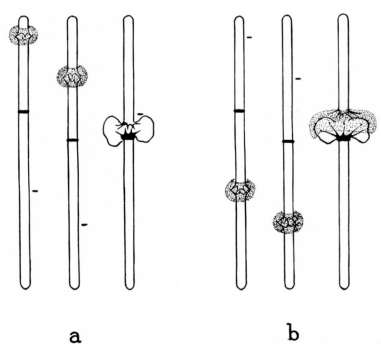

a   **b**

FIGURE 5. *Acricotopus lucidus*: Differential development of Balbiani-rings in two functionally different sections of the larval salivary gland. (a) posterior and lateral lobes, (b) anterior lobe. One of the three Balbiani-rings in b is situated close to the nucleolus.

Balbiani-rings in the granular cells, and, conversely, a third locus which is normal in the granular cells appears as a Balbiani-ring in the normal part of the gland. Intermediate conditions have never been observed.

Acricotopus lucidus (Mechelke, 1953) basically shows the same state of affairs as that encountered in *Trichocladius*. In *Acricotopus*, it is an entire lobe of the salivary gland which differs functionally from the rest. This functional difference becomes apparent at the onset of metamorphosis when the anterior lobe of the gland is filled with a dark brown secretion. Though such a secretion is not formed during larval life prior to metamorphosis, the special lobe is distinguishable morphologically and presumably produces a special component of larval saliva. Again the two types of cells, those of the special lobe and those of the rest of the gland, show clearcut specific differences with respect to the rings of Balbiani (Fig. 5). Two large Balbiani-rings, and, in addition, a puff of Balbiani-ring type adjacent to the nucleolus, were found in the special lobe at places where the banding pattern was unchanged in the chromosomes of the other lobes. Conversely, the latter show two Balbiani-rings at locations where the banding remains undisturbed in the special lobe. Again, intermediate types do not occur.

Summing up the above observations it seems obvious that the two types of gland cells, both in *Trichocladius* and in *Acricotopus*, fulfil different functions in the production of larval saliva. On the assumption that different types of protein are produced, specialisation for one or the other synthetic function could very well involve highly disproportionate activation of one or the other specific locus in the chromosomes. Mutually exclusive development of two or three different Balbiani-rings at least constitutes a striking demonstration of specific changes at single loci correlated to cellular differentiation. It is not meant to imply that simultaneous appearance of a Balbiani-ring in gland cells of different functions might not occur though such a situation has not yet been encountered (including *Cryptochironomus* and *Zavrelia*; Beermann unpub.).

DEVELOPMENTAL CHANGES: RE-DIFFERENTI-ATION OF THE NUCLEUS

It has been demonstrated that cellular differentiation in the larval tissues of Diptera is paralleled by specific local changes in the giant chromosomes. Whether or not this phenomenon is interpreted in the sense of differential activation of the genes, chromosome differentiation as such is a fact. Regardless of the structural nature of the differences observed, nuclear differentiation might or might not be final. Apart from experimental approaches, such as reciprocal transplantation of nuclei which seems hardly feasible in differentiated insect tissues, this crucial question is open to direct morphological examination in Dipteran larvae during metamorphosis.

In Chironomids, metamorphosis begins with a prepupal stage at the end of the fourth instar where the larvae cease to feed, and rapid growth of the gonads as well as the imaginal discs takes place. This stage lasts one day or longer and permits observation of metamorph changes in the giant chromosomes even of those tissues which are histolysed upon pupation, such as the salivary glands or the midgut. Conditions in Sciarids seem to be similar.

During the prepupal stage of *Chironomus tentans* a certain locus in chromosome 3 becomes puffed in the Malpighian tubules as well as in the rectum, a condition which persists into imaginal life. The same puff also appears in the salivary glands, along with several other new ones. Concurrent with the appearance of new puffs, others are seen to disappear regularly. This has been established (Beermann 1952a) for a short region in chromosome 1, by dissection of larvae and prepupae (20 each) from inbred laboratory stocks grown under identical conditions. It is clear from these findings alone that chromosomal differentiation is not final, as far as puffing is concerned, neither with respect to the ability to form new puffs nor with respect to the ability to return to the normal banded state. From the point of view of gene physiology it seems particularly interesting that homologous loci in cells of entirely different character may show identical reactions to changes in the internal environment of the animal. An explanation of this effect as a direct reaction to metamorphosis hormones may not be far from the truth.

From the point of view of nuclear differentiation, the fact of reversibility of puffing seems particularly meaningful. It would be in excellent agreement with the hypothesis of reversible gene activation. Even very large puffs of a highly specific nature such as the Balbiani-rings may be completely reversible as shown by Mechelke (1953) in *Acricotopus*, and by Breuer and Pavan (1953, 1955) in *Rhynchosciara angelae*.

In *Acricotopus lucidus*, the three specific Balbiani-rings of the anterior lobe of the salivary gland gradually revert to the normal banded state in the prepupa as a dark-brown secretion accumulates in this part of the gland. Fusion of all strands of the split chromosome cable does not take place, but is hardly to be expected anyway. That reversion in this case is not just a general degeneration effect is demonstrated by the persistence of the specific Balbiani-rings in the other lobes of the gland and, in addition, by the simultaneous appearance of small new puffs at other loci. Thus, reduction of puffed regions is a process no less specific than puffing itself. The cause of reduction in this case might be sought in the accumulation of the brown secretion, but the causal relation might just as well be vice versa so that the secretion appears because the Balbiani-rings have been inactivated by a third factor.

In *Rhynchosciara*, typical Balbiani-rings do not occur, though puffs ("bulbs" in the terminology of Breuer and Pavan) of comparable dimensions may develop. The prepupal stage of this species lasts ten days. Since, according to the authors named, larvae hatched from one batch of eggs develop synchronously, the sequence of changes in the salivary gland chromosomes can be timed simply by dissecting different larvae of one batch at different ages. Prepupal development of two puffs which were not present during larval life was followed in detail. It was found that one of them regularly attains its maximum extension two days before the other. Both disappear shortly before pupation. Some puffs begin to develop on the second day, others not until the 8th day of prepupal life. Furthermore, the pattern and sequence of puffing seem to be different in the Malpighian tubules, but this has not been worked out in detail. Reversible puffing similar to that found in the prepupae is said to occur also in larval life prior to the prepupal stage. It should be kept in mind that some of the changes observed might indicate changes in the external rather than internal environment of the larvae. Puffs in Sciarid chromosomes seem to be more variable than Balbiani-rings of Chironomids. As yet it is hardly possible to relate the pattern and sequence of puffing in *Rhynchosciara* to specific changes in the internal environment of the prepupae as metamorphosis approaches. The existence of such relations cannot be doubted in view of the situation in Chironomids. At any rate, *Rhynchosciara* furnishes an impressive demonstration of reversible and independent puffing at different loci induced by changes extrinsic to the cell.

Summing up, the evidence from cases such as *Chironomus*, *Acricotopus*, and *Rhynchosciara* may be interpreted as follows: The pattern of activation of the chromosomes is not an irreversibly fixed condition. It may be adapted to changes in the environment of the cells. Re-differentiation of the nucleus actually occurs.

Genetic Changes in Local Reactivity

Development and differentiation of the organism involve specific local changes in the chromosomes. As has been demonstrated these are not of a genetic, or mutational, nature. On the other hand, the genotype itself is subject to changes, either by recombination or by mutation, both of which must be expected to influence the pattern of puffing. Two kinds of genetic changes may affect the puffing behavior of a locus: 1) mutation at the locus itself, and 2) changes in the genetic background. Both have been found to occur.

Allelic differences in the puffing behavior of a locus are directly apparent in heterozygotes. Such cases are very rare and have been detected in *Chironomus* only, apart from certain parthenogenetic species of Chironomids where, however, structural heterozygosity generally is so extreme that homology becomes difficult to establish (Scholl, unpub.). In *Chironomus tentans*, two of the three Balbiani-rings in the salivary glands and, in addition, one puffed region have occasionally been found to be heterozygous in expression (Beermann, 1952a). Hsu and Liu (1948) have described a heterozygous "bulb" in a Chinese species of *Chironomus*. Keyl (personal communication) has seen heterozygous bulbs in *Chironomus thummi*. At first sight, it appears strange that heterozygous puffs are so seldom observed in species such as *Chironomus tentans* where natural inversion heterozygosity is extremely frequent. Even in species crosses between *C. tentans* and *C. pallidivittatus* (Beermann, 1955), puffs and Balbiani-rings of the F_1-chromosomes as a rule are homozygous in expression. However, mutation of a locus cannot a priori be expected to change its reactivity with respect to puffing. The ability to puff might depend on a specific molecular structure different from the one that was changed by mutation. Moreover, it is obvious that two alleles, though remaining different, might be activated to the same degree. Attempts are being made to induce mutations of puffing experimentally.

Experience with *Chironomus* has also shown differences in puffing behavior that must be due to differences in the genetic background of the individual larvae. For instance, a single individual out of about 100 collected at the same locality exhibited a very large homozygous puff at a locus where puffing does not occur normally. Breeding tests have not yet been made.

Structure, Chemistry, and Function of Balbiani-rings and other Local Changes

Research on the phenomenon of puffing as yet has been largely occupied with the establishment of clearcut correlations to cellular differentiation and function. Further work must concentrate on the nature of puffs and other local changes in themselves. A few preliminary observations relating to this subject will be reported subsequently.

Morphological comparison seems to indicate that different types of local changes occur. Poulson and Metz (1938) have distinguished between "puffs" and "bulbs" in *Sciara*. Bulbs are said to show a "blown-up" condition whereas puffs are characterized by a uniform, diffuse swelling of the chromosome locus in question. The same two types of changes have been observed in *Chironomus* salivary gland chromosomes. The difference between puffs and bulbs appears to depend on the quality of the specific product synthetized at a locus. If this product is not easily soluble in the nuclear sap, or if it has some other property such as an excessive viscosity which would slow down the rate of diffusion, it should accumulate in droplets and blow up the chromosome to a "bulb." Bulbs therefore might be formed without any intrinsic change in the structure of the locus itself. As a rule, however, the fine structure of a bulb locus, as judged by light microscopical examination, seems to be changed in a way similar to that of a true puff. Conversely, accumulation of droplets, or "accessory nucleoli" ("Nebennukleolen"; Bauer, 1936), may also occur in puffs under exceptional circumstances as show below. Hence, a sharp line between the two phenomena, bulbs and puffs, cannot be drawn. Balbiani-rings, on the other hand, should be considered as a special type of "puff," as stated earlier.

In this connection the status of the nucleolus proper should be defined as compared to puffs and similar structures. Development of true nucleoli is bound to specific loci, nucleolar organizers which are active in every cell of the organism, regardless of cellular function. In *Chironomus tentans* this is easily demonstrated because the two organizer loci are located in the euchromatin.

The ability of a given locus to accumulate nucleolar substance is genetically determined and hence may be lost or acquired by mutation. This follows from the situation encountered in hybrids of *C. tentans* and *C. pallidivittatus* (Beermann, 1955). In *C. tentans* two loci function as organizers which in *C. pallidivittatus* do not. Conversely, in *C. pallidivittatus*, a locus functions as organizer which does not do so in *C. tentans*. In hybrids all three organizers function in the heterozygous condition, that is, completely autonomously. Nucleolus formation has nothing to do with differentiation, but seems to be related to some elementary function of the cell. From the morphological point of view, the nucleolus and its organizer may be classified as a "bulb," *i.e.* a local change in chromosome structure that involves the accumulation of gene products. Organizer loci of *Chironomus* generally do not puff, but may sometimes do so owing to unknown factors. When not puffed, the organizer region is seen to be an interband space which appears slightly vacuolated and which stains more densely than usual.

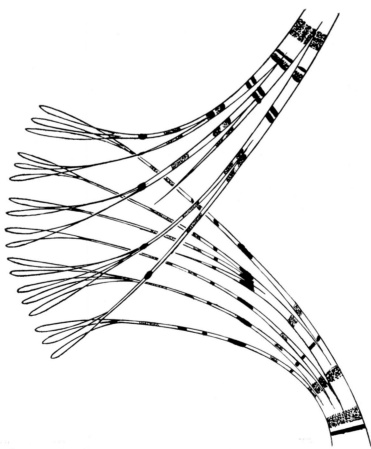

FIGURE 6. Diagrammatic representation of part of a helically wound bundle of chromonemata in a giant chromosome, at the location of a fully developed Balbiani-ring. Hypothetical loop formation of the ultimate chromonemata at the periphery. This interpretation has been verified by electron microscopy (see fig. 7).

The submicroscopic changes that occur during puffing have been investigated in the Balbiani-rings of *Chironomus*. Earlier light microscopical studies had led to the conclusion (Beermann, 1952a) that development of Balbiani-rings is due to the following factors: 1) a general torsional tension within the polytene cable; 2) local failure of the constituent fibrils, or "ultimate" chromonemata, to unite; 3) local mechanical weakening of the chromonemata. These factors together would cause the fibrils to bend out of the chromosome and to form loops. Thousands of such loops would compose the Balbiani-ring (Fig. 6). This view has been largely verified by electron optical studies on ultra-thin sections, carried out in Prof. Caspersson's institute at Stockholm (Beermann and Bahr, 1954). At the periphery of the Balbiani-ring, individual chromonemata can actually be seen forming loops. Differentiation of the polytene chromosome as a whole can thus be defined in terms of the single chromonema. Within the puffed region the chromonemata exhibit a kind of submicroscopic "lamp-brush" condition (Fig. 7). Each lamp-brush as a whole measures about $.2\mu$ in diameter, and up to 4μ in length, as opposed to a length of $.5$ to 1μ of the single band from which the lamp-brushes originate presumably. Considerable stretching of the locus in question must thus be involved. Axis and "bristles" of the lamp-brushes show slight zig-zagging, the bristles being about $.01\mu$ thick while the axis seems still thinner. One other structural detail is of particular interest. Numerous globules of about 300 Å diameter are seen to be attached to the lamp-brushes. Such globules have not been seen in normally banded sections of the chromosomes. It is tempting to assume that they are macro-molecules of a specific gene product, perhaps of an enzyme that is involved in saliva production and which at the same time causes the chromonema to unfold, or "puff." Speculations such as these must await further experimental work as well as comparative studies of other bulbs and puffs for confirmation.

Very little is known of the chemistry of puffs

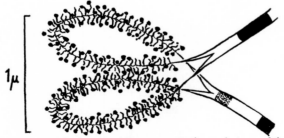

FIGURE 7. Diagrammatic representation of two ultimate chromonemata belonging to the same compound fibril, showing submicroscopic "lamp-brush" structure with attached globules (see text) in the puffed section which corresponds to one gene locus. From electron-optical studies.

and related phenomena. Toluidin blue tends to stain the Balbiani-rings of *Chironomus* metachromatically, that is, red-violet just like the cytoplasm and the nucleoli, and in contrast to the blue staining of most normal bands. Several smaller puffs as well as unpuffed bands may also stain violet. Some of the latter have been found to accumulate droplets after cold pretreatment, as shown below. Thus, activated loci of the chromosomes seem to differ from the rest in some general chemical property. By analogy with the nucleolus, it has been assumed that a higher RNA content might be involved.

Breuer and Pavan (1955) recently raised the question of DNA constancy of single bands in *Rhynchosciara* because some of the puffed regions in the salivary gland chromosomes of this species begin to develop from what appears to be a large increase in the concentration of stainable material. The same situation has also been found after reduction of some puffs. Cell-specific differences in the intensity of staining of a few bands had been found earlier in *Trichocladius* (Beermann 1952b) and have meanwhile been shown to be due to changes in the distribution of Feulgen positive substances. Whether actual changes in the quantity of DNA are involved must be decided by quantitative work.

It has been assumed throughout this review that puffing is indicative of increased local activity. One observation may serve to support this viewpoint (Beermann, 1952a). If larvae (*C. tentans*) have been kept at temperatures lower than 10°C for a few hours and are subsequently transferred to water of 20° for at least one hour, conspicuous changes in nuclear metabolism become apparent in the living glands as observed in phase contrast. Droplets of unknown composition begin to appear and accumulate at most of the sites where puffing normally occurs in the salivary gland chromosomes. This effect is particularly striking within one of the three Balbiani-rings of the 4th chromosome. The accumulation process may even proceed under the cover glass in liquid paraffin. After two hours in 20° the droplets slowly begin to dissolve until, after eight hours maximally, the chromosomes look normal again. The effect obviously is due to a temporary upset of the metabolic balance of chromosomes, nuclear sap, and cytoplasm. It demonstrates directly that the rate of turn-over is greatest at those loci which have been called "activated" on indirect evidence.

CONCLUDING REMARKS

Two major aspects of nuclear differentiation have been chosen for discussion in this review. Evidence has been presented to show that unequal distribution of genetic material is very often, if not regularly, involved in primordial germ cell differentiation during early embryonic development in arthropods and other animals. On the other hand, comparative morphological study of giant somatic chromosomes demonstrates conclusively that no such differential distribution of genetic elements occurs in somatic development. This apparent contradiction proves to be not a fundamental one on closer inspection of the facts. Unequal distribution and differential loss, or reduplication respectively, are processes confined to such elements in the nucleus which must be considered as supernumerary with respect to the normal, somatic, set of genes, that is, elements which have no specific function in somatic cells. Even in the germ-line itself these elements cannot have reached a level of differentiation comparable to that of the highly organized somatic chromosomes, though some of them seem to be euchromatic on morphological criteria. In somatic nuclei, the so-called heterochromatin would seem to constitute similar undifferentiated genetic material. With respect to this constituent of the chromosome set, differential distribution would be conceivable and cannot of course, be excluded on the evidence presented in this review which is solely concerned with normally banded euchromatic sections of giant chromosomes. Several authors have pointed to apparent deviations in the rate of growth of heterochromatin in polyploid and polytene nuclei (Heitz, 1934; Schultz, 1947); differential heteropycnosis might also be interpreted on this line.

Concerning those sections of the chromosomes which genetically as well as morphologically prove to consist of independent units of different genetic character the hypothesis of differential reversible gene activation has been accepted throughout this report. It finds ample support in comparative cytological studies of the behavior of single loci under different functional conditions. Local changes in polytene chromosomes have been shown to arise from structural modification of specific loci of the constituent fibers, and these changes have been demonstrated to be completely reversible under changing functional conditions. This does not exclude that nuclear differentiation as a whole might be irreversible in high differentiated somatic cells, a point which is open to experimental attack as shown by King and Briggs in this Symposium and earlier.

In conclusion it may be stated that the phenomenon of differential structural changes in giant chromosomes will probably help to put the classical theory of differentiation on a detailed cytological basis comparable to that provided for the chromosome theory of heredity when the true nature of giant chromosomes was first discovered. Further morphological, cytochemical, and genetical work must show if this expectation is justified.

References

BARIGOZZI, C., 1950, A general survey on heterochromatin. Portugaliae Acta Biol., Ser. A, R. B. Goldschmidt Vol.: 593–620.

BAUER, H., 1936, Beiträge zur vergleichenden Morphologie der Speicheldrüsenchromosomen (Untersuchungen an den Riesenchromosomen der Dipteren. II.). Zool. Jb. (Phys.) 56: 239–276.

1938, Die polyploide Natur der Riesenchromosomen. Naturwissenschaften 26: 77–78.

1953, Die Chromosomen im Soma der Metazoen (Referat). Zool. Anz. (Suppl.) 17: 252–268.

BAUER, H., and BEERMANN, W., 1952a, Der Chromosomencyclus der Orthocladiinen (Nematocera, Diptera). Z. Naturforsch. 7b: 557–563.

1952b, Die Polytänie der Riesenchromosomen. Chromosoma 4: 630–648.

BAYREUTHER, K., 1952, Extrachromosomale feulgenpositive Körper (Nukleinkörper) in der Oogenese der Tipuliden. Naturwissenschaften 39: 71.

1956, Die Oogenese der Tipuliden. Chromosoma 7: 508–557.

BEERMANN, W., 1950, Chromomerenkonstanz bei Chironomus. Naturwissenschaften 37: 543–544.

1952a, Chromomerenkonstanz und spezifische Modifikationen der Chromosomenstruktur in der Entwicklung und Organ-differenzierung von Chironomus tentans. Chromosoma 5: 139–198.

1952b, Chromosomenstruktur und Zelldifferenzierung in der Speicheldrüse von Trichocladius vitripennis. Z. Naturforsch. 7b: 237–242.

1955, Cytologische Analyse eines Camptochironomus-Artbastards. I. Kreuzungsergebnisse und die Evolution des Karyotypus. Chromosoma 7: 198–259.

BEERMANN, W., and BAHR, G. F., 1954, The submicroscopic structure of the Balbiani-ring. Exp. Cell. Res. 6: 195–201.

BOVERI, TH., 1904, Ergebnisse über die Konstitution der chromatischen Substanz des Zellkerns. Jena, G. Fischer.

BREUER, M. E., and PAVAN, C., 1953, Salivary chromosome and differentiation. Proc. 9th Intern. Congr. Genet., Caryologia 6 (Suppl.).

1955, Behavior of polytene chromosomes of Rhynchosciara angelae at different stages of larval development. Chromosoma 7: 371–386.

BRIDGES, C. B., 1935, Salivary chromosome maps. J. Hered. 26: 60–64.

1938, A revised map of the salivary gland X-chromosome of Drosophila melanogaster. J. Hered. 29: 11–13.

DEMEREC, M., 1934, The gene and its role in ontogeny. Cold. Spr. Harb. Symp. Quant. Biol. 2: 110–115.

FLEMMING, W., 1882, Zellsubstanz, Kern und Zelltheilung. Leipzig.

GEITLER, L., 1953, Endomitose und endomitotische Polyploidisierung. Protoplasmatologia, Handbuch der Protoplasmaforschung. Wien, Springer.

GÜNTHERT, T., 1910, Die Eibildung der Dytisciden. Zool. Jb. (Anat.) 30: 301–372.

HADORN, E., 1955, Letalfaktoren. Stuttgart, Thieme.

HEIDENHAIN, M., 1901, Plasma und Zelle. Jena.

HEITZ, E., 1934, Über α- und β-Heterochromatin sowie Konstanz und Bau der Chromomeren bei Drosophila. Biol. Zbl. 54: 588–609.

HSU, T. C., and LIU, T. T., 1948, Microgeographic analysis of chromosomal variation in a Chinese species of Chironomus (Diptera). Evolution 2: 49–57.

KOSSWIG, C., and SENGÜN, A., 1947, Vergleichende Untersuchungen über den Bau der Riesenchromosomen der Dipteren. C. r. Soc. Turque Sci. phys. nat. 13: 94–101.

MECHELKE, F., 1953, Reversible Strukturmodifikationen der Speicheldrüsenchromosomen von Acricotopus lucidus. Chromosoma 5: 511–543.

PAVAN, C., and BREUER, M. E., 1952, Polytene chromosomes in different tissues of Rhynchosciara. J. Hered. 43: 152–157.

POULSON, D. F., 1947, The pole cells of Diptera, their fate and significance. Proc. Nat. Acad. Sci. Wash. 33: 182–184.

POULSON, D. F., and METZ, C. W., 1938, Studies on the structure of nucleolus forming regions and related structures in the giant salivary gland chromosomes of Diptera. J. Morph. *63:* 363–395.

RUDKIN, G. T., 1955, The ultraviolet absorption of puffed and unpuffed regions in the salivary gland chromosomes of *Drosophila melanogaster*. Genetics *40:* 593.

SCHULTZ, J., 1947a, Nuclear differentiation and the origin of tumors. Cancer Res. *7:* 41–42.

1947b, The nature of heterochromatin, Cold. Spr. Harb. Symp. Quant. Biol. *12:* 179–191.

SLIZYNSKI, B. M., 1950, *Chironomus* versus *Drosophila*. J. Genet. *50:* 77–78.

STERN, C., 1954, Two or three bristles. Amer. Scientist *42:* 213–247.

WADDINGTON, C. H., 1954, The cell physiology of early development. Proc. VII. Symp. Colston Res. Soc.: Vol. VII of the Colston papers. London, Butterworth.

WHITE, M. J. D., 1947, The cytology of the Cecidomyidae (Diptera). III. The spermatogenesis of *Taxomyia taxi*. J. Morph. *80:* 1–24.

1955, Animal cytology and evolution, 2nd ed., Cambridge, Cambridge Univ. Press.

DISCUSSION

PAVAN: I would like to make some comments on Dr. Beermann's paper in relation to what we have done in two species of another Dipteran belonging to the Genus *Rhynchosciara*.

Our results are in a general way in complete agreement with those of Dr. Beermann, but in our case we have bands which go through a puffing process and then return to the original condition, thus appearing to go through a reversible process, while other bands do not. Although after the puffing the chromosome returns to the same number of bands which it had before the puffing, some of the bands which go through a puff show an increase of Feulgen positive material after it. The chromosome has returned to its original state. We interpret this increase of Feulgen positive material at a specific locus of the chromosome as being an increase in the number of the particular gene located at that position of the chromosome. Being so, the process in these bands is not always entirely reversible, since at the end of the process the amount of Feulgen positive material is increased.

Another point which I would like to bring up is that in our material, the examination, with the normal light microscope, of the puffing regions does not lead us to interpret the external region of the puff as being a section of an uncoiled chromonema, as Dr. Beermann sees it. We believe that the puffing region of the chromosome is an interaction between this specific locus and the nuclear sap in such a way that the chromosome at that specific locus would be disintegrated into its component genes which individually or in small groups would be surrounded by a Feulgen positive substance, increasing in this way the diameter of the chromosome at the particular locus.

The increase in diameter at the specific locus of the chromosome where the puff occurs will mechanically dissociate the proximal bands into several pieces. These last bands behave passively, while the bands which are responsible for the puff react actively with the nuclear sap, producing the Feulgen negative substance.

RUDKIN: We have projected a collaboration with Dr. Pavan in which we shall determine cytometrically the DNA content of the bands associated with some of the puffs that he has described to you.

In the meantime, we have been investigating puffs that change in *Drosophila* larvae at the time of puparium formation. One near the end of the second chromosome, in Section 60, arises within the first hour after the larval skin hardens while another near the end of the X chromosome, in Section 2, is present before puparium formation but shrinks in the prepupa. We have measured the total extinction of these chromosome sections in acetic acid fixed material at several stages of puff development. We employed the photographic method developed by Caspersson and modified by us (see Exp. Cell Res. *9:* 193, 1955); measurements were made at 275, 257, and 231 millimicra in the ultra violet.

The results (see preliminary note in Genetics *40:* 593, 1955) of the measurements on a region subject to puffing are expressed as per cent of a region not subject to puffing. In this way the effects of variability in total extinction between chromosomes and of the possibility of chromosome growth during the developmental period under study were minimized. We found the total extinction of a given region to be consistently but not significantly higher when the region was puffed.

There are two sources of error that remain to be studied before the observed changes can be referred to absorbing material. The first is that changes in the specific absorptivity of nucleic acid when it exists in compact (not puffed) as compared to diffuse (puffed) state would cause differences in the direction we observed. The second source of error is a purely technical one having to do with the demarcation of homologous regions in chromosomes with and without a puff. At the present time we can say that very little if any increase in acetic acid insoluble U.V. absorbing material is associated with puffing in the regions studied. The possibility remains that changes have occurred at earlier stages (as in some of Pavan's *Rhynchosciara* puffs). More specific cytochemical tests are being applied to our material at the present time.

We have reported briefly (J. Histochem. Cytochem. *2:* 458, 1954) preliminary results of a study begun three years ago with Mr. John Aronson on the difference between the X chromosome in male and female *Drosophila* salivary gland chromosomes. It has long been known that the X looks broader in the male than does an unpaired (therefore "haploid") X chromosome in the female. We were interested first to find out whether or not the size difference could be demonstrated, and second to find out what we could about the chemical basis of the difference. We measured the dimensions, the total extinction in the ultraviolet, and the total extinction of bound dye after the Feulgen reaction in the terminal section of the X (Section 1) and compared it in each case with a corresponding measurement made on a terminal segment of the second chromosome (Section 60) in the same nucleus.

In one stock in which we were able to compare the male X directly with an unpaired X in the female we found that in the male the X was about 21 per cent wider, corresponding to an increase in volume of about 50 per cent. Thus, the sex chromosome is normally in a slightly puffed condition in the male.

There were no differences between the sexes with respect to the total ultraviolet extinction at 275 millimicra or 257 millimicra, or with respect to the total dye bound in the Feulgen reaction. We conclude that there is no difference in the content of acetic acid fast nucleic acids of either type.

The total extinction at 231 millimicra was significantly ($.05 > P > .02$) higher (11%) in the males. We attribute absorption at this wavelength to end absorption of protein and conclude that there is relatively more of a protein poor state in cyclic amino acids in the X of the male than in the X of the female.

These two sets of data are consistent with the hypothesis supported by Dr. Beermann in his talk that enhancement of chromosomal activity is accompanied by swelling of the chromosome. Although we have no direct evidence as to which cellular activities the puffed regions may be concerned with, there is adequate evidence that cellular metabolism in the male is quantitatively different from that in the female. Most pertinent to our discussion here are microchemical analyses on the salivary glands of one of the stocks that we used (see Patterson *et al.*, Exp. Cell Res. *6:* 181–194, 1954), showing that cytoplasmic constituents (total N, peptidase activity, total RNA) are much larger on a per cell basis in females. The factors limiting the amount of cytoplasm under the control of a male nucleus must be sought in the X chromosome itself and ultimately in the balance between the X and the autosomes. Our results indicate that the increased demands on the single set of sex-linked genes in the male calls forth an increase in the protein, not in the DNA or RNA content of the fixed chromosome.

We may also note that the localized puffs in the X chromosome appear to be morphologically similar in both sexes; that is, they are superimposed upon the normally swollen chromosome in the male. Thus, a puff need not only represent the activation of an inactive portion of chromosome, but may be a temporary increase in an activity already in progress.

ALFERT: Following the elucidation of the fine structure of Balbiani rings by Bauer and Beermann (Chromosoma *4:* 630, 1952), I proposed that this discovery might have a bearing on the controversy about the structure of so-called "lampbrush" chromosomes in certain oocytes. (Alfert, 1954, Intern. Rev. Cytol. *3:* 131). It had long been maintained by Ris (*e.g.* Biol. Bull. *89:* 242, 1945) that the loops of lampbrush chromosomes represent chromonemata that were spun out sideways from the chromosome axis. However, few cytologists shared this view, presumably because they would not believe, in absence of corroborating evidence, that chromosomes were capable of such acrobatics. Bauer and Beermann's convincing demonstration of just such an occurrence in another system made Ris' hypothesis of lampbrush loop structure much more plausible. As a consequence, two very active present workers in this field, Callan and Gall, have adopted Ris' viewpoint concerning the chromonemal nature of the lampbrush loop, although they otherwise differ significantly from Ris in the interpretation of various structural details of oocyte chromosomes.

H. W. LEWIS: In our laboratory we have done some experiments, the interpretation of which may be integrated with Dr. Beermann's report on "puffs" and Balbiani rings. Our interest is in the macromolecular architecture of the salivary gland chromosomes and we view them not as cytological structures, but from the perspective of physical biochemistry as polyelectrolyte gels. That is to say, we consider the chromosomes to be composed of different species of macromolecules (DNA, RNA, proteins, etc.) which interact with each other to give parallel-packed aggregations of linear strands which are integrated into the whole system in a manner which gives rise to the banded pattern. The macromolecules are not connected directly with each other by end to end bonds, but by cross linkages between the interacting polymeric macromolecules by covalent bonds, van der Waals junctions and electrostatic links. These bonds are not all the same strength and one of the methods we have used to analyze the structure of the chromosome is by disassociating the component macromolecules by manipulating such variables as pH, ionic strength and temperature. Some of our treatments have resulted in the disruption of certain bands and reorganization of the material into structures resembling puffs and Balbiani rings. We have interpreted the thin threads which appear as micellar DNA. If our experimentally induced structural alteration of the bands are the same as the naturally occurring band reorganization described by Dr. Beermann, this would indicate that they do occur as the result of subtle, perhaps localized, changes in the cellular environment, as he suggested.

BIANCHI: I should like to ask Dr. Beermann two questions: 1) Is it possible to distinguish, at least in species of the insects he studied having low chromosome numbers, the somatic chromosomes from the germinal ones? If so, are the somatic chromosomes always the same or not? 2) In the species presenting individuals with different chromosomal numbers, are such individuals also different morphologically? I think that observations from these points of view could help in understanding the singular and very interesting phenomena that Dr. Beermann has described.

BEERMANN: In some species of Orthocladiinae the somatic set of chromosomes is distinguishable very clearly, even in metaphase I, in others this is not possible. All available evidence leads to the conclusion that the "somatic" chromosomes are not interchangeable with the supernumerary ones. Individuals of a given species do not differ morphologically if they possess different numbers of supernumerary chromosomes in their germ-line.

BALINSKY: The vast amount of interesting data presented by Dr. Beermann involves various biological problems; I will restrict myself to commenting on some aspects having a direct bearing on differentiations in the developing organism.

First, I should like to mention the supernumerary chromosomes occurring in Diptera. Dr. Beermann has implied that these are relatively unimportant for development, and that they may be considered as a kind of luxury some organisms can allow themselves provided a mechanism exists to eliminate them in due time so as to prevent their interfering with development. I should like to point out another possibility, namely that these chromosomes may be concerned in some way with the elaboration of the structure of the mature egg. The latter is a highly specialized cell, possessing a complex organization, which later manifests itself in the differentiation of the embryo. This organization is evolved in the oocyte at the time when the supernumerary chromosomes are present in the nucleus and, possibly, are functional. The eggs of Diptera are of the mosaic type, the amount of structural specialization prior to fertilization being therefore quite considerable.

The unequal distribution of chromosomes and other nuclear components reported by Dr. Beermann raises the old problem whether the differences in nuclear structures may be considered as causes of diverse differentiations of cells. Boveri long ago proved that it is not the case, at least in the *Ascaris* egg, that changes in nuclear structure are caused by the kind of cytoplasm in which a nucleus comes to lie. The data presented by Dr. Beermann do not appear to be inconsistent with this conclusion. In *Tipula lateralis*, for instance, although two cells in an ovarian cluster receive the Feulgen positive body, only one becomes an egg cell. The retinal cells of Vertebrates start differentiating their specific cytoplasmic structures in early stages, while their nuclei do not show the peculiarities found in the cells of the adults. These peculiarities are thus to be considered as concomitant to the other features of retinal rod cells rather than as the causes of a particular type of differentiation.

Lastly, I have been greatly impressed by Dr. Beermann's and also Dr. Pavan's observations on the puffing of chromosomes and on the Balbiani rings. I wonder whether it would be possible to correlate these phenomena with other indications about the time of action of specific genes? It would be interesting to know if puffing at specific loci of the chromosomes bears any relation to the time of activity of genes localized at such points as estimated from experiments on the production of phenocopies. If any relationship between these independent lines of evidence could be established, a very important step would be made toward understanding of gene action in development.

BEERMANN: As to role of supernumerary chromosomes in early development, Dr. Balinsky's hypothesis would constitute an elaboration of the idea of White, as mentioned in the manuscript. Differentiation of the mosaic type within the Dipteran egg would seem to preclude the possibility that supernumerary chromosomes are involved since the latter are identical in all nuclei at the stage when they become eliminated. The other points raised by Dr. Balinsky are in agreement with the discussion in the manuscript.

LEWIN: Has any case yet been found of a gene affecting salivary activity, the locus of which might be correlated with that of a "puff" in a salivary gland chromosome?

BEERMANN: No.

TOBIAS: Work on mammalian chromosomes and nuclei in Johannesburg over the last ten years has produced some parallels with the findings reported by Dr. Beermann. In approaching nuclear differentiation, we have used evidence from nucleoli. In the gerbil (*Tatera erantsii*) different tissue nuclei, although possessing the same number of nucleolar organizers, form nucleoli in varying patterns. In some cells (*e.g.* hepatic cells) a nucleolus develops alongside each of the four nucleolar organizers, while in others (*e.g.* spermatogonia) all four organizers produce a single nucleolus synergically. The addition of a different pattern of nucleolus-formation may accompany general changes in differentiation of cells (as from spermatogonium to spermatocyte). Thus, fine studies on nucleolus formation may provide a key to nuclear differentiation.

With regard to Dr. Bayreuther's observations on *Tipula*, I demonstrated some years ago that the large, Feulgen positive karyosome formed by mammalian sex chromosomes on pairing at meiosis is an example of "extra-chromosomal chromatin." Although its exact chemical composition remains to be determined, it strongly resembles the body reported by Bayreuther. It differs in its later behavior, however, as it disappears before metaphase of the first meiotic division in mammals. It may well be a reservoir of deoxyribose nucleotides.

Organization of the Chromosome

Berwind P. Kaufmann and Margaret R. McDonald

Department of Genetics, Carnegie Institution of Washington, Cold Spring Harbor, New York

The observational and experimental results presented here constitute another chapter in a continuing research program that is directed toward an understanding of patterns of organization of chromosomal materials. Evidence has been sought over the years at various levels of analysis, beginning with descriptive cytology, progressing into the areas of experimental and analytical cell research, and extending in recent months to the realm of fine detail afforded by the resolving powers of the electron microscope. Attention has been focussed throughout on the chromosomes of higher plants and animals, because their large size favored microscopic examination and because they offered the prospect of correlating chromosome activity with developmental processes. This progress report includes a brief examination of the background information accumulated in the earlier studies and then attempts to fit the more recent findings into that frame of reference.

The Frame of Reference

The microscopically discernible unit of chromosomal organization is the chromonema. Its pattern of coiling is most readily detectable in the condensed chromosomes during the stages from late prophase to anaphase. Within a chromosome several chromonemata lie in close approximation at all phases of the division cycle in both somatic and meiotic mitoses (summary of evidence in Kaufmann, 1948; Manton, 1950). The prophasic splitting and anaphasic separation of chromosomes in somatic cells thus represent a system for distribution of aggregates of subsidiary strands rather than for replication of individual units (see, for example, Huskins, 1947). Linearly, the chromonemata are subdivided into alternating zones of euchromatin and heterochromatin. Despite differences in their physical and chemical properties, euchromatic and heterochromatic regions break with equal facility when exposed to the action of ionizing radiations or such chemical mutagens as nitrogen mustard (Kaufmann, 1946; Kaufmann, Gay, and Rothberg, 1949). This suggests a high degree of uniformity throughout the length of the chromosome of the materials responsible for maintaining linear continuity, although we are mindful of the evidence that certain agents can act selectively on heterochromatin in some kinds of cells (*e.g.*, maleic hydrazide on chromosomes of *Vicia*, as reported by McLeish, 1953).

When fixed chromosomes are digested with deoxyribonuclease and ribonuclease, so that cytochemical tests no longer reveal either deoxyribose or ribose nucleic acids (DNA or RNA) there remains a structurally identifiable body, which presumably represents an aggregate of protein fibers (Kaufmann, Gay, and McDonald, 1950, 1951; Kaufmann, McDonald, and Gay, 1951). This body is not effaced by trypsin, or even by pepsin when used under certain experimental conditions (Kaufmann, 1952, 1953; Kaufmann, Pennoyer, and Rowan, 1953). Both structurally and functionally, however, the chromosomes of higher forms must represent an integrated fabric, in which histones and non-histone proteins can combine with both RNA and DNA (Kaufmann, McDonald, and Gay, 1951). The fabric may be disrupted by agents capable of degrading either nucleic acid or protein so that structure is deformed and cellular functions impaired. But the results of studies in which it was demonstrated that ribonuclease enters the living cell and effects structural deformation (Kaufmann and Das, 1954, 1955) suggest that ribonucleic acid is the most labile of the nucleoprotein constituents.

The Portrait of the Chromosome

It has been noted that the chromosome consists of a number of closely appressed subsidiary strands. But how many exist in a given chromosome? Observations made some 30 years ago indicated that the somatic anaphase chromosome contains at least two identifiable chromonemata and the metaphase chromosome four (Kaufmann, 1926a). Subsequent studies (Nebel, 1932) suggested that under appropriate conditions of treatment four chromonemata could be detected in telophase as well as in metaphase chromosomes. Since the structures under consideration approached in size the resolving powers of the best optical systems then available, the validity of the multiple-strand as compared with the single-strand pattern of organization was subjected to extensive debate. Nevertheless, as the concept of polyteny developed in the intervening years, most cytologists came to recognize the existence of types of chromosomes containing a number of component strands. The question that has arisen in many minds in recent years is whether the newer techniques of electron microscopy could serve in resolving some of the controversial aspects of interpretations of chromosome structure, particularly with respect to the form and arrangement of the ultimate replicating units. It seemed that progress in this direction could be furthered most satisfactorily by proceeding from the known to the unknown, using the large chromosomes of the salivary-gland cells of flies and of somatic cells of monocotyledonous plants, which had been described in considerable detail as a result of extensive studies with the light microscope. Some observations made in conformity with this plan of operation are listed below.

Salivary-gland chromosomes of Drosophila melanogaster. For many years there has existed a wealth of observational and experimental evidence that the salivary-gland chromosome is polytene, or composed of a large number of subsidiary chromonemata (summary of evidence in Alfert, 1954; Gay, 1955a). Although the constituent fibrillae are not readily discernible in the ordinary squash preparation, treatment with proteolytic enzymes will improve the "signal to noise ratio," so that the strands become more clearly defined (Kaufmann *et al.*, 1952). Each of the elements detected with the light microscope apparently represents, however, an aggregate of chromonemata rather than a single strand, since electron micrographs of ultrathin sections reveal a larger number of more slender coiled threads (Fig. 1). This figure includes two sections (not adjacent) from a series. In the thicker section lying to the left, the bands appear to be composed of chromomere-like bodies, connected with the "chromomeres" of adjoining bands by fibrillae that traverse the interband regions. In the thinner section shown to the right it is apparent that the so-called chromomeres are also composed of helically-disposed strands that continue across the interband regions. It is also apparent that the chromonemata crisscross or intertwine as they course along the chromosome; in other words, there is no indication in this or similar preparations that the salivary-gland chromosome is composed of fully extended chromonematic strands lying parallel to the longer axis.

Digestion of such a preparation with deoxyribonuclease reduces the electron-scattering properties of materials throughout the length of the chromosome, suggesting that DNA is not limited in its distribution to the banded regions (Fig. 2). Digestion with trypsin loosens up the fabric of the chromosome, disclosing large numbers of fine coiled threads, each about 125 Å in diameter (Fig. 3).

These illustrations are from material prepared by Dr. Helen Gay, and the essential findings have been described in detail in previous publications (Gay, 1955a, 1955b, 1956a). Her observations have led to the conclusion (Gay, 1955a) that the salivary-gland chromosome of *D. melanogaster* is not bounded by any discernible membrane, that it is composed of clearly delimited coiled fibrous elements in both the banded and non-banded regions, and that the finest discernible strands are about 250 Å in diameter (although more recent observations of trypsin-hydrolyzed preparations suggest that this dimension may encompass a pair of experimentally separable chromonemata rather than a single strand). It appears, more-

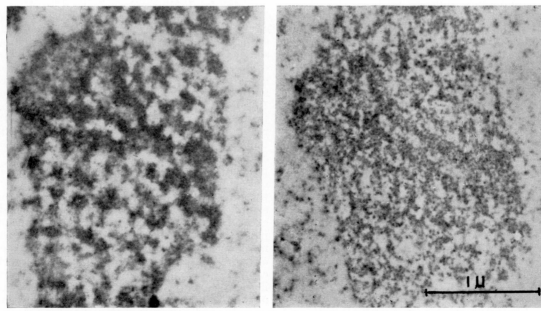

FIGURE 1. Electron micrographs of two sections (not adjoining) from a series through a salivary-gland chromosome of *D. melanogaster* fixed in buffered OsO₄, pH 7.5. Comparison of the thicker section (to the left) with the thinner one shows that helically-disposed strands constitute both the bands and interband regions. The chromomere-like bodies of the thicker section are shown in the thinner section to represent a complex of fine coiled threads. Note that these threads extend from the "bands" across the interband regions.

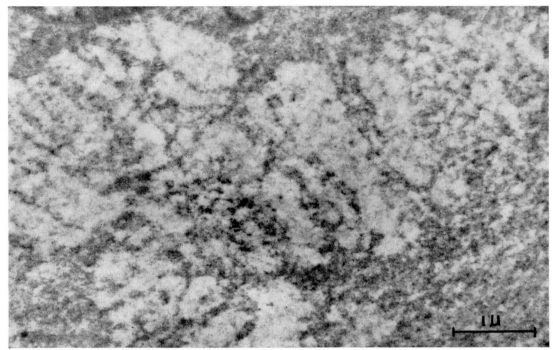

FIGURE 2. Electron micrograph of a section of a salivary-gland chromosome of *D. melanogaster* fixed in OsO₄ and digested in deoxyribonuclease. Digestion has reduced the electron-scattering properties of the chromosome, both in bands and interbands, so that the karyolymph appears more highly electron scattering than the chromosomal materials.

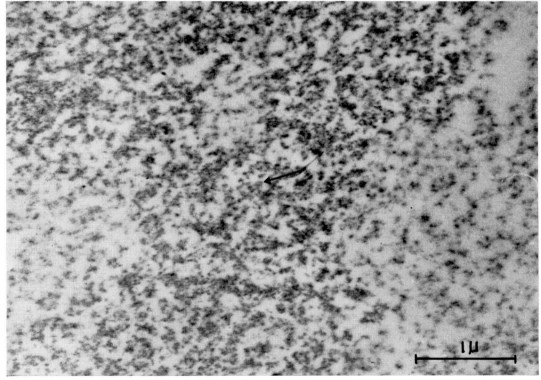

FIGURE 3. Electron micrograph of a section of a salivary-gland chromosome of *D. melanogaster* fixed in OsO₄ and digested in buffered trypsin. Loosening of the fabric of the chromosome brings into relief the delicate component chromonematic strands.

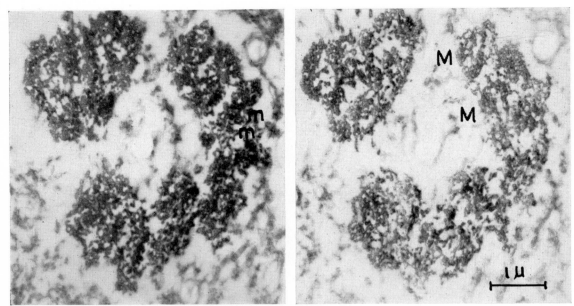

FIGURE 4. Electron micrographs of two sections (not adjoining) through first meiotic metaphase chromosomes of *Tradescantia reflexa* Raf. Major coils (M) and their component minor coils (m) are clearly defined, but there is in addition a wealth of fine detail. Sections were obtained from block prepared by imbedding an aceto-carmine smear preparation.

over, that these coiled threads are intertwined in pairs to form a hierarchy of pairs of pairs, but it cannot be stated with accuracy whether they are interlaced (a plectonemic arrangement that would not permit separation without breakage or untwisting) or whether they lie side by side without interlocking (a paranemic relationship that would permit their free separation). In either case the crisscrossing of the strands should give a low degree of nucleic acid orientation as measured by dichroism or birefringence, a type of result reported by Caspersson (1940) and Frey-Wyssling (1953; which includes a review of earlier studies). Differences in the stainability of band and inter-band regions with the Feulgen method appear to depend in part on differences in the amount of DNA and in part on the pattern of coiling of the threads. It is now known that materials, assumedly produced by the bands, sometimes accumulate at the edges of the chromosomes (Gay, 1956b). The states of hydration and aggregation of the coiled chromonemata, and the quantities of secreted materials preserved by different methods of fixation thus appear to account for the diverse interpretations of salivary-gland chromosome structure presented in past years. Apart from the bearing on specific problems of salivary-gland chromosome structure, the findings touch on the broader problem of interpretation of fixation images obtained at various pH's and in different ionic environments. The same questions that emerged during the second quarter of this century with respect to the validity of structural details revealed in the light microscope are now reappear-

ing with respect to the validity of fine structure disclosed in electron micrographs. One profitable method of seeking the answers that was not available 25 years ago seems to lie in the application of combined cytochemical and electron-microscope techniques similar to those outlined above.

Chromosomes of dividing cells. The discovery of chromonematic strands of about 250 Å (or perhaps 125 Å) diameter in the salivary-gland chromosome (Gay, 1955a) poses the question whether units of similar dimensions might be found in chromosomes of dividing cells. It seemed desirable, therefore, to turn to the chromosomes of the plant *Tradescantia*, which had figured so prominently in the original studies of chromosome structure with the light microscope.

The chromosomes of first meiotic metaphase in microsporocytes of this plant have become the classical material for demonstrating the so-called major and minor spirals. If an aceto-carmine (or orcein) smear preparation, which shows the coils clearly with the light microscope, is prepared for electron microscopy by imbedding in methacrylate (a method developed independently by Borysko and Sapranauskas, 1954; Gall, 1955; and Gay, 1955c), ultrathin serial sections can be obtained which reveal the gross patterns of coiling (Fig. 4). But there is in addition a tangle of indefinable elements that bespeaks a finer sub-structure. On theoretical grounds this finer structure should be more readily detectable when the chromosomes are extended in the earlier stages of meiotic prophase. Studies by Ris (1955) of Feulgen-stained

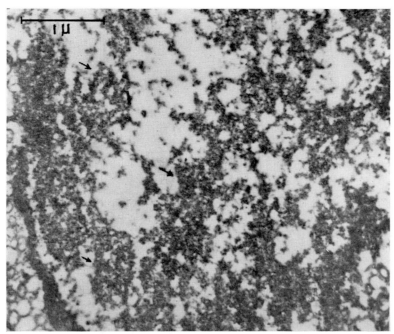

FIGURE 5. Electron micrograph of section of pachytene chromosomes of *Tradescantia* reflexa fixed in buffered OsO₄ . Chromosomes during "bouquet stages" appear multistranded and composed of finely coiled threads (see arrows).

and shadowed squash preparations of leptotene to pachytene chromosomes of the lily suggest, however, that the chromonemata are never fully extended, since the basic units of structure appear to be coiled threads about 250 Å in diameter. Electron micrographs of ultrathin sections of first meiotic prophase chromosomes of *Tradescantia* also disclose a large number of constituent coiled fibrillae (Fig. 5), the finest of which are approximately half the diameter of those detected by Ris in the squash preparations of the lily.

In the light of these findings, it seemed desirable to investigate the structure of chromosomes in somatic cells. Ris (1955) had observed fine coiled strands in sections of interphase nuclei of the lily after removal of the methacrylate and shadowing. For our studies we used the staminate hairs of *Tradescantia* in order to minimize problems of penetration of fixative, since these cells are cylindrical and arranged end to end in single file.

The preliminary aspects of the studies have been published elsewhere (Kaufmann and De, 1956), so that only a summary statement is essential to this discussion. Micrographs of thin sections of very early prophase cells reveal several orders of helically disposed strands. Each chromatid appears to be divided into two secondary or half-chromatids, and each of these in turn successively sub-divided into lower orders of chromonematic pairs. The smallest clearly defined units on the micrographs are about 125Å in diameter and present in end view the appearance of a rim of densely electron scattering ma-

terial surrounding a less dense "core." The wall of this "ring," which has a thickness of about 40 Å, assumedly represents the end-view pattern of a pair of coiled threads twining around a central axis, which is also about 40 Å in diameter. If this interpretation is correct, and here we must remark that we are approaching the limits of the resolving powers of the available equipment, this ultimate pair of intertwined strands would approach the dimensions of the type of nucleoprotein system described by Dr. Wilkins in this Symposium.

One point that merits emphasis is the similarity of pattern of end views of the subunits revealed in the electron micrographs and of the larger coiled aggregates revealed by the light microscope. In both cases a rim of more dense material surrounds a less dense core (*cf.* Kaufmann and De, 1956, Figs. 1–2 with Kaufmann, 1926b, Figs. 15–29). Such disposition of the chromonemata raises the question whether the pair rather than the single strand represents a functional unit, in the sense suggested by Ris (1956), in which protein surrounds the double helix of the nucleic acid. Ris' interpretation, based on isolation of fibrils and their subsequent shadowing, conforms in essence with the structure suggested for deoxyribonucleoprotein by Feughelman *et al.* (1955) and Wilkins (1956). Unfortunately, we have not been able to examine this interpretation in the light of cytochemical evidence, since our tests have not been perfected to the extent that we can identify with precision the densely electron scattering material and thereby define with accuracy the arrangement of nucleic acids and proteins in the ultimate chromonemata.

Examination of a series of micrographs and reconstruction of serial sections indicates that there are at least 64 subsidiary strands in these early prophase chromosomes (and perhaps as many as 128). One reaches the higher number also if one starts with assumptions about the size of the DNA molecule and associated materials and builds up to the known dimensions of the chromosome (cf. Darlington, 1955). By the same criterion thinner chromosomes should contain a smaller number of strands than the thicker ones. Our preliminary observations suggest that they do; what is important is the availability of techniques to make such determinations by direct observation rather than by analogy.

With respect to pattern of organization, the component chromonemata appear to be arranged in pairs of pairs, although the definitive observational evidence in support of this interpretation has not been obtained for all levels of organization. Nor can we determine from the electron micrographs whether the members of a pair are associated in plectonemic or paranemic relationship. There is considerable evidence from light-microscope studies (see Manton, 1950, for literature review) in favor of the latter alternative insofar as the standard, or minor coil, of plant chromosomes is concerned. In addition there are chromosomes, such as the ring-X of *Drosophila*, that maintain the form of a closed circle, although their chromatids are able to separate freely at anaphase and therefore must have been lying side by side without interlocking. A study of such material with the electron microscope has just been initiated in our laboratory in an effort to shed further light on these problems of interrelations and separation of chromonemata.

Accepting the validity of the interpretation of multiple chromonemata in somatic and meiotic chromosomes, a reevaluation seems required of such genetically and evolutionarily significant phenomena as coiling, chromosome pairing, crossing over, induced breakage and recombination, etc. In a general sense the problem had been posed by Huskins (1947) on the basis of interpretations derived from light-microscope studies. The electron-microscope studies have served to bring the problem into clearer focus, as has the accumulating experimental evidence that the chromosome is not a unitary structure. (For example, Friedrich-Freksa and Kaudewitz, 1953, interpret their radioisotope studies to indicate that the chromosomes of *Amoeba* have a number of subsidiary units; the same conclusion is reached with respect to the chromosomes of *Ephestia* by Henke and Pohley, 1952, and of *Drosophila* by Kaufmann, Gay, and Rothberg, 1949, and Fahmy and Fahmy, 1955, on the basis of radiation- or

chemical-induced mutational or structural changes; the older literature has been reviewed by Kaufmann, 1954.) These findings must eventually be correlated with the evidence that crossing-over occurs at a "four-strand" stage, that radiation-induced chromosome breakage and recombination usually involves whole chromosomes or chromatids, that the number of centromeres equals the number of chromatids, etc. Nevertheless, the presence of many strands raises serious questions about the adequacy of the models that have been proposed to explain such phenomena as crossing over and segmental interchange. And it forces us, in addition, to search for the materials or conditions that mould a bundle of strands into an aggregate that acts as a unit. But in which direction the search should turn needs to be considered with respect to a system in which discontinuities in different structural materials must be determined within diameters of a few dozen Ångstrom units.

Similar considerations emerge when one attempts to identify the "gene" within a multistranded chromosome. Is it definable as a functional unit in terms of a given segment in a single component strand, or does functional expression depend on the concerted activity of many structural subunits? In support of the first of these alternatives it might be pointed out that the polynemic structure affords a structural basis for the delayed expression of mutations, so frequently reported for microorganisms, and for the patterns of mosaicism sometimes detected in *Drosophila* and other higher forms. Mosaicism for structural rearrangements of chromosomes is not uncommon in salivary-gland cells of progeny of irradiated *Drosophila* males; and mosaics could account for some of the results obtained following chemical treatment of spermatozoa of *Drosophila*. Clearly the problem, insofar as it applies to these flies, requires some knowledge about the nature and distribution of the chromosomes in the sperm head. The problem gains greater importance in terms of the relation of chromosome organization to that of the DNA molecule because of the finding that sperm heads afford the same X-ray diffraction pattern as extracted DNA bound to protamine (Wilkins and Randall, 1953). Efforts to bridge the gap from the molecular to the chromosomal level are now in progress in many laboratories, and our current studies include an electron-microscope investigation of the spermatozoon of *Drosophila*.

FACTORS INFLUENCING STRUCTURAL INTEGRITY OF CHROMOSOMES

Changes effected by chelating agents. At this juncture the question arises, "What conditions serve to determine the lateral cohesion and linear continuity of the chromonemata?" With respect to the former, it might glibly be noted that if strands are intertwined they cannot fall apart, but this touches only part of the problem and in superficial manner. Some more profound considerations have been advanced by other workers. Thus, Ambrose and Gopal-Ayengar (1953) have suggested that the main lateral forces of cohesion within the chromosome are of an electrostatic character whereas the longitudinal cohesive forces appear to be largely due to hydrogen bonds. A somewhat similar proposal has been advanced by Mazia (1954) who suggests that divalent cations, such as Ca^{++} and Mg^{++}, play an essential role in maintenance of chromosomal integrity. This concept rests primarily upon experiments in which the chelating agent, ethylenediamine tetraacetic acid (EDTA) was used in treatment of cells. The cytologically-detectable effects were interpreted as indicating that this agent causes dissolution of chromosomes by removal of Ca or Mg ions, which presumably link the macromolecular complexes of component nucleic acids and proteins.

This stimulating interpretation has been accepted by other workers as the basis for further experimental work (Steffensen, 1955; see also his 1953 paper; Levine, 1955; Hyde, 1955; Eversole and Tatum, 1956) or for speculation about induced chromosome breakage (Muller, 1955) or the nature of the gene itself (Beadle, 1955). The interpretation rests, however, on the assumptions that EDTA is sufficiently specific in its action to permit formulation of conclusions about its mode of action and that the observational evidence of cellular damage convincingly demonstrates chromosomal dissociation.

We are not prepared to contest the first of these assumptions, although it is known that EDTA chelates a large number of metallic ions (The Versenes, 1953). But we can shed some light on the cytological interpretations, since the properties of chelating agents had been considered in connection with our studies of the effects of enzymes on the fixed cell and have been examined in greater detail in recent months.

In the earlier studies with EDTA we tentatively concluded that the action of this agent at the cellular level was essentially similar to that of trypsin, namely, that it did not dissociate the chromosomes by direct action but effected a marked modification in the gel-like properties of the chromosomal fabric. Our more recent observations confirm this interpretation. We shall not attempt to document this statement with the wealth of illustrative material now in hand, but will present the essential findings in summary form.

When used on salivary-gland cells of *Drosophila*, which had been fixed by freezing in water at pH 6 or 7 or in Ringer's solution at pH 6.4, deformation is a function of the concentration of EDTA (Versene). This confirms Mazia's findings. In the pH range of 6 to 7, a 0.1 M solution pre-serves the chromosomes with a reasonable degree of fidelity, a 0.01 M solution gives some deformation, and a 0.001 M solution causes considerable enlargement of nucleoli and peripheral displacement of the chromosomes. In contrast with Mazia we found that water caused deformation which differed only in degree from that obtained with 0.001 M EDTA.

Taken at face value these results may suggest that lower concentrations of EDTA cause dissolution of the chromosomes, but a few additional controls serve to cast the problem in a different perspective. If extensive rinsing of cells in water follows their treatment with a 0.001 M solution, the deleterious effect can be partially reversed. Moreover, if treatment with a 0.001 M solution is continued over long periods of time, such as 24 to 48 hours, there is less structural deformation than after short periods of treatment.

In the course of the studies it became apparent that there are many similarities between the action of EDTA on one hand and of pepsin or trypsin on the other. It will be recalled that the trypsin and pepsin studies showed that neither of these enzymes in itself caused disintegration of the chromosomes, but that either could effect their swelling or shrinking depending on the conditions of treatment (Kaufmann, 1952; 1953). Such findings suggested that "the products resulting from enzymatic hydrolysis of nucleoproteins have the properties of an elastic gel and are capable of undergoing marked changes in volume that lead to cellular deformation." Emphasis was placed on the properties of the nucleoprotein, since removal of the nucleic acids markedly modified the response of the cell to the action of proteolytic enzymes.

We have now found that pretreatment of cells with ribonuclease also modifies the degradational action of EDTA. Salivary-gland cells digested with this enzyme are not as sensitive to the action of a 0.001 M solution of EDTA as the controls.

Another way of demonstrating that changes in the gel-like properties of cellular materials are involved is to treat the cell with 0.1 M EDTA, and then with water. Addition of water causes a marked increase in the volume of the cell (Fig. 6). The swelling can be counteracted by replacement of the water with 0.1 M EDTA, and this process can be repeated time and again, with gradual loss of material from the cell and appreciable structural deformation. Neither 0.002 M $MgCl_2$ or $CaCl_2$ (or $MgCl_2$ plus $CaCl_2$) when used in place of water, wholly inhibits the swelling action.

We have some basis for assuming that RNA is involved in these reactions. It will be remembered that one of the first symptoms of cellular damage effected by ionizing radiations or by chemical treatment is the swelling of nucleus and nucleolus. Such swelling also occurs when cells are exposed to the action of low concentrations of EDTA; they then show a central ring in the light micro-

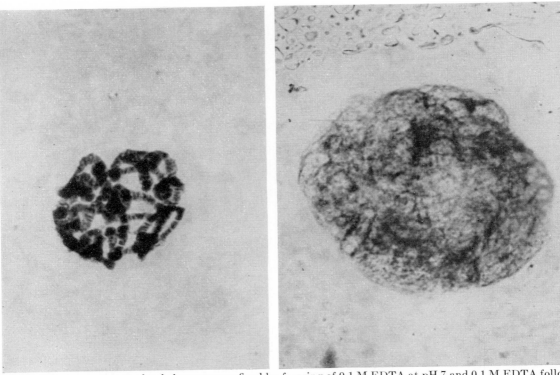

FIGURE 6. Effect on salivary-gland chromosomes fixed by freezing of 0.1 M EDTA at pH 7 and 0.1 M EDTA followed by water at pH 7. Stained after treatment in acetic-orcein.

scope and a loosening of the nucleolar fabric in the electron microscope.

To determine whether this represented an effect on RNA, EDTA-treated specimens were stained with dyes, such as pyronin-methyl green and azure B, that serve to localize basophilic materials. It was found that 0.001 M EDTA markedly reduced basophilia, whereas the 0.01 M and 0.1 M concentrations gave little or no detectable reduction. These experiments merely showed, however, that 0.001 M EDTA effected a loss of stainability that might be due either to a loss of RNA or to a masking of the stainable groups. It thus seemed desirable to obtain further evidence by chemical analysis.

Excised onion root tips, which had been frozen in water, were therefore homogenized and left at 3°C in various concentrations of EDTA at pH 7. Aliquots were removed at several time intervals and their nucleic acid, phospholipid, and protein content determined by a modified Schneider procedure (1945). The results are summarized in Figure 7. It is evident that EDTA did not alter the amount of protein. The spontaneous degradation of phospholipid and of DNA were inhibited, however, by concentrations of EDTA greater than 0.001 M, while that of RNA was markedly accelerated by 0.01 M, less so by 0.001 M, and unaltered by 0.1 M. This does not necessarily mean that RNA is degraded by EDTA *per se.*

The results could be due to an effect on the cellular enzymes involved in degradation. It is obvious that in any enzyme system affected by inorganic ions, removal of these ions by chelation will either raise or lower the observed enzymatic activity depending on the relative availability of activating or inhibitory ions. It is well known that pancreatic ribonuclease, and, to an even greater extent, that extracted from pea leaves, is markedly dependent on the ionic composition of the digestion medium (Holden and Pirie, 1955).

It has previously been stated that RNA is an extremely labile cellular component. Without attempting to summarize all of the supporting evidence, we might point to the fact that treatment of living onion roots with ribonuclease leads to the production of abnormalities of the types attributable to chromosomal stickiness and impairment of the spindle mechanism (Kaufmann and Das, 1954, 1955). Comparable types of abnormalities are produced in meristematic cells of growing onion roots by immersion in 0.002 M solutions of EDTA (Fig. 8). Similar end results do not necessarily imply the operation of similar pathways, however, and it is known that such abnormalities can be produced by a great variety of physical and chemical agents (Kaufmann and Das, 1955). As a matter of fact, treatment of onion roots with $CaCl_2$ or $MgCl_2$ (Fig. 8) gives results very similar to those obtained with EDTA

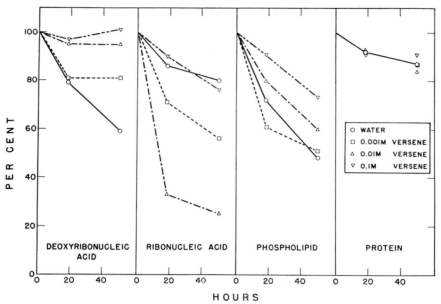

FIGURE 7. The effect of EDTA on the spontaneous degradation of various components of onion root-tip homogenates as determined by chemical assay.

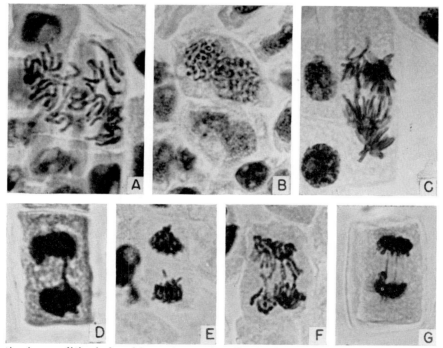

FIGURE 8. Mitotic abnormalities induced in meristematic cells of onion root-tips by treatment with 0.002 M EDTA, CaCl₂, or MgCl₂ in tap water at pH 6 for 4 hours with aeration. A–E, EDTA; F, MgCl₂; G, CaCl₂.

(*cf.* Sigenaga, 1944; VonRosen, 1954; Hyde, 1955). If the primary mode of action of EDTA in producing chromosome breakage were due to the removal of bivalent cations, which would normally bind together the macromolecular constituents of the chromosomes and thereby induce structural

instability, it is difficult to understand why addition of bivalent cations should have a similar effect. A more plausible interpretation of the results appears to be the following: Anything that alters the normal metabolism of the cell, whether it be changes in the ionic environment, or the removal of necessary cell constituents such as RNA, will produce chromosome instability.

Modification of crossing over in Drosophila. The foregoing experiments afforded a new basis for assessing the action of chelating agents on crossing over. Previous workers. had attacked the problem by using solutions containing Ca^{++} and Mg^{++} ions as controls (*e.g.* Levine, 1955), but it now seemed desirable to compare the action of EDTA with that of an agent capable of degrading RNA in the living cell, namely, ribonuclease.

An experiment was therefore designed in which treatment was given by immersing young, third-instar larvae of *Drosophila* for several hours in the solution to be tested, or by injecting the solution into the abdominal cavity. A set of markers was used that would permit ready diagnosis of large numbers of flies, namely, the white, miniature, forked, sex-linked genes. Both immersion and injection were effective methods of treatment, as revealed by failure of a proportion of the larvae to pupate and of pupae to eclose. Both types of treatment were also effective in modifying recombination values as compared with the controls within the intervals tested. The more extensive data obtained by immersion of larvae included counts of over 100,000 flies, as is shown in Table 1. The over-all X^2 value of 32.75 (N = 9; P < .0001) indicates a significant deviation from the distribution expected solely on the basis of sampling error. Comparison of pairs in all possible combinations shows that ribonuclease alone deviated significantly from all the others.

A more detailed analysis of the data for each of the intervals involved suggests that ribonuclease is more effective in increasing crossing over in the miniature-forked than in the white-miniature region. Such regional differences in recombination are not unexpected in the light of the findings of Schultz and Redfield (1951) that modifications of crossing over may be dependent on the structure of the region itself. The miniature-forked interval includes the extensive intercalary heterochromatic regions located in sub-divisions 11 and 12 of the salivary-gland chromosome, but whether heterochromatin *per se* is involved primarily in the effective action of ribonuclease would have to be determined by an analysis of recombination within shorter distances along the chromosome. The results suggest, however, that total crossing over may not be a valid index to the effective action of a given agent.

The data given in Table 1 showed no significant effect of EDTA on crossing-over when the immersion technique was used. This appears to contradict the results of Levine (1955), but it should be noted that he used both different markers and a different method of treatment, namely, inclusion of the chelating agent in the larval diet. A slight effect was found in our experiments when the injection technique was used; and, as will be described in detail elsewhere, our data indicate that different agents, or even different concentrations of the same agent may exert different influences on crossing-over in various regions of the chromosome. This would seem unlikely if the effect were dependent on the removal of some universally distributed bonding ionic substance. From our point of view, these findings again focus attention on the possibility that any agent capable of modifying the normal metabolism of the cell may lead to structural modification. At the moment the situation is analogous to that which exists with respect to production of chromosomal abnormalities; deformation of mitotic processes can be effected by almost any reagent capable of penetrating the cell, and in our experience the list includes distilled water, canned soup, coffee, and carbonated beverages, as well as enzymes, proteins, nucleic acids, nucleotides, etc. Under such conditions it is not the nature of the agent that is important in analyzing the phenomenon, but the materials that are affected and the reaction pathways that are disturbed. At the moment our studies focus on ribonucleic acid; but the pathways by which degradation is effected remain largely unknown.

This brief survey touches those aspects of our current efforts that are most directly related to the central theme of this symposium. We have presented some lines of evidence which suggest

TABLE 1. EFFECT OF EDTA ON CROSSING-OVER IN THE WHITE-MINIATURE-FORKED REGION OF THE X CHROMOSOME OF *Drosophila melanogaster*

	Non Cross-over	Cross-over w-m	Cross-over m-f	Cross-over w-m-f	Totals
Dry (not immersed)	10,967	4,503	2,814	494	18,778
RNase* 0.00007 M sol.	13,168	5,854	3,731	676	23,429
EDTA* 0.01M sol.	15,861	6,657	4,202	710	27,430
Water* (distilled)	17,740	7,753	4,636	804	30,933
Totals......	57,736	24,767	15,383	2,684	100,570
%..........	(57.41)	(24.63)	(15.30)	(2.67)	(100.01)

	X^2	P
RNase *vs.* Dry	21.46	ca. .0001
RNase *vs.* EDTA	15.46	ca. .0015
RNase *vs.* Water	14.74	ca. .0020
Dry *vs.* Water	7.88	ca. .05
Dry *vs.* EDTA	1.94	ca. .6
Water *vs.* EDTA	5.35	ca. .15

pH 7.0

that knowledge of genetic mechanisms in the years ahead will come to rely increasingly on information about changes in the fine structure of chromosomes under normal and experimentally-induced conditions. As L. J. Stadler noted in his valedictory article in Science (1954), "The central problem in biology is the physical nature of the living substance. It is this that gives drive and zest to the study of the gene, for the investigation of the behavior of genic substance seems at present our most direct approach to this problem."

Summary

Electron-microscope studies of chromosomes of salivary-gland cells of *Drosophila* and of dividing cells of *Tradescantia* indicate that the chromosomes are composed of a number of helically-disposed chromonemata. The finest clearly defined units have a diameter of about 125 Å, but each probably represents a pair of strands surrounding a central axis, since the end view presents the appearance of a ring of densely electron scattering material surrounding a less dense core. The strands thus seem to constitute a hierarchy of pairs of pairs. As many as 64 (or perhaps 128) separable units appear to exist, for example, in the somatic prophase chromosome of *Tradescantia*. The genetic implications of these findings are discussed briefly.

Attention has also been given to factors that determine lateral cohesion and linear continuity of the multistranded chromosome. Studies of the action of the chelating agent, EDTA, indicate that its degradational effects on chromosomes are due to changes in the gel-like properties of constituent nucleoproteins and not to dissolution or disruption of chromonemata (as some earlier studies had suggested). A comparison of the action of EDTA with that of ribonuclease in modifying crossing-over in *Drosophila* indicates that the latter agent may be more effective than the former under specified conditions of treatment. The results suggest that any agent capable of altering the normal metabolism of the cell, whether by changing the ionic environment or removing necessary cell constituents, such as RNA, can produce chromosomal instability.

Acknowledgments

The authors wish to express their sincere thanks to Dr. Helen Gay for her counsel and for permission to publish the electron micrographs of salivary-gland chromosomes shown in Figures 1 to 3. They also desire to express their appreciation to Mary McElderry, Kathryn Fuscaldo, Florence Powell, and Deepesh De for their assistance in collecting the data on crossing-over reported in this article.

References

ALFERT, M., 1954, Composition and structure of giant chromosomes. Intern. Rev. Cytology *3*: 131–169.

AMBROSE, E. J., and GOPAL-AYENGAR, A. R., 1953, Molecular orientation and chromosome breakage. In Symposium on Chromosome Breakage, Springfield, Illinois, Charles C Thomas. (Supplement to Heredity, *6*), pp. 277–292.

BEADLE, G. W., 1955, What is a gene? Bull. Amer. Inst. Biol. Sci. *5*: 15.

BORYSKO, E., and SAPRANAUSKAS, P., 1954, A new technique for comparative phase-contrast and electron microscope studies of cells grown in tissue culture, with an evaluation of the technique by means of time-lapse cinemicrographs. Bull. Johns Hopkins Hosp. *95*: 68–80.

CASPERSSON, T., 1940, Die Eiweissverteilung in den Strukturen des Zellkerns. Chromosoma *1*: 562–604.

DARLINGTON, C. D., 1955, The chromosome as a physico-chemical entity. Nature, Lond. *176*: 1139–1144.

EVERSOLE, R. A., and TATUM, E. L., 1956, Chemical alteration of crossing-over frequency in *Chlamydomonas*. Proc. Nat. Acad. Sci. Wash. *43*: 68–73.

FAHMY, O. G., and FAHMY, M. J., 1955, Cytogenetic analysis of the actions of carcinogens and tumour inhibitors in *Drosophila melanogaster*. III Chromosome structural changes induced by 2:4:6-tri (ethyleneimino) 1:3:5-triazine. J. Genet. *53*: 181–199.

FEUGHELMAN, M., LANGRIDGE, R., SEEDS, W. E., STOKES, A. R., WILSON, H. R., HOOPER, C. W., WILKINS, M. H. F., BARCLAY, K., and HAMILTON, L. D., 1955, Molecular structure of deoxyribose nucleic acid and nucleoprotein. Nature, Lond. *175*: 834–838.

FREY-WYSSLING, A., 1953, Submicroscopic morphology of protoplasm, 2nd. English Ed. New York, Elsevier Publishing Company, pp. 227–230.

FRIEDRICH-FREKSA, H., and KAUDEWITZ, F., 1953, Letale Spätfolgen nach Einbau von ^{32}P in *Amoeba proteus* und ihre Deutung durch genetische Untereinheiten. Z. Naturf. *8b*: 343–355.

GALL, J. G., 1955, On the submicroscopic structure of chromosomes. Brookhaven Symp. Biol. *8*. 17–32.

GAY, H., 1955a, Electron microscope studies on the nucleus and chromosomes of salivary-gland cells of Diptera. Thesis. University of Pennsylvania. Doct. Diss. Series, Pub. No. 11407, University Micro films, Ann Arbor, Michigan.

— 1955b, Nucleo-cytoplasmic relations in salivary-gland cells of *Drosophila*. Proc. Nat. Acad. Sci. Wash. *41*: 370–375.

— 1955c, Serial sections of smears for electron microscopy. Stain. Tech. *30*: 239–242.

— 1956a, Chromosome-nuclear membrane-cytoplasmic-interrelations in *Drosophila*. J. Biophys. Biochem. Cytol. *2*: Suppl., 407–414.

— 1956b, Nucleo-cytoplasmic relations in *Drosophila*. Cold Spr. Harb. Symp. Quant. Biol. *21*: 257–269.

HENKE, K., and POHLEY, H. J., 1952, Differentielle Zellteilungen und Polyploidie bei der Schuppenbildung der Mehlmotte *Ephestia kühniella*. Z. Naturf. *7b*: 65–79.

HOLDEN, M., and PIRIE, N. W., 1955, A comparison of leaf and pancreatic ribonuclease. Biochem. J. *60*: 53–62.

HUSKINS, C. L., 1947, Subdivision of the chromosomes and their multiplication in non-dividing tissues: Possible interpretations in terms of gene structure and gene action. Amer. Nat. *81*: 401–434.

HYDE, B. B., 1955, The effect of Versene on the structure of plant chromosomes. Biol. Bull., Woods Hole *109*: 347.

KAUFMANN, B. P., 1926a, Chromosome structure and its relation to the chromosome cycle. I. Somatic mitosis in *Tradescantia pilosa*, Amer. J. Bot. *13*: 59–80.

— 1926b, Chromosome structure and its relation to the chromosome cycle. II. *Podophyllum peltatum*. Amer. J. Bot. *13*: 355–363.

— 1946, Organization of the chromosome. I. Break distribution and chromosome recombination in *Drosophila melanogaster*. J. Exp. Zool. *102:* 293–320.

1948, Chromosome structure in relation to the chromosome cycle. II. Bot. Rev. *14:* 57–126.

1952, Cytochemical studies of the action of trypsin. I. Digestion of salivary-gland chromosomes. Proc. Nat. Acad. Sci. Wash. *38:* 464–468.

1953, Cytochemical studies of the action of trypsin III. The course of deformation of salivary-gland chromosomes. Exp. Cell. Res. *4:* 408–425.

1954, Chromosome aberrations induced in animal cells by ionizing radiations. In: Radiation Biology, Ed. A. Hollaender, New York, McGraw-Hill Book Company, Inc., Vol. 1, Part II: 627–711.

KAUFMANN, B. P., and DAS, N. K., 1954, Production of mitotic abnormalities by ribonuclease. Proc. Nat. Acad. Sci., Wash. *40:* 1052–1056.

1955, The role of ribonucleoproteins in the production of mitotic abnormalities. Chromosoma *7:* 19–38.

KAUFMANN, B. P., and DE, D. N., 1956, Fine structure of chromosomes. J. Biophys. Biochem. Cytol. *2:* Suppl., 419–424.

KAUFMANN, B. P., GAY, H., and McDONALD, M. R., 1950, Localization of cellular proteins by enzymatic hydrolysis. Cold Spr. Harb. Symp. Quant. Biol. *14:* 85–91.

1951, Enzymatic degradation of ribonucleoproteins. Amer. J. Bot. *38:* 268–275.

KAUFMANN, B. P., GAY, H., and ROTHBERG, H., Jr., 1949, The influence of near infrared radiation on the production by nitrogen mustard of chromosome rearrangements in *Drosophila*. J. Exp. Zool. *111:* 415–436.

KAUFMANN, B. P., McDONALD, M. R., and GAY, H., 1951, The distribution and interrelation of nucleic acids in fixed cells as shown by enzymatic hydrolysis. J. Cell. Comp. Physiol., Suppl. *1:* 71–100.

KAUFMANN, B. P., McDONALD, M. R., GAY, H., MOORE, E. C., VANDERBILT, G., and LARRABEE, J. B., 1952, Patterns of organization of cellular materials. Yearb. Carneg. Instn. *51:* 220–227.

KAUFMANN, B. P., PENNOYER, J. M., and ROWAN, M. E., 1953, Cytochemical studies of the action of trypsin II. Analysis of the swelling of salivary-gland chromosomes. J. Cell. Comp. Physiol. *41:* 79–102.

LEVINE, R. P., 1955, Chromosome structure and the mechanism of crossing over. Proc. Nat. Acad. Sci. Wash. *41:* 727–730.

MANTON, I., 1950, The spiral structure of chromosomes. Biol. Revs. Cambridge Phil. Soc. *25:* 486–508.

MAZIA, D., 1954, The particulate organization of the chromosome. Proc. Nat. Acad. Sci. Wash. *40:* 521–527.

McLEISH, J., 1953, The action of maleic hydrazide in *Vicia*. In Symposium on Chromosome Breakage, Springfield, Illinois, Charles C Thomas. (Suppl. to Heredity *6*) pp. 125–147.

MULLER, H. J., 1955, On the relation between chromosome changes and gene mutations. Brookhaven Symp. Biol. *8:* 126–147.

NEBEL, B. R., 1932, Chromosome structure in *Tradescantiae* I. Methods and Morphology. Z. Zellforsch. *16:* 251–284.

RIS, H., 1955, The submicroscopic structure of chromosomes. In: Fine Structure of Cells, New York, Interscience pp. 121–134.

1956, A study of chromosomes with the electron microscope. J. Biophys. Biochem. Cytol. *2:* Suppl., 385–392.

SCHNEIDER, W. C., 1945, Phosphorus compounds in animal tissues I. Extraction and estimation of desoxypentose nucleic acid and of pentose nucleic acid. J. Biol. Chem. *161:* 293–303.

SCHULTZ, J., and REDFIELD, H., 1951, Interchromosomal effects on crossing over in *Drosophila*. Cold. Spr. Harb. Symp. Quant. Biol. *16:* 175–197.

SIGENAGA, M., 1944, Experimental studies of abnormal nuclear and cell divisions I. Observation with living cells of the effects of neutral salts and heavy metal salts. Cytologia *13:* 380–404.

STADLER, L. J., 1954, The gene. Science *120:* 811–819.

STEFFENSEN, D., 1953, Induction of chromosome breakage at meiosis by a magnesium deficiency in *Tradescantia*. Proc. Nat. Acad. Sci. Wash. *39:* 613–620.

1955, Breakage of chromosomes in *Tradescantia* with a calcium deficiency. Proc. Nat. Acad. Sci. Wash. *41:* 155–160.

The Versenes, 1953, 6th ed., Framingham, Mass., Bersworth Chemical Co. Technical Bulletin No. 2.

VON ROSEN, G., 1954, Breaking of chromosomes by the action of elements of the periodical system and by some other principles. Hereditas, Lund *40:* 258–263.

WILKINS, M. H. F., 1956, Physical studies of the molecular structure of deoxyribose nucleic acid and nucleoprotein. Cold Spr. Harb. Symp. Quant. Biol. *21:* 75–90.

WILKINS, M. H. F., and RANDALL, J. T., 1953, Crystallinity in sperm heads: molecular structure of nucleoprotein *in vivo*. Biochim. Biophys. Acta *10:* 192–193.

DISCUSSION

MOSES: The morphology of chromosomes may also involve structures that are not coiled, at least at a level that can presently be resolved. The electron microscope has revealed linear axial structures in the spermatocyte chromosomes of a number of species. I reported seeing such laminated "cores" in crayfish (1956, J. Biophys. Biochem. Cytol. *2:* 215–218), grasshopper, *Xenopus*, and the rat. Fawcett has observed similar chromosomal structures in the pigeon, cat and man (*ibid.*, in press). By comparing electron micrographs of cells in thin sections with light microscope observations of the same cells in immediately adjacent thick sections stained with Feulgen reaction, I have identified the axial structures as being embedded in, and an integral part of, the DNA-containing material of the chromosome (*ibid. 2*, Suppl., in press). The "cores" appear at early prophase, persist until early metaphase and seem to be implicated in the process of chromosome separation.

KAUFMANN: We have no observational evidence comparable to that reported by Dr. Moses, but we have not been working with the same materials. As indicated, we have chosen to study in the electron microscope those chromosomes whose structural pattern has been reasonably well defined from extensive cytological and cytochemical studies using the light microscope, proceeding as it were from the known to the unknown. In the chromosomes we have described this afternoon, an axial "core" appears at all levels of resolution in both the light microscope and the electron micrographs and presumably reflects the pattern produced by helically arranged threads with respect to a central axis. But since we have not traced the chromonemata at the level of fine resolution throughout either somatic or meiotic mitoses, we do not know whether the "core" that separates chromatids or chromosomes bears any relationship to the structure noted by Dr. Moses. The suggestion given by Dr. Moses about the possible role of the type of "core" he describes should prove useful in consideration of structural mechanisms involved in chromosome pairing and repulsion.

STEFFENSEN: It might be predicted that chromosomes are bound together by at least three, four or more different types of secondary chemical bonds (hydrogen bonds, chelates or complexes with metals and "salt links" with protein). No single bond-type would explain adequately the present evidence. It is therefore necessary to examine interaction effects using two or more variables. The present evidence does suggest these kinds of experiments.

One essential point to consider is the known fact of molecular discontinuity. Recognizing discrete DNA and protein molecules, let us examine a possibility that genetic recombination is organized at least on two different levels. The first kind of organization can be that present in bacteriophage and bacteria where one or a few molecular species of DNA are involved. The

production of recombinant molecules may occur by synthesis or by molecule to molecule exchange. In the second kind of organization of higher organisms, the process of crossing over is likely to be different because the highly organized chromosomes with bundles of many strands or fibers must undergo a precise and orderly exchange. In order to break a multitude of covalent bonds within DNA (and protein) molecular species a considerable amount of energy and specific regulation would be required. A simple and quite precise method would be to have the exchange take place *between* molecules rather than within molecules. Control of the breaking of secondary bonds at the connective points (phosphate to phosphate end groups or carboxyl to amine, etc.) is chemically feasible. Bearing on the previous synthetic idea, the P^{32} uptake data of Taylor, Moses and others indicate that DNA is synthesized before leptotene. Crossing over would therefore not involve replication in the chromosomes of higher organisms. We might thereby

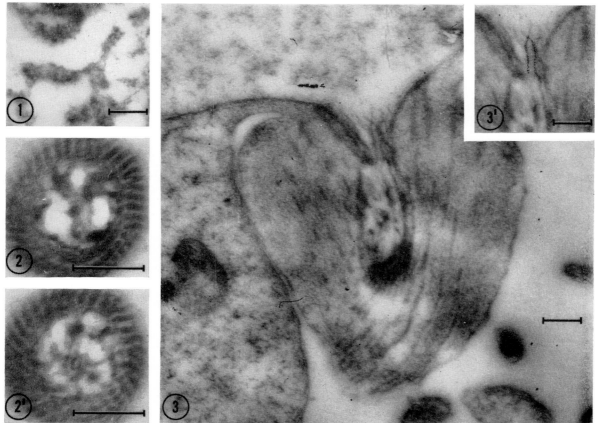

Electron microphotographs of *Tradescantia* and *Steatococcus*. Each bar in the figures corresponds to $\frac{1}{4}$ μ or 2500 A.
FIGURE 1. *Tradescantia palludosa* part of quartet nucleus, "Feulgen" stained with iodinated Rosaniline.
FIGURES 2 and 2', 3 and 3'. *Steatococcus tuberculatum*. Figures 2 and 2' cross-sections of sperm tails containing chromatin strands. (Impression: 16 or perhaps 32 strands per chromosome; while the former figure is preferred, the evidence to date is insufficient to support a sound numerical concept.) The chromatin strands are encased in a sheath made up of about 115 microfibrillae arranged in 3 concentric rings.
FIGURES 3 and 3'. Near sagittal section of "cap" showing bottle-shaped isthmopapillary bodies at exit from nucleus to tail. Figure 3' is identical with Figure 3 but one of the isthmopapillary bodies has been emphasized with India ink.

spend some effort studying intermolecular bonds, which although labile must have specificity.

With regard to the RNA and EDTA effects, Poulson and Bowen have indicated that high amounts of iron are in the nucleolus presumably bound to RNA. Iron-EDTA chelates are more stable than are chelates with calcium, magnesium or manganese. What a removal of iron might do to the RNA-protein complex should be examined.

Secondly, I should like to ask whether you have any idea or clue as to the mechanism of the ribonuclease effect on crossing over? Could not the free nucleotides with the groups of phosphate esters and purine and pyrimidine base be effective in some respect?

KAUFMANN: Dr. Steffensen has in essence concisely summarized what we have been trying to emphasize this afternoon, namely, that interference with any metabolic activity of the cell can be responsible for nuclear disturbances. I am sure that there is no fundamental difference in our points of view. I might add that it was an interest in EDTA-iron chelates that first led us to work with Versene, but the results with these compounds are still inconclusive.

We do not know the mechanism of the ribonuclease effect on crossing over. There are of course numerous possibilities, one of which you have mentioned, but these have not as yet been analyzed in detail.

NEBEL: Dr. Kaufmann's postulate for electron microscopy, namely to bridge adequately the gap between light microscopy and the macromolecular dimensions, I share. Figure 1 from a quartet nucleus in *Tradescantia* was obtained from material hydrolized for five minutes and then stained with an iodinated Rosanilin prepared by J. Pomeroy of the Argonne National Laboratory. I do not know the number of this type of unit per chromosome. Pappas has recently shown remarkable helices from the nuclei of *Amoeba proteus* (1956, J.B.B.C. *2*: 221). We do not know their genetical significance as yet.

In order to put Dr. Kaufmann's postulate to work it might be an advantage to start with species having the smallest and fewest chromosomes available. Dr. S. Hughes-Schrader recently supplied me with some male coccids (*Steatococcus tuberculatum*) in which she describes spermiogenesis (1946, J. Morph. *78*: 43–84). The spermatid nuclei present Feulgen positive content until the tail is formed. The Feulgen positive material constituting two chromosomes then migrates into the tail sheath formed by a special "cap" of cytoplasmic origin. The intact nucleus free of DNA is discarded while the tail alone enters and fertilizes the egg. Figures 2 and 2′ show cross sections of these early spermatozoa. The cytoplasmically derived sheath contains about 115 fibrillar structures arranged in three concentric rings, serving locomotion and surrounding the lumen containing the chromatin. The latter may be disposed in a possible 16 strand arrangement for each chromosome. Dr. M. H. F. Wilkins has worked on similar coccid spermatozoa and found their chromatin weakly U.V. absorptive. While the chromatin is being assembled in the tail, the old nucleus still contains electron dense materials as shown in Figures 3 and 3′. The cap is seen in near sagittal profile. Note the multiple bottle shaped bodies at the proximal "neck" of the tailcap. I have called them isthmopapillary bodies. Functionally they must aid in the rapid dispatch of the chromatin to its new site. I cannot forego the pun that this bottleneck must remain a "lucus a non lucendo" until more light is shed on the subject.

Chromosome Organization and Gene Recombination[1]

R. P. Levine

The Biological Laboratories, Harvard University, Cambridge, Massachusetts

The recombination of linked genes is a fundamental property of genetic systems ranging from those of the bacteriophages to higher plants and animals. Until recently, our consideration of gene recombination through crossing over has been directed toward those forms whose genetic material is clearly organized into a complex of macromolecules formed into chromosomes. As a logical consequence, the major hypotheses proposed to explain the mechanism of crossing over have drawn heavily upon cytological studies of various animal and plant chromosomes and in particular, they have been directed toward the differentiation of certain chromosomes into chromomeric and non-chromomeric regions (Belling, 1933) and to the coiling, uncoiling, and "opening out" of chromosomes early in meiosis (Darlington, 1935; Sax, 1930, 1932).

The discovery of linkage between genetic factors in bacteria (Lederberg, 1947), in bacteriophage (Hershey and Rotman, 1948), and in pneumococcus transformation (Hotchkiss and Marmur, 1954) and more recently in the transduction of genetic factors in *Salmonella* (Demerec and Demerec, 1955) has broadened the field of investigation into recombination mechanisms to organisms whose genetic systems were not as clearly defined as in many higher forms. However, in the genetic systems of higher and lower forms alike, deoxyribonucleic acid (DNA) is considered to be of fundamental significance. This is true of higher forms where DNA occurs in the nucleus and specifically in the chromosomes where its quantity is correlated with chromosome number. Similarly, it undergoes a duplication which is in turn associated with chromosome doubling. It is the active genetic material in phage (Hershey and Chase, 1952) and in the transforming principle of pneumococcus. In both of these cases recombination of genetic factors has been demonstrated (Hershey and Rotman, 1948 and Hotchkiss and Marmur, 1954). What is apparently a one to one relationship between DNA and genetic material, particularly in phage and pneumococcus along with the recombination of linked genetic factors points up the real possibility for a form of recombination or crossing over at the level of the DNA molecule.

The question now arises as to whether crossing over in organisms with a clearly defined chromosome organization has as its only *genetically important* result a recombination between DNA molecules. Or is something additional involved?

It is to the crossover phenomenon at the chromosome level that this discussion is directed. There are at least three sorts of experimental or observational evidence that can be drawn together in a consideration of crossing over among higher forms. This evidence is of great importance because it will set forth the requirements, conditions, and limitations of any sort of model proposed for the recombination mechanism. The first sort of evidence is derived from the familiar genetic analyses of crossing over as carried out in such organisms as *Drosophila*, mice, *Neurospora*, and maize. The second is evidence drawn from cytological studies of chromosomes at prophase of meiosis, and the third comes from experimental findings pertaining to chromosome chemistry and the molecular structure of DNA in protein.

These three sources of evidence taken together provide information on the following three aspects of crossing over: (1) pairing and chiasmata in crossing over, (2) the time of crossing over, (3) possible mechanisms of crossing over.

Much of the evidence to be presented has been familiar to us for some time. In using this evidence, however, we must bear in mind the distinction between conditions necessary for crossing over and conditions which merely modify it. For example, some form of pairing between chromosomes is necessary for crossing over whereas variations in the ionic environment of the chromosomes might be expected only to modify crossing over.

Pairing and Chiasmata in Crossing Over

The classical experiments of Stern (1931) and Creighton and McClintock (1931) demonstrate conclusively that genetic crossing over involves a physical exchange between homologous chromosomes. It is generally believed that chiasmata are intimately associated with this physical exchange. However it is apparent that there are some contradictory data as to whether or not there is always a one to one relationship between their formation and crossing over since there is a certain amount of evidence suggesting that chiasmata can be present in the absence of crossing over. Cooper (1948) suggests that chiasmata are present in male *Drosophila* where crossing over is a relatively rare event.

[1] The work of the author and his associates is supported in part by research grant No. RG-4000 (C) from the National Institutes of Health, U. S. Public Health Service and by an Institutional Grant from the American Cancer Society.

The recent work of Brown and Zohary (1955) has, however, provided detailed information of the close correspondence of chiasmata to crossing over in *Lilium formosanum*. They showed, with the use of terminal deficiencies, that a single chiasma in a deficient chromosome and the equational separation of that chromosome at anaphase were closely correlated. In addition, in chromosomes heterozygous for an inversion, it could be demonstrated that a chiasma between the centromere and the inverted segment led to a one to one ratio of dicentric bridge formation and loop chromatids at anaphase I.

If crossing over entails chiasma formation, it would seem logical to assume that pairing is a condition for such crossing over. If chiasmata were unquestionably concerned with crossing over, pairing would be an accepted condition but since no absolute relationship can presently be established, other evidence for pairing requirements should be cited. The simplest possible evidence comes from the examination of pairing configurations in polyploids during pachytene (Darlington, 1930; Darlington and Mather, 1932). Here, as has been seen in many cases, association of chromosomes is by twos and chiasmata are only observed between the paired chromosomes.

This sort of evidence indicates that chiasmata are seen when pairing occurs and if chiasmata are a consequence of crossing over then pairing is an essential step leading to crossing over. Without some sort of pairing crossing over would become a process dependent upon chance contacts between non-sister homologous chromatids. The rather great regularity in reproducibility of results in crossover experiments, particularly in *Drosophila*, does not support such ephemeral contacts as being the sole source of crossovers.

Clearly, if exchanges are possible on a submolecular level, the distance between the recombining molecules must be smaller than can be measured cytologically. The pairing of chromosomes observed cytologically is therefore not necessarily always close enough to permit crossing over. It is just such a situation that Pritchard (1955) visualizes when he refers to "effective" pairing. "Effective" pairing then would occur when chromosomes were close enough for an exchange to take place.

The Time of Crossing Over

The "time of crossing over," as used here, is in terms of the chromosome organization during those stages of meiosis when crossing over could occur. This time of crossing over can be demonstrated genetically, and it was done so by Bridges (1916) and Bridges and Anderson (1925). They demonstrated by genetic analysis that certain of the recoverable crossover types were multiple strand crossovers which could only arise when each chromosome had undergone replication so that four strands were present. Thus, crossing

over is said to occur at a four-strand stage of meiosis. Four strand crossing over was also demonstrated by Rhoades (1933) for maize, Whiting and Gilmore (1932) for *Habrobracon*, and Lindegren (1933) for *Neurospora*. Furthermore, the analysis of multiple strand crossovers has shown that they occur in frequencies predicted on the basis of four-strand crossing over. For example, two-strand, three-strand, and four-strand double crossovers occur in the expected ratios of $1:2:1$ (see Weinstein, 1954).

It is difficult to define the four-strand stage cytologically because the evidence for the earliest occurrence of a four-stranded condition is meager. Swanson (1943) has reported that the leptotene chromosomes of *Tradescantia* can be seen as visibly double, and therefore one might consider crossing over as being able to occur as early as zygotene, just as or following upon synapsis of homologous chromosomes. If, however, we believe, as does Darlington (1935), that the double condition is present later in prophase, then crossing over would occur during diplotene or possibly as early as pachytene. Surely four strands are visible at the diplotene stage, but it is certainly equivocal as to whether this is the earliest time in which crossing over could occur. Here, then, we are at a loss in trying to pin down cytologically a much needed point, that is, the actual structural organization at the time of crossing over; at least beyond the fact that each chromosome must have at some time undergo sufficient replication so as to permit the sorts of crossovers to occur as demanded by the results of genetic analysis.

It might be esthetically pleasing if crossing over and replication turned out to be different facets of the same process. Indeed, the assumption is made by Darlington (1935) and by Mather (1938) that crossing over occurs simultaneously with chromosome duplication at the end of pachytene. An extreme point of view is that of Belling (1933) who supposed that crossing over occurred as chromosomes replicated and that the newly forming chromatids, not yet fully linked, could join in non-sister unions. This hypothesis, at the chromosomal level of organization, is clearly unsatisfactory in light of our current knowledge. The fact that genetic analyses show crossing over occurring at a four-strand stage involving old and new chromatids immediately disqualifies this hypothesis. Modifications of the hypothesis such as sister strand crossing over can be made, but there is no clear cut evidence for its occurrence. A more logical modification, if it is worth while furthering a Belling-type of hypothesis, is to assume that all four strands are equally dissociated at the time of crossing over so that exchanges could occur between all of them.

I wish to turn briefly to another sort of approach which might be of value in localizing the time crossing over in relation to a four strand chromosome organization. The earliest time of visible chromosome doubling is debatable, since no really clear cytological picture of the early stages of prophase has been obtained. However, methods have been developed for the determination of DNA "doubling" or synthesis during both mitosis and meiosis (see Swift, 1953). We would like to know the relationship between the time of this synthesis and the time of crossing over. The two could occur simultaneously or crossing over could follow after DNA synthesis. In the former case, crossing over would be intimately tied into the gene replication process while in the latter it would occur subsequent to this replication. Whichever the case may be, if known it would have an important effect on the way in which an hypothesis for the mechanism of crossing over was phrased.

Numerous cytophotometric studies of DNA synthesis as measured by the intensity of the Feulgen reaction have shown that synthesis is completed very early in prophase of meiosis. In spermatogenesis for a number of organisms DNA synthesis appears to be completed by leptotene (see Swift, 1953). Studies of DNA synthesis during meiosis in plants show variable results. Taylor (1953) has shown through radioautographic techniques that DNA synthesis in *Lilium* as measured by P^{32} uptake is completed by leptotene. By similar methods Moses and Taylor (1955) have shown that synthesis in *Tradescantia* occurs during leptotene. In each of these cases both in animal and plant material the amount of DNA doubles abruptly. However, Sparrow, Moses, and Steele (1952) have shown that DNA synthesis in *Trillium* increases gradually through pachytene. Unfortunately, the resolution of experiments of this sort is not sufficient to localize the synthesis more accurately in time. Thus, as far as genetic units are concerned, as determined by DNA synthesis, a four-parted condition can exist as early as leptotene.

It is perhaps of value to recall that several different processes go in parallel during prophase of meiosis. These processes may not necessarily be synchronized. For example, nucleination in the sex chromosomes of certain grasshoppers takes place at a different time from that in autosomes (White, 1948). Some of the seeming contradictions in the evidence referred to above— that DNA seems to be synthesized at different prophase stages in different ogranisms—may result from the arbitrary definitions of these prophase stages on the basis of only one or two of numerous parallel processes. In short, the meaning of the prophase stages cannot logically be carried much beyond their definitions.

Here we are specifically interested in the relationship between DNA duplications and crossing over, and experiments effectively designed to relate crossing over to DNA synthesis must be carried out.

POSSIBLE MECHANISMS OF CROSSING OVER

The concept of a gene as a particulate unit has its basis in part in its definition as a unit of crossing over. Such a definition has given rise to the idea of a chromosome divided into units within which no crossing over occurs. The examination of many thousands of progeny in recombination experiments increases, as Pontecorvo (1952) points out, the resolving power for the genetic analysis of crossing over, and the size of the unit of crossing over decreases accordingly. The ultimate situation seems to be achieved in phage recombination at the *r* locus in T4 where Benzer (1955) has shown that a series of pseudoalleles recombine in such a way as to suggest that the unit of crossing over may be calculated in terms of at most a few nucleotide pairs of a DNA molecule. Such calculations, however, are based on many assumptions such as the linearity and homogeneity of the DNA distribution within the genetic material. Of significance in the present discussion is recombination analysis for certain factors in *Aspergillus nidulans* by Pritchard (1955) and Pontecorvo and Roper (1956). The latter have shown that the recombination distances between certain alleles can be calculated to yield the same order of magnitude of a limited number of nucleotide pairs as in Benzer's calculations. The significance of such calculations has been questioned (Pontecorvo, this Symposium). An important feature is the fact that in *A. nidulans* the genetic system is organized into chromosomes in the usual sense. Furthermore, the process of crossing over is identical, at least genetically, with that of other more "classical" forms. In particular crossing over occurs at a four-strand stage and reciprocal crossovers are normally recovered. Further evidence that suggests a molecular level of recombination comes from *Salmonella* in which Demerec and Demerec (1956) have shown that groups of loci can be transduced at various rates depending upon what is presumed to be their linear organization in donor bacteria. The order of this genetic material can be assumed to be translated to the DNA of the phage which in turn undergoes recombination with the genetic material of the host bacteria. Demerec and Demerec propose that the recombination occurs by crossing over between the replicating genetic fragment from the donor cell with that of replicating genetic material of the host cell. They suggest that this might be a process similar to that contained in the Belling hypothesis in which crossing over is assumed to occur only between the newly replicated chromosomes. Such a crossing over or cross over-like phenomenon in *Salmonella* can be explained on the submolecular level since we assume that the essential genetic material acting here is the DNA of the bacterial cells and the phage.

The step from the level of recombination in these organisms to that in those with a higher degree of genetic organization may appear to be a long one. Perhaps crossing over is different both in degree and kind at the two levels. A fundamental difference arises in the lack of recovery of reciprocal crossover types in numerous experiments with microorganisms and in particular with phage.

Let us turn then to an examination of hypotheses for crossing over as it occurs at the chromosome level since such an examination may be of some assistance in determining whether or not it is a long step from crossing over in a phage particle to that in a prophase nucleus in a higher organism.

The early ideas on the mechanism of crossing over were reviewed by Muller in 1916. The ideas expressed at that time were based upon Janssens' (1909) *chiasmatype theory* and crossing over was considered to be a "bending of the chromosomes across each other, a breaking of the threads, and then a fusion of adjoining pieces (or, perhaps, then the breaking of the original chromosomes at that point)" (Muller, 1916).

Only two enduring hypotheses have arisen since that time. One is the so-called Belling hypothesis (Belling, 1933). The difficulties associated with this hypothesis have already been described. The second hypothesis is due to the extensive cytological observations of Darlington which culminated in an hypothesis for the mechanism of crossing over which does not depart significantly from the early view stated by Muller. Darlington's hypothesis draws heavily upon cytological information concerning the relational coiling of chromosomes and the assumed mechanical stresses built up in such coils as opposed to the forces which cause chromosomes to pair. If I interpret Darlington correctly, there is coiling between a pair of homologous chromosomes. This results in part from the attraction between them. The sister chromatids are also coiled. He states that coiling can only develop between chromosomes in opposition to an equal amount of coiling within chromosomes, that is, between sister chromatids. As the chromosomes divide, there is the redistribution of these forces—the pairing force (lateral attraction) and the force maintaining the longitudinal cohesion of the chromatids. The strain will be translated to the chromatids and they will break. The break permits the union of non-sister chromatids, assuming that breaks occur at the same point in both non-sisters. This hypothesis is difficult to criticize except to say that we have little if any knowledge of the kinds and magnitudes of the forces suggested by Darlington and how chromatids might respond to them.

A most unfortunate feature of this hypothesis is that it does not permit the sorts of predictions and experimentation by which it can be tested so that even though the genetic and cytological requirements for crossing over might be fitted into it, we have no means of determining if it is in reality correct. It would be profitable, therefore, if some sort of working hypothesis could be devised which would be amenable to experimental tests. Such a hypothesis should be in a simple form and the experimentation should lead us to a more precise knowledge of the phenomenon. Belling began his 1928 paper by stating that, "In scientific investigations a working hypothesis is needed as a guide to the discovery of important facts and also serves to prevent distraction of the attention by unimportant facts. Even a wrong hypothesis may be better than none at all, *e.g.* the mutation hypothesis of *Oenothera*. If, however, a working hypothesis is in great part correct, then it may lead, as Janssens' has led, to fruitful work and discoveries of the first importance." Both the Belling and Darlington hypotheses for crossing over were working hypotheses of a sort but they have not necessarily lead to discoveries of first importance. We still do not understand how crossing over occurs.

An alternative hypothesis for crossing over, in view of the recombination picture in phage, bacterial transduction and transformation, and *Aspergillus nidulans* recombinations might profitably be phrased in terms of possible models for chromosome structure and crossing over at a molecular level. Let us assume simply that crossing over occurs as a result of exchanges at points along chromatids, and moreover it is possible that crossovers result from exchanges which are intimately associated with the molecular structure of the chromosomes. Further, if it is assumed that by altering the conditions to which chromosomes are sensitive because of their underlying molecular structure, such phenomena as the frequency of chromosome breakage and crossing over should in turn be altered in predictable ways.

The use of radiations, temperature shocks and chemicals in the induction of mutations has given us very tentative information regarding certain aspects of the chemical and structural nature of the gene. These agents have also been applied to crossing over but with uncertain results, at least as far as an understanding of the crossover mechanism is concerned. Their major difficulty lies in determining whether or not their effects are directly upon crossing over or upon the physiological state of the nucleus. If they act directly upon crossing over, we do not necessarily understand what their action would be.

Recently, data have been obtained from several different organisms which suggest that divalent cations are involved in the structural stability of chromosomes. A particular point of view concerning possible mechanisms for breakage and crossing over has arisen from some of this work. In particular, Mazia (1954) and Steffensen (1953, 1954, 1955a, b) have emphasized the possible significance of divalent cations in forming end to end linkages between DNA molecules. Mazia has distinguished two kinds of genetic effects, the *intergenic* of which he considers crossing over to be one and the *intragenic* such as gene mutation. According to Mazia the chromosome can be conceived of as having an organization of units of DNA and protein separated into particulate genetic units by divalent cations such as calcium and magnesium.

Studies of the relations between cations and the stability of chromosomes were initiated by Steffensen, who in 1953 reported that chromosomal alterations during meiosis in *Tradescantia* could be induced by raising plants under magnesium deficient conditions. Steffensen was able to give a quantitative evaluation of the chromosomal alterations he observed. The number of chromosome fragments was found to be approximately nine times greater in the magnesium deficient plants as compared with the controls. Similar differences were obtained upon growing plants under calcium deficient conditions (Steffensen, 1955a). In this case the number of chromosomal aberrations was approximately seventeen times that of the controls. Steffensen also reports (personal communication) that numerous other mineral deficiencies have no significant effect upon chromosome breakage.

Further evidence for a role of divalent cations in chromosome structure comes from studies by Mazia (1954) who reported that the salivary gland chromosomes of *Drosophila melanogaster* could be dispersed by treating them with chelating agents such as *Versene* or citrate at low ionic concentrations. He suggests that ionic factors are in part responsible for the assembling of macromolecules of DNA and protein into a chromosome. These factors are twofold. First, the particles are bound together lengthwise by bridges of divalent cations and secondly, the aggregation of the particles is dependent upon a nuclear environment of sufficient ionic strength to attract them. Lowering the ionic strength would tend to cause their repulsion. Both he and Steffensen propose therefore that chromosome stability depends at least in part upon the complexing of nucleoprotein by these metallic ions. If divalent calcium or magnesium ions are performing the function assumed by Steffensen and Mazia, it should be possible to demonstrate their role in chromosome stability in a number of ways. In particular they should effect the sensitive crossover process; a process which here is being considered as taking place on the molecular level.

Experiments concerned with the effects of calcium and magnesium on crossing over have been carried out with *Drosophila melanogaster* (Levine, 1955). This organism was chosen primarily because of the ease with which accurate data could be obtained free from bias due to differences in viability among different crossover types and because it represented a genetic system with a high level of chromosomal organization. The major drawbacks to experiments with this organism lie in the difficulty of controlling the nutritional conditions under which it can be easily raised, and, more important, the homeostatic mechanisms intervening between the medium and the chromosomes. The first experiments involved the feeding of excess quantities of calcium to young adult females heterozygous for a series of X-chromosome markers. The crossing over was measured in adults arising from eggs laid by treated and control females in successive two-day periods. The medium used both for the treatments and for the raising of a test cross progeny was the usual corn meal, molasses, agar, and yeast medium. In the case of the treated series, the medium was prepared in 0.1 molar calcium chloride. The adults were fed on this medium for four days, whereupon they were transferred to unmodified food for the remainder of a series of two-day egg-laying periods.

The results of this experiment (Table 1) showed that after the four-day feeding period the per cent of crossing over in the treated series became significantly lower than that of the control series and that this difference remained for a period of ten days whereupon crossing over returned to the control level.

Following this series of experiments another was carried out in which flies were maintained on a medium containing the chelating agent Versene. The concentration used was 0.01 M, and it was found that any higher concentration was toxic at all stages of the life cycle of the fly. In this experiment, both larvae and adults were fed but only among the former were adults obtained which laid fertile eggs. The results obtained (Table 2) showed that crossing over, at least in early egg-laying periods, was significantly increased upon the feeding of Versene.

The results of the experiments cited here suggest that metallic ions are acting in some fashion to alter crossing over, but they in no way indicate the manner in which such action is being carried out. It is impossible to decide on this basis whether the cations act directly upon the chromosomes and the process of crossing over or rather cause physiological changes in the flies which record themselves by changes in the frequency of crossing over. One thing is apparent, however, and that is the fact that the addition of calcium leads to decreased crossing over, while in the presence of the chelating agent crossing over was increased. Such results are in agreement with the predictions based upon the hypothesis advanced by both Steffensen and Mazia.

Upon obtaining these results, some earlier work of quite a different nature was re-examined. Ives, Fenton, Yost and Levine (1953) indicated that crossing over was reduced in *D. melanogaster* pupae when these were maintained under conditions of low relative humidity approaching that of zero per cent. The original experiments were repeated and they have been reported in part (Levine, 1955). Crossing over was indeed mark-edly reduced by water loss. Since these data were reported, a study has been undertaken of the cytological changes which are undergone in the ovaries under conditions of zero per cent

TABLE 1. CROSSING OVER IN FEMALES FED AS ADULTS ON THE USUAL MEDIUM SUPPLEMENTED WITH 0.1 M CALCIUM CHLORIDE (FROM LEVINE, 1955)

Two-Day Egg-Laying Periods		No. Flies	Per Cent Crossng Over				x^2	P
			y-ct	ct-ras	ras-f	Total		
1	T*	1,278	14.63	10.48	25.19	50.30	1.72	0.18
	C	1,433	17.94	10.00	24.91	52.85		
2	T	1,847	16.40	10.98	25.77	53.15	0.96	0.95
	C	1,858	18.46	11.52	24.81	54.79		
3	T	2,162	16.42	9.30	24.74	50.46	6.80	0.008
	C	2,189	17.95	11.43	23.16	52.54		
4	T	1,771	16.02	10.66	22.18	48.86	12.01	0.0005
	C	2,157	18.08	11.58	24.69	54.35		
5	T	1,846	13.87	9.26	22.64	45.77	7.73	0.004
	C	1,988	16.30	10.77	23.25	50.32		
6	T	954	13.52	10.48	22.64	46.64	8.77	0.003
	C	1,177	16.65	10.96	25.41	53.02		
7	T	1,179	12.38	8.73	22.99	44.10	98.59	<0.0001
	C	1,273	14.45	10.53	23.10	48.08		
8	T	864	14.94	7.76	25.47	48.17	0.04	0.85
	C	1,011	14.83	9.49	23.44	47.76		
9	T	624	15.54	11.38	25.63	52.55	0.00	—
	C	870	17.46	9.99	25.17	52.62		
10	T	357	18.20	10.92	24.37	53.49	0.84	0.36
	C	658	15.20	11.40	24.02	50.62		

* T represents the treated series; C represents the control series.

TABLE 2. CROSSING OVER IN FEMALES FED AS LARVAE ON THE USUAL MEDIUM SUPPLEMENTED WITH 0.01 M EDTA (FROM LEVINE, 1955)

Two-Day Egg-Laying Periods		No. Flies	Per Cent Crossing Over				x^2	P
			y-ct	ct-ras	ras-f	Total		
1	T	549	17.67	12.02	24.96	54.65	0.40	0.52
	C	5,158	19.15	11.38	25.47	56.00		
2	T	2,166	18.33	13.29	26.31	57.93	7.29	0.006
	C	8,897	19.06	11.39	24.27	54.72		
3	T	3,649	20.80	12.49	24.83	58.12	2.10	0.15
	C	9,874	19.99	11.43	25.31	56.73		
4	T	2,580	21.42	12.24	25.46	59.12	17.38	<0.0001
	C	6,499	18.67	11.05	24.55	54.27		
5	T	2,803	18.99	9.92	25.58	54.49	9.59	0.002
	C	6,207	16.22	10.74	24.01	50.97		
6	T	2,114	19.30	10.83	24.02	54.15	0.87	0.35
	C	5,140	17.66	10.01	25.27	52.94		
7	T	2,034	18.29	10.27	23.94	52.50	0.05	0.85
	C	4,954	16.81	10.96	25.03	52.80		
8	T	1,621	19.24	9.31	24.42	52.97	0.34	0.60
	C	4,358	16.03	10.27	25.81	52.11		
9	T	1,295	17.07	11.05	26.34	54.46	0.15	0.70
	C	3,468	17.76	10.98	25.05	53.79		
10	T	1,293	18.71	10.83	25.06	54.60	1.13	0.30
	C	3,001	17.56	10.64	24.59	52.79		

relative humidity and of the ionic changes within the flies themselves. The genetic events can be correlated with some conspicuous histological as well as with some more subtle cytological changes in the ovaries. This work is now in progress with Dr. T. O. Eisner and certain preliminary remarks may be made. The ovaries of the flies raised at zero per cent relative humidity are strikingly smaller than those of control insects, having become shrunken and retarded in their development. The nurse cells and oocytes are smaller than those of comparable ovariolar follicles of controls. The nuclei of the nurse cells show intensified Feulgen affinity and are frequently pyknotic.

The exposure of the pupae to low relative humidity can have an extreme physiological effect. In a series of preliminary experiments Dr. W. G. Van der Kloot has shown that the pupae kept at zero per cent relative humidity contain only 61.7 per cent water in contrast to the 69 per cent water in insects kept at 100 per cent relative humidity. Though the pupae at 0 per cent R.H. do lose water, they cannot lose salt. Measurements of Na, K, and Ca by flame photometry of ashed, whole flies showed that the 0 per cent R.H. pupae contained normal amounts of these ions, but when the results are expressed as concentrations of ion per kilogram body water, the 0 per cent R.H. animals were found to be 150 per cent as concentrated as the control animals. Since measurements were made on whole animals, it was not certain that individual tissues also increased in ionic concentration. To settle this point, the flight muscles and attached cuticle were dissected from 0 per cent and 100 per cent R.H. animals then rinsed in 0.24 M glucose, ashed, and the Cl⁻ contact measured by electrometric titration. Again the results showed normal amounts but higher concentration in the pupae kept at 0 per cent R.H. Their tissue Cl⁻ was 170 per cent as concentrated as the control pupae when Cl⁻ was expressed in terms of concentration of ions per kilogram at tissue water. In short, one physiological effect of keeping pupae at 0 per cent R.H. is a drastic increase in the tonicity of the body fluids.

The results of the studies summarized here point to alterations in the ionic environment as having effects on crossing over. However, the effects of ionic changes on crossing over, though statistically significant, are small in comparison with the degree to which the external ionic environment is altered. Thus, one is not assured that the data have a significant biological meaning. It is not possible, perhaps, to find in them strong support for an hypothesis such as Steffensen has proposed. It would be desirable though to have both genetic and either chemical or cytological information from another source, that is, from an organism whose culture medium permits more complete control of the internal ionic conditions than does *Drosophila*.

An approach to this has been achieved by Eversole and Tatum (1955) who have studied the effects of Versene on crossing over in *Chlamydomonas reinhardi*. They found that cells of opposite mating type treated with 10^{-4} M Versene for 24 to 48 hours, produced, upon mating, a highly significant increase in recombination frequency for a group of linked genes. In addition, they obtained recovery from the effect of the Versene by resuspending the cells in a calcium-magnesium solution. This resulted in bringing the frequency of crossing over back to normal. Finally, analysis for calcium and magnesium showed that these ions were significantly reduced in the treated cells.

Though the experiments with *C. reinhardi* fit the general hypothesis under discussion, we are still not able to distinguish between a specific role for divalent cations in chromosome structure in contrast to generalized ionic effects on chromosomes or an indirect physiological effect on the cell as a whole. As a step toward finding this out it is highly desirable to ascertain whether or not the changes in crossover frequency are due solely to changes in the concentration of the specific divalent ions such as calcium and magnesium rather than due to generalized changes in ionic concentration. *C. reinhardi* is ideally suited for experiments in which crossing over can be tested under a variety of ionic situations. Such experiments are currently underway in our laboratory and we hope to report the results in the near future.

On the basis of the findings discussed above which deal with cytological studies of chromosome breakage, and genetic analyses of crossing over an argument can be advanced for the importance of certain metallic ions in chromosome organization as they relate to both chromosome breakage and gene recombination. It is difficult, however, on only incomplete findings to point to a specific role for these ions. Both Steffensen and Mazia have advanced logical arguments for assuming the binding of these ions into the chromosome as a means of realizing its linear organization. Steffensen (1955b) has proposed a model whereby this role for metallic ions can be visualized. Calcium ions are presumed to be complexed by the terminal phosphate groups at the ends of DNA double helices. In this way different species of DNA could be linked. Since crossing over can be altered by calcium differences, it would appear on the basis of this model that exchanges would occur between DNA species at the sites where the calcium ions were loosely bound. A chromosome would then be separated into crossover and non-crossover regions in this way. In order that such exchanges could be effected, there would have to be some sort of flux of calcium ions between the chromatids so as to open up the terminal phosphate groups for non-sister unions or crossovers.

Steffensen's hypothesis assigns for divalent ions a role in a process necessary to crossing over rather than one whose variation could modify crossing over. This is not the only assumption that can be made, however. For example, the aggregation of macromolecules such as DNA and histone is dependent on the ionic concentration of their environment. Further, if there is a chromosomal membrane, it might be sensitive to ionic changes and its permeability affected by the concentration of a divalent cation such as calcium. In addition, it is known that divalent cations can play an important role in certain cellular movements affecting the expansion and contraction of long fibrous structures. Thus alterations in the concentration of these ions or their relative proportions might modify the expansion and contraction of chromosomes and in particular alter their pairing and coiling. Mechanical changes such as this could in turn affect the frequency of crossing over. It is known, for example, that isolated chromosomes become stiff and inelastic in calcium solutions (Duryee, 1941). Among the many possibilities for the function of metallic ions in chromosome organization there may be a number of indirect ones. For example, numerous enzymes activated by metals such as magnesium or calcium could, by their altered activity, change the physiological state of the nucleus so as to modify chromosome stability and crossing over.

Rather than raise various possibilities for means whereby divalent cations might be functioning in chromosome organization, and in particular, in gene recombination, it is essential to bear in mind two fundamentally different approaches to the recombination mechanism. The difference between these two approaches is whether or not a chromosome is divided into alternate crossover and non-crossover regions.

The role suggested for divalent cations in chromosome structure by both Mazia and Steffensen divides a chromosome into crossover and non-crossover regions. Therefore, crossing over would be an intergenic phenomenon. However, the crossover analyses in a number of organisms presents a contradictory view. The evidence from phage, *Aspergillus*, and *Drosophila* all suggest that a unit of crossing over is of the order of magnitude which can be calculated to equal to that of a few nucleotide pairs along the length of a DNA molecule. The question now arises as to whether DNA molecules are involved in recombination, what possible mechanisms exist for exchange between them, and whether or not such exchanges can operate at a chromosomal level.

We are most interested in the functional aspects of chromosomes and genes and in how structure and function are related. We wish to understand genetic mechanisms at all levels of organization. As the essential genetic material, the DNA molecule provides the framework on which structure and function can be drawn together. The properties of this molecule must then be considered and tested. First, crossing over could occur as a part of the DNA replication process. Such a view seems to be favored for recombination in certain microorganisms (Demerec and Demerec, 1955; Lederberg, 1956) and its mechanism has been likened to that in the Belling hypothesis. The alternative view is one of crossing over occurring after replication has been completed and as such involving some sort of breakage of already formed strands. This view probably would be favored by geneticists working with higher forms since crossing over after replication provides a means for crossing over at a four-strand stage.

It is possible to design model situations for crossing over under the two conditions mentioned above. However, such models are entirely speculative since many facts regarding chromosome structure are unknown and numerous simplifying assumptions must go into the models' design. These assumptions are dictated mainly by our lack of knowledge of the structural combination of DNA and protein in a chromosome and by only tentative ideas on the method for their replication.

Though speculation on crossing over models can be a valuable aid to our understanding of the process and a means of pointing out how little we know of it, a more significant contribution can be made by designing and undertaking experiments to test the alternative conditions discussed above. Specifically, what is needed is an experiment which determines the time relationship between DNA synthesis and crossing over. If the two occur simultaneously then the first condition becomes important in our studies. On the other hand, if crossing over follows upon synthesis the second condition is to be investigated. Such an experiment has been designed and is now underway. Since complete and definitive results have not yet been obtained only an outline will be given here. The organism for the experiment is *Chlamydomonas reinhardi* of which two different arginine requiring mutants are being used. These are linked and cross over with a frequency of about 10 per cent varying somewhat upon culture conditions. Cells of opposite mating type each carrying one of the arginine mutations are mated under standard conditions. Immediately after zygote formation (about 30 minutes) a large sample of zygotes (about 5–10 mg dry wt.) is taken for a DNA determination by the method of Ogur and Rosen (1950). Subsequent samples are taken every six or twelve hours after zygote formation for a period of six days during which the zygotes are maturing. This procedure provides a measurement of the time at which DNA is synthesized on the basis of a determination of when it doubles in amount. Fortunately, a large population of zygotes of *C. reinhardi* appear to develop with close synchrony. This is clearly shown by the method of determining when crossing over occurs. This time is determined most simply by the use of a temperature treatment. *C. reinhardi* in our laboratory is maintained at 25°C. However, zygotes germinate equally well at 35°C, at least after treatments up to 24 hours. It has been determined that a 35°C temperature treatment to zygotes at a specific time increases crossing over between the two arginine mutants two to three times above that of an untreated control series. It is assumed that the temperature treatment is effective during the time when crossing over is taking place. However, it must be borne in mind that the temperature treatment at any given time could have a delayed effect. Only by the use of several different temperature treatments and possibly through the use of other agents affecting crossing over can the time of crossing over be ascertained. The time of crossing over as determined by this temperature treatment (30° and 35°C) appears to be somewhere in a twelve-hour interval between the 24th and 36th hours after zygote formation. The effect of temperature is insignificant at any other time. The abrupt change is a fair indication of the synchrony of the large number of zygotes. We are currently reducing the temperature treatments to periods of six and three hours in order to pinpoint more accurately the effective time for the crossover process.

At present all that can be said is that both the DNA synthesis crossing over time are within the same 24 hour time period. However, their actual relationship and the statistical limits of each must be established, and many replicate experiments remain to be done.

Summary

In the earlier section of this paper an attempt was made to provide what information we have on the genetic requirements for crossing over at the chromosomal level of organization. In addition I have discussed some experiments which lead us to two approaches to the mechanism of crossing over. One approach considers crossing over to occur along a chromosome which is neatly separated into crossover and non-crossover regions. The other, stemming from recombination studies in phage, *Aspergillus*, and *Drosophila* leads to the idea that crossing over occurs at a sub-molecular level. If this is true, there are two conditions under which it might occur. The first is during the time of DNA replication and the second is after this time. Finally I have mentioned some experimental work which will aid us in distinguishing between these two possibilities.

It is clear that one of the most important and unexpected pieces of evidence in the study of crossing over has been that which supports the idea of crossing over on a sub-molecular level. Such evidence should focus our attention on

the molecular structure of chromosomes and in particular upon the structure and properties of DNA. By doing so we may arrive, perhaps by many false starts and devious routes, at a complete solution to one of the most perplexing and least understood of fundamental genetic phenomena–crossing over.

Acknowledgments

The author wishes to thank Dr. Dale Steffensen for permitting him to quote certain unpublished information. The numerous and stimulation conversations with Dr. Roger Milkman regarding various aspects of crossing over are gratefully acknowledged.

References

Belling, J., 1928, A working hypothesis for segmental interchange between homologous chromosomes in flowering plants. Univ. Calif. Pub. Botany *14:* 283–291.
1933, Crossing over and gene rearrangement in flowering plants. Genetics *18:* 318–413.
Benzer, S., 1955, Fine structure of a genetic region in bacteriophage. Proc. Nat. Acad. Sci. Wash. *41:* 344–354.
Bridges, C. B., 1916, Non-disjunction as proof of chromosome theory of heredity. Genetics *1:* 1–52, 107–163.
Bridges, C. B., and Anderson, E. G., 1925, Crossing over in the X-chromosome of triploid females of *Drosophila melanogaster*. Genetics *10:* 418–441.
Brown, S. W., and Zohary, D., 1955, The relationship of chiasmata and crossing over in *Lilium formosanum*. Genetics *40:* 850–873.
Cooper, K. W., 1949, The cytogenetics of meiosis in *Drosophila*: Mitotic and meiotic autosomal chiasmata without crossing over in the male. J. Morph. *84:* 81–119.
Creighton, H. B., and McClintock, B., 1931, A correlation of cytological and genetical crossing over in *Zea mays*. Proc. Nat. Acad. Sci. Wash. *17:* 492–497.
Darlington, C. D., 1930, A cytological demonstration of crossing over. Proc. Roy. Soc. B. *107:* 50–59.
1935, The time, place, and action of crossing over. J. Genet. *31:* 185–212.
Darlington, C. D., and Mather, K., 1932, The origin and behaviour of chiasmata. III. Triploid Tolipa. Cytologia *4:* 1–15.
Demerec, M. and Demerec, Z. E., 1955, Analysis of linkage relationships in *Salmonella* by transduction techniques. Brookhaven Symp. Biol. *8:* 75–87.
Duryee, W. R., 1941, The chromosomes of the amphibian nucleus. In: Cytology, Genetics, and Evolution. Philadelphia, Univ. of Pennsylvania Press.
Eversole, R. A., and Tatum, E. L., 1956, Chemical alteration of crossing over frequency in *Chlamydomonas*. Proc. Nat. Acad. Sci. Wash. *42:* 68–73.
Hershey, A. D., and Rotman, R., 1948, Linkage among genes controlling inhibition of lysis in a bacterial virus. Proc. Nat. Acad. Sci. Wash. *34:* 89–96.
Hershey, A. D., and Chase, M., 1952, Independent functions of viral protein and nucleic acid in growth of bacteriophage. J. Gen. Physiol. *36:* 39–56.
Hotchkiss, R. D., and Marmur, J., 1954, Double marker transformations as evidence for linked factors in deoxyribonucleate transforming agents. Proc. Nat. Acad. Sci. Wash. *40:* 55–60.
Ives, P. T., Fenton, B. J., Yost, H. T., and Levine, R. P., 1953, The effects of infra-red radiation and desiccation on crossing over in *Drosophila melanogaster*. Proc. Nat. Acad. Sci. Wash. *39:* 1134–1141.
Janssens, F. A., 1909, La theorie de la chiasmatypie. Le Cellule *25:* 387–411.

LEDERBERG, J., 1947, Gene recombination and linked segregations in *Escherichia coli*. Genetics *32:* 505–525.

LEVINE, R. P., 1955, Chromosome structure and the mechanism of crossing over. Proc. Nat. Acad. Sci. Wash. *41:* 727–730.

LINDEGREN, C. C., 1933, The genetics of *Neurospora*. III. Pure bred stocks and crossing over in *N. crassa*. Bull. Tor Bot. Cl. *60:* 133–154.

MAZIA, D., 1954, The particulate organization of the chromosome. Proc. Nat. Acad. Sci. Wash. *40:* 521–527.

MOSES, M. J., and TAYLOR, J. H., 1955, Deoxypentose acid synthesis during microsporogenesis in *Tradescantia*. Expl. Cell Res. *9:* 474–487.

MULLER, H. J., 1916. The mechanism of crossing over. Amer. Nat. *50:* 193–434.

OGUR, M., and ROSEN, G., 1950, The nucleic acid of plant tissues. I. The extraction and extimation of desoxypentose nucleic acid and pentose nycleic acid. An. Biochem. *25:* 262–276.

PONTECORVO, G., 1952, Genetical analysis of cell organization. Symp. Soc. Exp. Biol. *6:* 218–229.

PONTECORVO, G., and ROPER, J. A., 1956 Resolving power of genetic analysis in terms of DNA. Heredity *10:* 124 (abst.).

PRITCHARD, R. H., 1955, The linear arrangement of a series of alleles in *Aspergillus nidulans*. Heredity *9:* 343–371.

RHOADES, M. M., 1932, The genetic demonstration of double strand crossing over in *Zea mays*. Proc. Nat. Acad. Sci. Wash. *18:* 481–484.

SPARROW, A. H., MOSES, M. J., and STEELE, R., 1952, A cytological and cytochemical approach to an understanding of radiation damage in dividing cells. Brit. J. Radiol. *25:* 182–189.

STEFFENSEN, D., 1953, Induction of chromosome breakage at meiosis by a magnesium deficiency in *Tradescantia*. Proc. Nat. Acad. Sci. Wash. *39:* 613–620.

1955a, Breakage of chromosomes in *Tradescantia* with a calcium deficiency. Proc. Nat. Acad. Sci. Wash. *41:* 155–160.

1955b, Interaction effects of metal ions in the production of spontaneous chromosomal aberrations in calcium deficient *Tradescantia*. Genet. Soc. Rec. *24:* 598 (abst.) and Genetics *40:* 598 (abst.).

STERN, C., 1931, Zytologisch-genetische Untersuchungen als Beweise fur die Morgansche Theorie des Faktorenaustauschs. Biol. Zbl. *51:* 547–587.

SWANSON, C. P., 1943, The behavior of meiotic prophase chromosomes as revealed through the use of high temperatures. Amer. J. Bot. *30:* 422–428.

SWIFT, H., 1953, Quantitative aspects of nuclear nucleoproteins. Intern. Rev. Cytol. *2:* 1–76.

TAYLOR, J. H., 1953, Autoradiographic detection of incorporation of P[32] into chromosomes during meiosis and mitosis. Exp. Cell. Res. *4:* 164–175.

WEINSTEIN, A., 1955, Unravelling the chromosomes. J. Cell. Comp. Physiol. *45:* 249–269. (Suppl. 2).

WHITE, M. J. D., 1948. Animal Cytology and Evolution. Cambridge, Cambridge Univ. Press.

WHITING, P. W., and GILMORE, K. A., 1932, Genetic analysis of synapsis and maturation in eggs of *Habrobracon*. Proc. Sixth Intern. Cong. Genetics *2:* 210–211.

DISCUSSION

ALFERT: With respect to the experiment described by Dr. Levine concerning the relation between DNA replication and crossing over, there are quite a few data already available but the situation is far from clear at the moment. If we assume, just for the purpose of the present argument, that DNA duplication can be taken as an indication of chromosome duplication and that crossing over occurs after cytologically detectable chromosome pairing in meiotic prophase, both of the alternatives mentioned by Dr. Levine appear to be realized in different materials. During spermatogenesis in the centipede *Scutigera forceps* (Ansley, 1954, Chromosoma *6:* 656) and in microsporogenesis of *Trillium* (*e.g.* Moses *et al.*, 1950, J. Nat. Cancer Inst. *10:* 1345) DNA synthesis was found to extend through pachytene; in *Tradescantia* DNA synthesis extends into the earliest prophase stages: zygotene, according to photometric Feulgen-DNA measurements by Swift, and leptotene, according to radioautographic studies by Taylor (1953, Exp. Cell Res. *4:* 164). Swift (1953, Intern. Rev. Cytol. *2:* 1) has reviewed photometric and radioautographic data by several workers showing that DNA synthesis is *completed before onset* of meiotic prophase in spermatogenesis and oogenesis in the mouse and in a grasshopper, and in microsporogenesis of the lily. These last named findings are of interest in another connection, namely with regard to their bearing on Darlington's "precocity theory." Basing himself solely on the result of Ansley (*loc. cit.*) Darlington (1955, Nature, Lond. *176:* 1139) has generalized his former speculations in physico-chemical terms by relating them to chromosomal DNA and protein synthesis during meiotic prophase. Such a generalization appears hardly justified in view of the observations that in at least three higher organisms mitosis and meiosis are indistinguishable as far as the time relationship between DNA synthesis and onset of prophase is concerned.

Nucleocytoplasmic Relations in *Drosophila*[1]

HELEN GAY

Department of Genetics, Carnegie Institution of Washington, Cold Spring Harbor, New York

The methods of genetic analysis in higher organisms involve classification of phenotypes that usually are removed by many cell generations from the initial stages of operation of the genetic system. Consideration of this factor and related aspects of gene action has led in recent years to reevaluation of the concept of "the gene," until it is now frequently regarded as a physiological reaction system (see, for example, Pontecorvo, 1952; Gerard, 1954). The integration of developmental processes is controlled by this system. Some evidence concerning the pathways involved has been provided by studies in genetics and experimental embryology. Biochemical genetics has shown that specific chemical reactions in the cytoplasm are controlled by the nucleus. Results of removal or inactivation of the nucleus indicate that its presence is essential for sustained synthetic activities of the cell. These findings imply that the nucleus provides materials necessary for controlling specific cytoplasmic reactions and synthetic activities. The nature of this nuclear control has long been a subject of inquiry.

Biologists at the turn of the century were concerned with this problem. The classical studies of Driesch, Boveri, Weismann and Roux were directed toward an understanding of mutual interactions of nuclear and cytoplasmic materials during early cleavages. On the basis of theoretical considerations of the role of the nucleus, deVries postulated migration of invisible pangens to the cytoplasm, whereas Hertwig, Schaxel and others espoused the chromidial hypothesis of extrusion of "chromidia," or chromatin-like particles, from the nucleus into the cytoplasm. Based on such assumptions, many well-known cytoplasmic elements, such as mitochondria and ergastoplasmic structures, were considered to be of nuclear origin. Changes in nuclear size, shape, and staining properties during growth or secretory activity suggested a causal relationship between nuclear activity and cytoplasmic function. The cytological tools and methods of the era were not sufficiently refined, however, to afford unequivocal evidence about the mechanisms responsible for nucleocytoplasmic transfers.

In recent years, improved methods for detecting nucleic acids, for example, by the Feulgen reaction and ultraviolet microspectrophotometry, have enabled the cytologist to determine the nature and location of cellular materials. Caspersson and Schultz's observations (summarized in Caspersson, 1950) on the changes that occurred in the ribonucleic acid (RNA)/protein ratio in cells that were actively growing or functioning in secretion, and Brachet's similar observations on embryogenesis (Brachet, 1950) led to the formulation, independently by these two groups, of the hypothesis that protein synthesis is correlated with changes in RNA concentration which in turn is dependent on nuclear changes. More recent studies on extrusion of nuclear materials into the cytoplasm have shown that Feulgen-positive granules are indeed found in the cytoplasm of some isolated cell types (Sparrow and Hammond, 1947; Cooper, 1952). It has not been conclusively determined, however, whether this process is a manifestation of degeneration or not (Rasch and Swift, in Swift, 1953). Observations made on oocytes of Amphibia and fishes (Duryee, 1940, 1950; Wittek, 1952; Dodson, 1953; Chaudry, 1951) have been interpreted as demonstrating eversion of nucleolar material (containing RNA) from nuclei. Although many who have studied these cells agree that nucleoli may be seen in pseudopodial processes projecting from the older germinal vesicles of amphibian oocytes, they do not concur that actual extrusion of nucleoli occurs under normal conditions (Painter and Taylor, 1942; Gall, 1954). The evidence provided by these types of investigation does suggest, nevertheless, that distinct and chemically definable nuclear materials of submicroscopic or larger proportions may be transferred from the nucleus to the cytoplasm; but the actual mechanism of the transfer is not known.

In the course of a study of the chromosomes and nuclei of larval salivary-gland cells of *Drosophila melanogaster*, electron micrographs were obtained in which details of cellular organization suggested a mechanism for exchange of materials between nucleus and cytoplasm. The original report of these findings (Gay, 1954, 1955a) and more recent observations (Gay, 1955b, 1956) have been published elsewhere and will merely be summarized here. This precis will serve as a background for interpretations and hypotheses that have been derived from the additional data now available. The present observations on *Drosophila* salivary-gland cells thus supplement the earlier reports and the previous hypotheses of nucleocytoplasmic interrelations based on light microscopy by demonstrating a possible structural mechanism for transfer to the cyto-

[1] This study was supported by a research grant (RG-149) from the National Institutes of Health, United States Public Health Service, to Dr. Berwind P. Kaufmann.

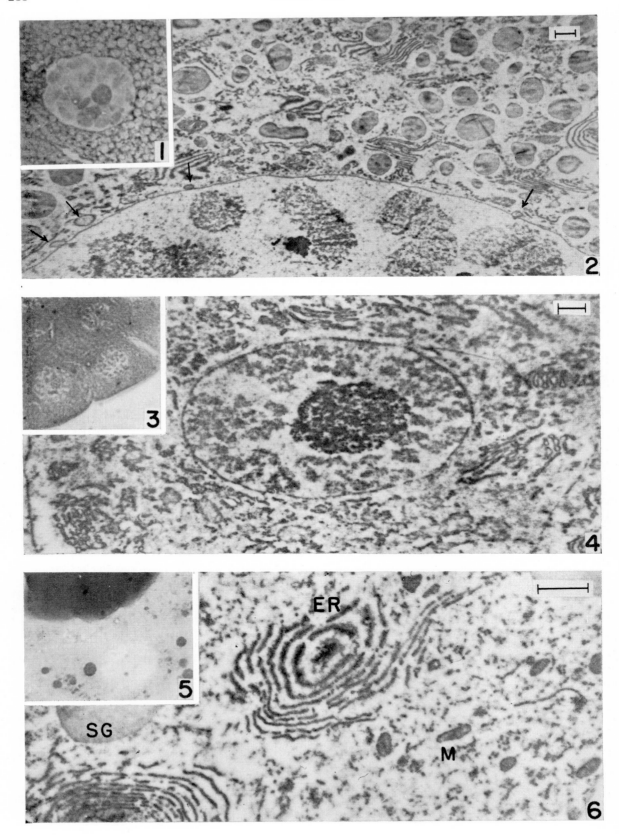

plasm of nuclear materials originating at specific chromosomal regions and the subsequent role of these materials and structures in the formation of cytoplasmic organelles.

MATERIALS AND METHODS

Salivary glands of larval *Drosophila melanogaster* (a Swedish-b, wild-type strain, devoid of detectable chromosomal aberrations) raised according to standard culture methods for larvae were preserved in a variety of fixatives, mostly containing osmium tetroxide (Palade, 1952; Dalton, 1955), and imbedded in n-butyl methacrylate (Newman, Borysko and Swerdlow, 1949). Thin sections for electron microscopy were cut on the Porter-Blum microtome (Porter and Blum, 1953). Adjacent thick sections were stained and examined in the light microscope to facilitate identification of the cellular structures seen in the electron micrographs. It was found that examination of serial sections in the electron microscope (Gay and Anderson, 1954) was necessary to determine the relationship between the cellular components involved in nucleocytoplasmic transfer. Cytochemical methods (utilizing enzymatic hydrolysis—Kaufmann, McDonald, and Gay, 1951) were employed in analysis of the nature of the structures involved in this phenomenon.

RESULTS

The structural relationships that suggest nucleocytoplasmic interchange in *Drosophila* were observed in salivary-gland cells during the second half of the third larval instar. In *D. melanogaster*, the embryonic salivary-gland cells are set aside in definitive number during the first twelve hours of development (Sonnenblick, 1950). Subsequent growth of the gland, throughout the three larval instars, occurs solely through increase in cell size, since no mitotic division takes place. The large cells of the third or last instar furnish the familiar giant chromosomes which have been used so extensively in cytogenetic research. Cells in this stage of development were those first used in the present electron microscope study (Gay, 1954, 1955a). Figures 1 and 2 show respec-

tively a light-microscope picture and an electron micrograph of such a cell.

The salivary glands of *Drosophila* as their name implies are assumedly concerned with the function of digestion. It is generally agreed that secretion occurs early in development, since the glands are functional when the larva hatches from the egg. During the middle of the third instar, however, the larvae leave their food supply, reduce food intake and eventually become quiescent, preparatory to pupation. At about this time changes occur in the cytoplasm of the cells of the salivary gland which suggest that another intracellular synthetic process has superseded that of saliva production. Secretion granules that are not seen in the cytoplasm of the younger cells (see Figs. 3 and 4) are formed. These granules contain a mucoprotein, giving a positive test for proteins when stained with acidic dyes in combination with pepsin digestion and for polysaccharides when treated with the periodic acid-Schiff reagent (Gay, 1956). Just before pupation the material of the granules is discharged into the lumen and the cytoplasm again contains few PAS secretion granules (Figs. 5 and 6).

The observations of Fraenkel and Brookes (1953) further substantiate the interpretation that the cells of the salivary gland of *Drosophila* assume a second secretory function during the middle of the third instar. These authors recognize that the salivary glands of younger larvae of *Drosophila* may produce digestive enzymes during the feeding period but believe that the secretion of the salivary glands of larvae preparing to pupate is used in attaching the puparium to the substrate. They observed that fluid was ejected from the mouth of the prepupa and correlated this secretion with the simultaneously decreased volume of the salivary gland. In addition, their analysis of the amino acids of the secretion found in the lumen of the prepupal salivary gland showed that this material contained the same 15 amino acids found in the proteins of the puparial glue. These findings, in conjunction with the cytological evidence of the present study, confirm the dual secretory function of the salivary gland.

In the figures, the following abbreviations are used: SG—secretion granules, ER—ergastoplasmic lamellae, M—mitochondria, CHR—chromosome, NU—nucleus, NM—nuclear membrane. The bar indicates 1 μ.

FIGURE 1. Light-microscope picture of a mid-third-instar salivary-gland cell stained with Azure B. The cytoplasm is filled with secretion granules which do not stain with this dye but are outlined by the basophilic cytoplasmic materials. × about 1000.

FIGURE 2. Electron micrograph of an ultrathin section of a cell from the same gland as shown in Figure 1. Arrows indicate nuclear-membrane blebs.

FIGURE 3. Light-microscope picture of several cells of a salivary gland from a larva at the beginning of the third instar (immediately after molting). This preparation was stained with the periodic acid-Schiff reagent and no P.A.S.-positive granules are discernible in the cytoplasm. × about 1000.

FIGURE 4. Electron micrograph of an ultrathin section of a cell from the same gland as shown in Figure 3. The cytoplasm contains ergastoplasmic lamellae and mitochondria but no secretion granules.

FIGURE 5. Light microscope picture of a salivary-gland cell from a quiescent late third-instar larva whose anterior spiracles had just been everted. The preparation has been colored with the periodic acid-Schiff technique, and the material within the lumen stains intensely. A few large granules are seen in the cytoplasm. The nucleus is colorless. × about 1000.

FIGURE 6. Electron micrograph of an ultrathin section of the same cell shown in Figure 5. This portion of the cytoplasm shows mitochondria, ergastoplasmic lamellae and a large secretion granule.

Salivary-gland cells of the mid-third instar larva have apparently already acquired the capacity to produce secretion granules, since a moderate number of these spherules are present in the cytoplasm. In electron micrographs of these cells it was observed that the nuclear membrane had formed blebs or outpocketings which protruded into the cytoplasm. The nuclear membrane of the salivary-gland cells of *Drosophila* is about 250 Å thick and, as has been shown in many other types of cells (for literature survey, see Watson, 1955), consists of two layers (Fig. 7). The blebs seen in the salivary-gland cells were formed by the outpocketing of the entire dual-layered membrane (Fig. 8). Tangential views of these outpocketings (Fig. 9) show the characteristic "pore" pattern of tangential sections of the nuclear membrane (Fig. 10).

An analysis of serial sections revealed that these minute projections from the nucleus were

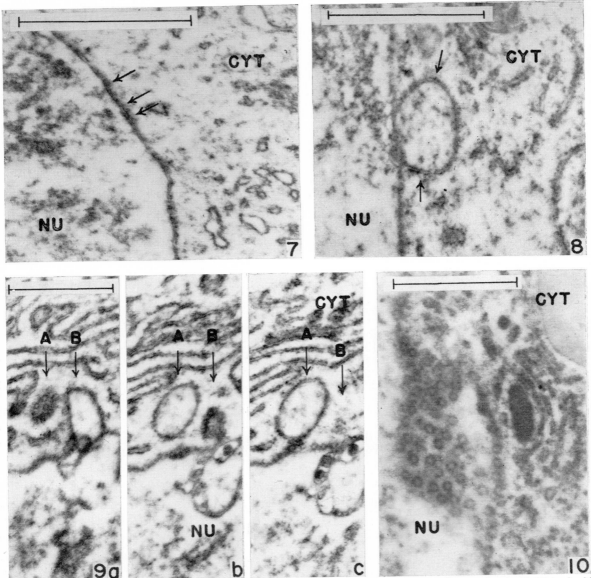

FIGURE 7. Electron micrograph showing a cross section of the nuclear membrane of a salivary-gland cell. Note double layered structure. Arrows denote places where outer and inner layers are fused or continuous with each other.

FIGURE 8. Electron micrograph of a cross section of a nuclear-membrane bleb in a salivary-gland cell. The doubleness of the membrane of the outpocketing is most pronounced at regions indicated by arrows.

FIGURE 9. Three sections through two nuclear-membrane blebs in a salivary-gland cell. The arrow marked A indicates a bleb which shows the characteristic "pore" pattern of a tangential section in Figure 9a and cross sectional views in Figures 9b and c. Arrow indicates a second outpocketing. (Figs. 9b and c are at same magnification as 9a.)

FIGURE 10. Tangential view of the nuclear membrane of a salivary-gland cell. Note "pores."

invariably associated with highly differentiated chromosomal material. The giant chromosomes of these nuclei are polytene in nature, being composed of about 2000 closely appressed chromonemata each of which is about 200 Å in width. In the band regions, the chromonemata are denser to the electron beam than they are in the interband regions. The chromosomal strands in the vicinity of the nuclear-membrane blebs were found to be highly electron scattering (more so than most other parts of the nucleus, with the exception of the nucleolus cr the densest bands) and frequently contained dense homogeneous material or distinct structural elements, such as granules, thick fibers, or lamellae. These highly differentiated chromonemal strands and materials were oriented toward the nuclear membrane and lay in contact with it at the region of the blebbing. In some instances chromosomal materials could be observed within the outpocketings. In all cases in which enough serial sections were available to trace a bleb through its entirety, its association with highly differentiated chromosomal material was confirmed, sometimes as a connection to a single intercalary band, and in other cases, apparently to terminal chromatin. In several instances, the intercalary band was located in what appeared to be a "reverse repeat," some of which have been shown to contain heterochromatin (Kaufmann, 1946; for summary of literature on intercalary heterochromatin, see Hannah, 1951).

It was necessary to establish with certainty that the nuclear membrane blebs were not attributable to distortion due to fixation, polymerization-embedding or other techniques used. Consequently numerous modifications of technical procedures were undertaken, such as varying the ionic strength, pH, or osmium-concentration of the fixative; utilization of chromate as well as osmium tetroxide in the fixing fluid; and use of prepolymerized—as well as monomer—methacrylate for imbedding. All these studies have led to the conclusion that blebbing is not due to distortion produced by fixation or other technical procedures, but is a characteristic feature of the salivary-gland cell at this stage of development.

In the earlier observations electron micrographs had been made of the large cells of the mid-third instar salivary gland cells in one stage of development, that is, at the time when the larvae were just beginning to leave their food supply. The question was accordingly raised whether blebbing occurred in cells of glands in earlier or later stages of development. The dual secretory function proposed for these gland cells suggested that the formation of the nuclear-membrane outpocketings might be a manifestation of a change in cellular activity. In order to trace the cellular changes that occur during development, a combined light microscope and electron microscope study was made of salivary glands of *D. melanogaster* during

seven stages of larval development selected at regular time intervals over the period extending from the end of second instar to pupation. This study indicated that during the early stages of development blebbing of the nuclear membrane is either entirely absent or so rare that our samples (10 individuals at each stage) did not reveal it. Until the first third of the third instar has been completed, a cell of the salivary gland contains a nucleus with a relatively smooth membrane and a cytosome without secretion granules (Figs. 3 and 4). The nuclear-membrane blebs first appear when about one-third to one-half of the third instar has been completed. At about the same time secretion granules are first seen in the cytoplasm. The number and size of secretion granules increased throughout the later hours of larval life, and although no comparative counts have been made, it seemed apparent that the number of outpocketings per nucleus and the number of nuclei with outpocketings also increased during the second half of the third instar period. Just prior to puparium formation, however, fewer blebs were found, the secretion granules disappeared from the cytoplasm and the strongly PAS-positive secretion was discharged into the lumen of the gland (Figs. 5 and 6). This series of events suggested a correlation between the appearance of nuclear-membrane outpocketings and the production of secretion granules, which act as a puparial glue when discharged from the cell.

The salivary gland of *Drosophila* undergoes degradational changes at pupation. The question accordingly arose whether the production of nuclear-membrane blebs represents the first stages of nuclear degeneration. Earlier workers (Hsu, 1948; Lesher, 1951; Bodenstein, 1950) had suggested that the accumulation of the secretion granules, which some considered deutoplasmic substances, was the first evidence of cytolysis. Our observations (also determined by Schultz, personal communication) indicate that the salivary gland of the late third instar enlarges and becomes "puffy," but that later, in the prepupal organism, the gland is reduced in size. The electron micrographs reveal that the cells of the late third instar gland have discharged their granules into the lumen but still maintain very definite cellular boundaries, with well-defined chromosomes, nuclei, ergastoplasmic lamellae, and mitochondria. Patterson, Dackerman and Schultz (1949) have shown that peptidase activity is high in glands of *Drosophila* until the puparium is formed. If the nuclear-membrane blebs and chromosomal material are indications of nuclear or chromosomal degeneration, their association with specific chromosomal bands indicates that this is not an indiscriminate phenomenon. Such a specific type of degeneration seems unlikely. Moreover, the cytological picture of an autolyzing salivary gland from an individual with a well-formed pupal case, shows that cytoly-

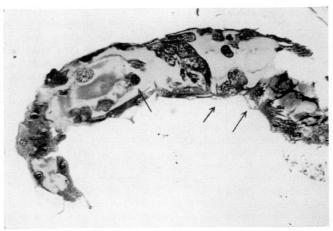

FIGURE 11. Light microscope picture of a degenerating salivary-gland cell taken from an individual shortly after puparium formation. The cells have separated from each other and the cytoplasm shows signs of cytolysis, but the chromosomes within the intact nuclei (arrows) are clearly banded and identifiable. × 250.

sis occurs first in the cytoplasm and that nuclei and well-banded chromosomes at this time are still intact (Fig. 11). By all available criteria the salivary glands of the mid-to-late third instar of *Drosophila* are composed of functionally active cells.

It is believed that the structural relationships that are observed in mid-third instar salivary-gland cells reflect the functional activity of chromosomes producing materials which subsequently are contributed to the cytoplasm. Cytochemical studies utilizing enzymatic hydrolysis have been undertaken to determine the nature of the different materials and structures involved in the transfer. Use of the enzyme deoxyribonuclease on OsO_4-fixed salivary-gland cells has resulted in complete reduction of Feulgen stainability in the chromosomes as determined by light-microscope examination. Electron micrographs of thin sections taken from these same tissues indicate that a considerable reduction in the electron-scattering capacity of the chromosomes has taken place both in the band and interband regions. Deoxyribonuclease treatment has reduced the density of the chromonemal strands in the vicinity of the nuclear-membrane outpocketing and within the bleb, indicating that these regions contain chromosomal material which most probably includes DNA. The more homogeneous highly differentiated chromosomal material which is always associated with the blebs does not seem to be reduced in density by this enzyme. A preliminary cytochemical analysis of this material suggests that ribonuclease may cause a partial reduction in its density. A more thorough investigation of the effect of ribonuclease and other enzymes must be pursued together with other cytochemical tests before this preliminary result may be considered as conclusive.

DISCUSSION

The intimate structural and configurational association observed between chromosomal materials and nuclear-membrane outpocketings suggest that this phenomenon may be a manifestation of a mechanism for transport of materials of chromosomal origin to the cytosome. In this case the outpocketings from the nucleus would be detached and released into the cytosome. In considering this hypothesis the possibility must be evaluated that the outpocketings are not manifestations of indiscriminate surface activity of the nucleus, through which blebs are formed and withdrawn, more or less as pseudopodial processes. This possibility seems to be negated, however, by the observation that rather special chromosomal materials associated in some cases with a single band extend into the blebs, suggesting that they are formed at specific regions of the nuclear membrane. The possibility must also be considered that blebs formed by the action of particular chromosomal regions could be retracted after their specific functional activity had ceased. The fact that the blebs protrude into the cytoplasm, sometimes as flask-shaped or finger-like projections, and are constricted at their point of attachment to the nucleus, frequently forming a narrow neck or tube, varying in diameter from 750 Å to 2000 Å, suggests that the outpocketings do indeed become detached.

The similarity in structure of the ergastoplasmic lamellae and nuclear membrane in cross-sectional and tangential views of salivary-gland cells has been demonstrated previously (Gay, 1955a, 1956). These similarities suggest that nuclear-membrane blebs freed from their connection with the nuclear membrane could become flattened to form the saclike membranes of the ergastoplasm. In several instances, a double-membraned structure, similar to ergastoplasmic lamellae and having the form of a bleb, was observed adjacent to the nucleus but completely detached therefrom (Fig. 12). Serial sections which traversed the whole bleb showed no attachment of these structures to the nuclear membrane. In some of the electron micrographs of nuclear-membrane blebs, we have observed structures resembling a thin lamella or membrane closely appressed to the chromosomal strands near the base of the bleb at its point of origin from the nucleus. Such structure might presumably function as an abscission layer facilitating loss of the bleb (Fig. 13). For the reasons mentioned above, it seems plausible to accept the interpretation that nuclear-membrane protrusions become detached from the nucleus and rapidly assume the aspect of the ergastoplasmic lamellae. Under such circumstances, the contents of the outpocketing could also contribute to the production of cytoplasmic material (see Fig. 14). Although cytochemical tests indicate that DNA-containing material is found within the blebs, no Feulgen-positive material has been observed in the cytoplasm when examined in the light microscope. It is believed that the small size of most of the nuclear-membrane outpocketings would preclude detection of their contents as Feulgen-positive granules in the cytoplasm. The possibility must also be entertained that a rapid conversion of the DNA to some other material, such as polysaccharide (Schrader and Leuchtenberger, 1952), might obtain. The analysis by electron microscopy of serial sections of deoxyribonuclease-treated glands is now in progress to determine whether any completely detached blebs with enzyme-reduced contents can be found.

Several lines of evidence obtained in the present study suggest that the ergastoplasmic lamellae are associated with the formation of secretion granules. The time sequence in the development of the salivary-gland cells indicates that secretion granules begin to form when the large aggregates of granular ergastoplasmic lamellae arise—that is, during early to mid-third instar. What appear to be small secretion granules are often associated with ends of the lamellae (Fig. 15) and large granules are frequently surrounded by whorls of ergastoplasm (Fig. 16). Weiss (1953) has suggested that zymogen granules of the pancreas are formed by the ergastoplasmic sacs, and more recently Rebhun (1956b) has shown that in various types of oocytes the yolk nuclei which form the yolk-platelets are composed of aggregates of basophilic ergastoplasmic lamellae.

If the ergastoplasm of the salivary-gland cells is associated with the formation of secretion granules, an elaborate scheme could be formulated for the role of specific chromosomal regions in directing cytoplasmic functions. It is tempting to speculate that the double-layered lamellae in the young larval salivary-gland cells represent sites of formation of saliva and that the new function

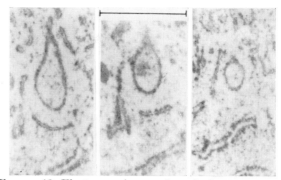

FIGURE 12. Electron micrographs of three non-consecutive sections of a bleb-like structure observed in the cytoplasm of a salivary-gland cell. The complete series of sections which traversed this tear-drop-shaped structure from tangent to tangent showed no attachment to the nuclear membrane.

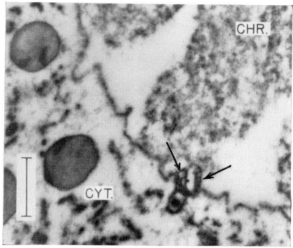

FIGURE 13. Electron micrograph of a salivary-gland cell in which the chromosomal fibers adjacent to the membrane are very dense (see arrows) and seem, from study of serial sections, to be lamellar in structure. It is suggested that these structures might function as an abscission layer facilitating detachment of the outpocketing.

of forming a cementing substance may be attributed to the ergastoplasmic lamellae produced later in larval life. (This proposition is based on the concept that in the broad sense the term ergastoplasm subsumes numerous kinds of functionally-different double-membraned structures which in the future may be characterized both structurally and functionally.) The foregoing inference is supported by several lines of evidence. In addition to those enumerated above, it may be noted that with Azure B staining the material between the secretion granules shows a pronounced basophilia which is reduced by ribonuclease digestion. Electron micrographs have indicated that the ergastoplasmic lamellae are located in these regions. The capacity of RNA

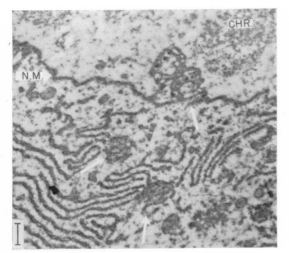

FIGURE 14. Electron micrograph of a salivary-gland cell. Arrows indicate cytoplasmic structures showing some similarity to structures within the nucleus.

and cytochemical data point to the ergastoplasmic lamellae as the cytoplasmic structures having a high RNA content. These various circumstantial lines of evidence present an array of related facts that require interpretation.

A mechanism has consequently been postulated whereby chromosomal loci and adjacent segments of the nuclear membrane participate in the transfer from nucleus to cytosome of materials that serve to regulate the synthetic activities of the living cell. Operation of the mechanism involves production of blebs along the nuclear membrane, their detachment into the cytosome and conversion into the ergastoplasmic membranes or so-called endoplasmic reticulum and the release of the contents of the blebs to augment and modify existing stores of cytoplasmic materials. This method would thus afford a rapid transfer from the nucleus to cytosome of materials essential for synthetic activities.

From this viewpoint, the mechanism proposed above, involving formation and detachment of

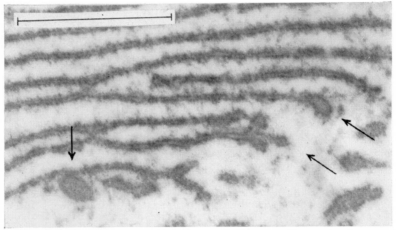

FIGURE 15. Cross section of ergastoplasmic lamellae. Arrows indicate swollen ends of some of the double-layered membranes. In serial sections these structures appear to form small spherules of the same density as the large secretion granules.

to facilitate protein synthesis has been well established. According to Caspersson, Schultz, and Brachet, RNA accumulates on the cytoplasmic side of the nuclear membrane. This situation might be explicable on the basis of accumulation of detached blebs which had become converted to layers of the ergastoplasm with their associated RNA. Palade and Siekevitz (1956), and Novikoff (1956) have demonstrated recently that the microsomal fraction of tissues homogenates consists in great part of vesicles and lamellae of the ergastoplasm. Palade and Siekevitz have also indicated that the microsomal RNA may be derived from the granular portion of these lamellae. Dalton and Felix (1954b) suggest that the membranes themselves may contain a high concentration of RNA. In any event, the biochemical

nuclear membrane blebs, might represent a unique adaptation, an expression of a latent potentiality serving to produce a given type of secretion in one kind of cell at a particular stage of development. This may actually be the case, but the unique feature would not be the production of ergastoplasmic lamellae from the nuclear membrane but only the method of detachment of the nuclear-membrane, that is, by blebbing. Ergastoplasm, or endoplasmic reticulum, has been found in the cytosome of cells of many types (Palade, 1955), being very abundant in secretory and nerve cells, and oocytes. Its similarity in structure to the nuclear membrane has frequently been noted in these materials (Dalton and Felix, 1954a; Sjöstrand and Hanzon, 1954; Watson, 1955; Swift, 1956; Rebhun, 1956a, b) as

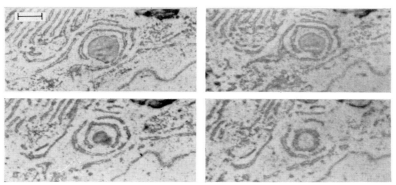

FIGURE 16. Electron micrographs of four non-consecutive sections of a secretion granule and the surrounding ergastoplasmic lamellae. The innermost layer of the ergastoplasm forms a cup around the secretion granule.

well as in *Drosophila*, and this suggests a relationship of widespread occurrence and general functional significance. In some cells the innermost membranes of the ergastoplasm lie so close to the nuclear membrane as to suggest origination by a process of exfoliation. In fact, Swift (1956) and Rebhun (1956a) recently demonstrated the active participation of the nuclear membrane of oocytes of *Spisula* and *Otala* in formation of basophilic cytoplasmic structure, which may in turn be involved in protein synthesis. Swift's hypothesis of the synthetic cycle involved may be summarized as follows: Active chromosomal loci may serve as synthetic sites for formation of protein filaments, which radiate to the nuclear membrane in bundles. Where these bundles intersect the membrane, annuli and subannuli are formed and RNA material is apparently synthesized. The filaments may extend into the cytoplasm and synthesize new membrane systems parallel to the nuclear surface. Detachment of a series of these lamellae from the nuclear surface may then constitute the aggregates of the basophilic lamellae seen in the cytoplasm. Rebhun (1956b) has extended these observations and hypotheses to demonstrate the probable production by these lamellae of the protein-containing yolk platelets. Although the mechanism by which the end result is attained in oocytes may be different from that in the salivary-gland cell of *Drosophila*, the structures involved seem to be similar. Swift's hypothesis of production of ergastoplasmic lamellae would be more conducive to maintenance of a nuclear membrane with constant properties than one in which segments were continually lost through detachment of outpocketings. Indeed, a situation may be visualized in which structural constancy of the nuclear membrane is essential for sustained activity of the cells and in which repeated diminution by blebbing would lead to the onset of such degenerative changes as the salivary-gland cells undergo in early pupal life. In either case, attention focusses on the potentialities of the nuclear membrane for the production of cytoplasmic organelles.

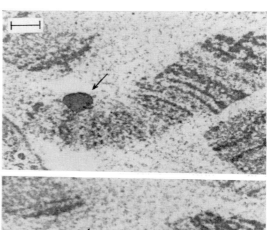

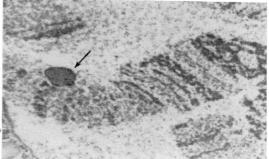

FIGURE 17. Two serial sections of a salivary-gland nucleus in which a nucleolus-like body (arrow) is confluent with a well-banded intercalary chromosomal region.

The condition responsible for blebbing during third instar may be the high degree of polyteny attained by the chromosomes which permits accumulation of a favorable level of some essential chromosomal products. In fact, as has been pointed out by Painter (1945), polyteny may represent a device for facilitating functional activity of the salivary-gland cell in secretion.

We have found several examples of accumulation of nucleolus-like material in well-banded regions that apparently are not located in the proximal heterochromatic region of the X, the position occupied by the nucleolus organizer in *D. melanogaster* (Fig. 17). Cytochemical analysis of these structures is now in progress. In the cases of bleb formation, it is of interest to note that some of the blebs seem to be associated with chromosomal regions that are heterochromatic. The phenomenon may therefore reflect some general property of heterochromatin and this may in turn account for the fact that many blebs are present in a cell, since all chromosomes of *D. melanogaster* contain heterochromatin.

One such general property of heterochromatin—postulated by Caspersson and Schultz—is its role in protein synthesis. They assume that this proceeds by way of the nucleolus—the nucleolus organizer in *D. melanogaster* lies in the proximal heterochromatic region of the X chromosome. We have shown above that the increased basophilia observed near the nucleus may be due to the formation of basophilic ergastoplasmic lamellae which originate from nuclear-membrane blebs, which may in turn be associated with heterochromatic regions of the chromosomes. This offers a more precise definition of the role of heterochromatic loci other than the nucleolus-organizing region, and recognizes the active—rather than the passive—participation of the nuclear membrane. It does not afford any evidence concerning the activity in these synthetic processes of the nucleolus, unless intercalary heterochromatin has properties comparable with those of the nucleolus-organizing region (as suggested by Poulson and Metz (1938) in an analysis of the "puffs" in *Sciara*).

The interpretations presented above concern those properties of heterochromatin that are operative in influencing metabolic activities of a cell during the course of its normal development. There is another aspect of the action of heterochromatin that is related to the behavior of euchromatic loci brought into its vicinity by structural rearrangment of chromosomes, since it leads to variegation in somatic cells. The phenomenon was first recognized in *Drosophila*, but a somewhat analogous situation appears to exist in maize and may have more widespread distribution in nature. The question arises whether such differences in the eventuation of gene-controlled reactions as appear in adjoining cells of a variegated tissue could be attributable in some cases to the operation of a mechanism comparable to that described for the salivary-gland cell of *Drosophila*.

No definitive answer can be given since the relevant empirical data are not in hand, but a survey of the factors that are known to modify the manifestation of variegation, such as change in temperature and alteration of balance between euchromatin and heterochromatin, serve to focus attention on the integrative mechanisms involved. Since the establishment of patterns of variegation requires not only the operation of the displaced identifying chromosomal differential but also of the adjoining and even the more remote heterochromatic regions within the complex, it is conceivable that here again some general property of heterochromatin is brought

into play in the eventuation of the resulting phenotypes, perhaps by modifying the nucleic acid balance as suggested by Schultz and Caspersson (1939). The problems that arise in such considerations also seem sufficiently challenging to warrant studies of variegation at the level of analysis now afforded by the electron microscope, not only in *Drosophila* but in other organisms such as maize—in which the genetic factors responsible for variegation have been so skillfully elucidated by McClintock—in order to determine whether displacement of the nuclear membrane by blebbing or some analogous process is involved in the production of cytoplasmic organelles.

In the foregoing discussion it has been implied that the detached segments of the nuclear membrane might convey the specificity afforded by the chromosomes that participated in their formation. The observations of classical cytology suggest that the chromosomal vesicles at telophase fuse to form the nuclear membrane. Watson (1955) has proposed that the nuclear membrane represents a modified element of the endoplasmic reticulum. Although cytoplasmic structures and substances may be involved in the actual formation of the membrane, the chromosomal strands in close proximity to these materials could conceivably determine the way these materials are put together and impart a specificity to the nuclear membrane. Watson (1955) has pointed out that the inner nuclear membrane of nerve cells is noticeably thicker than the outer one, and has suggested that accumulation of nuclear material could produce this differentiation. Just this sort of specificity either during or after formation of the envelope could be transposed from chromosomal strands to the nuclear membrane.

Detachment of nuclear-membrane segments thus appears to represent a method for the production of "plasmagenes." If the hypothesis is sustained that the ergastoplasmic lamellae formed from the nuclear membrane convey genetic specificity, it is suggested that they be termed genoplasmic membranes to avoid the ambiguity that now derives when the term "plasmagene" is employed. Transfer of representatives of nuclear genes to the cytosome was the primary criterion on which the concept of the plasmagene was based, in conjunction with the assumption that they could then divide and mutate in the cytoplasm. On the basis of evidence now available in *Drosophila*, it is not known whether the ergastoplasmic lamellae produced by nuclear membrane blebs are capable of either duplicating or mutating. Swift has suggested that in the oocytes which he has studied the ergastoplasmic lamellae may form new lamellae on the free margins of the basophilic lamellar aggregates. This would then constitute evidence for replication.

We have proposed that gene-controlled reactions might be mediated through reproduction and transfer of segments of the nuclear membrane to the cytoplasm. These hypotheses involve intracellular transfer of specificity. The question might be posed whether intercellular transport of specificity might likewise be effected by passive transfer of similar cytoplasmic organelles from one cell to another.

The concept of the nuclear membrane as an actively functioning component of the cell has not been considered in earlier theoretical discussions of nucleocytoplasmic interrelations. Schultz (1952) has suggested that the properties of the nuclear membrane might vary according to the chromosomes most intimately associated with it during its production, and that this variation might afford a basis for differential cell function and cell differentiation. The present findings in *Drosophila* salivary-gland cells sustain this point of view and extend the concept to include a nuclear membrane that is capable of continuous displacement and reformation. Eventuation of the genetic potentialities of a cell can accordingly be visualized in terms of the sequential operation of independent loci within a numerically unvarying chromosome complex and the subsequent activity of specifically endowed cytoplasmic organelles.

In 1925 Wilson noted that those hypotheses are more accessible to investigation which assume differentiation is effected "by transformation of visible cytoplasmic granules or other definite bodies, arising either by migration from the nucleus or independently in the cytosome." Efforts along these lines have not been lacking as was pointed out in the introductory remarks about the "chromidial hypothesis," but the evidence represents for the most part a series of reports of cytoplasmic particles of unknown chemical composition and uncertain origin. Whether the hypothesis of the production of ergastoplasmic membranes from the nuclear membrane will serve to narrow the existing dichotomy between the biochemical and morphological factors involved in differentiation remains to be decided. An effort along these lines seems justified, however, in an investigation at the level of resolution now afforded by the electron microscope of some of the classical materials that served in laying the foundations of modern cytology and experimental embryology.

It would be hazardous to imply that the mechanism proposed in this discussion is anything more than one of a possible series of alternative methods by which nucleocytoplasmic transfer of materials may be mediated. But the blebbing phenomenon in *Drosophila* salivary-gland cells, even though it may be unique in nature, offers a mechanism whereby nucleo-cytoplasmic exchanges involving specific chromosomal regions may be effected. The possible intermediation of a nuclear membrane in gene-controlled reactions thus affords a new perspective in consideration of problems of gene action and development.

ACKNOWLEDGMENTS

The author wishes to acknowledge with thanks the use of the electron microscope at the Biology Department of Brookhaven National Laboratory during the past year, and prior to that date, at the cytology laboratory of the Rockefeller Institute for Medical Research. In addition she wishes to express her appreciation to Dr. Berwind P. Kaufmann for many profitable discussions concerning the theoretical implications of this study and to Miss Kathryn E. Fuscaldo for valuable assistance in the experimental procedures.

REFERENCES

BODENSTEIN, D., 1950, The postembryonic development of Drosophila. In: Biology of Drosophila. New York, John Wiley and Sons.

BRACHET, J., 1950, Chemical Embryology. New York, Interscience Publishers, Inc.

CASPERSSON, T., 1950, Cell growth and cell function. Salmon Lectures. New York, W. W. Norton and Co.

CHAUDRY, H. S., 1951, Nucleolar activity in the oocytes of some marine teleostean fishes. J. Roy. Micr. Soc. 71: 87–93.

COOPER, D., 1952, The transfer of desoxyribose nucleic acid from the tapetum to the microsporocytes at the onset of meiosis. Amer. Nat. 86: 219–229.

DALTON, A. J., 1955, A chrome-osmium fixative for electron microscopy. Anat. Rec. 121: 281.

DALTON, A. J., and FELIX, M., 1954a, Cytologic and cytochemical characteristics of the Golgi substance of epithelial cells of the epididymis—in situ, in homogenates and after isolation. Amer. J. Anat. 94: 171–187.

1954b, A study of the Golgi substance and ergastoplasm in a series of mammalian cell types. In: Fine Structure of Cells, pp. 274–293. New York, Interscience Publishers, Inc.

DODSON, E. O., 1953, Nucleoli and the formation of yolk in the eggs of vertebrates. J. Roy. Micr. Soc. 72: 177-178.

DURYEE, W. R., 1940, The chromosomes of the amphibian nucleus. Univ. Penn. Conference on Cytology, Genetics, and Evolution, pp. 129–141.

1950, Chromosomal physiology in relation to nuclear structure. Ann. N. Y. Acad. Sci. 50: 920–953.

FRAENKEL, G., and BROOKES, V. J., 1953, The process by which the puparia of many species of flies become fixed to a substrate. Biol. Bull. 150: 442–449.

GALL, J. G., 1954, Lampbrush chromosomes from oocyte nuclei of the newt. J. Morph. 94: 283–351.

GAY, H., 1954, Nuclear-cytoplasmic interrelations as revealed by electron micrographs of Drosophila salivary-gland cells. Anat. Rec. 120: 728.

1955a, Nucleo-cytoplasmic relations in salivary-gland cells of Drosophila. Proc. Nat. Acad. Sci., Wash. 41: 370–375.

1955b, Structural evidence for nucleo-cytoplasmic relations in Drosophila. Anat. Rec. 122: 469.

1956, Chromosome-nuclear membrane-cytoplasmic interrelations in Drosophila. J. Biophys. Biochem. Cytol. 2: suppl. 407–414.

GAY, H., and ANDERSON, T. F., 1954, Serial sections for electron microscopy. Science 120: 1071–1073.

GERARD, R. W., 1954, Experiments in microevolution. Science 120: 727–732.

HANNAH, ALOHA, 1951, Localization and function of heterochromatin in Drosophila melanogaster. Adv. Genet. 4: 87–125.

HSU, W. S., 1948, The Golgi material and mitochondria in the salivary glands of the larva of Drosophila melanogaster. Quart. J. Micr. Sci. 89: 410–414.

KAUFMANN, B. P., 1946, Organization of the chromosome. I. Break distribution and chromosome recombination in *Drosophila melanogaster*. J. Exp. Zool. *102:* 293–320.

KAUFMANN, B. P., McDONALD, M. R., and GAY, H., 1951, The distribution of nucleic acids in fixed cells as shown by enzymatic hydrolysis. J. Cell. Comp. Physiol. *38:* Suppl. 1: 71–100.

LESHER, S., 1951, Studies on the larval salivary gland of *Drosophila*. I. The nucleic acids. Exp. Cell Res. *2:* 577–585.

NEWMAN, S. B., BORYSKO, E., and SWERDLOW, M., 1949, New sectioning techniques for light and electron microscopy. Science *110:* 66–68.

NOVIKOFF, A., 1956, Preservation of the fine structure of isolated liver cell particulates with polyvinyl-pyrrollidone-sucrose. J. Biophys. Biochem. Cytol. *2:* Suppl. 65–66.

PAINTER, T. S., 1945, Nuclear phenomena associated with secretion in certain gland cells with especial reference to the origin of cytoplasmic nucleic acid. J. Exp. Zool. *100:* 523–544.

PAINTER, T. S., and TAYLOR, A. N., 1942, Nucleic acid storage in the toad's egg. Proc. Nat. Acad. Sci., Wash. *28:* 311–317.

PALADE, G. E., 1952, A study of fixation for electron microscopy. J. exp. Med. *95:* 285–298.

1955, Studies on the endoplasmic reticulum. II. Simple dispositions in cells *in situ*. J. Biophys. Biochem. Cytol. *1:* 567–582.

PALADE, G. E., and SIEKEVITZ, P., 1956, Liver microsomes. An integrated morphological and biochemical study. J. Biophys. Biochem. Cytol. *2:* 171–200.

PATTERSON, E. K., DACKERMAN, M. E., and SCHULTZ, J., 1949, Peptidase activity accompanying growth of the larval salivary gland of *Drosophila melanogaster*. J. Gen. Physiol. *32:* 623–645.

PONTECORVO, G., 1952, Genetic formulation of gene structure and gene action. Adv. Enzymol. *13:* 121–149.

PORTER, K. R., and BLUM, J., 1953, A study in microtomy for electron microscopy. Anat. Rec. *117:* 685–712.

POULSON, D. F., and METZ, C. W., 1938, Studies on the structure of nucleolus-forming regions and related structures in the giant salivary-gland chromosomes of Diptera. J. Morph. *63:* 363–395.

REBHUN, L. I., 1956a, Electron microscopy of basophilic structures of some invertebrate oocytes. I. Periodic lamellae and the nuclear envelope. J. Biophys. Biochem. Cytol. *2:* 93–104.

1956b, Electron microscopy of basophilic structures of some invertebrate oocytes. II. Fine structure of the yolk nuclei. J. Biophys. Biochem. Cytol. *2:* 159–170.

SCHRADER, F., and LEUCHTENBERGER, C., 1952, The origin of certain nutritive substances in the eggs of Hemiptera. Exp. Cell Res. *3:* 136–146.

SCHULTZ, J., 1952, Interrelations between nucleus and cytoplasm: Problems at the biological level. Exp. Cell. Res., Suppl. *2:* 17–43.

SCHULTZ, J., and CASPERSSON, T., 1939, Heterochromatic regions and the nucleic acid metabolism of the chromosomes. Arch. exp. Zellforsch. *22:* 650–654.

SJÖSTRAND, F. S., and HANZON, V., 1954, Membrane structures of cytoplasm and mitochondria in exocrine cells of mouse pancreas as revealed by high resolution electron microscopy. Exp. Cell Res. *7:* 393–414.

SONNENBLICK, B. P., 1950, The early embryology of *Drosophila melanogaster*. In: Biology of Drosophila. New York, John Wiley and Sons.

SPARROW, A. H., and HAMMOND, M. R., 1947, Cytological evidence for the transfer of desoxyribose nucleic acid from nucleus to cytoplasm in certain plants. Amer. J. Bot. *34:* 439–445.

SWIFT, H., 1953, Quantitative aspects of nuclear nucleoproteins. Intern. Rev. Cytology *2:* 1–76.

1956, The fine structure of annulate lamellae. J. Biophys. Biochem. Cytol. *2:* Suppl. 415–418.

WATSON, M. L., 1955, The nuclear envelope. Its structure and relation to cytoplasmic membranes. J. Biophys. Biochem. Cytol. *1:* 257–270.

WEISS, J. M., 1953, The ergastoplasm. Its fine structure and relation to protein synthesis as studied with the electron microscope in the pancreas of the Swiss Albino mouse. J. Exp. Med. *98:* 607–618.

WILSON, E. B., 1925, The Cell in Development and Heredity. 3rd Ed. New York, Macmillan Co.

WITTEK, M., 1952, La vittelogenese chez les Amphibiens. Arch. Biol., Paris *63:* 133–197.

DISCUSSION

POULSON: Have you made any estimates of the number of nuclear-membrane blebs per section, or per nucleus? If so, is there as yet any indication of changes at different times?

GAY: We can easily count the number of nuclear-membrane blebs per section but it is difficult to transpose these data into an estimate of the number of blebs per nucleus. In our study of serial sections we have found that one section of a nucleus may have as many as six or seven outpocketings whereas at another level of the same nucleus only one or two are seen. It is therefore only useful to make counts of nuclear-membrane blebs when we have a long series of sections through a nucleus. Unfortunately they are not easily obtained, but we have made an estimate on one mid-third-instar cell from which we secured 35 serial sections. Since the diameter of this nucleus is about 20 μ and the average thickness of each ultrathin section about 500 Å, we have sampled in this case less than one tenth of the depth of the nucleus. However, in these 35 sections we found 19 nuclear-membrane blebs. As we do not know at what level our sample traversed the nucleus it is not possible to calculate the number of blebs in the nucleus, which is an oblate spheroid. A rough estimate can be made in terms of a cylinder, which gives about 200 nuclear-membrane blebs per nucleus, a figure that is obviously too large but which is probably correct within the order of magnitude, 20–200.

There do seem to be changes in the number of nuclear-membrane blebs with development during the third instar, that is, none just after the molt, initiation of blebbing at the end of the first third of this period, increase in number of outpocketings throughout the rest of the third instar period, and finally, somewhat of a decline in number at the end of this period. These evaluations are subjective, however, and not based on counts such as those given above, since extensive series of ultrathin sections are only rarely obtained.

MOSES: For many years an understanding of the functional relationship between nucleus and cytoplasm was limited by conjectures about the nuclear membrane. Watson's (J. Biophys. Biochem. Cytol. *1:* 257–270, 1955) demonstration of the continuity between the double membrane at the nuclear periphery and the membrane lamellae of the endoplasmic reticulum defined the morphological continuity between nucleus and cytoplasm as well as the physical boundary through which materials must pass if actual transfer is to take place. Dr. Gay's observations of nuclear blebbing, particularly as it is associated with specific chromosomal regions, are indicative of a possible mechanism of transfer. Nuclear blebbing, however, may well be a fairly common phenomenon. I have observed an extreme example of it associated with cell differentiation (Jour. Biophys. Biochem Cytol. 2 Suppl., in press). In the spermatid of crayfish, large and frequent nuclear outpocketings are associated with the formation of an elaborate system of convoluted cytoplasmic membranes. These membranes surround the acrosome and nucleus and make up the balance of the aflagellate sperm. DNA lines the interior of the blebs in the early stages, but does not appear to be included in the resultant membrane system.

GAY: Watson's beautiful demonstration of nuclear membrane structure and of the relationship between the double membrane of the nucleus and the endoplasmic reticulum in certain types of mammalian cells does indeed suggest that materials may be transferred between nucleus and cytoplasm through "pores," which may be bridged by a diaphragm, as Watson has suggested, or through a connection between the perinuclear space, that is, the space enclosed by the two layers of the nuclear membrane, and the cavities of the endoplasmic reticulum. Whether this latter type of connection between nucleus and cytoplasmic membrane systems also exists in cells containing less endoplasmic reticulum than those studied by Watson and in cells of non-mammalian organisms remains for future investigation to determine. It should be kept in mind, at any rate, that in this type of transfer, the inner nuclear membrane still remains as a barrier to passage of materials of macromolecular dimensions directly from nucleus to cytoplasm. The present interpretation of observations made on *Drosophila* salivary-gland cells does not ignore the fact that materials may pass from nucleus to cytoplasm

for metabolic purposes through the channels suggested by Watson. The interpretations that have been drawn from this study do recognize, however, that the salivary-gland chromosomes have become highly polytene by mid-third instar, and that such growth establishes a new set of chromosome-nuclear membrane-cytoplasmic relationships that may be conducive to nuclear-membrane blebbing. Cytologists are familiar with the extraordinary adaptations developed among the insects at the cellular level for meeting many types of functional requirements, such as elimination of whole sets of chromosomes or extrusion of particular chromosomes at specific periods in development. It is suggested the nuclear-membrane blebbing phenomenon in *Drosophila* may be a related type of "demand reaction" and thus represent an adaptive mechanism for gross transfer of materials in a very rapid manner to the cytoplasm.

The observations presented in my paper can obviously apply only to the activity of one type of cell at one stage in its development, but the reports of Swift and Rhebun suggest that in some oocytes the ergastoplasmic lamellae apparently are associated with nuclear-membrane origin and are concerned in the production of additional lamellar material. Dr. Moses' description of cellular differentiation in the crayfish spermatid also involves nuclear-membrane activity in the formation of cytoplasmic membrane systems. A recent personal communication from Dr. T. C. Hsu indicates that nuclear blebbing may occur in tissue-culture cells. It thus seems possible that the process of transfer of material from nucleus to cytosome may take many different forms in different types of cells. As long as my observations of nuclear-membrane blebbing in *Drosophila* represented the only evidence of this type of phenomenon, it seemed advisable to suggest that it might represent a unique pattern of cellular differentiation, but now that additional evidence has been presented indicating involvement of the nuclear membrane in the formation of cytoplasmic membrane systems, it does not seem premature to suggest the possibility of its more general significance in the operation of genetic systems.

Serial Transplantation of Embryonic Nuclei[1]

THOMAS J. KING AND ROBERT BRIGGS

Lankenau Hospital Research Institute and Institute for Cancer Research, Philadelphia, Pennsylvania

Over the past many years genetical research has revealed large numbers of gene effects on cell differentiation. These are usually effects on the final phases of differentiation, but may also be manifested at early developmental stages (Glucksohn-Waelsch, 1954; Hadorn, 1948, 1956; Poulson, 1945; and others). In principle, the analysis of these effects depends upon the permanent alteration or deletion of a chromosome segment, and the subsequent detection of a change in differentiation—usually a deficiency. The evidence so obtained permits the conclusion that a particular gene or gene set is required for a particular type of differentiation to proceed normally. However, in general it leaves unanswered the questions which are of greatest concern to students of development. First, the genetic evidence as yet provides no explanation of the orderly segregation of cell types during development—of the fact that a given gene comes to have one effect in one part of the organism while in another part it has no effect or a different one. This must, of course, involve interactions of the geneticist's nucleus with the embryologist's cytoplasmic localizations, but the nature of this interaction is unknown. Second, the available evidence fails to account for the stability or irreversibility of differentiation. In other words, while genes have particular functions in differentiation, in general, it is not known how they acquire them, nor whether they are themselves altered in the performance of these functions in such a way as to confer stability on the differentiated cells.

It has been apparent for some time that in order to obtain answers to the questions posed above it would be necessary to devise new methods for detecting changes in gene function in somatic cells. Essentially, such methods should yield recombinations of nucleus and cytoplasm and of different types of nuclei of somatic cells, comparable with the natural recombinations of germ cells from which most genetic information is obtained.

Experiments of the type mentioned above, involving artificial transfer of cytoplasm or nucleus, were accomplished with unicellular organisms some years ago. Hämmerling (1934, 1953), using the unicellular uninucleate alga, *Acetabularia*, grafted stalk pieces from one species to the nucleated rhizoidal ends of another and demonstrated that the form of the cap that regenerated from the grafted stalk was controlled by the nucleus. Later Hämmerling (1953) produced heterokaryons and showed that the form of the regenerated cap was intermediate between the forms characteristic of the species contributing the nuclei. This and other evidence led to the conclusion that the nucleus produces specific morphogenetic substances which pass into the cytoplasm and there control the differentiation of the cap.

Another instance in which new combinations of nucleus and cytoplasm have been produced artificially is provided by the studies of Danielli and co-workers on amoebae. Using a method devised by Comandon and deFonbrune (1939), these investigators transferred nuclei from one species of amoeba to another (Lorch and Danielli, 1950). In the best analyzed case, a combination of *A. proteus* nucleus with *A. discoides* cytoplasm, a clone was obtained which has survived more than six years. Some properties of the individuals in this clone (division rate, nuclear diameter) are determined by the cytoplasm, others (shape when migrating) are intermediate, while the type of antigen(s) produced is under nuclear control (Danielli, Lorch, Ord and Wilson, 1955). Similar experiments, involving transfers of nuclei between different species of *Stentor*, have been done by Tartar (1953). The ciliates, with their highly organized cytoplasmic structures, possess obvious advantages over amoebae for this type of study. Tartar was able to make successful intraspecific transfers, but unfortunately the interspecific combinations did not survive long enough to permit an analysis of the relative contributions of cytoplasm and nucleus in the control of cytoplasmic differentiation.

So far, we have restricted ourselves to those instances in which nucleo-cytoplasmic recombinations have been produced artificially in unicellular organisms. There is, of course, a much larger body of information, not to be reviewed here, which is based on regeneration studies in ciliates and on various naturally occurring genetic recombinations in a variety of microorganisms. In the majority of cases, it appears that cell type is determined by nuclear genes, but cytoplasmic particulates or conditions have also been shown to be a part of the genetic system (Sonneborn, 1954; Ephrussi, 1953; Weisz, 1951). This work with unicellular organisms is extremely valuable in revealing a larger range of recombination mech-

[1] The experimental work reported in this paper was aided by a research grant from the National Cancer Institute of the National Institutes of Health, United States Public Health Service, and in part by an institutional grant from the American Cancer Society.

anisms, both natural and artificial, than had been suspected 25 years ago. It has also provided us with a set of beautifully analyzed types of nucleo-cytoplasmic interactions, which have led to several theories of metazoan differentiation. However, as Lederberg (1956) has pointed out, the problems of embryology cannot be solved with microbes, and we should now pass to a consideration of some of the attempts that have been made toward an analysis of nuclear function in metazoan differentiation.

This subject was of intense interest in the early years of experimental embryology, largely as a result of the stimulus provided by the somatic segregation theory of differentiation proposed by Weismann and by Roux. The large literature of the period has been summarized by Wilson (1925). Of this, we should like to mention only two experiments. The first, by Jacques Loeb (1894), involved placing fertilized sea urchin eggs in diluted sea water, in which they swell and sometimes burst the egg membrane. When this happens a portion of the cytoplasm protrudes as a hernia. This may not at first contain a nucleus, but after a few divisions of the main part of the egg one of the cleavage nuclei may migrate into the herniated portion and initiate its development, which then proceeds to the formation of either a complete embryo or half a double monster. A similar result was obtained later in the famous constriction experiment of Spemann (1914), who observed a delayed nucleation of one half of the newt egg resulting from the migration into it of a nucleus from the other half after it attained the 16 to 32 cell stage. Again the part experiencing the delayed nucleation developed into a complete embryo.

In both Loeb's and Spemann's experiments, as well as in numerous other investigations, the results showed that the cleavage nuclei are equivalent and "totipotent." However, the actual evidence was restricted to the first few cleavages and, as Spemann (1938) later pointed out, it remained undecided whether the nuclei might come to have different properties in different tissues later in development. Spemann further suggested that decisive information on the question might perhaps be afforded if it were possible to transfer nuclei from cells of older embryos to non-nucleated eggs, the development of which should then reveal the character of the transplanted nucleus. This type of experiment was also suggested independently by Schultz (personal communication, 1943; 1952), Ephrussi (1951), Rostand (1943) and perhaps others.

To the best of our knowledge, the transfer of nuclei (by pricking frog's eggs coated with embryonic brei) was first attempted by Rostand in 1943, with uncertain success. A few years later, we began to work on the problem, and after a considerable number of failures devised a different procedure for the transplantation of living nuclei from embryonic cells into enucleated eggs of the frog, *Rana pipiens* (Briggs and King, 1952). More recently transfers of embryonic nuclei have also been made by Waddington and Pantelouris (1953), Lehman (1955, 1956), Markert (referred to in Lehman, 1956) and Subtelny (1956). The method used is not without its difficulties and complications, but it appears to represent the most direct experimental approach for obtaining evidence of the genetic condition of nuclei in differentiating embryonic cells.

NOTE ON METHODS

A brief description of the nuclear transplantation procedure was given in previous papers (Briggs and King, 1952, 1953; King and Briggs, 1955). Since then, certain refinements, particularly in the construction and use of micropipettes, have been added, which will be described elsewhere. Here we wish to mention only the main features of the method—those which are essential to an appraisal of the significance of the results obtained with it.

The transplantation operation is carried out in two main steps. First, the recipient eggs (*Rana pipiens*) are activated with a glass needle and subsequently enucleated, following Porter's (1939) technique. With practice and care, the enucleation operation is 100 per cent successful. The second part of the procedure involves the isolation of the donor cells and the nuclear transfer itself. Free donor cells may be obtained by the appropriate use of Versene (Ethylene diamine tetra acetic acid, Na salt) alone or in combination with trypsin, as previously described (King and Briggs, 1955). A given cell, in Niu-Twitty (1953) solution, is then drawn into the tip of a micropipette, the inner diameter of which is somewhat smaller than that of the cell. When this is properly done the cell surface is broken but the contents are not dispersed. In this way the nucleus is protected by its own cytoplasm until the pipette is inserted into the recipient egg and the broken cell ejected, liberating the nucleus into the egg cytoplasm. The technique sounds deceptively simple, but it takes practice to perform these operations consistently well.

Two features of the method that bear on the interpretation of results are first the inclusion of donor cell cytoplasm along with the injected nucleus, and second, the possibility of inadvertently damaging the nucleus in the course of the operation. Nuclear damage can be appraised by a study of control eggs injected with undifferentiated blastula nuclei, and by observations on cleavage patterns and chromosomes of test eggs. With reference to the donor cell cytoplasm, it should be mentioned that it represents in volume only $\frac{1}{40,000}$ to $\frac{1}{500,000}$ the volume of cytoplasm of the recipient egg. Still, the possibility that it might contain self-replicating units controlling differentiation must be considered, and where necessary, control transfers of cytoplasm from differentiating cells must be carried out—as will be mentioned in a subsequent section of this paper.

TRANSPLANTATION TESTS OF BLASTULA NUCLEI

The first successful transplantations were carried out with nuclei of mid- to late blastulae. The donor blastulae were 18 to 24 hours old (at 18°C) and consisted of approximately 8,000 to 16,000 cells (estimates of cell number based on Sze's (1953) determinations). Only nuclei of undetermined animal hemisphere cells were used. In the first set of experiments, about one-third of the transfers led to normal cleavage and blastula formation on the part of the recipient eggs, and the majority of these blastulae, some 75 per cent, developed into complete embryos. Half of the embryos appeared to be perfectly normal while the remainder displayed minor abnormalities (Briggs and King, 1952). In more recent experiments, the number of transfers of this type leading to normal cleavage has been larger (40% to 80%) and the majority (ca. 80%) of the resulting embryos develop normally to larval or later stages (King and Briggs, 1955 and unpub.).

The proof that the nuclear transfers are successful, and that the test eggs contain only the transplanted nuclei, consists of the following:

1) Control operations for removal of the egg nucleus, performed on normally fertilized eggs, show that all eggs develop as androgenetic haploids. Failures would lead to the development of diploids, of which there were none in control series of more than 500 embryos during the past two years.

2) Sections of eggs which cleave following enucleation and nuclear transplantation reveal the egg nucleus outside the egg, in the enucleation exovate, while the blastomeres contain nuclei derived from the transferred nucleus (Briggs and King, 1952).

3) Enucleated eggs which were injected with diploid nuclei and which begin cleavage at the normal time after activation, develop into diploid embryos, ploidy being determined by cell size, nucleolar number, and chromosome counts (see Table 2 of this paper for chromosome counts). If the first cleavage is initiated one cleavage interval late, the resulting embryos are tetraploids.

4) Enucleated eggs injected with haploid nuclei develop into haploid embryos unless there is a delayed initiation of cleavage—in which case the embryos become diploids (Subtelny, unpub.).

5) When enucleated *Rana pipiens* eggs are injected with *R. catesbeiana* nuclei the resulting development duplicates exactly that of the normally produced lethal hybrid between these two species (King and Briggs, 1953).

The results summarized above proved that late blastula nuclei could be transplanted in undamaged condition, and since the test eggs developed normally it was further demonstrated that the nuclei were unchanged, that is, equivalent to the nucleus at the beginning of development.

This result has been independently confirmed in this Institute by Subtelny, who also worked with *Rana pipiens*. So far as we are aware, the only other work on this species which has been mentioned in the literature (by Lehman, 1956) is that of Markert and Freedman. From 256 transfers these workers obtained 32 blastulae of which 20 gastrulated and 9 neurulated. While this represents a positive result, the yield from the transfers is relatively low and it would be difficult on this basis to draw conclusions concerning the properties of the nuclei tested.

Some attempts have been made to transfer embryonic nuclei into newt's eggs. The newt embryo would seem to offer important advantages for this work, with its large cells, relatively small chromosome number, and ease of handling in the usual tissue grafting and explantation techniques. However, the results so far have been disappointing. Waddington and Pantelouris (1953) transferred nuclei from blastula and later stages of *Triturus* (*Triton*) *palmatus* into non-nucleated egg fragments, which had been previously produced by constricting normally fertilized eggs. About 12 per cent of the fragments developed into blastulae which failed to gastrulate. No chromosome studies of these blastulae were reported and for this and other reasons the interpretation of the results was uncertain.

More recently, H. E. Lehman (1955) has reported on the transplantation of *Triton* blastula nuclei into enucleated eggs. Apparently the *Triton* egg cannot be activated with a glass needle and then enucleated in the manner which works so well with the frog's eggs. Furthermore, attempts to inject nuclei and then enucleate eggs also failed; eggs so treated did not cleave. Either the egg cytoplasm is damaged by these manipulations, or the injected nucleus for one reason or another fails to provide an effective cleavage center. In any event, Lehman was forced to resort to a more complicated procedure in which the eggs were first fertilized with heavily irradiated sperm (50,000 r), then pricked and enucleated, and finally injected with a blastula nucleus. About 65 per cent of the recipient eggs cleaved, and one-third of these formed blastulae which failed to gastrulate. Since the enucleations were only 50 per cent successful, and there was in addition some question of the survival of chromosome fragments from the irradiated sperm, the interpretation of this experiment depended on an accurate chromosome analysis. This Lehman did, finding haploid, diploid and hyperdiploid numbers. The occurrence of diploid, and particularly of hyperdiploid chromosome numbers, indicated that the injected nuclei or chromosomes therefrom were participating in the cleavage. As Lehman pointed out, the reasons for the failure of the embryos to gastrulate could have been a) irregular distribution of chromosomes during cleavage, leading to lethal chromosome imbalance (Fankhauser, 1934b), b) operative damage to the egg or the transferred nucleus or both, and c) nuclear

determination at the blastula stage. In view of
the fact that the blastula donor cells are not themselves determined, and in view of the results obtained with the frog, it seems likely that the failure
of the recipient newt eggs to develop normally
is due principally to their greater susceptibility
to damage in the course of transfer.

Nuclei of Early Gastrulae

As has been appreciated for a long time, the
beginning of gastrulation is a crucial phase of
development. At this time the regional localizations of materials present from the beginning in
the egg cytoplasm have their first morphogenetic
expression. For example, in the amphibian egg
the gray crescent material, localized on the dorsal
side of the egg shortly after fertilization, is known
to determine the position of the dorsal lip of the
blastopore, and consequently the point of origin
of the chorda mesoderm and the whole axial organization of the embryo. While the position of
the dorsal lip is thus determined by the gray crescent cytoplasm, it is also known that in order for
it to invaginate and form chorda mesoderm, it
must be provided with a "normal" set of chromosomes. Prior to gastrulation, cleavage and
blastula formation may proceed with nuclei containing variable numbers of chromosomes (Fankhauser, 1934b), no chromosomes (Fankhauser,
1934a; Stauffer, 1945; Briggs, Green and King,
1951); or with various foreign genomes (see review
by Moore, 1955). However, in all these cases development stops at or before the beginning of
gastrulation, from which it is concluded that
gastrulation and later phases of development
require the participation of a balanced chromosome set. Furthermore, nucleus and cytoplasm
must be of the same or closely related species.
This and other information indicates that the
nuclei come to have specific essential functions
at the beginning of gastrulation. Whether they
undergo irreversible or quasi-irreversible changes,
and whether these are the same or different in
different parts of the early gastrula, are questions
we have approached by means of nuclear transplantation. The work is not quite finished yet,
and will be described in full elsewhere. Here we
may give only a brief account to provide a background for the following portions of this paper.

Nuclei from the following portions of the early
gastrula were tested: 1) animal hemisphere, near
the pole, 2) dorsal lip region, 3) endoderm including the floor of the blastocoel, and a region
between the vegetal pole and the dorsal lip. The
nuclei were transplanted to enucleated eggs in
the usual way, giving the following results:

1) Animal hemisphere nuclei—39 per cent of
33 test eggs formed complete blastulae, 69% of
the blastulae developed into tadpoles.

2) Dorsal lip nuclei—25 per cent of 77 test
eggs formed complete blastulae, of which 74 per
cent developed into tadpoles.

3) Endoderm nuclei—54 per cent of 107 recipient eggs cleaved normally, 66 per cent of the
blastulae so produced developed into tadpoles.

These preliminary experiments provide no
definite evidence of differences among the nuclei
from the various regions of the gastrula. The
proportion of recipient eggs forming complete
blastulae was smaller in the case of animal hemisphere and dorsal lip nuclear transfers than it
was in the case of the endoderm transfers, but
this is probably due to differences in donor cell
size and ease of isolation. With respect to the
development of the complete blastulae, there
was some indication (in one experiment) that
blastulae containing endoderm nuclei were more
frequently arrested in gastrula or post-neurula
stages. However, in the majority of experiments
endoderm, dorsal lip, and animal hemisphere
nuclei appeared equally capable of promoting
normal development to the early larval stage, at
least.

This result, indicating equivalence of early
gastrula nuclei, is to some extent to be expected.
One of the donor regions, the animal pole, is definitely undetermined and would not be expected
to contain differentiated nuclei. The dorsal lip
area is, of course, determined to form chorda-
mesoderm. However, the determination is on a
regional and not a cell basis, for if parts of the
region are explanted they are found to be capable
of differentiating into neural and endodermal as
well as mesodermal structures (Holtfreter, 1938).
The endoderm, on the other hand, gives evidence
of being already determined in the early gastrula
(Holtfreter, 1938). Whether the individual cells
are irreversibly set in their path of differentiation
appears uncertain, but the endoderm cell mass
and portions of it are apparently determined to
form gut and gut derivatives. Yet the endoderm
nuclei, along with nuclei of other regions, give
no definite evidence of differentiation in the transplantation experiments. This could mean either
that the individual endoderm cells are not irreversibly determined, or that if they are, the determination does not involve irreversible nuclear
changes. Since our experiments involve the transfer of donor cell cytoplasm along with the nuclei,
the results also indicate that there are no genetic
units in the cytoplasm which are capable of directing the differentiation of the recipient eggs.

The nuclear transplantation work summarized
above emphasizes a point which has been familiar
to embryologists for some time; namely, that
the morphogenetic events in the early gastrula
depend on the regional localization of cytoplasmic
materials present in the egg at the beginning of
development. Normal nuclei are essential for
morphogenesis to proceed, but neither the nuclei
nor the individual cells (except possibly endoderm
cells) are irreversibly specialized at this stage.
In other words, the intrinsic properties of the
individual cells provide no explanation of the

morphogenetic events, which are directed by the aforementioned cytoplasmic localizations. Thus, the role of the nucleus in this early phase of development will eventually have to be studied prior to fertilization, when these materials are being laid down in the oocyte.

NUCLEI OF LATE GASTRULAE

During gastrulation the germ layers are established, and by the late gastrula stage are determined in the sense that they cannot be transformed, one into the other, by grafting to inductive sites. In order to see if the determination of the layers involves detectable changes in the nuclei, we have made transplantation tests of nuclei from chorda mesoderm, presumptive medullary plate, and endoderm. The first tests were done on nuclei of the presumptive plate and the chorda mesoderm. These nuclei elicited normal cleavage in a considerably smaller proportion of the test eggs than had been the case with the blastula nuclei. Furthermore, about half the normally cleaved eggs were arrested in blastula and gastrula stages, and of the ones completing gastrulation the majority displayed abnormalities later in development (King and Briggs, 1954). However, a few embryos did develop normally, indicating that at least some of the chorda mesoderm and medullary plate nuclei were undifferentiated. The significance of the cases in which development was arrested or abnormal remained in doubt because of the technical problems in handling the small donor cells. At the time, these cells were being isolated with glass needles with some risk of injury; and being small they were difficult to handle in the micropipette without some dilution of the cytoplasm with the Niu-Twitty medium and consequent damage to the nucleus. In order to circumvent these problems, we began to use trypsin as an aid in separating embryonic layers, and Versene to dissociate the cells (King and Briggs, 1955). In addition, it was decided to concentrate on the endoderm since this tissue appears to be definitely determined in the late gastrula, and still consists of large cells which are as readily managed in the transfer procedure as are those of mid- to late blastulae.

Late gastrula endoderm nuclei. In view of the considerations mentioned above, an extensive series of transfers of late gastrula endoderm nuclei has been made, the donor cells being taken usually from the presumptive anterior midgut region (King and Briggs, 1955 and unpub.). These nuclei elicited normal cleavage and blastula formation in about 40 per cent of the test eggs, and were therefore equivalent to undifferentiated blastula nuclei in this respect. However, the later development of the "endoderm blastulae" differed from that of the controls. Approximately 80 per cent of the control blastulae, containing transplanted blastula nuclei, developed into normal larvae. By contrast, the majority of the endoderm blastu-lae displayed pronounced abnormalities in their development. About one-third were arrested in late blastula or gastrula stages, one-half gastrulated normally but later displayed deficiencies, while the remaining minority developed normally into tadpoles.

The nature of the abnormalities in the endoderm embryos has been studied, and will be described in more detail elsewhere. In brief, the embryos had the following characteristics.

Arrested late blastulae or early gastrulae were uniformly cleaved, contained nuclei of uniform size, and possessed a normal blastocoel. Before the onset of arrest the cleavages occurred at about the normal rate, and the cells contained the normal number of chromosomes ($2N = 26$) although in some cases the form of the chromosomes was changed (see below). After the embryos were arrested the nuclei tended to become vacuolated, and some loose cells appeared in the blastocoel.

Abnormal post-neurula embryos. These embryos completed gastrulation in apparently normal fashion, but later showed in varying degrees the following conditions. First, there was a reduction, sometimes extreme, in size and degree of differentiation of the central nervous system, sense organs, and neural crest derivatives, accompanied by nuclear pycnosis in the affected organs. The inductor system (notochord and somites) was well developed and displayed no significant pycnosis. However, somites were usually abnormal in form. Other mesodermal organs (cardiovascular system, pronephros) were generally less well developed. Endoderm, in the stages studied, is not normally highly differentiated. In the endoderm embryos, its differentiation was retarded, in keeping with the general retardation in development, but it did not display significant numbers of pycnotic nuclei.

Endoderm nuclei from later stages. Nuclei from the anterior midgut region of mid-neurulae elicited normal cleavage and blastula formation in only 16 per cent of the test eggs, compared with 40 per cent or more in the case of the late gastrula nuclei. Of the blastulae obtained, a larger proportion (70%) were arrested early, in blastula or gastrula stages. The remaining embryos gastrulated, but the large majority later displayed the abnormalities mentioned above. Endoderm nuclei from the same region of tail bud embryos displayed a still further reduced capacity to promote cleavage of recipient eggs. Only seven per cent of the test eggs developed into complete blastulae 9 in number. Seven of these blastulae were arrested in late blastula or early gastrula stages, and two were abnormal "endoderm embryos."

These results on endoderm nuclear transfers indicate that the nuclei are going through definite changes. Nuclei from the late gastrula show an undiminished ability to promote cleavage and blastula formation. However, in their subsequent development the endoderm blastulae fall into three general classes—(a) embryos which are arrested before or during the formation of chorda mesoderm, (b) embryos which complete gastrulation but later show deficiencies, especially in ectodermal derivatives, and (c) normal embryos. This suggests that in the late gastrula some endoderm nuclei are unchanged; others are limited in their capacity to promote ectodermal differentiation; and still others are incapable of participating in chorda mesoderm formation. Results of transfers of mid-neurula and tail bud endoderm nuclei indicate that as differentiation proceeds the number of unchanged nuclei decreases, and that some nuclei may lose their capacity even to promote cleavage of recipient eggs.

That the changes described above occur in the nucleus or some nucleus-associated structure is indicated by the fact that endoderm cytoplasm, injected into normally nucleated eggs, has no influence on their development. This does not exclude cytoplasmic participation in the effects observed, but does indicate that cytoplasmic factors would be nucleus-dependent in their activity. In what follows, we shall refer to the changes detected by the transplantation procedure as nuclear changes, with the understanding that these changes may actually involve either the nucleus itself or some perinuclear organelle, or both.

Serial Transplantation of Endoderm Nuclei

From the experiments described above, it looks very much as if there is, during development, a progressive restriction of the capacity of endoderm nuclei to promote the coordinated differentiation of the various cell types required for the formation of a normal embryo. The two most pressing questions concerning these nuclear changes are 1) are they specific? and 2) are they stable or irreversible? For various reasons it seemed that the question of specificity could be solved more readily if that of irreversibility were first settled. A method of doing this is illustrated in Figure 1.

The experiment consists of first making transfers of a series of endoderm nuclei to enucleated eggs. Each egg receives one nucleus as usual, and a sizable proportion of the eggs then cleave and form complete blastulae. Each blastula will be, so to speak, populated by descendants of a single endoderm nucleus. Different blastulae contain nuclei derived from different endoderm cells, and develop in the different ways shown in the figure. Now, in order to test the descendants of any given endoderm nucleus we may sacrifice one of the original recipient eggs at the blastula stage, and make from it a new series of nuclear transfers. All of the new group of recipient eggs will contain descendants of one original endoderm nucleus. If the expression of the nucleus with respect to differentiation is uniform and not much affected by vagaries of experimentation all of this new

generation of test eggs (called the 1st blastula generation) should develop in the same fashion. It will, in effect, represent the first generation of a clone of embryos all containing descendants of a single nucleus, and is referred to as a nuclear clone. The characteristics of the clone may be studied further by sacrificing an individual of the first blastula generation to provide nuclei for another group of test eggs, referred to as the second blastula generation. The development of this group of eggs will tell us not only how uniform is the differentiation-promoting activity of the nucleus but also, by comparison with the preceding generation, how stable.

The actual experiments were carried out in the following way. In any given experiment we first transferred approximately 15 endoderm nuclei to the same number of enucleated eggs. Anywhere from 6 to 12 of these eggs cleaved and formed complete blastulae. The first two or three cleavages were observed and recorded, and the eggs were then placed in a water bath at 14°C. On the following day (ca. 24 hours later) the blastulae were removed from the 14° tank to the 18° room, three donors were selected, and the remaining embryos were set aside for observation. The donors were always blastulae of perfectly normal appearance which had records of having initiated cleavage at the normal time. It was important to select the donors on this basis to avoid the complication of polyploidy (see page 273). Nuclei from each of the three donors were transferred to ten enucleated eggs to give the first blastula generation of three nuclear clones. Again cleavages were observed and on the following day one of the resulting blastulae in each clone was selected as the donor for the second blastula generation, while the remaining blastulae were allowed to develop. Usually the experiments were not carried beyond the second blastula generation, and as outlined above, each such experiment, producing three nuclear clones, required at least 75 nuclear transfers. The work reported below on 27 nuclear clones (9 control nuclei, 18 endoderm nuclei) is based on a total of about 850 nuclear transfers.

Results

Results of serial transplantation of nuclei are given in the form of actual records of representative experiments and in a summary table and chart (Figs. 1–8 and Table 1). The experimental records reproduced here include only the test eggs that cleaved completely forming normal blastulae. Not included are eggs that failed to cleave, or cleaved abnormally or partially, since for one reason or another these provide no test of the capacity of the transferred nuclei to promote differentiation.

Figure 1, illustrating the principle of the experimental procedure, is also an accurate record of the development of one nuclear clone. In this experiment, the original transfers of endoderm

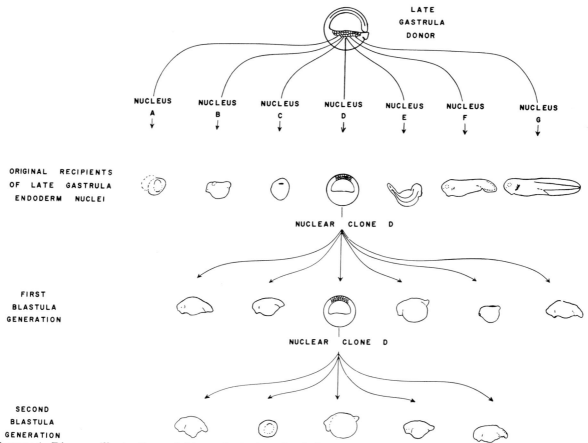

FIGURE 1. Diagram illustrating serial transplantation of endoderm nuclei. Donor nuclei are actually taken from the presumptive anterior midgut region of the late gastrula. Transferred to enucleated eggs they promote the various types of development shown for the "original recipients" in the diagram. One of the original recipients, sacrificed at the blastula stage, provides nuclei for a single clone which shows the more uniform development illustrated for the first and second blastula generations. In this and subsequent figures the illustrations of embryos are in the form of either camera lucida drawings or photographs.

nuclei as usual led to quite different types of development, ranging from arrested gastrulae to normal embryos, as illustrated by the camera lucida drawings. One blastula was sacrificed to provide nuclei for transfer to a new group of enucleated eggs, giving rise to a nuclear clone which, in the first blastula generation, displayed a quite uniform type of development—in contrast to the wide variety of developmental types seen among the original recipients of the different endoderm nuclei. The embryos of this generation gastrulated normally, but later showed marked deficiencies, particularly in the ectodermal derivatives. One of the blastulae of this generation was sacrificed to provide nuclei for the second blastula generation, which also developed fairly uniformly and in a manner nearly identical with that of the first generation.

Figure 2 is a camera lucida record of another experiment in which three different original donors were used. Endoderm nuclei from each of these donors were transferred to ten enucleated eggs,

which then showed the usual range of developmental types, as illustrated in the three groups of drawings in the upper part of Figure 2. One blastula from each group of embryos was sacrificed to provide nuclei for the first blastula generation. Endoderm nuclei from blastula "A" promoted completely normal development in practically all of the recipient eggs that showed complete cleavage, in both the first and second blastula generations. Nuclei from blastula "C" also promoted uniform development, stopping in late blastula or early gastrula stage. Nuclei from blastula "B", on the other hand, elicited normal blastula formation in only three of the test eggs, of which one developed normally, one arrested in neurulation, while one was sacrificed at blastula stage to provide nuclei for the second blastula generation. The second generation developed abnormally and displayed somewhat greater variability than usual. The variable development of this clone poses a problem of interpretation. Possibly some nuclei, chosen by chance at the time

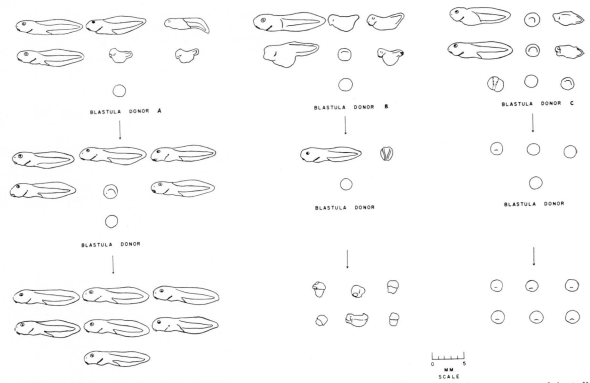

FIGURE 2. Camera lucida record of serial transplantation experiment. Three late gastrula donors were used (not diagrammed in above record). Nuclei from these donors were transferred to 3 groups of enucleated eggs, which developed in the various ways illustrated in the upper part of the figure. The derived clones developed much more uniformly

when they are beginning to undergo a change, will continue to change following transfer to egg cytoplasm. An alternative explanation would be that the variations in development within clone "B" are accidentally induced.

Another serial transplantation experiment is summarized in Figure 3. In this experiment all three nuclear clones were derived from a single donor. Descendants of nucleus "A" promoted development only to gastrula stages, in both the first and second blastula generations. Descendants of nucleus "B" promoted development of abnormal post-neurula embryos. The abnormalities were similar to those described in the previous section of this paper, being most pronounced in the ectodermal derivatives, and were quite uniformly expressed in the first blastula generation. The majority of embryos of the second generation were similar to those of the first, but two out of the eight embryos were arrested earlier, at gastrula stage. Embryos of nuclear clone "C" also developed to an abnormal post-neurula stage. In the first blastula generation they were uniformly somewhat better developed than individuals in clone "B," but none the less displayed typical characteristics of endoderm embryos. In the second generation two of the five individuals were apparently identical with the embryos of the first generation while the remainder showed more marked deficiencies, as shown in Figure 3.

The actual appearance of the embryos is shown in the photographic record of another experiment. Figure 4 consists of photographs of living embryos and illustrates clearly how uniform are the individuals within a given clone, and how distinct the clones are from each other. Some of the internal morphology of these embryos is illustrated in Figure 5. Figure 5 shows sections through the eye region. In clone "A" the brain is poorly developed, the eye is in the form of a small vesicle, there is no lens, head mesenchyme is poorly formed, and the development of the foregut is retarded. Although it is not visible in the low power photographs, there is pycnosis in the nuclei of the brain, eye, and dorsal mesenchyme, but not significantly in the ventral mesenchyme and foregut. Sections through the trunk show the notochord well formed and of about the same diameter as the notochord in the controls. Somites are also present, although abnormal in form. On the other hand, both the spinal cord and the dorsal mesenchyme are very poorly developed and contain pycnotic nuclei. The midgut is still in the form of a large endoderm mass in controls and experimental embryos at this stage. In clone "A" it is distorted by swelling of the coelomic space, but does not contain pycnotic nuclei.

Clone "B" displays more advanced differentiation than clone "A" but is still deficient compared with the controls. The deficiencies, although less

SERIAL   TRANSPLANTATION   OF   ENDODERM   NUCLEI

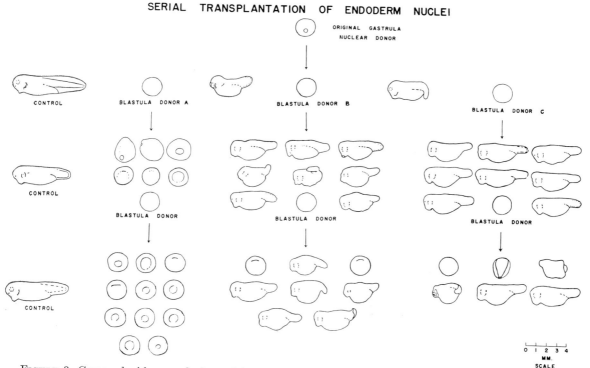

FIGURE 3. Camera lucida record of a serial nuclear transplantation experiment. See text for description.

pronounced, are of the same general character as those in clone "A". Brain and dorsal head mesenchyme contain numerous pycnotic nuclei. The eye cup has induced a lens which is still in the form of a simple vesicle whereas in the controls it has differentiated into the main body of the lens and the lens epithelium. Foregut and ventral mesenchyme are somewhat retarded but contain no significant number of pycnotic nuclei. Sections through the trunk show a modest but definite reduction in the size and degree of differentiation of the spinal cord.

Clone "C" shows extreme deficiencies, the brain and head mesenchyme being absent or very poorly formed and containing numerous degenerating nuclei. In the trunk the notochord and somite material is present. A rudimentary spinal cord is present in three of four cases examined. The gut is poorly developed, but contains no pycnotic nuclei.

Figure 6 gives the results of one experiment in which the serial nuclear transfers were carried on for a total of four blastula generations. The experiment was unique in that the original transfers of late gastrula endoderm nuclei led to only two types of development. The recipient eggs were either arrested in the very early gastrula stage, or they developed into perfectly normal postneurula embryos, as shown in the top line of photographs of Figure 6. There were no embryos of intermediate type. Correspondingly, clones derived from this group of embryos also expressed

at first only the two types of development. Clones "A" and "B" showed uniformly an arrest of development in early gastrula stage, and even though the transfers were carried on for four blastula generations there was no evidence of reversal to a more normal type of development. Clone "C" embryos, on the other hand, developed normally for the first two blastula generations, but in the third and fourth generations the development changed, giving rise to abnormal post-neurula embryos of the type commonly seen in the other endoderm experiments.

A summary of the serial transplantation tests of endoderm embryos is given in Table 1 and Figure 7. The main point to be emphasized concerning the data in Table 1 is that the same types of embryos occur in about the same proportions in both the original population of endoderm embryos and in the derived clones. Each clone displays a fairly uniform type of development and as a clone corresponds to one or another of the individual embryos in the original population. In other words, in the process of deriving the clones we obtain a faithful representation of the original types.

We have included also in Table 1 the data on serial transfers of undifferentiated blastula nuclei, for the purpose of showing that in the majority of experiments these give rise to clones of normal embryos. A detailed record of one of these experiments is given in Figure 8.

Figure 7 gives a comparison of the development

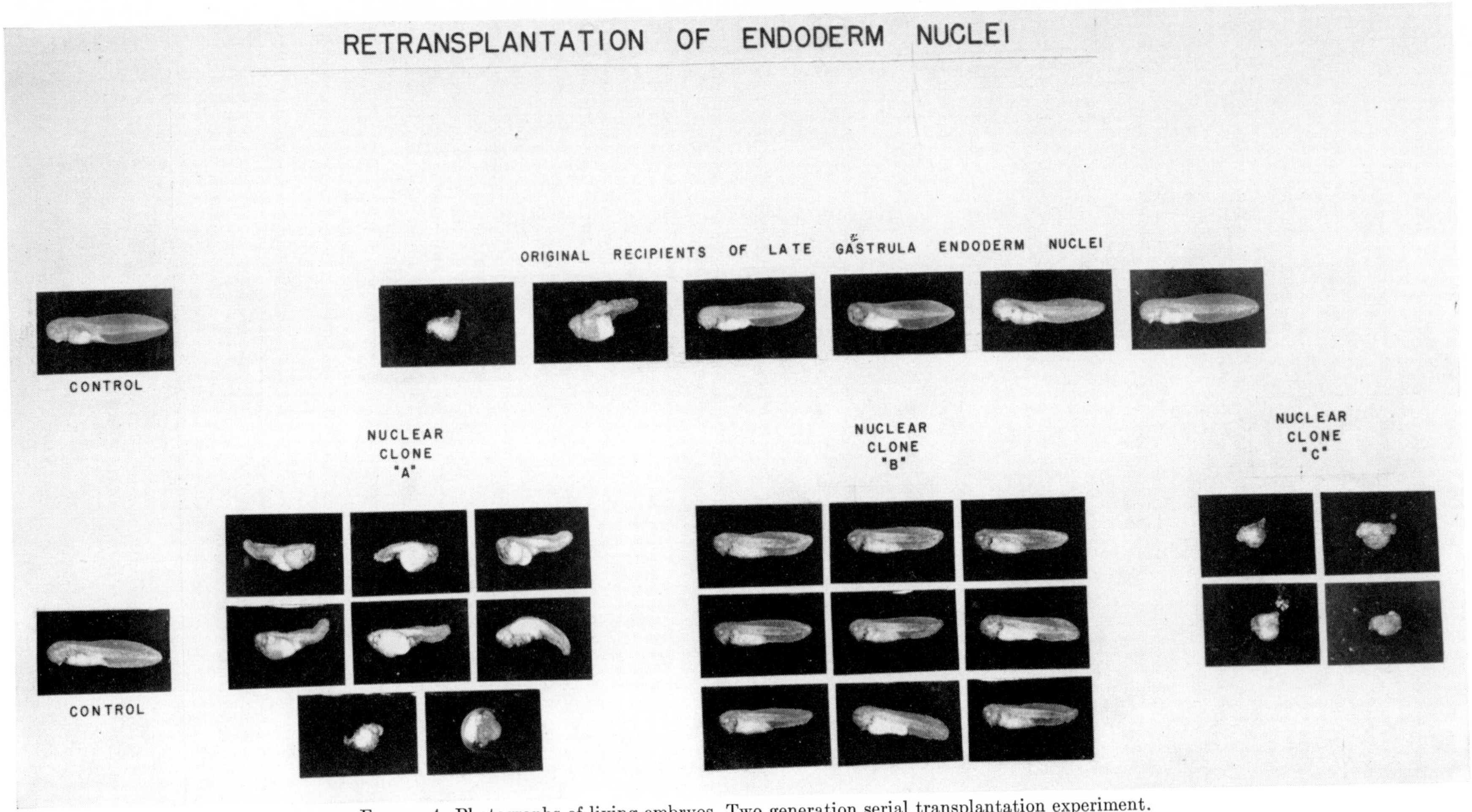

RETRANSPLANTATION OF ENDODERM NUCLEI

ORIGINAL RECIPIENTS OF LATE GASTRULA ENDODERM NUCLEI

CONTROL

NUCLEAR CLONE "A"

NUCLEAR CLONE "B"

NUCLEAR CLONE "C"

CONTROL

FIGURE 4. Photographs of living embryos. Two generation serial transplantation experiment.

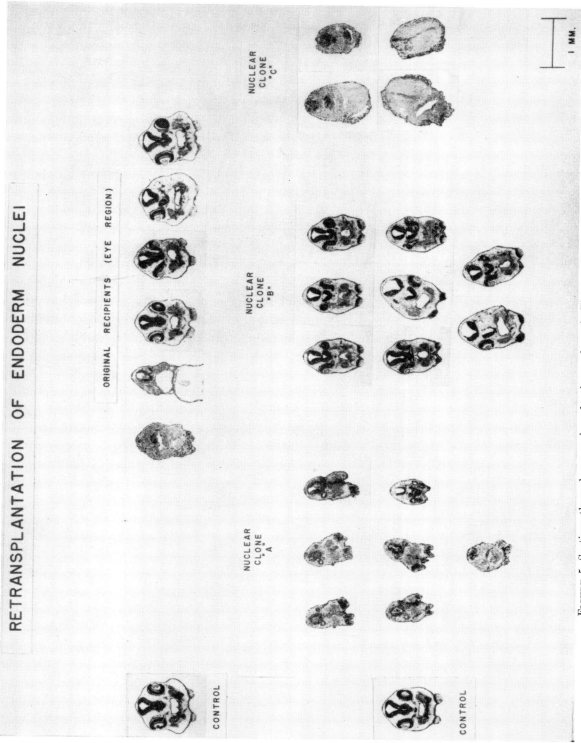

FIGURE 5. Sections through eye region of embryos shown in Figure 4. Description given in text.

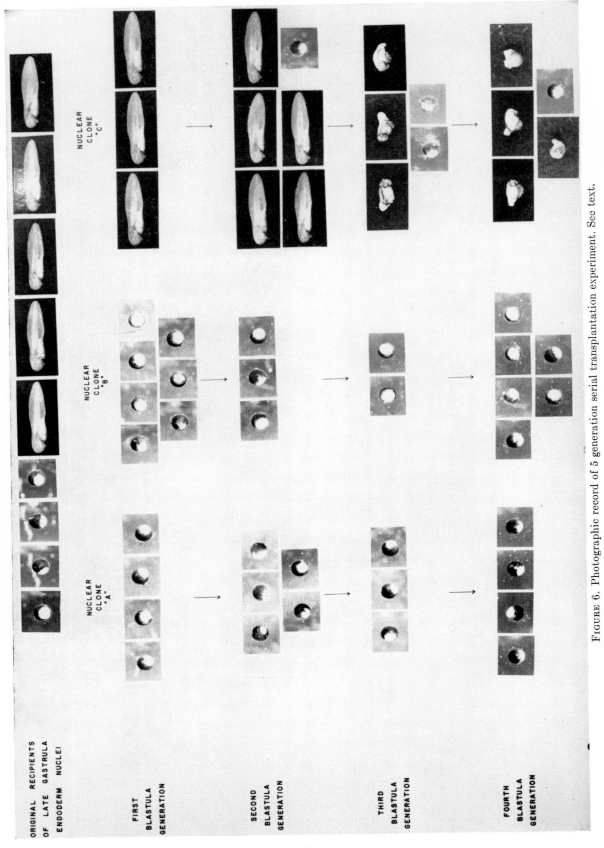

FIGURE 6. Photographic record of 5 generation serial transplantation experiment. See text.

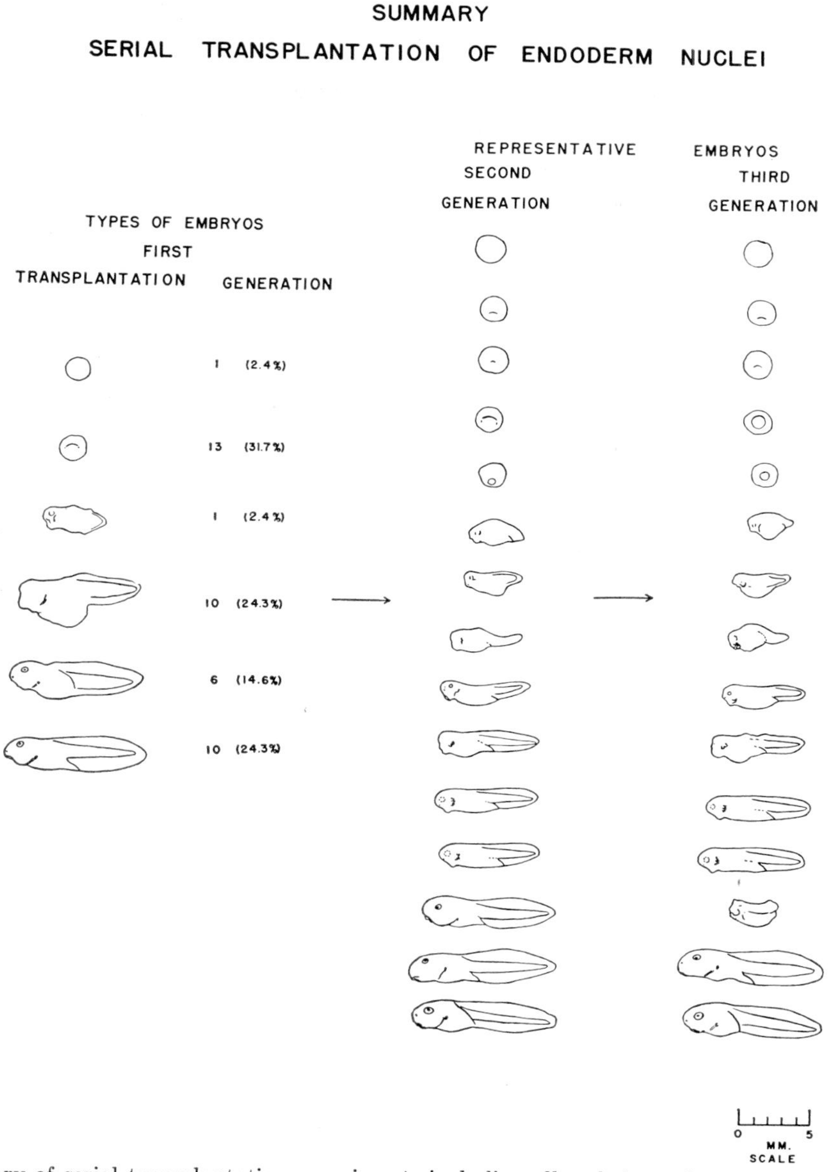

SUMMARY
SERIAL TRANSPLANTATION OF ENDODERM NUCLEI

FIGURE 7. Summary of serial transplantation experiments including all endoderm clones except the ones shown in Figure 4 (not included because the experiment was carried on for only 2 generations). The row of drawings on the left illustrates the types of embryos developing from the original recipient eggs injected with endoderm nuclei. The middle row shows typical embryos from the clones in the second generation (referred to in text as the first blastula generation). Each embryo represents a single clone. The same clones in the third generation are represented in the right hand row of drawings. Note that in general the development in the third generation is similar to that in the second, with no evidence of change to a more normal type of differentiation.

of the endoderm clones in the successive blastula generations. Each generation of each clone is represented in the figure by a single typical embryo. The important fact emerging from this summary is that in no case so far studied is there a reversal to a more normal type of development in the second (or later) blastula generation compared with the first. In other words, the nuclear condition responsible for given deficiencies in differenti-

ation is irreversible under the conditions of these experiments. However, it is possible that nuclear changes leading to more restricted development may sometimes progress in the course of repeated transfers. Two instances of a more restricted development in the later generations have been noted (Figs. 2 and 6) and it is possible, though far from certain, that endoderm nuclei may continue "differentiating" in egg cytoplasm.

TABLE 1. DEVELOPMENT OF ORIGINAL RECIPIENTS OF
ENDODERM NUCLEI COMPARED WITH DEVELOPMENT
OF ENDODERM CLONES

Source of Nucle	Total No. Complete Blastulae	Development		
		Blastulae and gastrulae	Abnormal postneurulae	Normal larvae
Endoderm (late gastrula) Original recipients (individual eggs)	44	14 (32%)	20 (45%)	10 (23%)
Clones	18	5 (28%)	8 (44%)	5 (28%)
Control (blastulae) Original recipients (individual eggs)	22	2 (9%)	2 (9%)	18 (82%)
Clones	9	0	2 (22%)	7 (78%)

the endoderm embryos described above. This was done as follows:

In each experiment portions of the original donor gastrula and of the blastula donor for each transplant generation were handed over to Miss Marie DiBerardino, who immediately prepared acetic-orcein squashes of the material. All the subsequent work on the chromosomes was done by Miss DiBerardino.

The preparation of satisfactory squashes of blastula chromosomes posed some problems. If the cells are squashed directly from the Niu-Twitty medium it is very difficult to obtain adequate separation of the chromosomes. A photograph of a typical metaphase plate is reproduced in Figure 9A, showing the long blastula chromosomes intertwined and impossible to count accurately. Adequate separation of chromosomes can be produced by pre-treating the cells with hypotonic medium and colchicine (Hungerford, 1955), but still better results can be obtained by pre-treatment for 30 minutes with a Niu-Twitty

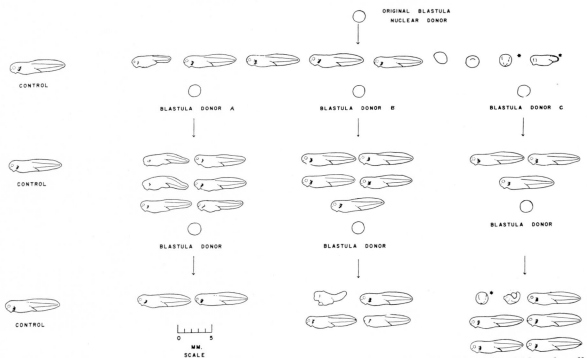

FIGURE 8. Camera lucida record of serial transplantation experiment with nuclei of undifferentiated blastula cells. Embryos marked * died from some infectious or toxic process after developing normally to the stages shown.

CHROMOSOME STUDIES

Since it is known that embryos with unbalanced chromosome sets develop abnormally and are frequently arrested at early developmental stages (Fankhauser, 1934b), it was important to determine the condition of the chromosomes in

medium lacking Ca^{++} and Mg^{++}, and buffered to pH 7.5 with phosphate. A photograph of a plate from such a preparation is given in Figure 9B. The effect of pre-treatment with the modified Niu-Twitty medium is immediately reversed if the cells are returned to the normal medium before squashing. The effect is also different for tissues

mosome lengths is the same or different in the different clones. The results of this analysis are illustrated in Figure 11. In general, the distribution of chromosome lengths did not appear to differ in the different types of clones. One of the clones containing ring chromosomes did differ from the others in displaying a wider range of chromosome lengths (Figure 11). Otherwise, there were no differences that could be definitely related to type of development. This does not eliminate the possibility that deletions, etc. may have occurred, but does suggest that they would have to be on a relatively small scale. It also does not mean that more subtle types of chromosomal (or other) changes may not be occurring as a regular concomitant of differentiation (for example, see Beermann, this volume).

DISCUSSION

The serial transplantation experiments described above show that the changes occurring in endoderm nuclei during differentiation are highly stabilized, in the sense that they are not reversed in egg cytoplasm. Each transfer is followed by cleavage of the recipient egg to produce a donor blastula consisting of approximately 8,000 cells, requiring about 13 divisions (or generations) of the original nucleus. In the majority of experiments, three such transfers were done serially and therefore involved about 39 nuclear generations. In the most extensive experiments (5 serial transfers) there would have been 65 reproductions of the original endoderm nucleus, with still no evidence of reversal. Thus, regardless of its exact character and mode of origin, we are dealing with a heritable change in the capacity of the nucleus to promote differentiation. At the least, it could be a change induced in the original endoderm nuclei accidentally during the transfer operation. At the most, it would represent a specific genetic change elicited somehow by particular cytoplasmic localizations, and responsible in turn for the stabilization of differentiation of individual cells.

The idea that nuclear changes such as we see in endoderm cells might be accidentally induced cannot be ignored. The hazard of nuclear damage is always present in this kind of experimentation. The arguments against it are as follows:

1) The technical problems of making nuclear transfers from endoderm cells are no greater than they are for blastula cells. Yet, the blastula nuclei promote normal differentiation of recipient eggs while the endoderm nuclei generally do not.

2) Although the original transfers of endoderm nuclei give a variety of types of development, subsequent transfers of descendants of a particular nucleus lead to fairly uniform development of the recipient eggs. If the variation were accidentally induced one would expect to find it in the clones as well as in the recipients of the original nuclei. (Unless, of course, endoderm nuclei are

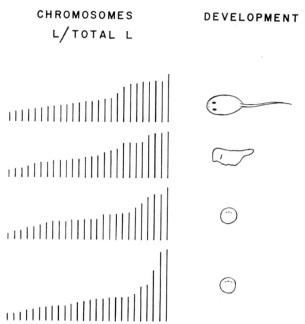

CHROMOSOMES L/TOTAL L   **DEVELOPMENT**

FIGURE 11. Relative lengths of chromosomes were measured on a total of 78 metaphase plates from 14 endoderm embryos and 6 controls. The results shown above for endoderm embryos are representative. Differences in relative lengths, from embryo to embryo, are not significant being within the range observed in different plates from single embryos. The one exception, in which the range in relative lengths is greater than normal, is plotted at the bottom of the figure.

somehow much more sensitive to damage in their own cytoplasm than they are in egg cytoplasm.)

3) While the original endoderm transfers usually lead to a variety of types of development, this is not always so. In one experiment (Figure 6) we observed only two classes of embryos, which would be hard to account for on the basis of chance injury to the nuclei.

4) In the majority of clones there was no evidence of chromosome changes such as might be expected to result from nuclear damage.

On the basis of this evidence we may assume that the restrictions in the capacity of endoderm nuclei to promote differentiation are real and not artificially induced. Other points about which definite statements can be made are: 1) that the nuclear changes are highly stabilized, as shown by the serial transplantation experiments, and 2) that they do not occur in all cells at once. Rather it appears that in the late gastrula the endoderm nuclei fall into three general classes: 1) undifferentiated nuclei, 2) nuclei restricted to varying degrees in their capacity to promote normal post-gastrula development, particularly of ectodermal derivatives, and 3) nuclei incapable of participating in the formation of chorda mesoderm, resulting in arrest at gastrulation. In later stages of development the number of nuclei in class 1) (undifferentiated) decreases while those showing restrictions of differentiation-promoting capacity increase. This indicates that a progressive and "irreversible" nuclear change occurs during differentiation. Whether in any given cell this restriction in differentiating-promoting ability occurs slowly or rapidly, continuously or in distinct steps, we do not know, although a study of nuclear changes during the post-blastula development of the clones might eventually give answers to some of these questions. Also, it is unknown which of the nuclear or peri-nuclear structures are involved. Control experiments have shown that the endoderm cytoplasm by itself is incapable of modifying the differentiation of normally nucleated eggs. However, we cannot yet determine whether it is the nucleus itself or some replicating perinuclear organelle which is responsible for the restricted developmental potencies.

Finally, we should consider briefly the question of the specificity of the nuclear changes in endoderm cells. We have seen that these changes result first in a loss of the capacity to promote normal differentiation of ectodermal derivatives, and presumably later the ability to promote differentiation of chorda mesoderm is also lost. Thus, the nuclear changes are consistent with the fact that the nuclei are derived from endoderm. But whether they are specific for endoderm is uncertain. In order to settle this point it would be necessary to explore the capacity for various types of differentiation by appropriate grafting experiments with parts of the arrested endoderm embryos, and the same sort of analysis would have to be done on embryos containing other types of nuclei. Now that the nuclear changes in endoderm cells are known to be highly stabilized and to give a fairly uniform type of development in the clones, this central problem of specificity may be attacked.

SUMMARY

Nuclei of late gastrula endoderm, transplanted to enucleated eggs (*Rana pipiens*) promote the following general types of development: 1) arrest at gastrula stages, 2) normal gastrulation followed by deficient development in later stages, especially in the ectodermal derivatives, 3) normal development throughout.

In order to determine if the nuclear changes responsible for the deficient development are stable, serial transfers of endoderm nuclei were carried out. Individual nuclei were transplanted to enucleated eggs, which cleaved and produced blastulae. In a given test, one of these blastulae was sacrificed to provide nuclei for transfer to a new group of eggs. Such a group represents a clone, all members of which are nucleated by descendants of one original endoderm nucleus. One member of such a clone may be sacrificed at the blastula stage to provide nuclei for transfer to a new group of enucleated eggs, giving in effect a second blastula generation of the clone. The same process may be repeated to provide several generations.

Analysis of the development of 18 clones revealed the following: Whereas test eggs containing different endoderm nuclei developed in the different ways mentioned above, eggs within one clone developed much more uniformly. In some clones all embryos were arrested at gastrula stage, in others they displayed a fairly uniform set of deficiencies in post-gastrula development, and in a few clones almost all embryos developed normally throughout. Furthermore, within any given clone the development in the second and later generations were generally of the same type as that observed in the first generation. In a few clones the deficiencies became more severe in the later generations, but no case of reversal to a more normal type of development was noted.

Chromosome studies on donor embryos in the clonal experiments showed that chromosome number generally remained unchanged at the diploid value (26). In three clones, all consisting of embryos arresting at early gastrula stage, a few small ring chromosomes were present. Otherwise, no chromosome changes were detected even though the clones exhibited quite different types of development.

These experiments show that descendants of individual endoderm nuclei have a fairly uniform expression with respect to differentiation, which does not reverse to a more normal expression in the course of the serial transfers. In other words, compared with nuclei of undifferentiated cells, the endoderm nuclei show stabilized changes in capacity to promote differentiation. How these changes arise, whether they are specific, and which of the nuclear or peri-nuclear structures are involved, are problems remaining to be worked out.

ACKNOWLEDGEMENTS

We wish to thank Dr. Jack Schultz for the benefit derived from many discussions we have had with him on problems of differentiation. We also wish to acknowledge the assistance of Miss Marie DiBerardino, who carried out the chromosome studies described in this paper and provided valuable assistance in many other ways as well.

REFERENCES

BEERMANN, W., 1956, Nuclear differentiation and functional morphology of chromosomes. Cold Spr. Harb. Symp. Quant. Biol. *21:* 217–232.

BRIGGS, R., GREEN, E. U., and KING, T. J., 1951, An investigation of the capacity for cleavage and differentiation in *Rana pipiens* eggs lacking "functional" chromosomes. J. Exp. Zool. *116:* 455–500.

BRIGGS, R., and KING, T. J., 1952, Transplantation of living nuclei from blastula cells into enucleated frogs' eggs. Proc. Nat. Acad. Sci. Wash. *38:* 455–463.

1953, Factors affecting the transplantability of nuclei of frog embryonic cells. J. Exp. Zool. *122:* 485–506.

COMANDON, J. and DE FONBRUNE, P., 1939, Greffe nucleaire totale, simple ou multiple, chez une *Amibe.* Compt. rend. soc. biol. *130:* 744–748.

DANIELLI, J. F., LORCH, I. J., ORD, M. J., and WILSON,

E. C., 1955, Nucleus and cytoplasm in cellular inheritance. Nature, Lond. *176:* 1114–1115.

EPHRUSSI, B., 1951, Remarks on cell heredity. In: Genetics in the 20th Century. New York, Macmillan Company, pp. 241–262.

1953, Nucleo-cytoplasmic relations in microorganisms. Oxford, Clarendon Press.

FANKHAUSER, G., 1934a, Cytological studies on egg fragments of the salamander *Triton*, IV. The cleavage of egg fragments without the egg nucleus. J. Exp. Zool. *67:* 349–394.

1934b, Cytological studies on egg fragments of the salamander *Triton*. V. Chromosome number and chromosome individuality in the cleavage mitoses of merogonic fragments. J. Exp. Zool. *68:* 1–57.

GLUECKSOHN-WAELSCH, S., 1954, Some genetic aspects of development. Cold Spr. Harb. Symp. Quant. Biol. *19:* 41–49.

GROBSTEIN, C., 1952. Effects of fragmentation of mouse embryonic shields on their differentiative behavior after culturing. J. Exp. Zool. *120:* 437–456.

GROBSTEIN, C., and ZWILLING, E., 1953, Modification of growth and differentiation of chorio-allantoic grafts of chick blastoderm pieces after cultivation at a glass-clot interface. J. Exp. Zool. *122:* 259–284.

HADORN, E., 1948, Gene action in growth and differentiation of lethal mutants of *Drosophila*. Symposia Soc. Exp. Biol. *2:* 177–195.

1956, Patterns of biochemical and developmental pleiotropy. Cold Spr. Harb. Symp. Quant. Biol. *21:* 255–382.

HÄMMERLING, J., 1934, Über genomwirkungen und Formbildungsfähigkeit bei *Acetabularia*. Arch. Entwickmech. Org. *132:* 424–462.

1953, Nucleo-cytoplasmic relationships in the development of *Acetabularia*. Intern. Rev. Cytol. *2:* 475–498.

HOLTFRETER, J., 1933, Die totale Exogastrulation, eine Selbstablösung des Ektoderms vom Entomesoderm. Entwicklung und funktionelles Verhalten nervenloser Organe. Arch. Entwick-mech. Org. *129:* 669–793.

1938, Differenzierungspotenzen isolierter Teile der Anurengastrula. Arch. Entwick-mech. Org. *138:* 657–738.

HUNGERFORD, D. A., 1955, Chromosome numbers of ten-day fetal mouse cells. J. Morph. *97:* 497–510.

KING, T. J., and BRIGGS, R., 1954, Transplantation of living nuclei of late gastrulae into enucleated eggs of *Rana pipiens*. J. Embryol. Exp. Morph. *2:* 73–80.

1955, Changes in the nuclei of differentiating gastrula cells, as demonstrated by nuclear transplantation. Proc. Nat. Acad. Sci. Wash. *41:* 321–325.

LEDERBERG, J., 1956, Infection and heredity. Growth Symp. *13:* 101–124. Princeton Univ. Press.

LEHMAN, H. E., 1955, On the development of enucleated *Triton* eggs with an injected blastula nucleus. Biol. Bull. *108:* 138–150.

1956, Nuclear transplantation, a tool for the study of nuclear differentiation. AAAS Symp. (In press).

LOEB, J., 1894, Über eine einfache Methode, zwei oder mehr zusammengewachsene Embryonen aus einem Ei hervorzubringen. Pflüger's Arch. *55:* 525:530.

LORCH, I. J., and DANIELLI, J. F., 1950, Transplantation of nuclei from cell to cell. Nature, Lond. *166:* 329–333.

MOORE, J. A., 1955, Abnormal combinations of nuclear and cytoplasmic systems in frogs and toads. Adv. Genet. *7:* 139–182.

NIU, M. C., and TWITTY, V. C., 1953, The differentiation of gastrula ectoderm in medium conditioned by axial mesoderm. Proc. Nat. Acad. Sci. Wash. *39:* 985–989.

PORTER, K. R., 1939, Androgenetic development of the egg of *Rana pipiens*. Biol. Bull. *77:* 233–257.

POULSON, D. F., 1945, Chromosomal control of embryogenesis in *Drosophila*. Amer. Nat. *79:* 340–363.

ROSTAND, J., 1943, Essai d'inoculation de noyaux embryonnaires dans l'oeuf vierge de grenouille. Rev. sci. *81:* 454–456.

SCHULTZ, J., 1952, Interrelations between nucleus and cytoplasm: problems at the biological level. Exp. Cell Res. Suppl. *2:* 17–43.

SONNEBORN, T. M., 1954, Patterns of nucleocytoplasmic integration in *Paramecium*. Proc. 9th Intern. Congress Genetics. Caryologia, suppl. 1954: 307–325.

SPEMANN, H., 1914, Über verzögerte Kernversorgung von Keimteilen. Vergandl. deut. zool. Ges., 1914: 16–221.

1938, Embryonic Development and Induction. New Haven, Yale Univ. Press, pp. 211.

STAUFFER, E., 1945, Versuche zur experimentallen Herstellung haploider Axolotl-Merogone. Rev. suisse zool. *52:* 231–327.

SUBTELNY, S. S., 1956, Personal communication.

SZE, L. C., 1953, Changes in the amount of desoxyribonucleic acid in the development of *Rana pipiens*. J. Exp. Zool. *122:* 577–601.

TARTAR, V., 1953, Chimeras and nuclear transplantations in ciliates, *Stentor coeruleus* × *S. polymorphus*. J. Exp. Zool. *124:* 63–103.

WADDINGTON, C. H., and PANTELOURIS, E. M., 1953, Transplantation of nuclei in newt's eggs. Nature, Lond. *172:* 1050.

WEISZ, PAUL B., 1951, A general mechanism of differentiation based on morphogenetic studies in ciliates. Amer. Nat. *85:* 293–311.

WILSON, E. B., 1925, The Cell in Development and Heredity. 3rd ed. New York, Macmillan Company.

DISCUSSION

BALINSKY: The persistence of the same types of development in each of the different clones makes it plausible that there are differences in the nuclei propagating in each clone. Do you have any suggestion as to why the initial nuclei used to start each clone could have been different, seeing that they were all taken originally from the same part of the embryo, the floor of the archenteron of a late gastrula stage?

KING: The embryological evidence for the determination of late gastrula endoderm is based on explantation and transplantation experiments which involved large groups of cells. We cannot distinguish whether this determination depends upon differentiation of the individual cells or is to be regarded as a property of the mass as a whole. Grobstein (1952) and Grobstein and Zwilling (1953), working with cultured explants of mouse embryonic shield and chick blastoderm, find that the extent of differentiation depends upon the degree to which the explant cells are dispersed. Large explants will differentiate into neural tissue, but if these explants are divided into eighths or sixteenths the differentiation fails to occur or is poorly expressed. Thus it appears that in chick and mouse embryos organ determination occurs while the individual cells are still undifferentiated or in various states of differentiation. The same situation may exist in the amphibian gastrula.

Another source of heterogeneity is suggested by Holtfreter's (1933) observation that the midgut contains "lethal" cells, as well as cells which later form the gut epithelium. In urodeles the lethal cells can be seen to degenerate in the gut lumen during late embryonic life. However, we could find no evidence of cell lethality in the developing gut of the anuran (*R. pipiens*) used in our experiments.

STERN: It has been suggested that if embryonic nuclei from prospective germ cells were transplanted they would demonstrate unrestricted potentialities in development. This expectation implies the belief that the genetic totipotency of the nuclei of germ cells at the time of their presence in mature germ cells is equivalent to developmental totipotency of these nuclei at other stages. However, it may well be that nuclei of immature germ cells are just as restricted developmentally as those of somatic cells, while on the other hand, developmentally restricted nuclei of somatic cells may be totipotent genetically.

KING: We would agree with Dr. Stern's comment, especially since we do not yet know what part of the nuclear complex is involved in the changes reported in this paper, and whether these changes might not be reversible under different conditions than those existing in our experiments.

MARKERT: The range of variation in developmental capacity shown by nuclei taken from a restricted area would seem to support the concept that the state of differentiation of a tissue reflects the average state of differentiation of its constituent cells. These cells apparently do not undergo synchronous transformations but gradually differentiate as variable members of a complex population. Such a process of tissue differentiation based on the additive individual contributions of diverse, although related, cells should be relatively "well-buffered" against transitory abnormal influences to which the embryo might be exposed during development. Only those influences which persisted long enough to transform a substantial number of cells with initially different degrees of sensitivity could effectively alter the course of tissue differentiation. Over any short period of time that fraction of the tissue cells in any particular phase of development would be dispensable so far as the development of the entire tissue was concerned.

The Effects of Nuclear Genes on the Structure and Differentiation of Cytoplasmic Particles[1]

Ernst Caspari and Ingbritt Blomstrand

Wesleyan University, Middletown, Connecticut

Introduction

One of the characteristics of living systems is the phenomenon of organization. Living matter appears at every level arranged in an orderly manner related to function. The factors which are responsible for this organization of living matter constitute therefore one of the most attractive problems of biology. It is proposed to discuss in this paper organization at the cellular level.

The organization of the cell shows itself in the fact that a number of structures can be found in cells, some of which are constantly found throughout all types of cells, such as the nucleus, the chromosomes, mitochondria, the cell membrane, the submicroscopic reticulum, while others are restricted to particular species or particular types of cells. The functional aspects of these elements of cellular organization are in part understood for some of them, while their interplay in the regulation of cellular activities is less well investigated.

The fundamental fact of genetics is the similarity, not only in composition but also in organization, between ancestors and progeny. The organization of the cytoplasm of the egg cell seems to be of high importance in the early developmental stages. In later stages of development, the organization of the cells seems to be predominantly determined by the action of genes. It should be noted that the genes, the chromosomes and even whole genomes show the character of organization, as demonstrated by the phenomenon of genic homeostasis (Lerner, 1954; Dobzhansky and Wallace, 1953).

The present contribution proposes to deal with the genetic control of the organization of the cytoplasm. This will be done by attempting to analyze the genic control over some of the structural elements of the cytoplasm. This problem has actually two aspects: the structural elements show themselves the characteristics of structural and functional organization, and at the same time they form a part of the organized structure of the cell. It will be seen that these two aspects cannot be neatly divided from each other.

A further aspect of this problem concerns the changes in cellular organization in the course of development. Differentiation at the cellular level consists in part in the formation of cytoplasmic structures characteristic of the particular type of cell. The control by genes of cytodifferentiation in the course of development is therefore another aspect of the influence of genes on the organization of the cytoplasm.

Strain Differences in Mitochondria

The mitochondria seem to be a favorable system for the investigation of the question of the genic control of cytoplasmic constituents because of the fact that their role in intracellular metabolism is relatively well understood. Their importance as carriers of organized enzyme systems seems to be well established, and the facts on which this concept is based have been extensively reviewed recently (Schneider and Hogeboom, 1951; Schneider, 1953; Lindberg and Ernster, 1954; Green, 1954). It was therefore decided to look for differences in the mitochondria between inbred mouse strains.

The strains BALB/Ci and C57/11 were the first ones investigated. It has been possible to establish the fact that in preparations fixed in Regaud and stained according to Altmann, differences in the appearance of the liver mitochondria between males of these two strains can be demonstrated (Caspari, 1955a). More suitable for a genetic analysis are differences in the chemical composition of the mitochondrial preparations obtained by centrifugation of liver homogenates at 24,000 g in .88 M sucrose, according to the method of Hogeboom, Schneider and Palade (1948). In preparations obtained in that way, phosphorus and nitrogen were determined, and it could be shown that consistent differences between the two strains with respect to P/N ratio exist (Caspari and Santway, 1954). In evaluating the P/N ratios obtained, it must be kept in mind that significant variation occurs between the P/N ratios of preparations obtained in different experiments. It is therefore not the absolute difference obtained from a number of pooled experiments which is significant, but the consistency with which a difference in P/N ratio appears between the two strains in many independent experiments. In the tables, a standard error is attached to each value of P/N ratios, for the sake of convenience. This standard error is, however, not a measure of the significance of a difference, since it is based both on the variance within and between experiments. Only the variance within

[1] Work reported in this paper was supported by Grants RG-2645 of the National Institutes of Health, U. S. Public Health Service, and G 1812 of the National Science Foundation.

TABLE 1. MEAN PHOSPHORUS/NITROGEN RATIOS OF MITOCHONDRIA FROM MALES FROM DIFFERENT STRAINS

Strain	Mean P/N Ratio ± SE	n
BALB	97.7 ± 0.93	109
C57	102.3 ± 0.70	110
BALB	93.3 ± 0.97	52
C3H	95.8 ± 0.88	82

experiments can be used legitimately to establish the significance of a difference. The experiments have therefore been designed in such a way that in each case mitochondria from eight individual animals were prepared, two of which belonged to the same genotypic constitution. The significance of the results of a number of independent experiments can then be evaluated by means of analysis of variance, or by comparing the mean values for the genotypes from each experiment with each other.

In this way it could be demonstrated that a difference between the P/N ratios of the mitochondrial preparations of the two mouse strains exists. The difference is small, about 5 mg phosphorus per g nitrogen, but its existence has been confirmed in the meantime on a large body of material collected over more than five years. (Table 1.)

The nature of this difference between the two strains was more thoroughly investigated. It has been shown by Novikoff *et al.* (1952), Kuff and Schneider (1954) and Paigen (1954) that by differential centrifugation mitochondrial preparations can be divided into subfractions which differ in enzymatic activity and chemical composition, amongst them P/N ratio. The question arises, therefore, whether the difference in P/N ratio of the mitochondrial preparations from C57 and BALB livers is restricted to a particular subfraction, or whether it may be due to differences in the amounts of the different subfractions present. The results of fractionation of the mitochondrial preparations into three subfractions by differential centrifugation have shown that there are at least two factors involved in the strain difference, a qualitative difference in P/N ratio in the heaviest fraction and a greater contribution of the lightest, phosphorus-rich fraction to the total preparation in C57 (Caspari and Santway, 1954)

A further observation points in the same direction. It was observed that the pellets obtained from centrifugation of the homogenates of the two strains show striking differences. The pellets obtained at the bottom of the centrifuge tube are not a homogeneous mass of evenly colored mitochondria but show a definite and characteristic color pattern. Four major regions can be distinguished. The center of the pellet is divided by a darker ring from the peripheral layer of the pellet. In addition, there is always a distinct dark line

which extends from the center of the pellet up, usually through the ring into the peripheral layer of the pellet. The extent and coloration of the areas is so different in the two strains that it is easy to distinguish the pellets obtained from C57 and BALB by simple macroscopic observation. The central area is lighter in BALB than in C57, having a tan to light brown color as opposed to the dark brown color of C57. The ring dividing the central from the peripheral layer is narrow and of equal width throughout in BALB. In C57 it is broader and less distinct at the borders. The dark line going from the center to the periphery is narrow and distinct in BALB and of equal width throughout its length. In C57 it is somewhat less distinct, narrow at the upper end but becoming considerably wider towards the center; it is usually somewhat darker than the corresponding line in BALB.

It appears likely that these different zones of the pellet represent different subfractions of mitochondria which may correspond to the differentially colored bands obtained by Kuff and Schneider (1954) by centrifugation of mitochondria in narrow tubes. The observation would therefore constitute a further confirmation of the conclusion that at least part of the difference between the mitochondrial fractions of the two strains is due to the fact that they are composed of several different subfractions which contribute to the total sediment in different relative amounts. Whether there exist, besides this difference in relative quantities of subfractions, qualitative strain differences in the chemical and physical constitution in any one subfraction cannot be decided on the basis of the evidence presented.

Mr. A. C. Schwenk has extended these studies to include a third mouse strain, C3H/hepatoma 98/15 which was obtained through the courtesy of Dr. J. Walter Wilson. It appears from the data in Table 1 that C3H has a higher P/N ratio than BALB, although the difference does not appear to be as large as that between BALB and C57. In 21 independent experiments, 2 BALB and 2 C3H males of approximately equal ages were compared. The mean difference between the values from these determinations was 2.49 ± 0.609 mg P/gN (t = 3.21, df = 20, P < .01), a highly significant difference.

The sedimented mitochondrial pellet of C3H males is different in appearance from both BALB and C57, but the difference is not as striking as that between the other two strains. The center appears slightly darker than in BALB, and the ring dividing the center from the periphery is darker than in BALB but faint and frequently indistinct. The line going from the center to the periphery is dark and very distinct in C3H, narrow at the periphery but broader in the center. In the latter respect it resembles C57.

Since it is well known that several enzyme systems are found in the mitochondria it appeared possible that such significant differences in mitochondrial composition as have been demonstrated might be reflected in their enzymatic activities. Mr. Schwenk therefore investigated the succinoxidase activity of mitochondria from the livers of C3H and BALB males, again in paired experiments.

The isolation of mitochondria was done in the same way as for the determination of P/N ratios, except that the mice used were not starved, and that the mitochondrial preparations were kept in 0.25 M instead of 0.88 M sucrose. The final suspension was made up to be 20 per cent per wet weight of liver. Succinoxidase activity was determined manometrically according to the method of Schneider and Potter (1943) at two and three levels of enzyme concentration.

It was found that the succinoxidase activity was concentrated in the mitochondrial fraction, though some activity was found in the nuclear fraction, probably due to contamination with mitochondria and cell debris. The results of four experiments, each one with mice of the two strains BALB and C3H, are shown in Figure 1. It appears that at the concentrations used the amount of enzyme is limiting. There is no consistent difference in the O_2 uptake between the two strains. But there appears to be a difference in the variability between individuals. In C3H the values from four experiments arrange themselves easily in one line, so that an average enzyme activity per mg nitrogen could be easily established. This is not true for BALB where the different individuals show great differences in the level of activity. This may either be due to a greater variability in the level of activity, or to a greater variability in the content of inactive nitrogen containing substances. With regard to this latter possibility it should be pointed out that it was found previously that with regard to P/N ratio BALB shows a significantly higher variance within experiments than C57 (Caspari, 1956). Both observations can be interpreted in the same way if it is assumed that BALB mitochondria are characterized by high variability between individuals in a nitrogen containing component which is not involved in succinoxidase activity.

It can be imagined that the different types of mitochondria may be derived from different types of liver cells. It has indeed been shown by Noël (1923) and since been confirmed by many authors that the mitochondria in cells belonging to one liver lobule show regular morphological differences: the mitochondria in the cells close to the central blood vessel are filamentous, those in the intermediate zone more frequently rod shaped, and those at the periphery of the lobule short or even globular. The possibility that the different types of mitochondria are derived from different cells cannot be decided by a study of preparations isolated from homogenates. But morphological studies on Regaud-Altmann preparations indicate that in every one of the three zones the mito-

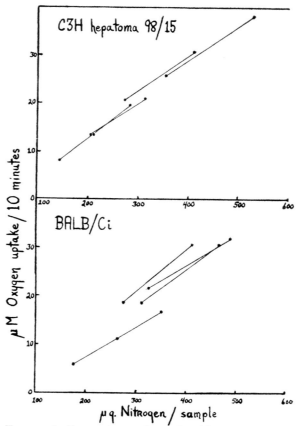

FIGURE 1. Comparison of succinoxidase activity of liver mitochondria from males of strains C3H and BALB. 4 paired experiments.

chondria of the strains BALB and C57 appear characteristically different. This may be taken as suggesting that the mitochondrial population of individual liver cells is different in the two strains.

INHERITANCE OF THE STRAIN DIFFERENCE IN MITOCHONDRIAL COMPOSITION

The difference in P/N ratio between strains BALB and C57 is sufficiently consistent that an attempt to analyze its behavior in crosses was made. The results of different types of crosses are summarized in Table 2. In this table, only experiments are included in which two animals of different crosses were compared to BALB and C57 controls. The only exception is the first backcross of the reciprocal F_1 females to males of the pure strains in which in each experiment two animals each of the four possible crosses were compared.

It is apparent that in all cases the difference between the BALB and C57 controls is in the expected direction. The variation between different independent experiments is particularly clear in the data from the fourth backcross which have generally low values.

The F_1 males have a low P/N ratio, similar to

TABLE 2. PHOSPHORUS/NITROGEN RATIOS OF
MITOCHONDRIA FROM MALES OF CROSSES
BETWEEN C57(C) AND BALB(B)

Paired experiments only, with C57 and BALB controls

	Cross	Mean P/N Ratio ± SE	n
F_1	B	99.6 ± 1.72	28
	C	102.9 ± 1.46	28
	CB	97.8 ± 1.33	27
	BC	98.7 ± 1.48	27
F_2	B	95.6 ± 1.51	40
	C	100.9 ± 1.07	42
	(CB)(CB)	100.0 ± 1.09	38
	(BC)(BC)	97.8 ± 1.21	41
Backcrosses	(CB) C	99.6 ± 1.20	24
	(CB) B	99.6 ± 1.35	24
	(BC) C	101.7 ± 1.49	24
	(BC) B	102.2 ± 1.74	24
	B	99.5 ± 1.61	15
	C	103.0 ± 1.68	16
	(CB) B2	104.4 ± 2.14	15
	(BC) C2	106.6 ± 1.49	16
	B	88.2 ± 1.25	28
	C	94.2 ± 1.70	28
	(CB) B4	89.3 ± 1.50	27
	(BC) C4	93.5 ± 1.59	28

BALB, and significantly lower than C57. No difference between the reciprocal F_1s is indicated. In F_2, on the other hand, a difference between the reciprocal crosses becomes apparent. (CB)(CB) has a mean value close to C57, and significantly higher than BALB ($t = 3.455$, df = 92, $t < .01$), while (BC)(BC) is intermediate between the two strains. The difference between the reciprocal F_2s has been established with the aid of four more experiments, not included in Table 2, in which only mitochondria from (CB)(CB) and (BC)(BC) males were compared. Both analysis of variance and a comparison of the means from experiments indicate that the difference between the two reciprocal crosses is significant at the .05 level ($F = 5.484$ for 1 and 71 df, $F_{.05} = 3.98$; $t = 2.225$, P < .03).

Two facts in F_2 have to be explained: the appearance of a reciprocal difference which was not apparent in F_1, and the high P/N values found in both F_2s in view of the fact that both the BALB derived genes in homozygous condition and the heterozygotes should be expected to induce low P/N values. Since the reciprocal F_2s are identical genetically except for the cytoplasm and the Y-chromosome, the difference must be due to either one of these structures. The fact that in cytoplasmic inheritance differences are frequently expressed only in the presence of homozygotes, as first shown by Bateson and Gairdner (1921) and later repeatedly confirmed,

led to the supposition that the cytoplasm may be responsible. It is unlikely that the high P/N value obtained in the cross (CB)(CB) is due only to homozygous genes from C57, since they should represent only 25 per cent of the genes. This difficulty could be avoided if it is assumed that some genes derived from BALB in homozygous condition cause a high P/N ratio in the cytoplasm derived from C57, but not in that of BALB. This hypothesis would account for the data obtained from F_1 and F_2.

This proposition has been tested by means of backcrosses. The four different types of backcross show no significant differences whatsoever. In these experiments no C57 and BALB controls were run, but four experiments in which (CB)C males were compared to C57 and BALB showed that they have a P/N ratio similar to C57 and higher than BALB. The same may therefore be assumed for the other backcrosses. The high P/N ratio of the cross (BC)(B) is unexpected, but it must be mentioned that this cross showed an unusually high variance within experiments.

The second backcross seems to be in agreement with the proposed hypothesis, since the backcross (CB)(B) has a high P/N ratio. The average difference between the means of BALB and the second backcross to a BALB male, obtained in the eight experiments, is below the .01 level of significance ($t = 4.15$, df = 7, P < .01). In other words, even though the genome of the backcross consists partly of homozygous BALB genes and partly of genes in heterozygous condition which according to the F_1 data should also have a low P/N ratio, the backcross seems to possess mitochondria of a higher P/N ratio than BALB.

This effect does not continue to the fourth backcross. In the fourth backcross, the backcross to BALB is very similar to BALB, while the backcross to C57 agrees with C57. In other words, no cytoplasmic effect can be detected, the P/N ratios can be accounted for exclusively by the genotype. This conclusion is borne out by macroscopic inspection of the mitochondrial pellets: (CB)B4 could not be distinguished from BALB while (BC)C4 was identical with C57.

These data show beyond doubt that the P/N ratio and the pellet pattern of the mitochondria are under the control of chromosomal genes. The reciprocal difference demonstrated in F_2 can therefore best be interpreted as a maternal effect which seems to continue through three generations but finally disappears under the influence of the paternal genotype. The physiological nature of a maternal effect of such duration which resembles the phenomenon of dauermodification is hard to visualize, and alternative interpretations may have to be taken into consideration. But on the basis of the data presented, it seems to be the best interpretation.

The Genetic Behavior of Mitochondria

The data reported show the existence of a dependence of the composition of the mitochondria on genes in the mouse. This is not unexpected since genes affecting the biochemical activities and composition of mitochondria have been demonstrated in yeast (Ephrussi and Hottinguer, 1951) and in *Neurospora* (Mitchell, Mitchell and Tissières, 1953).

In addition, Ephrussi (1953) and Mitchell and Mitchell (1952) have demonstrated that in yeast and in *Neurospora* mitochondrial differences of a similar kind occur which are transmitted through the cytoplasm, independently of the genic constitution. This has been taken as evidence that the mitochondria may have the capacity of identical selfreproduction and the ability to transmit their own specific characteristics to the daughter cells. In higher organisms, an orderly transmission of mitochondria to the offspring may be indicated by the fact that in some animals the distribution of the mitochondria to the male gametes at meiosis is brought about by an orderly process reminding one of chromosomal distribution (Meves and Duesberg, 1907 in the yellow jacket, Pollister in *Gerris*, 1930, Wilson, 1931 in scorpions). The fate of the mitochondria contributed by the sperm cell seems to be different in the development of different animal species, according to the older literature (see Lillie and Just for review, 1924). In the mouse, there exists evidence that a considerable amount of mitochondrial material is transmitted to the zygote by the sperm cell (Gresson, 1940).

If it is assumed that the mitochondria have the ability of selfreproduction, the question of the origin of the different subfractions of mitochondria arises. They may either constitute different independently reproducing types of particles or they may represent differentiated types of the same original particle. In this way, this question is closely allied to that of mitochondrial differentiation. The fact that mitochondria undergo differentiation during development has been well demonstrated, for example, by Hutchens, Kopac and Krahl (1942) and by Gustafson and Lenicque (1952) for the developing sea urchin egg, by Boell and Weber (1955) for the Amphibian embryo, by Sippel (1954) for the cardiac development of the chicken and the rat. An analogy in *Neurospora* may be found in the observation that during the growth of a culture the enzymatic activities of mitochondria in the cytoplasmic mutant undergo changes (Haskins, Tissières, Mitchell and Mitchell, 1953). The result of this mitochondrial differentiation in development may well be the differences in the mitochondrial composition and activities in different tissues, examples of which have been cited by Schneider (1953) and Green (1954). The observed changes in mitochondrial characteristics during development may represent shifts in mitochondrial population structure in the cells by differential reproduction, or differential organization of originally undifferentiated mitochondria.

The question arises whether and how genes control this differentiation of cytoplasmic particulates. For the investigation of this question, the differences in the mitochondrial composition of mouse strains are not suitable, since different reactions of different subfractions on the same genotype have been demonstrated, and the genes involved have not been isolated. A system favorable for this investigation is constituted by the pigment granules of the moth *Ephestia*.

The Effect of Genes on Pigment Granules in the Testis of *Ephestia*

The possibility that pigment granules may be related to the mitochondria has been suggested by the fact that isolated pigment granules may show at least some of the enzymatic activities usually associated with mitochondria, as shown by Herrmann and Boss (1945) for pigment granules from the ciliary body of cattle, and DuBuy, Woods, Burk and Lackey (1949) for melanin granules from mouse melanomata. This fact does not necessarily indicate a genetic relationship between mitochondria and pigment granules, since it may be assumed that pigment granules are of independent origin and take over the functions of the mitochondria in pigment forming cells.

The origin of the pigment in the eyes and testes of *Ephestia* is well investigated. It is an ommochrome (Becker, 1942), derived from tryptophane by the series:

tryptophane → kynurenin →

3-hydroxykynurenin → ommochrome

An ommochrome pigment, xanthommatin, has recently been isolated by Butenandt and collaborators from the feces of *Vanessa* and the eyes of *Calliphora* (1954). Its chemical constitution has been confirmed by synthesis. It may be assumed to have arisen from the oxidative condensation of two molecules of 3-hydroxykynurenin under loss of one amino group.

The formation of the pigment granules in the eye has been investigated by Hanser (1948). She found that the pigment is deposited on precursor granules which appear shortly before the first appearance of the pigment. The precursor granules form a continuing part of the pigment granule and can be demonstrated by dissolving the pigment in acidified methyl alcohol or destroying it according to the method of Lustgarten-Pal. The association of pigment with a cytoplasmic precursor structure has also been described by Tsujita (1948) for a kynurenin derived pigment in the Malpighian tubules of *Bombyx*. Tsujita considers the precursor granules to be derived from "chondriosomes."

The gene *a* inhibits the formation of pigment

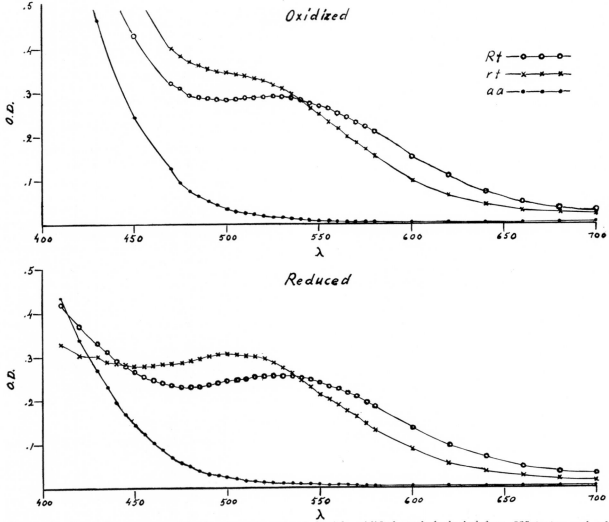

FIGURE 2. Absorption spectra of testis pigments extracted with acidified methyl alcohol from 925 testes each of strains *Rt Rt* —O—O—O—, *rt rt* —✕—✕—✕— and *aa* —O—O—O—. a. oxidized with NaNO₂ ; b. reduced with stannous chloride.

by blocking the oxidation of tryptophane to kynurenin. The block is incomplete, and some pigment is deposited on the precursor granules in the eye. The testes of *aa* animals are, however, usually colorless under the conditions used in our laboratory, although colored testes do occasionally occur. A second gene *wa* inhibits the pigmentation of both eyes and testes completely. Hanser (1948), investigating the eyes of *wa wa* animals, found that the precursor granules were completely absent. She concluded that the gene *wa* interferes with the formation of the precursor granules. This would constitute the dependence of a particular type of cytoplasmic structure on a particular gene. Because of the importance of this finding, the

formation of the pigment granules in the testis of *Ephestia* was investigated.

Precursor granules can be stained with hematoxylin, pyronin or azure B. Because of their small size, they cannot, in stained preparations, be easily distinguished from pigment granules. The best method of observation consists therefore in the study of unstained preparations, fresh or fixed in Carnoy, with the phase contrast microscope. Both pigment granules and precursor granules are apparent under phase contrast, whereas, if the same preparation is observed or photographed in bright field, only the pigment shows up.

In wild type animals, the pigment appears

first in the last larval instar. Before the appearance of pigment, no precursor granules can be seen, only dark haloes around the nuclei which can be stained with pyronin. Precursor granules can be clearly seen, particularly in the neighborhood of the nuclei, as soon as the first minute amount of pigment appears (Fig. 3). The amount of pigment increases fast, resulting in a larger number of granules of larger size, as may be seen in the host tissue in Figure 9.

In *wa wa* testes, no definite precursor granules could be found (Fig. 4 and 5). Haloes in the surroundings of the nuclei could be seen. In addition, Figure 4 shows dark particles in the cytoplasm; they appear however larger in size than the precursor granules and show a more irregular shape.

In *aa* males, it might be expected that precursor granules without pigment would be found. This expectation has not been borne out. In unpig-

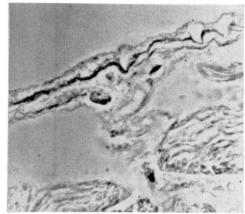

FIGURE 5. Testis sheath of *wa wa* adult. Phase contrast. 1200×.

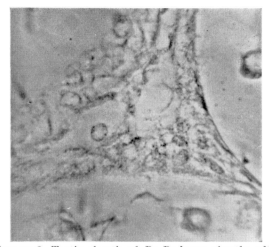

FIGURE 3. Testis sheath of *Rt Rt* larva shortly after the last larval molt. Phase contrast. 1200×. Precursor granules around nuclei.

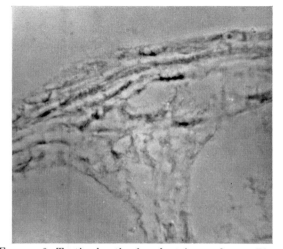

FIGURE 6. Testis sheath of *aa* last instar larva. Phase contrast. 1200×.

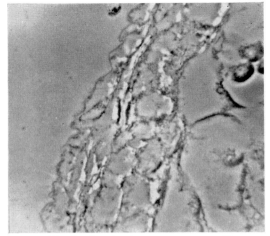

FIGURE 4. Testis sheath of *wa wa* prepupa. Phase contrast. 1200×.

mented testes of *aa* animals, pyronin staining matter could be found in the neighborhood of the nuclei, but no indication of precursor granules (Fig. 6). If, however, a slight trace of pigment is formed in the testis, numerous precursor granules appear (Fig. 7). It appears, therefore, that the presence of a small amount of pigment is necessary for the formation of precursor granules.

This hypothesis was tested by implanting *aa* larval testes into wild type pupae. Since wild type pupae contain kynurenin in their body fluids, *aa* transplants are able in the host environment to form pigment. The implanted testes were removed after a certain time and investigated under the binocular microscope whether or not they had formed at least a trace of pigment. The results are given in Table 3. Only completely colorless testes are indicated as unpigmented. It should be mentioned that even the pigmented testes had usually formed only minute amounts

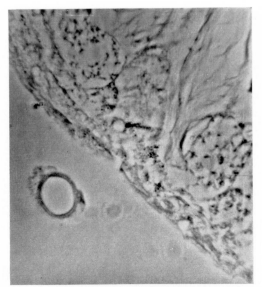

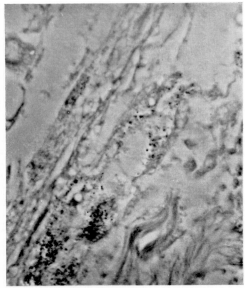

FIGURE 7. Testis sheath of *aa* adult, slightly pigmented. Phase contrast. 1200×. At left a trachea. Considerable number of granules in testis sheath.

FIGURE 9. Tests sheath of *aa* larval testis transplanted into +pupa. Removed after 2 days. Fused to host testis. Phase contrast. 1200×. At right host testis; sheath with many pigment granules. At left transplant; sheath contains few granules, particularly around nucleus.

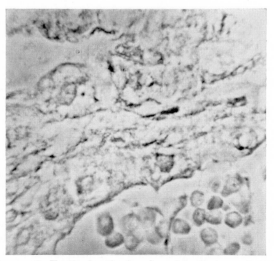

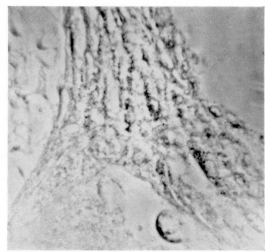

FIGURE 8. Testis sheath of *aa* larval testis transplanted into + pupa. Removed after one day. Phase contrast. 1200×. No granules.

FIGURE 10. Testis sheath of *aa* larval testis transplanted into +pupa. Removed after 3 days. Phase contrast. 1200×. Many granules.

of pigment. The recovered grafts were fixed in Carnoy for microscopic observation.

Table 3 shows that after one day in the host most testes are still colorless. Such testes show large nuclei with well developed haloes, but no precursor granules (Fig. 8). After two days, a large proportion of the grafts shows traces of pigment. Figure 9 shows such a graft which has fused with the well pigmented host testis. The graft was pigmented only where it was attached to the host. There are well developed precursor granules visible in the graft. After three days in the host, most testes are slightly pigmented. Fig-

ure 10 shows a large number of granules in such a transplant, most of which are precursor granules.

The experiments agree with the previously mentioned observations that precursor granules first appear when the slightest amount of pigment is deposited. They appear first in individual cells, leaving other cells free of precursor granules. Not all cells containing precursor granules show visible pigment. The number of precursor granules increases fast once they have appeared, while the increase in the amount of pigment proceeds more slowly. The formation of some pigment seems therefore necessary to either induce the formation of precursor granules or at least to stabilize them. The fact that in *wa wa* animals no precursor granules are found does therefore not necessarily indicate that the gene *wa* controls primarily the formation of precursor granules. Any interference with the formation of pigment would have the same result.

The Genic Control of the Time of Pigment Formation

Another pair of alleles controls the quality of the pigment in wild type animals. In *Rt-* animals, the testes appear brownish-blue, in *rt rt* red. The individual pigment granules from the two strains are different in size and color (Caspari, 1955b). The difference in color is due to qualitatively different pigments, as shown by their absorption spectra (Fig. 2). Both pigments are typical ommochromes, as shown by their insolubility in water, alcohol and organic solvents, their solubility in acidified methyl alcohol, and their behavior as oxidation-reduction indicators. The absorption curve of *Rt Rt* pigment corresponds completely to that of the eye pigment of *Ephestia* according to Becker (1942). There appears to be no difference in the amount of pigment between the two strains, since both curves are based on the pigment extracted from somewhat over 900 testes.

In addition to controlling the quality of the pigment, the alleles *Rt* and *rt* determine the time at which pigment is first formed. In *Rt Rt* animals, pigment appears first about the time of the last larval molt (Fig. 3), whereas in *rt rt* pigment is not formed until the beginning of the pre-pupa stage.

The conditions for the inability of *rt rt* testes to form pigment during most of the last larval instar has been investigated. Lack of kynurenin may be *a priori* excluded since other characters depending on kynurenin, the pigmentation of the ocelli and the hypodermis, are present in *rt rt* larvae. The possibility that *rt rt* larval testes are unable to react on the presence of kynurenin with pigment formation was tested by establishing an *aa rt rt* strain and transplanting larval testes into wild type hosts. The results, as indicated in Table 3, give no evidence of a difference between *aa Rt Rt* and *aa rt rt* testes with respect to their ability to form pigment in a wild type host.

Another condition must therefore prevail in the intact larva which inhibits pigment formation. Some information concerning this question has been obtained by experiments involving the tying of last instar larvae. If larvae are tied behind the head shield or behind the thorax before the critical period, the abdomen cannot pupate because the pupation hormone secreted by the prothoracic glands cannot reach the abdomen (Kühn and Piepho, 1936). The release of pupation hormone by the prothoracic glands is in turn

TABLE 3. PIGMENTATION OF *aa* LARVAL TRANSPLANTS AFTER DIFFERENT LENGTH OF TIME IN A WILD TYPE HOST

Percent pigmented transplants. The number in parentheses indicates the number of grafts.

Genotype of Donor	Days in a^+a^+ Host				
	1	2	3	4	6
aa Rt Rt	12 (49)	47 (94)	76 (25)	100 (10)	100 (18)
aa rt rt	0 (2)	72 (25)	60 (15)		

controlled by a hormone secreted by the brain. The abdomina become therefore permanent larvae which can survive in the larval state for a considerable amount of time.

Rt Rt larvae were tied in the earlier parts of the last larval instar, when their testes were already slightly pigmented. The abdomina were kept for 12 days and the testes dissected out. They had continued to form pigment and became much darker than they usually are. The same experiment was performed on *rt rt* larvae whose abdomina were kept isolated for 14 days. If at the time of the operation pigment formation had not yet started, the testes were completely colorless when removed. In a small number of cases pigment formation had just started, as could be observed by seeing a slight indication of the presence of a testis through the dorsal abdominal wall. In all of these cases, pigment formation proceeded, so that at the time of removal of the testes they were well pigmented, though not unusually dark. These experiments permit the conclusion that in *rt rt* animals the initiation of pigmentation is depending on some factor reaching the abdomen from the anterior part of the body. It may be suggested that this factor may be the pupation hormone. At all events, the gene *rt* controls the dependence of the testis on some stimulus for the initiation of pigmentation. Since in *Rt* animals pigment formation starts earlier and is not inhibited by isolation in the last larval instar, it must be dependent on a different stimulus or the stimulus must appear at an earlier developmental stage.

The general picture of the genic control of the formation of pigment granules in *Ephestia* is therefore complex. The granules are themselves complex structures and their formation is controlled by genes affecting the synthesis of their components. The syntheses of the different components are, however, not independent of each other: block of ommochrome formation by the gene *a* inhibits the formation of the precursor granules, and, according to Hanser's hypothesis, inhibition of the formation of the precursor granules by the gene *wa* would inhibit ommochrome formation from proceeding beyond the stage of kynurenin or hydroxykynurenin. Finally, there are control mechanisms which integrate the formation of pigment granules with the development of the whole organism, as indicated by the dependence of *rt* testes on the thoracic stimulus.

CONCLUSIONS

The effect of genes on two types of cytoplasmic structures has been studied. The structures are different from each other in so far as one type, the pigment granules of *Ephestia*, is restricted to particular cells and appears at a particular time in development. The origin of new cytoplasmic structures in development is not clear, but the electron microscope work of Porter (1954) suggests that the so-called dense bodies may be involved in the production of myofibrils, even though they may not directly participate in their formation. As far as genic control is concerned, it appears that genes do not control the formation of the pigment granules *in toto*, but by means of controlling the formation of their constituents and of the conditions under which they appear.

The mitochondria are different from the pigment granules in so far as they are of ubiquitous occurrence and are transmitted from generation to generation by the gametes. But, as mentioned earlier, they show similarly the feature of differentiation. This is shown by the fact that increases in the number of visible mitochondria per cell have been repeatedly observed (Goss, 1940; Gustafson and Lenicque, 1952) in the course of differentiation, that the mitochondrial populations in cells from different adult tissues are different in their constitution and activity, and that the enzymatic activities of isolated mitochondria change in the course of differentiation (Boell and Weber, 1955). In addition, the strong variability of mitochondria under the influence of environmental factors should be mentioned. This has been particularly shown by morphological methods (Roberts, 1949), but the well demonstrated influence of hormones such as thyroxin on the metabolic activities of mitochondria, both *in vivo* and *in vitro*, seems also to indicate the variability in the activity of these particles (Martius and Hess, 1951; Maley and Lardy, 1953; Mudd, Park and Lipmann, 1955). The fact that variability of mitochondria under external influences has been observed raises the question whether the genic influence on mitochondrial constitution may be ascribed to a more or less direct influence of the genes, or whether it would represent an influence via control of the cellular environment or even the activities of other tissues, such as hormone glands. The genetic situation in our mouse experiments is not sufficiently clear to give a definite answer, but analogy to the much simpler situation in the pigment granules of *Ephestia* suggests that indirect effects are quite likely to be expected.

Wagner and Mitchell (1955) point out that the known facts concerning inheritance of cytoplasmic structures can be interpreted in two different ways. It may be assumed that different types of particles exist which are selfreproducing, giving rise to new particles with the same characteristics, and which are transmitted through the gametes. Differentiation might then consist in a differential multiplication of different types of particles, giving rise to different particle populations in different types of cells. The other possibility would be that the whole of the cytoplasm, including its particulate constituents, forms a relatively stable steady state which may be transmitted at cell division and at zygote formation. Wagner and Mitchell state: "According to this scheme the specific properties of the cellular particles, the appearance and activities of which may be different in different cytoplasms, are determined by the interrelated chemical activities of the cytoplasm." Differentiation under this assumption would consist in change from one pattern of metabolism to another. In either case, genic control by an influence on metabolic processes would be expected.

The data presented do not allow a decision between these possibilities. However, the fact that a maternal effect was transmitted through three generations and disappeared after that time could be more easily described under the picture of a stable state, selfreproducing to a certain degree, and involving both the genotype and the cytoplasmic particles. But since alternative interpretations of the maternal effect are not excluded, caution is indicated concerning this conclusion.

The different cells of an adult animal show more or less stable morphological characteristics and metabolic patterns even in the presence of variations in external and internal environment. Mechanisms may therefore be postulated by which this stability of the metabolic pattern is maintained. Lindberg and Ernster (1954) have suggested that the mitochondria themselves may constitute part of the mechanism responsible for the regulation of the metabolic equilibrium, since by changes of their permeability and possibly by other mechanisms they may be imagined to control the rate of particular reactions and in this way may decide between alternate possible pathways for a metabolite. The great variability of the mitochondria may be an expression of this particular function in cellular metabolism and may be expected to be itself under genic control. It has been pointed out earlier (Caspari, 1956) that mouse strains may differ from each other not only in the mean P/N ratios of their mitochondria, but also in the variability of this character. This observation, and the indication that different mouse strains may differ in the variability of the succinoxidase activity of their liver mitochondria may be regarded as indicative of one possible way in which genes may control the stability of the cellular metabolic pattern.

REFERENCES

BATESON, W., and GAIRDNER, A. E., 1921, Male sterility in flax subject to two types of segregation. J. Genet. *11:* 269–276.

BECKER, E., 1942, Über Eigenschaften, Verbreitung und diegenetisch-entwicklungsphysiologische Bedeutung der Pigmente der Ommatin- und Ommingruppe (Ommochrome) bei den Arthropoden. Z. ind. Abstam. Vererb.-lehre *80:* 157–204.

BOELL, E. J., and WEBER, R., 1955, Cytochrome oxidase activity during Amphibian development. Exp. Cell Res. *9:* 559–567.

BUTENANDT, A., SCHIEDT, U., BIEKERT, E., and CROMARTIE, R. J. T., 1954, Über Ommochrome, IV. Mitteilung. Konstitution des Xanthommatins. Liebig's Ann. *590:* 75–90.

CASPARI, E., 1955a, The role of genes and cytoplasmic particles in differentiation. Ann. N. Y. Acad. Sci. *60:* 1026–1037.

——— 1955b, On the pigment formation in the testis sheath of *Rt* and *rt Ephestia kühniella* Zeller. Biol. Zbl. *74:* 585–602.

——— 1956, The inheritance of the difference in the composition of the liver mitochondria between two mouse strains. Genetics *41:* 107–117.

CASPARI, E., and SANTWAY, R. W., 1954, Differences in composition between mitochondria from two mouse strains. Exp. Cell Res. *7:* 351–367.

DOBZHANSKY, TH., and WALLACE, B., 1953, The genetics of homeostasis in *Drosophila*. Proc. Nat. Acad. Sci. Wash. *39:* 162–171.

DUBUY, H. G., WOODS, M. W., BURK, D., and LACKEY, M. D., 1949, Enzymatic activities of isolated amelanotic and melanotic granules of mouse melanomas and a suggested relationship to mitochondria. J. Nat. Cancer Inst. *9:* 325–336.

EPHRUSSI, B., 1953, Nucleo-cytoplasmic Relations in Microorganisms. Oxford, Oxford Univ. Press.

EPHRUSSI, B., and HOTTINGUER, H., 1951, Cytoplasmic constituents of heredity. On an unstable cell state in yeast. Cold Spring Harbor Symp. Quant. Biol. *16:* 75–84.

GOSS, C. M., 1940, First contractions of the heart without cytological differentiation. Anat. Rec. *76:* 19–27.

GREEN, D. E., 1954, Enzymes in metabolic sequences. In: Chemical Pathways of Metabolism, ed. by D. M. Greenberg, New York, Academic Press: 27–65.

GRESSON, R. A. R., 1940, Presence of the sperm middle-piece in the fertilized egg of the mouse (*Mus musculus*). Nature, Lond. *145:* 425.

GUSTAFSON, T., and LENICQUE, P., 1952, Studies on mitochondria in the developing sea urchin egg. Exp. Cell Res. *3:* 251–271.

HANSER, G., 1948, Über die Histogenese der Augenpigmentgranule bei verschiedenen Rassen von *Ephestia kühniella* Z. und *Ptychopoda seriata* Schnk. Z. ind. Abst. Vererb.-lehre *82:* 74–97.

HASKINS, F. A., TISSIÈRES, A., MITCHELL, H. K., and MITCHELL, M. B., 1953, Cytochromes and the succinic oxidase system of poky strains of *Neurospora*. J. Biol. Chem. *200:* 819–826.

HERRMANN, H., and BOSS, B., 1945, Dopa oxidase activity in extracts from ciliary body and in isolated pigment granules. J. Cell. Comp. Physiol. *26:* 131–138.

HOGEBOOM, G. H., SCHNEIDER, W. C., and PALADE, G. E., 1948, Cytochemical studies of mammalian tissues I. Isolation of intact mitochondria from rat liver; some biochemical properties of mitochondria and submicroscopic particulate material. J. Biol. Chem. *172:* 619–635.

HUTCHENS, J. O., KOPAC, M. J., and KRAHL, M. E., 1942, The cytochrome oxidase content of centrifugally separated fractions of unfertilized *Arbacia* eggs. J. Cell. Comp. Physiol. *20:* 113–116.

KUFF, E. L., and SCHNEIDER, W. C., 1954, Intracellular distribution of enzymes XII. Biochemical heterogeneity of mitochondria. J. Biol. Chem. *206:* 677–685.

KÜHN, A., and PIEPHO, H., 1936, Über hormonale Wirkungen bei der Verpuppung der Schmetterlinge. Nachr. Ges. Wiss. Göttingen, Math.-Phys. Kl., N. F., Fachgr. II., Nachr. Biol. *2:* 141–154.

LERNER, I. M., 1954, Genetic Homeostasis. Edinburgh and London, Oliver and Boyd, III + 134 pp.

LILLIE, F. R., and JUST, E. E., 1924, Fertilization. In Cowdry ed.: General Cytology. Chicago, Univ. of Chicago Press: 451–536.

LINDBERG, O., and ERNSTER, L., 1954, Chemistry and Physiology of mitochondria and microsomes. Protoplasmologia, ed. by L. V. Heilbrunn and F. Weber, III A *4:* 1–136.

MALEY, G. F., and LARDY, H. A., 1953, Metabolic effects of thyroid hormones *in vitro* II. Influence of thyroxine and triiodothyronine on oxidative phosphorylation. J. Biol. Chem. *204:* 435–444.

MARTIUS, C., and HESS, B., 1951, The mode of action of thyroxin. Arch. Biochem. Biophys. *33:* 486–487.

MEVES, F., and DUESBERG, J., 1907, Die Spermatocytenteilung bei der Hornisse (*Vespa crabro* L.). Arch. mikr. Anat. *71:* 571–587.

MITCHELL, M. B., and MITCHELL, H. K., 1952, A case of "maternal" inheritance in *Neurospora crassa*. Proc. Nat. Acad. Sci. Wash. *38:* 442–449.

MITCHELL, M. B., MITCHELL, H. K., and TISSIÈRES, A., 1953, Mendelian and non-Mendelian factors affecting the cytochrome system in *Neurospora crassa*. Proc. Nat. Acad. Sci. Wash. *39:* 606–613.

MUDD, S. H., PARK, J. H., and LIPMANN, F., 1955, Magnesium antagonism of the uncoupling of oxidative phosphorylation by iodothyronines. Proc. Nat. Acad. Sci. Wash. *41:* 571–576.

NOËL, R., 1923, Recherches histo-physiologiques sur la cellule hépatique des mammifères. Arch. Anat. mic. *19:* 1–156.

NOVIKOFF, A. B., PODBER, E., RYAN, J., and NOE, E., 1952, Biochemical heterogeneity of the cytoplasmic particles isolated from rat liver homogenate. Federation Proc. *11:* 265–266.

PAIGEN, K., 1954, The occurrence of several biochemically distinct types of mitochondria in rat liver. J. Biol. Chem. *206:* 945–957.

POLLISTER, A. W., 1930, Cytoplasmic phenomena in the spermatogenesis of *Gerris*. J. Morph. *49:* 455–507.

PORTER, K. R., 1954, Cell and tissue differentiation in relation to growth (animals). In: Dynamics of Growth Processes, ed. E. J. Boell, Princeton, Princeton Univ. Press: 95–110.

ROBERTS, H. S., 1949, Changes in mitochondrial form. Anat. Rec. *104:* 163–183.

SCHNEIDER, W. C., 1953, Biochemical constitution of mammalian mitochondria. J. Histochem. Cytochem. *1:* 212–233.

SCHNEIDER, W. C., and HOGEBOOM, G. H., 1951, Cytochemical studies on mammalian tissues: the isolation of cell components by differential centrifugation. A review. Cancer Research *11:* 1–22.

SCHNEIDER, W. C., and POTTER, V. R., 1943, The assay of animal tissues for respiratory enzymes II. Succinic dehydrogenase and cytochrome oxidase. J. Biol. Chem. *149:* 217–227.

SIPPEL, T. O., 1954, The growth of succinoxidase activity in the hearts of rat and chick embryos. J. Exp. Zool. *126:* 205–221.

TSUJITA, M., 1948, Cytological studies of the Malphigian tubules in the silkworm larva II. Relation between chondriosomes and "lactoflavin." Bull. Sericult. Exp. Station, Tokyo *12:* 649–666 (Japanese).

WAGNER, R. P., and MITCHELL, H. K., 1955, Genetics and Metabolism. New York and London, Wiley and Chapman & Hall, ix + 444 pp.

WILSON, E. B., 1931, The distribution of sperm-forming materials in scorpions. J. Morph. *52:* 429–483.

An Attempt to Compare the Sarcosomes of Diploids and Triploids in *Drosophila melanogaster*

George T. Rudkin and Jack Schultz

Lankenau Hospital Research Institute and Institute for Cancer Research, Philadelphia, Pennsylvania

About five years ago when Dr. Levenbook called our attention to insect flight muscle sarcosomes, it occurred to us that these organelles might be suitable for a study of nuclear control of cytoplasmic elements. The work, especially of Dr. Carroll Williams' laboratory at Harvard, had indicated that these bodies had all of the enzyme systems of mitochondria and they are now regarded as giant mitochondria (see Levenbook and Williams, 1956). With the establishment of genetic control over respiratory enzymes in microorganisms (Ephrussi, 1953), it seemed that the wide range of genetic types available in *Drosophila melanogaster* could immediately be used for comparisons. Although enzymatic studies have not been carried out, an exploratory morphological examination of two genotypes is of interest to the present Symposium.

An attempt was made to discover any change in the sarcosome that could be brought about by a change in the number of chromosome sets. It is well known that triploid *Drosophila* have a larger cell size than their diploid sisters, although their total mass is only slightly increased (thus fewer cells). The increase in ploidy might affect the dimensions of sarcosomes in several ways: the size might remain constant, the number changing; the number might remain constant, the size of individual sarcosomes increasing. Changes in constitution or shape are also possible with or without changes in dimension. The diameters of sarcosomes from the two types were therefore measured and information regarding possible changes in constitution was sought from microspectrophotometric measurements of individual sarcosomes. As will be seen, the diameters of the sarcosomes (*i.e.*, size) turned out to be quite variable from muscle fiber to muscle fiber and from fly to fly. On the basis of present data, the most likely interpretation is that the constitution of the sarcosomes in triploid and diploid *Drosophila* is similar; but their size may be influenced by chromosomal as well as other factors.

Material

The diploid stock used was the "Oregon R" wild type, *D. melanogaster*, inbred in this laboratory for about one hundred generations. Triploids were derived from two sources, one newly arisen in the Oregon R stock, the other from stocks kept by Dr. Helen Redfield and made available to us. The newly arisen triploids arose from colchi-cine treatment of female larvae of the Oregon R stock; tetraploid portions of the ovary give diploid eggs which, when fertilized by X-bearing sperm, produce triploids used for two sets of diameter measurements (Tables 1 and 2) and for all of the microspectrophotometric measurements. In all cases, diploids are compared with their triploid sisters.

The second series of triploids came from a long established stock carrying two of the three X-chromosomes attached, and made heterozygous by outcrossing to various wild stocks. As is usual with long established stocks of triploids, these individuals probably carried only two of the small fourth chromosomes.

Methods

All flies were aged two to three weeks to avoid the variation during the growth period. Muscle from the dorsal half of the thorax was teased from unetherized flies into a drop of 2.5 per cent serum albumin in 0.16 M phosphate buffer (Watanabe and Williams, 1953), covered with a coverslip and sealed. Measurements under a 90× Leitz phase objective (NA 1.15) with a 10× filar micrometer eyepiece are converted to μ. For convenience, however, variance analyses were performed on the micrometer readings. A "field" consisted of a row of sarcosomes, apparently *in situ* along muscle fibers. Genotypes were measured in pairs; the observer did not know which one he was measuring in the attached-X stock.

Malphigian tubules were mounted in Versene solution (Slater and Cleland, 1952) and fields of yellow pigment globules photographed with the Zeiss 2.5 mm quartz objective at a magnification of 1320 diameters with the 2750A Cd line. Relative globule diameters, estimated from enlarged images of films so obtained, are not directly reducible to μ, but are of the order of 1 μ. The distribution of pigment globules becomes fairly uniform in the different cells of the tubule at some distance from its junction with the gut. The posterior tubules were chosen for measurement, and the attempt made to use cells in the uniform region. It is believed that this was successful in most cases.

Flies used for the data in Table 3 were weighed one day after hatching and classified into three classes: those within five per cent of the mean and those between five and ten per cent heavier or lighter, respectively, than the mean.

TABLE 1. MEAN DIAMETERS OF SARCOSOMES FROM DIPLOID AND TRIPLOID OFFSPRING OF COLCHICINE TREATED *Drosophila*

Diploid			Triploid		
Fly no.	Number of sarco-somes	Mean diameter	Fly no.	Number of sarco-somes	Mean diameter
69	33	2.80 μ	73	33	2.85 μ
77	33	2.85 μ	81	33	3.45 μ
93	100	2.27 μ	85	100	2.98 μ
			89	100	2.47 μ
Total......	166	2.49		266	2.83

TABLE 2. MEAN DIAMETERS OF YELLOW PIGMENT GLOBULES FROM MALPHIGIAN TUBULES OF DIPLOID AND TRIPLOID OFFSPRING OF COLCHICINE TREATED *Drosophila*

Diploid			Triploid		
Fly no.	Number of globules	Mean diameter*	Fly no.	Number of globules	Mean diameter*
69	202	5.25	73	239	5.61
77	170	5.73	81	125	6.51
			89	221	5.23
Total.......	372	5.47		585	5.66

* Arbitrary units; mean diameters about 1 μ.

TABLE 3. MEAN DIAMETERS OF SARCOSOMES FROM DIPLOID AND TRIPLOID FLIES FROM AN ATTACHED-X STOCK OF *Drosophila*

Diploid			Triploid		
Fly no.	Weight class	Mean diam-eter*	Fly no.	Weight class	Mean diam-eter*
94	±5% mean	2.92 μ	95	±5% of mean	2.66 μ
96	5–10% less	2.88	97	5–10% less	2.58
98	5–10% less	2.80	99	5–10% less	2.80
			(100)	5–10% more	2.76)
			(101)	±5% of mean	2.52)
Total..		2.87 μ			2.69 μ

* Mean of 100 sarcosomes (5 fields of 20 each).

Brownian motion and radiation effects were minimized for microspectrophotometry by dehydrating *in vacuo* sarcosomes dispersed in the Versene solution and frozen to a quartz slide with dry ice. Glycerin was added and a quartz coverslip sealed in place for observation. A Zeiss 2.5 mm and a Cooke 2 mm quartz monochromat (2750A) were used with a Cooke quartz condenser in a photographic apparatus according to Caspersson as recently described by us (Rudkin *et al.*, 1955). Plate calibration followed Caspersson, but in our hands variations between plates could not reliably be kept below ±10 %. Absorption images were scanned with a Jarrel-Ash microphotometer, the output of which was put through an electronic function transformer to record extinction directly on a Brown recording potentiometer.

THE DIAMETERS OF SARCOSOMES

The measurement of small microscopic objects is limited by the resolving power of the microscope, the error at any discontinuity being of the order of ±0.1 μ. The exact meaning of a statistically significant difference in diameter of the same order of magnitude is dubious. It is this problem which is raised by the case of the attached-X triploid stock, where a statistical difference of 0.18 μ between genotypes is found. It is likely that the differences represent a real difference between sarcosomes of the two types, since the measurements were randomized insofar as possible.

Table 3 gives the data upon which this difference is based. Analysis of variance was carried out to detect possible variability due to fly weight, to other variation between individuals and to differences between different measured fields (*i.e.*, sarcosomes on different muscle fibers). If the variance of the diameters within fields is chosen as the error variance, then neither fly weight nor differences between individuals had a significant effect on sarcosome size, but differences between fields are shown to be larger than chance would allow (.01 > P > .001). The implication is that sarcosome size varies in the musculature of the dorsal thorax. Comparison of the variance contributed by genotype with that from the fields shows the effect of genotype to be just significant at the five per cent level.

It should be emphasized that the comparison is between a genotype unbalanced for the fourth chromosome (triploids with only two fourth chromosomes instead of three), and normal diploids. Hence the difference observed cannot be directly attributed to ploidy, but does show an effect of the chromosomal constitution on the mitochondria.

The measurements of sarcosomes summarized in Table 1 are from another group of triploids, those freshly derived from colchicine treatment and containing three sets of all chromosomes. The triploids appear to have sarcosomes larger than those of their diploid sisters, on the average. However, the difference could have been a reflection of the variability among flies in each genotype, significant at the .001 level in this case. Comparison of the appropriate variances (genotype and fly) gives a probability between 0.3 and 0.2 that the genotypic difference is a chance one. The difference between the sizes of malphigian tubule yellow pigment globules from the same flies (Table 2) is likewise not significant when its variance is compared to the very large one contributed by the differences between the fields photographed. The differences between flies are not significant for the same reason, but positive correlation ($r = 0.94$; $0.01 > P > 0.001$) between mean pigment globule size and the mean diameters of sarcosomes from the same individuals suggests that the two cytoplasmic "organelles" are being influenced in the same way by factors independent of ploidy.

EXTINCTION COEFFICIENTS OF SARCOSOMES

The larger sarcosomes have a diameter adequate to permit measurement of their U.V. absorption by the photographic method of microspectrophotometry. However, there was considerable variability between the different preparations when the diameters of the sarcosomes were compared before and after lyophilization. Because of this variability only a striking difference in the shape of the absorption curves could have significance.

The sarcosome turns out to be an even more difficult object for microspectrophotometry than was anticipated. The extinction of the frozen-dried sarcosome is at the lower limit of the range for the method; and a large percentage of the extinction is due to non-specific light loss. The presence of Becke lines made an accurate estimate of diameter impractical, and measurements of total extinction unreliable. Attempts were made to avoid these errors by matching the index of refraction of the medium to that of the sarcosome by adding chloral hydrate to the glycerin. Under these circumstances, both sarcosomes and muscle fibers became invisible in the "finder" of the ultra-violet microscope as well as in the phase microscope.

The measure finally adopted was the maximum of the extinction given in the microphotometer runs, a quantity proportional to the diameter of the sarcosome and therefore subject to the same variability plus that introduced by lyophilization. Although slightly larger mean values were found in triploids, the difference between the two classes must be regarded as fortuitous because of that variability. The average absorption curves obtained would not be inconsistent with the known composition of mitochondria (60 % protein, 29 % lipid) superimposed upon a high non-specific absorption. A high nucleic acid content (e.g., 8–10 %) would certainly have shown as a hump at 2570 Å, wherefore the mean RNA content of these bodies is set well below that level and in the range held by mammalian mitochondria. No qualitative difference between the two classes is indicated.

DISCUSSION

Thus, in respect to size, mitochondrial structures show a wide variability at the intracellular level. Although this variability is influenced by genetic constitution, other factors not well controlled in these experiments are also important. Williams and co-workers (see Levenbook and Williams, 1956) have found as a result of studies on sarcosome preparations pooled from several flies that the growth and maturation process appears to be complete about one week after eclosion. It would appear likely that in our material (all aged over one week) variations in the rate of growth of individual sarcosomes as well as the variability from place to place within the musculature could completely mask differences conditioned by the genotypes we employed.

These findings point to caution in the comparison of measurements made on mitochondria derived from different sources. Differences in diameter showed up here within a given type of tissue and between individuals because they could be compared with the variability of sarcosomes themselves. They would have been undetected if only mean values were available as is usually the case for populations extracted from tissue homogenates. It is difficult to estimate how much this type of variability could have contributed to the variability observed by Dr. Caspari.

Our extinction data, it should be emphasized, were obtained on mitochondria that were morphologically free from microsomes. Thus, our failure to detect RNA absorption is strong evidence that these mitochondria do not contain any; more refined methods will be required to detect the presence of less than five per cent. We can, thus, lend some support to Dr. Novikoff's comments on Dr. Caspari's paper in this Symposium, to the effect that the variability in RNA values may reflect variations in percentage contamination by non-mitochondrial cytoplasmic granules.

ACKNOWLEDGMENT

We have Messrs. John F. Aronson and David A. Hungerford to thank for great help during the course of this work.

Supported by research grant C1613 from the National Cancer Institute of the National Institutes of Health, Public Health Service, and by an institutional grant from the American Cancer Society.

REFERENCES

CASPARI, E., and BLOMSTRAND, I., 1956, The effects of nuclear genes on the structure and differentiation of cytoplasmic structures. Cold Spr. Harb. Symp. Quant. Biol. *21*: 291–301.

EPHRUSSI, B., 1953, Nucleo-cytoplasmic Relations in Micro-organisms. Oxford, Clarendon Press.

LEVENBOOK, LEO, and WILLIAMS, C. M., 1956, Mitochondria in the flight muscles of insects. III. Mitochondrial cytochrome in relation to the aging and wing beat frequency of flies. J. Gen. Physiol. *39:* 497–512.

RUDKIN, G. T., ARONSON, J. F., HUNGERFORD, D. A., and SCHULTZ, J., 1955, A comparison of the ultraviolet absorption of haploid and diploid salivary gland chromosomes. Exp. Cell Res. *9:* 193–211.

SLATER, E. C., and CLELAND, K. W., 1952, Stabilization of oxidative phosphorylation in heart muscle sarcosomes. Nature, Lond. *170:* 118. (See also K. W. CLELAND and E. C. SLATER, 1953, Respiratory granules of heart muscle. Biochem. J. *53:* 547–556.)

WATANABE, M. I., and WILLIAMS, C. M., 1953, Mitochondria in the flight muscles of insects. II. Effects of the medium on the size, form, and organization of isolated sarcosomes. J. Gen. Physiol. *37:* 71.

The Relation of the Heterochromatic Chromosome Regions to the Nucleic Acids of the Cell[1]

JACK SCHULTZ

The Institute for Cancer Research and The Lankenau Hospital Research Institute, Philadelphia, Pennsylvania

The attraction which the heterochromatic regions of the chromosomes holds for investigators resides in the fact that they are differentiated chromosome regions. This fact provides the possibility that by their study, one might gain insight into some quality which could itself serve as a guide to generalities of the nature and function of all genes.

The origin of genetic interest in these regions is history which need not be recounted in detail here (for earlier summaries see Hannah, 1951; Schultz, 1947). The absence of notable effects of duplication or deficiency on morphogenesis, and an association with the origin (by position effects) of variegation, early gave rise to the consideration of these regions in *Drosophila* as controllers, in a general way, of chromosome metabolism—a concept finding its uses in other organisms at present.

Some association with the nucleic acids was inherent in Heitz' original characterization of these regions as Feulgen-positive blocks of chromosome in interphases. The hypothesis that these blocks were an indication of the genetic function of these chromosome regions, and that this function had to do with the nucleic acid metabolism of the cell, came later; I believe I must bear the initial responsibility for it (Schultz, 1936). The nucleic acids as substances specifically concerned with heterochromatin occurred to me as the common denominator between such diverse observations as the changed cytology in position effects at heterochromatic regions, and the maternal effects of the Y chromosome on variegation. To test this hypothesis quantitation was necessary, measurements of the nucleic acids in different parts of the cell were needed; and at this point it was possible—some years ago now—to work with Professor Caspersson on these problems.

We were able at that time to sketch only the outline of an answer. What I propose to do now is to report some of the more recent work that has been going on at the Fox Chase laboratory, designed to explore further the validity of the hypothesis connecting heterochromatic regions with the nucleic acid metabolism of the cell.

Such an hypothesis—and indeed any hypothesis relating a genetic unit to a metabolic process—can be approached in different ways. First, the nature of variations in the synthesis of the particular group of substances may be compared in different genotypes; second, the utilization of metabolic precursors may be studied; and third, the sensitivity of the activities associated with the genetic change may be studied in relation to antimetabolites to the suspected reaction participants.

EFFECTS OF HETEROCHROMATIC REGIONS ON THE SYNTHESIS OF THE NUCLEIC ACIDS

We shall consider first the evidence that the kinds or the amounts of the nucleic acids of the cell are affected by the balance of heterochromatic regions. Balance is of course the operative word here; we start with a genetic system in which our simplest comparisons are made by using a whole chromosome, the Y chromosome, and studying its effects on the nucleic acids of the cell when added to or subtracted from the chromosome complement as a whole.

The situation would be better if our information regarding the genetic makeup of the Y chromosome were more detailed, so that one knew more about the relations between loci for the bobbed bristle effect, the factors for sterility in the male, the nucleolar organizer, and the heterochromatic blocks, before interpreting the behavior of the chromosome as a whole as a property of its heterochromatic regions. For simplicity, I shall be equating the Y chromosome with its heterochromatic regions in this discussion, and shall not take time here to go into the genetic complexities of this situation, some of which are being studied by Lindsley (1955); except to say that one of the chief difficulties is that the conventional type of linkage analysis, or the localization of mutants by genetic deficiencies is extremely difficult where multiple duplications have occurred, and position effects are rife.

Perhaps the best point of departure for these comparisons is the original series of measurements performed by Caspersson and myself. What we did was to make use of the suppressing effect of the Y chromosome on variegation, in order to distinguish females carrying a Y chromosome

[1] This work has been supported by grants from the American Cancer Society, recommended by the Committee on Growth of the National Research Council; from the National Cancer Institute of the U. S. Public Health Service (C1613); and from the Women's Auxiliary of the Lankenau Hospital Research Institute (Northern Branch); and an Institutional Grant of the American Cancer Society.

TABLE 1. THE EFFECT OF THE Y CHROMOSOME ON THE ULTRA-VIOLET ABSORPTION (257 mμ) OF *Drosophila melanogaster* OOCYTES

(Caspersson and Schultz, data of 1938; for methods see Caspersson, 1950.)

Series		No. of Cells		Relative Extinction		Ratio of Extinction
		XX	XXY	XX	XXY	XXY/XX
T(1;2) N^{264-10}/ ywdim	1.	12	11	0.75	1.01	1.34
	2.	10	11	0.64	0.73	1.12
	3.	2	2	0.72	1.05	1.45
	4.	5	5	0.81	1.10	1.35
	5.	4	4	0.93	0.81	0.88
T (1;2) yw^{258-18}/ ydim	1.	14	11	0.69	0.85	1.24
	2.	3	3	0.75	0.99	1.32
	3.	7	7	0.54	0.84	1.55
y, XX; In(2LR) Pm^2/ bltbw		5	5	0.69	0.96	1.41
T (1;4) w^{258-21}/ $w^e spl$	1.	20	22	0.89	1.03	1.15
	2.	8	8	1.01	1.07	1.06

Mean of Ratios $\pm$SE$_m$ = 1.27 $\pm$0.10

from those which were of the normal 2X2A constitution for a female *Drosophila*. The ultra-violet absorption of immature oocyte cytoplasm in such females was measured, and the result was consistently that the oocytes from XXY females showed a higher extinction than those from the XX females regardless of oocyte size. Table 1 shows a summary of the series of eleven experiments, the largest of which when taken alone has a statistically significant increase in the extinction of the egg cytoplasm. If these differences are calculated as the ratio of XXY to XX for each of the eleven groups, the mean of the ratios for all the sets is 1.27 $\pm$ 0.1—a mean difference of 27 per cent. This difference from an expectation of 1, for equality in the two groups, is significant at the 2 per cent level.

At that time therefore, when nucleic acid chemistry was innocent of differences in base composition, we felt free to conclude (since the absorption spectrum of the cytoplasm was a clean nucleic acid one, with little evidence of protein) that this meant a difference in the amount of the pentose-nucleic acids of the cytoplasm. The further conclusions were fairly obvious: A nuclear component was influencing the synthesis of cytoplasmic nucleic acids. Presently this conclusion that a difference existed in the amounts of the nucleic acids, was challenged by Callan (1948). He performed a series of experiments on fertilized eggs from XX and XXY mothers, testing the amount of RNA by the furfural reaction. He found no difference in RNA content between the two types of egg. These experiments had a

number of serious deficiencies for a comparison with the ultra-violet work: The eggs were at diverse stages of development, the furfural reaction is not a specific one for RNA determination; nor could one easily compare the immature oocyte with even the unfertilized egg in a simple way. It was obvious however that more work needed to be done, to understand what really was going on in these ovaries, and whether there was an effect of the Y chromosome on the nucleic acids of the egg.

As it happened the next approaches to the problem were both chemical. In our laboratory Dr. Elizabeth Patterson had become interested in the nucleic acids of the salivary glands, and had modified the standard methods of chemical determination to allow estimations on samples of 36 glands (Patterson et al., 1954).

By this time the genetic techniques were more elegant. Lindsley and Novitski (1950) had synthesized an X chromosome to which the limbs of a Y were attached at opposite ends, making an asymmetrical V out of the metaphase rod. Actually this has more than a normal Y; it contains also an indeterminate duplication of the heterochromatic region of the X, which should not be lost sight of in making comparisons; and also a duplication of the loci from yellow to achaete, which can be disregarded for its own DNA content. We shall designate this chromosome $\overline{XY}^{sc8}$.

With this chromosome available it was possible to arrange comparisons in which the rest of the genome was maintained constant, the variable being the attached $\overline{XY}^{sc8}$ chromosome in the female, or the normal Y in the male. Thus normal XX females are compared with the $X\overline{XY}^{sc8}$; and XY males compared with those lacking a Y, the so-called XO type. No cytoplasmic maternal effects can be involved: the cytoplasm is all from the same type of female.

As it turned out, the effect of the Y on the amount of RNA in the salivary gland cells was negligible; in fact the differences were in opposite directions in the $\overline{XX}Y$—XX, and XY—XO comparisons. The DNA differences were slight also—it will be remembered that the Y in the salivary glands is a small section at the chromocentral region. We shall return to the DNA value later.

Altorfer in Brachet's laboratory approached the problem somewhat differently, determining the total RNA per imago, comparing XO to XY males, using measurement of ultra-violet absorption, cold perchloric acid extracts (the method of Ogur and Rosen) as her technique (Altorfer, 1953). In these experiments also, no effect of the Y on the RNA content could be detected.

It would obviously have been naive at this stage to conclude that the results of the microspectrophotometric experiments were in error. Clearly if the hypothesis that the ribonucleic acids have a function in cell growth and differentiation has any meaning at all, the effects of a genetic change cannot be blindly predicted from one tissue to another. Chemical analyses of unfertilized eggs were needed, to give a reference point from which the oogenesis could be reevaluated, and the relations to the other tissues determined.

Dr. Leonidas Levenbook undertook this analysis several years ago. We were able to obtain the large quantities (gram lots) of unfertilized eggs that were required for nucleic acid isolation, by mating sterile XO males to the females of the type desired. The same comparisons were made as were used in the experiments with the salivary glands; the results from the two types of cell should then be comparable. The eggs were collected over a three-hour egg-laying period. At that time they have not yet undergone the degenerative changes which occur as the unfertilized egg ages. As they were collected, the eggs were either analyzed immediately or were quickly frozen in an acetone-dry-ice mixture, and were ready for the appropriate washings, homogenizations and series of ether, alcohol and cold and hot acid extractions. The thought at this point was not only to measure the amounts of the nucleic acids, but also to get some idea of the kinds of nucleic acid precursors present.

For the quantitation of the RNA per egg, Levenbook used the three standard methods of comparison—the ultra-violet absorption, the orcinol reaction for pentose, and the determination of phosphorous, as Dr. Patterson had done for the salivary gland. These methods all require comparison with a standard; the earlier measurements used a yeast nucleic acid as standard. Levenbook however, thought it advisable to isolate the nucleic acids from the respective types of egg, and purify them sufficiently for use as a proper standard; for by this time the differences in base composition between nucleic acids from different sources were sufficiently well known to make this a reasonable precaution, particularly for the ultra-violet measurements.

Table 2 shows the results of measurements made on fresh eggs, and repeated on the frozen samples by Miss Elizabeth Travaglini. The units

are micrograms of nucleic acid per egg. The situation is quite clear: if there is a difference in the amount of RNA between the two types of egg, it is the XX that has the greater amount. And this shows in the two series of measurements, made several years apart, one by Dr. Levenbook on the fresh eggs, the other by Miss Travaglini on frozen samples. It would seem that despite the crudity of his methods, Callan's conclusions were correct. However, the story does not end here.

Levenbook was primarily interested not in the amount but in the kind of nucleic acid present in the insect egg; and he set out to determine the base analysis first of the $X\overline{XY}^{sc8}$, easily procurable in large quantities, and then of the XX egg. He did this on samples prepared by successive alcohol reprecipitations from hot NaCl extractions of the egg residues after a previous cold one per cent perchloric acid treatment. The base analysis was carried out by ionophoresis of an alkaline hydrolysate, after the procedures of Markham and Smith (1952), and checked by independent analysis of the purines, following the procedure of Loring and his group (1952).

The results are fairly clear (Table 3). In the eggs from the three hour group, the $X\overline{XY}^{sc8}$ samples show a consistently higher proportion of adenine in their RNA than do those from XX eggs. The two types of nucleic acid are different in their composition. The data from the purine analysis agree with the electrophoretic analysis.

As I have already said, the unfertilized eggs undergo degenerative changes on standing. Are these differences possibly artifacts due to different rates of degeneration in the two types of egg? An approach to this question is made by the analysis of eggs which have been allowed to remain on the culture medium for a 24-hour period before the extractions. In these, presumably the degenerative process has come to completion, and any differences due to it might be accentuated. As Table 3 shows, the opposite is the case. The two samples are now very similar in their base ratios. This indicates that the results on the

TABLE 2. RNA CONTENT OF XX AND $X\overline{XY}^{sc8}$ EGGS OF *D. melanogaster*

Values in parenthesis give the ranges of the determinations. Units are micrograms per egg.

Egg Type	Method of Collection	Method of Analysis		
		Ultra-violet	Phosphorus	Orcinol
$X\overline{XY}^{sc8}$	Fresh 125 eggs	0.190 (0.188–0.192)	0.179 (0.173–0.185)	0.178 (0.177–0.179)
(3 hour)	Frozen α 4000 eggs	0.162 (0.160–0.164)	0.170 (0.167–0.172)	0.199 (0.192–0.205)
XX	Fresh 125 eggs	0.205 (0.196–0.213)	0.189 (0.178–0.197)	0.185 (0.174–0.199)
(3 hour)	Frozen α 4000 eggs	0.214 (0.211–0.216)	0.187 (0.168–0.206)	0.196 (0.195–0.196)

TABLE 3. DISTRIBUTION OF PURINE AND PYRIMIDINE BASES IN THE RNA OF XX AND $\overline{XXY}^{sc8}$ EGGS

Values are moles of base/100 moles of phosphorus. Abbreviations: A, adenine; G, guanine; C, cytosine; U, uracil; Pu, purine; Py, pyridine.

Max. age	Prep. #	Sample #	Egg Type									
			$\overline{XXY}^{sc8}$					XX				
			A	G	C	U	Pu/Py	A	G	C	U	Py/Pu
hours												
3	1	a	29.7	24.1	18.1	28.0		23.6	25.4	20.0	31.0	
		b	29.9	23.1	18.7	28.5		24.0	25.2	20.6	30.4	
	2	a	29.8	25.0	18.3	27.2		24.2	25.4	20.5	29.9	
		b	30.1	23.6	18.4	27.7		24.2	24.5	19.5	31.9	
	3	a	29.5	22.4	19.0	29.5		27.9	23.0	20.8	28.1	
		b	29.5	21.9	18.4	30.1		26.9	22.8	21.5	29.0	
		Mean	29.9	23.4	18.5	28.5	1.13	25.0	23.2	20.4	30.3	0.97
24	1	a	24.9	23.2	21.7	30.2		26.2	24.6	21.1	28.3	
		b	25.5	23.0	21.0	30.5		25.7	25.9	20.8	27.8	
		Mean	25.2	23.1	21.4	30.4	0.94	26.0	25.2	21.0	28.1	1.04

three-hour group may be taken as a close approximation to the values to be expected in the fresh egg, and the difference in the nucleic acids regarded as truly physiological.

It follows that if we consider this effect as due to the heterochromatic nature of the Y chromosome, the thesis that such regions have to do with nucleic acid metabolism receives considerable support from Levenbook's data. But how about the apparent quantitative differences found in the microspectrophotometric work on oocytes?

It turns out that at least part of the answer here lies also in the base analyses. In recent years, following Chargaff (Chargaff and Zamenhoff, 1948; Beaven and Holliday, 1955), increasing emphasis has been placed on the necessity for determining the extinction per mole phosphorus ($\epsilon(P)$) for each nucleic acid, and attention has been paid to the variability of the $\epsilon(P)$, after different treatments of the molecule. Table 4 shows the $\epsilon(P)$ for the different types of RNA, worked out by Miss Travaglini. The $\epsilon(P)$ of the $\overline{XXY}^{sc8}$ nucleic acids is consistently higher than that of the XX.

It would be expected that the $\epsilon(P)$, if it reflected the absorptions of the constituent bases of the nucleic acids, would agree with the expectations calculated from the analysis of the bases. In fact the hydrolyzed samples agree not too badly with the expectations (Table 4). In the unhydrolyzed nucleic acids, whose state is closer to that of the acid fixed oocyte cytoplasmic nucleic acids, the differences are even greater.

It is odd that the first attempt to use ultraviolet absorption as a quantitative measure of nucleic acid content in the cytoplasm of two genetic types should lead to a situation like this.

The original data were correct, the differences were real; apparently their correct interpretation, namely, that the difference is one of nucleic acid composition, is more favorable to the theory we were testing than a simple quantitative difference. For we must now seek more specific steps in the synthesis of the nucleic acids as affected by the heterochromatic regions. We can therefore proceed to examine the status of possible precursors of the nucleic acids. These would be contained in the cold one per cent perchloric acid extract already referred to, and from the beginning of Dr. Levenbook's work, an attempt was made to analyze these substances. The major part of the story that follows is the work of Miss Travaglini, whose accomplishment it was to put through a tedious and annoying job of chromatography.

The annoyance came in the presence of pigments in the egg, probably both pterins and kynurenine derivatives, as the work of Hadorn and others tells us. In the solvents used (those finally settled on, after numerous trials, were H_2O and butanol-ammonia), the pigments smear and no clear spots are obtained. The problem was solved by running the substances as bands on the chromatogram, treating the chromatogram as coordinate paper, cutting the strips, eluting, rerunning the band, cutting strips of known R F, running these individually as two-dimensional chromatograms, eluting the spots, hydrolyzing, and comparing the hydrolysate on a new chromatogram with known standards. In the meantime at each stage aliquot strips had been analyzed for phosphorus by a molybdic acid spray, for deoxyribose by a cysteine sulfuric acid spray, and the ultra-violet absorption taken at three pH's.

The results of this analysis appear in Tables 5

and 6. We may consider the purine compounds first, and begin by noting the enormous loss in the successive stages of elution evidenced by comparing the totals for each base from the identified compounds, with the totals found from complete hydrolysis of the initial sample. Caution is necessary therefore in evaluating quantitative differences in the different types, and due regard must be paid to the size of the initial sample in making comparisons.

In these analyses of the contents of the cold acid extract, once more the comparisons, between the samples extracted at the three hour period and those extracted 24 hours after the collection, are useful in evaluating the enzymatic systems in the unfertilized egg. These must operate to influence some of the degenerative changes which occur on standing; and, as we have already said, they allow an inference of the extent to which these degenerative changes are involved in the differences between genotypes.

The interesting point is the presence of significant amounts of deoxyriboside and relatively little free base in the three-hour eggs as compared with the situation in the 24-hour eggs. It is worth noting that free adenine only appears rarely in the extracts of three-hour $\overline{XXY}^{sc8}$ eggs, and irregularly in the XX eggs (Table 5). The other differences between the two types for the purine compounds are of doubtful significance.

TABLE 4. MOLAR ABSORPTIVITY ($\epsilon(P)$) OF UNHYDROLYZED AND HYDROLYZED RNA FROM $\overline{XXY}^{sc8}$ AND XX *D. melanogaster* EGGS

Max. Age	Egg Type	$\overline{XXY}$	XX
	Treatment of RNA	($\epsilon(P)$) 260 pH 7	($\epsilon(P)$) 260 pH 7
hours			
3	non-hydrolyzed	9,450	7,605
	KOH-hydrolyzed	12,200	10,350
	st'd ribotides*	11,210	10,950
24	non-hydrolyzed	7,500	8,900
	KOH-hydrolyzed	11,750	12,550
	st'd ribotides*	10,950	11,000

* ($\epsilon(P)$) values for standard nucleotides are based on values obtained from graphs of Beaven, Holliday and Johnson (Chargaff and Davidson, Nucleic Acids I, Chap. 14).

The 24-hour eggs show that a great deal has been going on, confirming breakdown as an interpretation of the change in type of RNA. There is an increase in free base, and the disappearance of many of the compounds. Oddly, there is the impression of an increase in deoxyguanosine, a point to which we shall return.

Table 6 shows the same kind of data for the pyrimidine bases. And two things become ap-

TABLE 5. CHROMATOGRAPHIC ANALYSIS OF PURINE COMPOUNDS IN COLD 1% HClO₄ EXTRACT OF VARIOUS TYPES OF *D. melanogaster* EGGS

(Micromoles/egg)

Egg Type	$\overline{XXY}^{sc8}$, 3 hour					XX, 3 hour		$\overline{XXY}^{sc8}$, 24 hr.	
Sample No.	1	2	3	Mean	Total base*	1	Total base*	1	Total base*
No. of eggs × 10³	226	333	422			178		134	
Nucleic Acid Component									
Adenine	0.11					0.10		0.15	
Adenosine	0.19	0.24	0.36			0.21		0.61	
Deoxyadenosine		0.07	0.17			0.02			
Total	0.30	0.31	0.53	0.38	25.2	0.33	4.0	0.76	16.3
Guanine									
Guanosine	0.49	1.47	0.31			0.31		0.18	
Deoxyguanosine		0.22	0.35					0.64	
Total	0.49	1.69	0.66	0.95	12.2	0.31	5.7	0.82	14.9
Hypoxanthine		0.38	0.36			0.45		0.23	
Inosine	1.48	2.25	1.77			0.24			
Deoxyinosine		0.14	0.18						
Total	1.48	2.77	2.31	2.19	—	0.69	—	0.23	8.5

* Bases obtained by complete hydrolysis of initial cold 1% HClO₄ extract.

TABLE 6. CHROMATOGRAPHIC ANALYSIS OF PYRIMIDINE COMPOUNDS IN COLD 1%
HClO₄ EXTRACT OF VARIOUS TYPES OF *D. melanogaster* EGGS

(Micromoles/egg)

Egg Type	$X\overline{XY}^{sc8}$, 3 hour					XX, 3 hour		$X\overline{XY}^{sc8}$, 24 hour	
Sample No.	1	2	3	Mean	Total base*	1	Total base*	1	Total base*
No. of eggs × 10³	226	333	422			178		134	
Nucleic Acid Component									
Cytosine			0.02			0.07		0.03	
Cytidine						0.11			
Deoxycytidine									
Total			0.02	0.01	0.00	0.18	2.7	0.03	0.00
Thymine									
Thymidine	0.48	0.67	0.12					0.48	
Total	0.48	0.67	0.12	0.43	0.88	0.00	0.0	0.48	1.25
Uracil	0.44	1.70				0.36		1.08	
Uridine		3.65	1.64			0.72		2.14	
Deoxyuridine	0.18	0.27	0.42			0.51		0.92	
Total	0.62	5.62	2.06	2.77	12.80	1.59	6.80	4.14	5.60

* Bases obtained by complete hydrolysis of initial cold 1% HClO₄ extract.

parent. In the purines, the deoxyribosides were present; but among the pyrimidines, the identification of deoxyuridine in sizable amounts is significant. This is a precursor of thymidine, as we know from the studies of Friedkin on isotopically labelled substances.

Differences between the two genetic types are now significant. Cytosine compounds appear in low or insignificant amounts in the $X\overline{XY}^{sc8}$ eggs; regularly in the XX eggs. But the most striking and consistent results are the thymidine quantities regularly present in the $X\overline{XY}^{sc8}$, and not detectable by these methods in the XX eggs. It should be noted that free thymine has not been found, even in the 24-hour eggs.

With these data we are in a position to ask whether it is really the Y chromosome, or some peculiar quality of the attached Y^{sc8} complex that is responsible for these differences. This means extending the work to comparisons involving the normal Y chromosome. Such comparisons are feasible, using an attached-X strain made isogenic with Oregon-R for all the X except the portion adjacent to the centromere, and being phenotypically normal for the bobbed locus. The enormous labor of the chromatographic method both in the quantity of the samples required, and the successive elutions, caused a recourse to the microbiological assay methods. These had been

used extensively for folic acid determinations by Dr. Toennies and his group at our Institute, and Miss Travaglini was able to adapt their methods to our uses, for two types of assay. One was the assay for deoxyribosides with *Thermobacterium acidophilus*, originated by Hoff-Jørgensen and Zeuthen (1952a, b); the other an assay for thymine or thymidine, using Roepke's thymine requiring mutant of *E. coli*, for the strain of which (15T⁻) we must thank Dr. Seymour Cohen (Roepke, Libby and Small, 1944; Elson and Chargaff, 1952; Cohen, 1954). By the combination of these two methods, it has been possible, not only to extend the analyses to the free Y chromosome, but also to get an idea of the interrelations of the deoxyribosides and the DNA of the egg.

We may consider the overall picture first: Do the deoxyribosides as a group show any relationship to the presence of the Y chromosome in the genotype? The total deoxyribosides can be determined on extracts from samples of about a thousand eggs, using the *Thermobacterium* assay. Using samples of about 4000 eggs, determinations of the following are also carried out: Pyrimidine deoxyribosides, by the *Thermobacterium* assay after a mild acid hydrolysis of the original extract; purine deoxyribosides plus free deoxyribose by the diphenylamine reaction; and the ultra-violet absorption spectra of the extract at acid, alkaline and neutral pH.

Figure 1 shows the relationship between the total content of free deoxyriboside and the amount of pyrimidine deoxyriboside in the samples prepared for extraction immediately after the three hour collection period. The pyrimidine compounds of the unfertilized egg form a constant proportion of the deoxyribosides, although the total varies over a five-fold range. Some grouping appears in the $\overline{XXY}$ and $\overline{XX}$ points, the set without the Y chromosome giving on the whole the higher values. This relation does not hold for the $X\overline{XY}{}^{sc8}$, XX comparisons.

Figure 2 shows the same comparisons in the eggs which have been allowed to age for twenty-four hours. The linear relationship is maintained and now all genotypes seem distributed at random around the line. It would seem that there is no obvious consistent effect of the Y chromosome on the relationship between these substances.

The relationships with the materials sensitive to the diphenylamine reaction are more complex. These materials are free deoxyribose as well as the purine deoxyribosides. The purine deoxyribosides should show a relation complementary to that already found in the pyrimidines. Evidently, this is not the case (Fig. 3) in the three hour egg; presumably there is a sufficient amount of free deoxyribose to obscure this relation. In the twenty-four hour egg, however, the relation is linear (Fig. 4). The values for total deoxyribosides being generally higher in the 24-hour egg, it may be inferred that deoxyriboside synthesis has proceeded with time so there is no longer the excess of free deoxyribose.

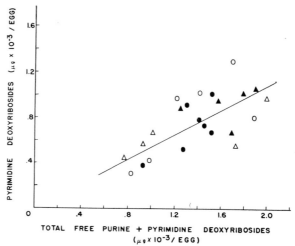

FIGURE 2. Pyrimidine and total deoxyribosides in eggs allowed to remain on culture medium for 24 hours before beginning of extraction procedure. Methods and symbols as in Fig. 1. Note the absence of low values in these samples as compared with Fig. 1, indicating increase in total deoxyriboside as the egg stands.

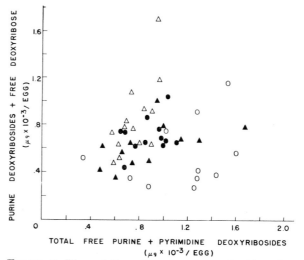

FIGURE 3. The relation of purine deoxyribosides plus free deoxyribose to the total deoxyriboside content in the same three hour group of eggs as those in Fig. 1. The ordinates are measured by Dische's diphenylamine reaction; the abscissae are as in Fig. 1, so also the symbols for the genotypes.

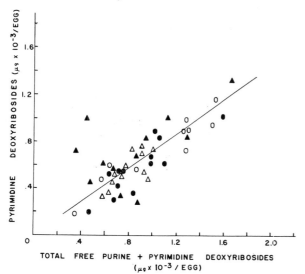

FIGURE 1. The relation of pyrimidine deoxyriboside content to total deoxyribosides in eggs of different genotypes collected over a three hour period. Deoxyribosides were measured by the *Thermobacterium acidophilus* assay; pyrimidine deoxyribosides are given by measurement of an aliquot after mild acid hydrolysis. Symbols for genotypes: ▲ $X\overline{XY}{}^{sc8}$; ● XX; △ $\overline{XXY}$; ○ $\overline{XX}$.

For the measurement of DNA content per egg, or more cautiously, of the bound deoxyribosides, treatment of the egg residue after the cold perchloric extraction by a combination of DNA-ase and phosphatases was found necessary. Figure 5 shows the results of the assay of this preparation for deoxyribosides by the *Thermobacterium* test. It is evident that a great deal of material is released—an amount per egg equivalent, if calculated as DNA, to a 500-ploid nucleus in the salivary gland. Again, there is no evidence that

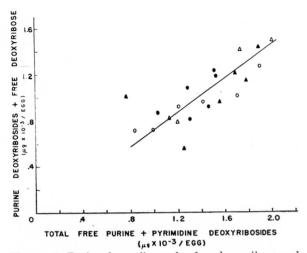

FIGURE 4. Purine deoxyribose plus free deoxyribose and total deoxyribosides in the same 24 hour old group of eggs as Fig. 2. Methods and symbols as in Fig. 3.

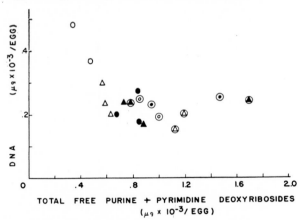

FIGURE 5. DNA values per egg as related to the total free deoxyriboside contents. DNA measured by *Thermobacterium* assay following enzymatic (DNA-ase + phosphatase) digestion of residue after cold 1% perchloric acid extraction. Symbols as follows: 3 hour eggs: ▲ XX̄Y[sc8], ● XX; △ X̄X̄Y, ○ X̄X̄. 24 hour eggs: solid triangle in circle XX̄Y[sc8], ◉ XX; open triangle in circle X̄X̄Y, ◎ X̄X̄.

the Y chromosome increases the total amount of this material; in fact the highest values on the graph are two from attached-X females without a Y chromosome. Nor is there any relation to the amount of free deoxyribosides in the same eggs; the deoxyriboside precursors are present in excess.

Thus the situation observed in the ribonucleic acids repeats itself here: the total amounts of these substances are not obviously affected, in the present data, by the Y chromosome. But when we turn among the free deoxyribosides to the one for which we have a specific test, thymidine, we find a definite effect of the Y chromosome.

Table 7 gives the results of the *E. coli* thymine-mutant assays, of the cold acid extracts of the eggs. In the three-hour eggs, no free thymidine is detected in quite large samples of the two XX types; whereas the much smaller samples of both XXY types show appreciable amounts of this substance. They show also that the amount of thymidine per egg from the XX̄Y[sc8] is almost six times that found in the free Y group. This is significant since the Y[sc8], from its genetic origin, must have in it a duplication of the heterochromatic region of the X. All this adds up to a curiously specific effect of the Y on thymidine synthesis. At this point it is useful to recall the differences in cytosine content (Table 6) and that the effect on the ribonucleic acid appears to be on the purine moiety; we have a system of considerable complexity in which the interrelationships must be worked out.

The 24-hour eggs serve as a reminder of this (Table 7). For now thymidine appears in both the XX and the XXY groups in increased amounts. This could be due to either breakdown of the DNA, or to a real synthesis of deoxyribosides. The test is obviously to measure both substances at different times after egg-laying. The results of such an experiment appear in Figure 6.

In this experiment, Miss Travaglini compared the free deoxyribosides, and what we may call the DNA in both unfertilized and developing eggs over the 20-hour period of embryonic development at 25°. As expected, with development the amount of DNA rises rapidly, and there is apparently a decline in the amount of free deoxyribosides.

In the unfertilized egg, on the other hand, there is a slight but probably significant increase in the amount of DNA, and also a definite rise in the free deoxyribosides. The increase agrees with the comparisons of three and twenty-four hour eggs already presented. This means therefore that the indication of an increase in deoxyguanosine, from the chromatographic data, and the discussion just presented of thymidine content,

TABLE 7. THE EFFECT OF THE Y CHROMOSOME ON THE FREE THYMIDINE CONTENT OF THE UNFERTILIZED *Drosophila* EGG

Egg Type	No. Samples	Ave. No. Eggs	μmole, TDR/egg	
			3 hr.	24 hr.
XX̄Y[sc8]	5	743	0.244 ± .006	
	4	1740		0.669 ± .005
X̄X̄Y	5	645	0.045 ± .008	
	2	1015		0.345 ± .002
XX	2	4015	0.000	
	2	2750		0.317 ± .003
X̄X̄	4	4175	0.000	
	2	2700		0.475 ± .002

are best interpreted in terms of a synthesis of these substances in the egg. And it follows further that the XX eggs contain in them enzyme systems which allow the accumulation of thymidine under proper circumstances. Presumably the role of the Y chromosome has to do with defining what these circumstances are.

I should digress for a moment to consider briefly the possible cytoplasmic synthesis of DNA indicated here. These data are not isolated: Dr. Liselotte Metzger-Freed in Dr. Briggs' laboratory has carried out independent experiments on the enucleated *Rana pipiens* egg. Hoff-Jørgensen and Zeuthen (1952b, 1954) had reported considerable quantities of DNA in the frog egg, as well as others. Using the same methods as those used by us, she finds an approximate doubling (over a 24-hour period) of the bound deoxyriboside from the initial range of .06–0.10 micrograms per egg, and also an increase in the free deoxyribosides—with the only nucleus present, that in the attached exovate. If this is really DNA, that is being measured both in *Drosophila* and the frog, and not some complex of deoxyribosides released also by DNA-ase and phosphatase, it is obvious that many of the proponents of plasmagenes would expect such a result, in view of the genetic relations of DNA. The key question however is the real relation of these substances in the egg cytoplasm to chromosomal DNA, which remains to be established.

To return to the effects of the heterochromatic regions. How can we summarize the constellation of facts recounted here? If we knew more in detail about the constitution of the cytoplasmic DNA, and the relationships of the free ribosides, we would be in a better position; nor is our information about any free nucleotides adequate. But the increment of adenylic acid in the RNA of the XXY, the appearance of the free base in the XX; the decrease in cytosine compounds accompanied by an increase in thymidine, all indicate a change in the balance of purine and pyrimidine utilization. This is simply a restatement of the facts; but it is helpful in considering where to go next in the study of what metabolic process the heterochromatic regions might be influencing.

Effects of the Y Chromosome in Oogenesis

So much for the egg; but the early results were on the oocyte. Obviously the oogenesis needs reinvestigation. We have made only a beginning at this, and have deferred the study of the cytoplasm for a variety of reasons, concentrating on the behavior of the nuclei for the present. There are two points of consequence for the preceding discussion, one having to do with the replication of the heterochromatic regions, the other with the origin of the deoxyribonucleic acids of the egg cytoplasm.

The formation of the egg in *Drosophila* is a complex process involving three types of cell: a sheath of follicle cells around the egg chamber, the egg cell itself, and 15 nurse cells originating from the same oogonium as the oocyte. Each egg chamber forms one egg, the follicle cells secreting the chitinous covering, the nurse cells contributing a good portion of the egg cytoplasm. As the egg is laid, the nurse cell nuclei can be seen to be left behind.

The interesting point about the nuclei of such nurse cells was made by Bauer (1938), and by Painter and Reindorp (1939), a good many years ago; they are endopolyploid. Painter (1940) suggested that they did in fact become incorporated into the egg, and were themselves therefore precursors of the DNA required for the synthesis of cleavage nuclei. The situation is certainly more complicated than that in detail, since the nuclei of the nurse cells themselves are not incorporated into the egg cytoplasm.

The story that I have to tell now is the work of Dr. Jerome Freed (Freed and Schultz, 1956), who has been studying the DNA changes in the nurse cells as related to their content of Y chromosomes. It begins with an observation I made some

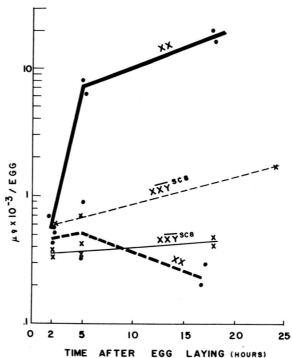

FIGURE 6. Comparison of DNA and free deoxyriboside content in fertilized and unfertilized *Drosophila* eggs over a period of 24 hours after egg laying. Measurements by *Thermobacterium* assay of deoxyribosides, on cold 1% perchloric acid extract, and on residue after DNA-ase + phosphatase treatment. Symbols: ●——● DNA, fertilized eggs (XX mothers). ✕——✕ DNA, unfertilized eggs (XXY^sc8 mothers). ●---● free deoxyribosides, fertilized eggs (XX mothers). ✕---✕ free deoxyribosides, unfertilized eggs. (XXY^sc8 mothers).

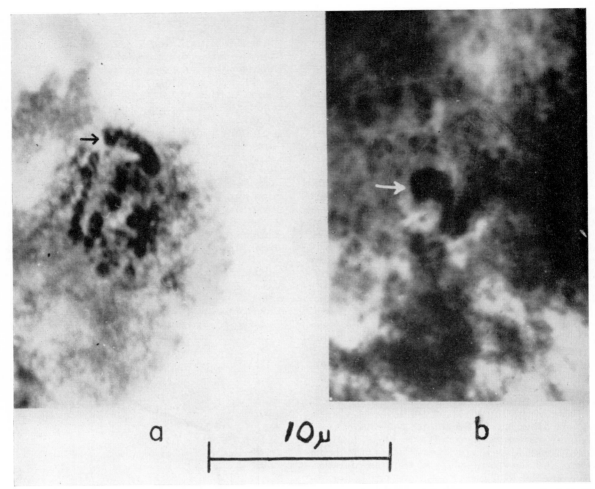

Figure 7. Nuclei from $\overline{XX}Y$ ovary. Aceto-orcein preparation, photographed in the ultra-violet microscope at 257 mμ. a) nucleus from cell in germarium, either presumptive nurse cell or oöcyte; arrow marks section of chromocenter identified as Y chromosome. b) sector of ca. 500-ploid nurse cell nucleus; arrow marks element identified as Y chromosome.

time ago (Schultz, 1941), that the Y chromosome could be detected in the nurse cells of females carrying it, as a discrete heterochromatic body. This finding was quite reasonable; but what was unexpected was the behavior of this body as the nurse cell nuclei increased in size. Figure 7 shows an ultra-violet photograph of an aceto-orcein preparation, taken by Dr. George Rudkin, in which at one side the prophase from a cell in the germarium, at the beginning of growth, at the other a small sector of one of the largest nurse cells is seen. The difference in the dimensions of the Y chromosome is not great. I made the suggestion therefore that the Y chromosome was not replicating at the same rate as the other chromosomes in these cells, a situation which would have consequences for general theory. It seemed not unlikely either, on the basis of the cytological behavior, that the other heterochromatic regions of the nurse cell behaved in the same way. And

one could go on to embroider a hypothesis involving the antithetical nature of gene activity and replication.

Dr. Freed set out to make a quantitative test of the nature of this phenomenon. If the Y is not replicating at the same rate as the other chromosomes, a simple expectation would be that the difference in DNA content per nucleus, between the XX and the XXY types, should decrease as the ploidy value became higher. We shall now see the results of his experiments.

The material for these was taken from the same groups as those already mentioned in the chemical experiments on the eggs. That is, the same two types of Y chromosome, and the two types of XX female with which each is to be compared. The measurements were made in a variety of ways: using the so-called plug method on squashes of isolated nuclei, whose structure is made more or less homogeneous by pretreatment

TABLE 8. TEST OF POLYPLOID RELATION OF NURSE CELL CLASSES
Prediction based on average C value of each cell

Class	XX		XX̄Ȳ^{sc8}		X̄X̄		X̄X̄Y	
	Exp.	Obs.	Exp.	Obs.	Exp	Obs.	Exp.	Obs.
16C	4.34	4.65	5.82	6.28				
32	8.67	9.92*	11.7	13.4*	9.92	12.1*		
64	17.3	17.3	23.3	24.1	19.8	20.1	20.5	21.7
128	34.7	35.7	46.6	48.7	39.7	42.4	41.1	46.6*
256	68.4	65.4	93.2	87.4	79.4	76.3	82.2	83.5
512	139	108*	186	170	159	134*	164	159
1024	277	290	372	310*	317	282	329	304
2048							657	585*

* Significant difference at 5% level.

in isotonic sucrose, or fixed in neutral formalin; and, as a necessary check on these methods, by scanning photomicrographs on a densitometer. Units could be calculated as DNA because of the presence on the same slides of standard mouse kidney tubule nuclei, whose DNA content is known chemically; this procedure also has its dangers, but it is a help.

The analysis has not been simple, as it turns out. It involves populations of nuclei ranging from diploid to 1024-ploid, and since the growth is not necessarily synchronous, all stages of synthesis can give values transitional between the groups. From direct measurements of follicle cell anaphases, Dr. Freed was able to ascertain a value for the diploid content, and to use this in the subsequent calculations of the degree of ploidy. The follicle cells measured are chiefly in the 8 and 16 C groups; and the XX̄Ȳ^{sc8} values for this group are higher than those of the comparable XX group. As I have already said, the distributions for the nurse cells are much wider. Again the attached-Y (Y^{sc8}) is higher than the free Y.

From the frequency distributions of the DNA per nucleus, the mean value per class can be calculated, using the minima in a frequency distribution as dividing lines between classes. For each class value obtained in this way, a computation of the haploid value (C) can be made by dividing it by the assigned ploidy number. In this way, a set of C values is obtained from the data, which provides a mean. This can now be used to test the correctness of the class distribution, by giving an expectation for each member of the polyploid series. The results of this test are shown in Table 8.

The bulk of the values agree very nicely with expectation, even the differences that are significant finding a possible explanation in relative frequencies of cells at different stages of synthesis in the older and younger egg chambers. For our present discussion the important thing we learn is that the agreement is the same both in the

Y-bearing and in the XX individuals. Obviously, if the DNA increment due to the Y were different in the different ploidy levels, there should be a systematic departure from the mean at the higher levels.

We are now prepared to study the difference between the two series. The ratios between the XXY and XX values, for both sets, are given in Table 9. In the XX̄Ȳ^{sc8}/XX group, the mean ratio is 1.36, equivalent to a 36 per cent increase in DNA per nucleus due to the Y^{sc8}. But the X̄X̄Y/X̄X̄ value is only 1.11, an increase of only 11 per cent. The difference between the two increases is obviously significant. If we recall that the X̄Y^{sc8} complex contains duplication of heterochromatin in addition to the Y, it is not unreasonable that they have a different effect on the DNA content. Moreover, the thymidine values in the same groups of eggs show similar differences. But can this difference of 35 per cent for the XX̄Ȳ^{sc8} series, or even the lower value for the other, be accounted for by the tiny clump of chromatin which I identified with the Y?

Dr. Freed tested this question by making measurements with the photographic scanning method, of the contribution in the Y-bearing nurse cells not of the Y alone, but of all the

TABLE 9. THE RATIOS OF DNA VALUES
BETWEEN NURSE CELLS OF XXY
AND XX FEMALES

Class	XX̄Ȳ^{sc8}/XX	X̄X̄Y/X̄X̄
16C	1.35	—
32C	1.35	—
64C	1.39	1.08
128C	1.37	1.10
256C	1.34	1.11
512C	1.57	1.19
1024C	1.14	1.08
Mean..................	1.36	1.11

TABLE 10. PERCENTAGE OF TOTAL FEULGEN POSITIVE
MATERIAL (DNA) IN HETEROCHROMATIC REGIONS
OF Y-BEARING NURSE CELL NUCLEI

Units are Total Extinction (E_T), area of the nucleus
times the mean extinction at 546 mμ; $E_{,T}{}^H$ the same for
the heterochromatic areas of the same nuclei.

$\overline{XXY}^{sc_8}$			$\overline{XXY}$		
E_T	$E_T{}^H$	%	E_T	$E_T{}^H$	%
73	5.8	7.9	36	1.3	3.7
75	6.1	8.2	85	5.9	6.9
118	5.5	4.6	97	5.3	5.4
148	7.6	5.1	118	4.7	4.0
150	8.2	5.5	127	2.7	2.9
			159	9.0	5.7
			189	10.9	5.8
Mean......		6.26			4.91

heterochromatic clumps, to the total absorption
of the nucleus. In this way, a maximum estimate
is obtained. What he found is shown in Table 10.
It is clear that these heterochromatic clumps
cannot account for more than a fraction of the
contribution of the Y chromosome. Instead of
solving a problem, we seem to have come up with
a new one. And there are indications, from
measurements of the oocyte nucleus itself, that
the problem may be still more complex; but these
things are not far enough advanced to take time
with now.

The point that is clear, is that in the nurse cell
the Y chromosome is synthesizing more DNA
than we should expect from its cytological appearance. Is this related to the DNA-carrying
body that Bayreuther has discovered in the
oogenesis of Tipulids? Are we facing a change in
our concepts of the relation of DNA to nucleoli?
Or is this simply a dispersal of the body of the Y
chromosome, and will it all straighten out into a
conventional pattern of DNA constancy?

If this large difference between the DNA
contents of the XX and the XXY nurse cell
nuclei is a somehow warped reflection of a picture
of DNA constancy per nucleus, it becomes important to examine the situation in other tissues
than the ovary. The chemical determinations in
the salivary glands, already referred to (Patterson
et al., 1954), provide an indication of what we
may find. The observed values of DNA per
nucleus were 245 picograms for the XX nucleus,
281 for the XXY. If the relationship were the
same as exists in the nurse cell, the XXY value
should be 36 per cent more than the XX; the
expectation would then be 323 picograms, which
is significantly different from the observed value
of 281. We have not yet made measurements on
the salivary glands cytophotometrically; but I
should be surprised, in view of tests on other
material, if this difference in the reaction of the

nurse cell and salivary gland cell nuclei, to the
addition of a Y chromosome, were due to the
difference in methods; although this possibility
cannot be excluded completely. If the difference
should be substantiated, it would follow that the
DNA content of a nucleus depends not only on
the intrinsic constitution of the chromosomes, but
also on their function in a particular type of
nucleus (see also Breuer and Pavan, 1955).

The situation may turn out to be somewhat of
this nature: in the salivary gland cell, at the time
of analysis, DNA synthesis is completed. But
DNA synthesis is actively proceeding in the nurse
cells at the stage measured, only a few of which
belong to the very largest group. Perhaps the
special role of the heterochromatic regions in
nucleic acid synthesis is exposed in these deviations from DNA constancy in the nurse cell as
compared with the salivary gland. It is obvious
that many detailed hypotheses exist which can be
tested by experiment, both in the nurse cells and
in other tissues. This possible difference in the
effects of the Y on DNA synthesis in the nuclei
of different tissues has obvious relevance to the
nature of nuclear differentiation: we shall return
to this point.

HETEROCHROMATIC REGIONS AND NUCLEIC ACID REQUIREMENTS

The evidence presented so far shows effects of
the Y chromosome on the nature of the ribonucleic acids, and on the interrelations of the
nucleosides of the Drosophila egg, and indicates a
cytochemical approach to the analysis of the
process of DNA synthesis as affected by the Y
chromosome in the nurse cells. We may now turn
to the second approach, the attempt to detect
changes in the nutritional requirements of the
organism associated with diversion of the paths
of synthesis by the presence of the Y chromosome
in the genotype.

The nutritional requirement of a multicellular
organism is a gross measure of the requirements
of the different tissues which compose it; and, as
we have reason to believe is the case with the Y
chromosome effects on the nucleic acid metabolism, when the effect of a change in genotype is
different in different tissues, the change in nutritional requirements of the organism as a whole
will only reflect the changes that dominate the
overall balance. Thus, the inability to synthesize
the ommatins for which tryptophane is a precursor
is reflected in a decrease of the tryptophane requirements of the vermilion larva in Drosophila
(Rudkin and Schultz, 1949). What are we to expect in the nucleic acid requirements? These
must be examined against the background of the
general nutrition of Drosophila, by which they
are conditioned. We shall do this here only briefly.

The nutritional requirements of Drosophila
fall into the conventional pattern for most animals: Growth (not optimal, but forming a normal

imago) is obtained on a medium consisting of the ten amino acids essential for the mammal; glycine and glutamic acid among the non-essentials; sucrose; the conventional assortment of the B vitamins; cholesterol; and ribosenucleic acid (Schultz, St. Lawrence and Newmeyer, 1946). The nucleic acid requirement is facultative on a medium of either whole casein or a mixture of the 21 amino acids in the appropriate proportions; but on the minimal medium of the ten essentials plus glutamic acid, it is obligatory for the standard Oregon R wild type strain. Of the nucleic acid components, adenylic acid seems to be the most important (Villee and Bissell, 1948); but growth is further aided by cytidylic acid, indicating a balance in the utilization of the purine and pyrimidine components (Hinton, 1956).

These results suggest that the *de novo* synthesis of the nucleic acid components in *Drosophila* is not rapid enough to promote optimal growth, and that the preformed components can be directly incorporated into the nucleic acid molecule. This is a situation not infrequently met with in animal nutrition, as the incorporation of labeled purine and pyrimidine nucleosides has demonstrated (for a review, see Brown and Roll, 1955). The system in *Drosophila* differs in its details, some of which may turn out to be of interest. For example, we have found that certain levels of adenosine are inhibitory to growth on a whole casein diet, and that the inhibition can be reversed by orotic acid (Schultz and Rothman, unpub.); the latter having no substantial growth promoting effect in the absence of adenosine. Thus the utilization of the nucleosides and nucleotides by *Drosophila*, while in general conforming to pattern, has peculiarities of its own.

The *de novo* synthesis of purines and pyrimidines in vertebrates is based on the assemblage of the bases from the metabolism of glycine and CO_2 for the purines; and for the pyrimidines, by the metabolism of certain offshoots of the Krebs cycle (see the appropriate chapters in Volume II, Chargaff and Davidson, 1955). In *Drosophila*, the Krebs cycle enzymes have been shown to be present in the larva (Spirtes, 1951); and the interrelation of the requirements for glycine and those for folic acid may serve as presumptive evidence that the transformylation mechanism, important both for purine synthesis and for the synthesis of thymidine from uracil deoxyriboside, is operative here also.

From this sketch of a nucleic acid metabolism in which both *de novo* synthesis and the utilization of the nucleic acid components take part, it might be expected that many types of genetic change could occasion differences in the requirements for the participants in these reactions. This is indeed the case. A survey of a group of morphological mutants revealed differences between them in the optimal ratio of glycine in the medium, when no ribonucleic acid was present (Schultz and Service,

1951). The glycine requirements being related to the amount of folic acid present, to the serine content of the diet, and doubtless to other permutations of the untested nutrilites, it becomes obvious that, for example, a difference in the adenine requirement might depend on the proportions of the other nutrients present. Thus a great variety of metabolic patterns is possible, with derangements of nucleic acid metabolism contingent on many types of primary genetic change.

But the problem with respect to the heterochromatic regions, and specifically the Y chromosome, is somewhat different: given an influence on the type of RNA in the egg, and on the proportions of the different nucleoside precursors, how will this be reflected in the nutrition of the larva? Since the ovary enters its grand phase of growth only after pupation, its nucleic acid requirements will not have much weight in the total balance of the diet. It is not surprising therefore that in the diverse tests made in our laboratory only minor effects have so far been found. No key nutritional requirement has yet appeared, opening the analysis of the specific reactions involved. This statement covers not only studies of glycine, adenine and orotic acid interrelationships; but also experiments with a variety of purine and pyrimidine analogues, as well as antimetabolites to folic acid. As always in such cases, negative results may mean only that a particular critical constellation of conditions has not been arranged; whatever this constellation may be, it is not an obvious one, following directly from the known reactions of nucleic acid metabolism. In a sense these results are the counterpart in terms of nutritional chemistry, of the absence of major morphological effects of the Y chromosome. It may well be that the same considerations apply in both cases; that the effect of the Y is not limiting for the synthesis of critical reaction participants.

One apparent case of a drastic requirement for adenine has been described by Hinton (1955), who believes this to be associated with a rearrangement involving the heterochromatic regions of chromosome 2. The genetic analysis however indicates a complex situation, the interaction of a number of factors. Inspection of the data suggests that such factors are reasonably frequent; in the absence of an analysis of the strain from which the rearrangement originated, it is difficult to accept the interpretation given by Hinton—a position effect on a heterochromatic region. Further work in this direction is undoubtedly needed in view of the results presented here, with which such a possibility would be consistent.

Modification of the Activities of Heterochromatic Regions by Influences on Nucleic Acid Metabolism

On the showing of this discussion, the second of our three approaches has not yielded striking results: the nutritional requirements of the larva are not strikingly modified by the presence or the absence of a Y chromosome. Let us now examine the third of the approaches I outlined at the beginning, the attempt to modify the activities of the heterochromatic regions by diversion of the course of nucleic acid synthesis, either by changes in the proportions of the dietary constituents, or by the introduction of antimetabolites to the participants in nucleic acid synthesis.

The known activities of the heterochromatic regions have been detected in two ways: By deficiency or duplication of chromosome regions; and by the analysis of the effects of these regions in chromosome rearrangements occuring at or near them. Two major types of effect have been observed. One is on the terminal stages of spermiogenesis. Males lacking a Y chromosome, having too many Y chromosomes, or containing rearrangements of the X to euchromatic autosomal regions, are sterile. The other effect is a type of somatic variegation, observed in rearrangements for genes adjacent to the points of translocation; or to a degree, also in individuals containing a high number of supernumerary Y chromosomes (Cooper, 1956). Minor effects include a change in cell size, but these are far from distinctive.

The effects on spermiogenesis may turn out to be relevant to the Y chromosome effects already discussed, on the nucleic acids in female gametogenesis. They have not been studied from this point of view as yet. Therefore, although the effect on the sterility of the male is most dramatic, further discussion of it is better deferred until more is known of the cytochemistry.

The phenomenon of heterochromatin-induced variegation in *Drosophila* has a different status. This it was that originally stimulated speculation about the relation of the heterochromatic regions to the nucleic acids and their genetic effects, as I have already said. Loci transposed to heterochromatic regions in general, the proper detecting genes being present, produce mutant areas in the bodies of individuals containing these rearrangements. This somatic variegation is sensitive to the balance of heterochromatic and other chromosome regions in the nucleus. No summary of the evidence will be attempted here; references to the earlier work will be found in the reviews of Hannah (1950) and Lewis (1950). The relationship of modifier to localized agent has some similarities to the two-component systems discussed by Dr. McClintock in maize; and it is not out of reason that the basic principles are the same in the two cases, even though the definitions of the nature of the modifying agents are clouded by ignorance of all but their end effects on the genetic system. An outstanding question is whether the phenotypic changes observed are due to changes in gene activity or to changes in the nature of the genetic locus. In the *Drosophila* cases particularly this is difficult, since the genetic behavior of the changed cells cannot be studied by breeding tecniques,

and we are led immediately into the questions relating nuclear changes to the differentiation process.

The variegation problem has therefore concentrated in it many of the most vexing problems of genetics: the function of the heterochromatic regions, the nature of position effects, the balance of genetic factors in the nucleus, and the primary mode of action of the genes as related to these genetic variables. Add to these the cytological problems arising from the observations on the structure of the heterochromatin-affected regions in the giant salivary gland chromosomes (Schultz, 1941, 1952). Changes occur, which parallel the somatic variegation for the characters in these regions. Under conditions when the normal phenotype (no variegation) appears, the bands in these regions have a normal structure. As the extent of variegation increases, the structure approximates more and more closely to that of the heterochromatic regions themselves, and in extreme instances the bands cannot be detected as such. These are the changes that suggested a nucleic acid involvement in genetic activity, with their reversal by addition of the Y chromosome indicating a relation of heterochromatic regions to general nucleic acid metabolism.

For our present purposes, I shall confine the discussion to three questions, pertinent to the main theme. Do the changes in the chromosomes really have to do with nucleic acid content? What is the nature of the nuclear change giving rise to the altered phenotype: is it a change in gene "expression" or in the nature of the genetic complex whose action is observed? And can these changes be altered by substances having to do with nucleic acid metabolism?

The first of these questions turns out to have a more complex answer than anticipated. In the original case that Caspersson and I studied (Schultz and Caspersson, 1939; Caspersson and Schultz, 1951), the rearrangement was a translocation between the X and the 4th chromosomes, detected by variegation for the white-Notch region. I had found a difference in the apparent amount of Feulgen reaction in the translocated segment of X adjacent to chromosome 4, but in which no loci displaying variegation exist. The ultra-violet absorption measurements of translocated region and homolog showed a comparable difference which seemed greatest in the bands closest to the rearrangement point. The fragment in which the white-Notch region lies presented greater technical difficulties and no measurement was accomplished in the early work. More recently, Dr. Rudkin, Miss Sally Corlette and I have returned to this problem; the work has not yet gone far enough to yield definitive conclusions. Table 11 gives a series of measurements from larvae raised at 25°C. In these the variegation does not extend to section 3C, in which the white-Notch loci are placed, but is restricted to the genes in 3D, close to the rearrangement point. 3D is not analyzable in these figures; there would seem to be a decrease in the amount of absorbing material, as well as a transformation of structure. Section 3C, on the other hand, may be behaving like the bands in 3F, the ones measured in the earlier work I have just referred to; there is an indication of an increase in the amount of absorbing material, but I hesitate to claim any significance for it at this point. The real complication, however, comes when we consider that we already know, from the work on the RNA composition presented earlier, of influences on the kind of nucleic acid. These we cannot yet measure, but they could certainly complicate quantitative changes; so this part of the work is still in its beginnings. It does even now, however, indicate that the changes that lead to the variegation have to do with the composition of the chromosomes, something to keep in mind in considering the effects of antimetabolites, as we shall do presently.

The existence of changes in chromosome composition, however, does not in itself clear up the second question raised above—the nature of the nuclear change, to which we must have an answer. With the type of reversible change in chromosome structure that we have heard about from Dr. Beermann and Dr. Pavan, and which Dr. Rudkin has studied in *Drosophila* also, some independent evidence is needed before conclusions can be drawn about the relation of the variegation process to either gene activity or "mutation."

The answer must come on a cellular basis. The requirements are two: 1) The effect of the change should be detectable in a single cell; and 2) the determination of the genetic difference should occur at a different time than its expression in development. The reason for the first requirement is obvious, since it is the relation of the nucleus and cytoplasm in the individual cell that concerns us. The second requirement has a more complex rationale. Assume a genetic change in one of the members of a pair of sister chromosomes at or following replication. If differentiation is immediate, this will be manifest in one of the sisters, in whom the expression of the genetic change would be irreversible. Contrariwise, assume the variegation to be a reversible change affecting the activity of the gene; if the process affected continues during the growth of the cell, it should be responsive to changes in the environment. Hence, by studying the effects of environmental factors at different times in the cell cycle, it should be possible to distinguish between reversible and irreversible changes in the nucleus. The presumption would then be that reversible changes were more likely to be changes in activity of the gene; this is by no means a critical demonstration, in the present state of our knowledge of gene action, but it will have to suffice at present.

The malpighian tubules showing variegation for the white locus are a good system for analysis

TABLE 11. ULTRA-VIOLET ABSORPTION IN SECTIONS 1A–3C OF SALIVARY GLAND CHROMOSOMES IN TRANSLOCATION (1; 4) w^{258-21}/w^{48h}

Total extinction in μ^2 at 257 mμ, obtained by photographic densitometry.

Preparation No	Section 1A–3B		Section 3C	
	T(1;4) w^{258-21}	w^{48h}	T(1;4) w^{281-21}	w^{48h}
231 B	13.91	14.90	1.65	1.79
231 E	10.20	11.40	1.59	1.30
199 A	5.88	6.89	1.10	1.01
310 × D	8.15	7.91	1.13	1.07
310 × F	15.95	21.58	2.50	2.45
282 C	8.90	7.17	1.28	1.30
Totals	62.99	69.85	9.28	8.92
$\dfrac{\text{T (1;4) } w^{258-21}}{w^{48h}}$	0.90		1.08	

of this kind. The individual cells are easily distinguished; the white mutant cells do not possess the yellow globules present in the wild type. Like other larval tissues the cells of the malpighian tubules do not divide after the embryonic stages; thus after the larva hatches from the egg, the cells grow only in size and not in number. The pigment globules make their appearance in the cells shortly after the malpighian tubules are differentiated, before the larva hatches; and they increase in number as the cells grow larger. In contrast to other larval tissues, the malpighian tubules are retained in the adult. Consequently, the variegation pattern of the adult malpighian tubule, insofar as it depends on the mitotic history of the tissue, is a record of events occurring during the embryonic stages. Therefore, any factor effective in changing the extent of variegation applied during the embryonic period, should change the variegation in the malpighian tubules. It is well known that the temperature at which development occurs is such a factor. The grade of variegation is more extreme at 18° than at 25°, as evidenced in the imaginal tissues. This is also true for the malpighian tubules and for the cytological abnormalities in the salivary glands.

The experiments carried out made use of the translocation already mentioned, designated T(1;4) w^{258-21}. In heterozygotes for this rearrangement and the mutant white, at 25° the eyes show the normal red color, with occasional flecks of brown ommatidia. A low frequency of individuals appears with its wings slightly notched. Raised at 18°, individuals of the same type are extreme Notch, the eye color being cream or ecru, with patches colored apricot or darker. The malpighian tubules at 25° are yellow, with an occasional single white cell. At 18°, there are frequent groups of white cells, amounting to about 50 per cent of the total cells in the tubule. The difference is striking, and the tubules from individuals raised at the different temperatures can easily be classified into their respective groups.

The malpighian tubules from four groups of individuals were therefore compared. Two of these had in common an embryonic period passed at 18.6° C. They differed in the temperature at which larval growth occurred, one having remained throughout at 18.6°, the other having been transferred to 25°C within several hours of hatching from the egg. The other two groups were reciprocal to these, one being at 25° throughout, the other having been transferred to 18.6° on hatching from the egg. The adults of each group were classified for their eye and wing variegation, after which the malpighian tubules were dissected out and mounted in insect Ringer's solution. Examined under the dark field microscope at about 500×, individual cells could easily be classified as white or wild type, and the tubule as a whole classified as having either around 90 per cent or 50 per cent yellow cells.

The results, shown in Table 12, are unequivocal. As expected, the imaginal characteristics depend on the temperature during larval growth, when the important divisions of the imaginal discs are still occurring. There are peculiarities of detail, which are tangential to our main theme. But the characteristics of the variegation in the malpighian tubules are definitely determined in the embryonic period, when the cell divisions occur to form this organ. Neither of the transfers had any discernible effect on the malpighian tubules, from the lower to the higher temperature, or *vice versa*. Any effect during the growth of the cells after the hatching from the egg would seem to be excluded. If the white phenotype were due to an inhibition of a gene activity continuous during the growth phase, the transfer to the lower temperature should have brought about this change, and one should see patches of pale cells (assuming that the few yellow globules present at hatching from the egg are maintained). Conversely, the transfer from 18.6° to 25° should have released the inhibition and the condition approximate the 25° malpighian tubule. Since neither of these things occurred, it follows that an irreversible differentiation, with respect to the activity of the white locus, occurs in the variegation phenomenon. We may now ask what the nature of this differentiation is, whether this is a process related to nucleic acid metabolism.

The attempt to determine the sensitivity of heterochromatin-induced variegation to changes in the diet influencing nucleic acid synthesis suggested itself fairly early in this analysis. In some of the early work on the nutrition of *Drosophila*, effects of a variety of deficiencies were noted, on the grade of white variegation (Schultz and Rudkin, 1949). These were consistent with a relationship to nucleic acid synthesis, but could not be considered demonstrative at that time. The reason lies in the lack of specificity in such effects, which could involve the general energy metabolism of the organism. Since then, the steps in both purine and pyrimidine biosynthesis have proved susceptible to analysis, both *in vivo* and *in vitro*; and a barrage of compounds has been made available to act as antimetabolites to critical substances (see, for example, the contributions of Hitchings and of Brown to the Symposium on Antimetabolites and Cancer; ed. Rhoads, 1955).

Before considering the results of these experiments, let us ask what information is required to identify the biochemical reactions involved in a particular biological process such as variegation, from studies of the effects of antimetabolites upon it. Clearly, it is not enough that there be an effect of the specific antimetabolite. It is necessary to show that this effect is not simply a by-product of some general influence on the metabolism of the organism. Moreover, in order to delimit the system, it must be shown not only that antimetabolites to the suspected group of substances have an effect on the process; but also that antimetabolites to substances participating in remotely related reactions have only slight or no effect.

In the experiments that were carried out, the attempt was made to satisfy both these requirements. A group of some 27 compounds was studied for their effects, not only on variegation, but also

TABLE 12. EFFECTS OF TEMPERATURE CHANGES ON THE DEVELOPMENT OF VARIEGATION

Individuals are w^{258-21}/w^{48h} females

Grades of Variegation:

0 = Wild type.

1 = Few white cells or mutant spots; slight notching of wing.

2 = Standard notch phenotype; eyes mostly a dark allele of white.

3 = Standard notch phenotype; eyes mostly a light white allele; malpighian tubules >50% white cells.

4 = Extreme notch, eyes mostly a light allele of white.

Temperature °C	Individuals Showing Grades of Variegation						
	Eyes and wings					Malpighian tubules	
	0	1	2	3	4	0-1	3
25.0	54	27	—	—	—	57	—
18.7	1	1	7	5	34	—	44
18.7–25.0*	—	6	19	25	—	2	40
25.0–18.7*	19	27	1	—	—	49	

* Eggs collected over 3 hr. periods at 25°C; transferred to designated temperature; retransferred to new temperature at beginning of first larval instar.

on the growth and morphogenesis of the wild type *Drosophila* (Schultz, Rothman and Aronson, 1955). In addition, since it seemed desirable to study some other type of genetic change occurring in the same tissues as the variegation, parallel experiments were carried out in which the mosaics due either to somatic crossing over, or to the elimination of a ring X chromosome, could be detected.

It is evident that this type of experiment is like the conventional screening experiment in chemotherapy. Actually, part of our data derive from a project of the American Cancer Society, in which this group of compounds, selected for relevance to the chemotherapy of cancer, were tested on a variety of biological systems. Among these compounds, analogs of the purines and pyrimidines were present; mitotically active compounds such as colchicine; analogs of the amino acids such as ethionine and β-thienylaline; of such coenzyme precursors as the folic acids and pyridoxine. This group of compounds, therefore, tested on variegation, somatic crossing over and for effects on morphology and growth during development, should allow deductions concerning the metabolic process involved in variegation.

Only the general conclusions of these experiments will be given here; they will be presented in detail elsewhere. Somatic crossing over in chromosome 2 and the elimination of the ring X chromosome were affected by the same three compounds: the nitrogen mustard methyl bis (β-chloroethyl) amine, azaserine and colchicine. That the nitrogen mustard is effective is not surprising, since Auerbach (1945) had already shown an effect of the sulfur mustards on this process. Colchicine is in a different category, being spindle active; and it is possible that the mosaics in this group result from some type of abnormal segregation. The azaserine effect, one of the most striking, presents a different problem: this substance is an antagonist of purine synthesis *de novo*, at a stage subsequent to the formation of the imidazole-carboamide precursor (Hartman, Levenberg and Buchanan, 1955). For these three compounds, the best experiments contained as high as ten per cent of the individuals with mosaic areas resulting from somatic crossing over or ring elimination, where the per cent in the controls was negligible. The 25 other compounds were inactive under these conditions. This includes the purine and pyrimidine analogues, urethane, and other substances each of which produced its own characteristic morphogenetic defects. Most significant is the failure of the folic acid analogue amethopterin to have any effect on somatic crossing over: if azaserine acts primarily by virtue of its effect on purine synthesis *de novo*, amethopterin should also be effective. Since this is not the case, a further analysis of the azaserine action is needed, particularly with respect to reversing agents, to determine whether the block to purine synthesis is critical for somatic crossing over.

We turn now to the effects of this same series of compounds on several types of variegation: One, the same white-Notch translocation already discussed; and two other types which gave concordant results in general. I shall confine this discussion to the white-Notch variegation. In these experiments the individuals were classified as wild type, Notched wing, and variegated eye (the variegation at this temperature in all cases being a brown flecking). The frequencies of the different classes were calculated as percentages, and the difference between the experiment and a parallel control served as a measure of the effect of the compound.

The important point for the present discussion is that the most effective compounds proved to be those having to do with the *de novo* synthesis of the pyrimidine and purine bases. The pyrimidine analogues had no effect; purine analogues in some cases (diaminopurine, benzimidazole) had a slight suppressing effect; 8-azaguanine showed a just statistically significant increase in the frequency of flecking in the eye. The alkylating agent nitrogen mustard was ineffective. Where deoxypyridoxine [among its other effects, antagonist to a cofactor for serine synthesis (Alexander and Greenberg, 1956)—a reaction also involving transformylation] was ineffective on somatic crossing over, it exerted a strong suppressing effect on variegation. Azaserine and colchicine were both effective here also. Ethionine showed a moderate enhancing action, although it had no significant effect on somatic crossing over. Most effective of all was the folic acid analogue amethopterin. Of these four most effective compounds, colchicine is the only one not having an overt connection with purine or pyrimidine synthesis *de novo*; and it is not excluded that here, as in the somatic crossing over effect, there is not still some aberrant type of segregation to be discovered. The other three compounds are two of them (amethopterin and ethionine) concerned with single carbon unit transfer; and azaserine, as already said, with purine synthesis.

The results of this screening program are to be regarded as preliminary, requiring a more intensive analysis. The beginning of such an analysis has been carried out for the amethopterin effect, which seemed the likeliest place to identify the chemical step involved. Amethopterin has been shown to be a metabolic antagonist to folic acid in the synthesis of coenzymes (the citrovorum factors) for transformylations of various kinds. These have been shown to be involved in the synthesis of purine ribosides (see the Chapters by Reichardt and Schlenk in Volume II of Chargaff and Davidson, 1955) and also in the synthesis of thymidine from uracil deoxyriboside. Friedkin and Roberts (1956) have shown that incorporation of uracil deoxyriboside to DNA (thymidine synthesis) is easily inhibited by amethopterin; but thymidine incorporation is not affected by much

TABLE 13. REVERSAL OF MORPHOGENETIC EFFECTS OF AMETHOPTERIN BY THYMIDINE

Values are percentages of individuals showing different combinations of the following characters:
ro—rough eyes. crip—crippled legs.
py—polychaete (extra bristles). N—Notch wings.

Treatment conc. = mg 1 cc	Sex	+	ro	py	crip	py, N	py, crip	N, crip	ro, py, N	ro, py, crip	py, N, crip	ro, py, N, crip	N
Controls (autoclaved	♂	99		1									146
10% yeast agar)	♀	100											121
1.0 Thymidine	♂	96	1.0	3									273
	♀	96	0.5	3	0.4	0.4							288
.001 Amethopterin	♂	1		62		16.0	8				3	10	205
	♀			63	1.0	11.0	8			1	11	5	198
.001 Amethopterin + 1.0	♂	99						1					368
Thymidine	♀	96	1.0	2					1				365

TABLE 14. PERCENTAGE OF INDIVIDUALS SHOWING MORPHOGENETIC EFFECTS OF AMETHOPTERIN IN THE PRESENCE OF DEOXYURIDINE

ro—rough eyes. crip—crippled legs.
py—polychaete (extra bristles). N—Notch wings.

Treatment	Sex	+	py	crip	py, N	py, crip	N, crip	ro, py, N	rp, py, crip	py, N, crip	ro, py, N, crip	N
Controls (autoclaved 10%	♂	99	1									146
yeast agar)	♀	100										121
1.0 Deoxyuridine	♂	100										171
	♀	98	2									195
.001 Amethopterin	♂	1	62		16	8				3	10	205
	♀		63	1	11	8			1	11	5	198
.001 Amethopterin + 1.0 De-	♂	0.5	65		0.5	1						100
oxyuridine	♀		54		1	5	1	1		2		92

higher amounts of the antagonist. It follows therefore that one of the critical steps in DNA synthesis is affected by the folic acid system, and that the effects of amethopterin on *Drosophila* can be analyzed in terms of DNA synthesis.

Let us first examine the highly specific morphological defects produced by amethopterin from this point of view. It might be presumed that these could be traced to changes in the patterns of proliferation, ultimately due to changed rates of DNA synthesis. Thus the special tissues which showed the morphological changes might be relatively low in their coenzyme content as compared with others; or, again they might require a higher than normal concentration of precursors to maintain a necessary pattern of cell division.

This specific pattern of effects on morphogenesis in the different tissues is of importance in evaluating the nature of the variegation effects of amethopterin. From the temperature experiments on the malpighian tubule variegation, we learned that this process does not go on during the period of polytene growth that occurs during larval life; but it is concerned with an earlier process analogous to the embryonic determination of the tissue. By the comparative analysis of the mechanism of the amethopterin effect on morphogenesis and variegation, we can pursue the question further.

An obvious question—the sensitive step in morphogenesis—can be approached by attempting to reverse the morphogenetic effects of amethopterin by the incorporation of the missing reaction product into the diet. From the experiments of Friedkin and Roberts, it would be likely that thymidine should reverse the amethopterin effect, and that its precursor deoxyuridine would be, relatively ineffective. As Tables 13 and 14 show, this is indeed the case for morphogenetic effects of amethopterin on the wild type *Drosophila*. There is a complete reversal to normality by thymidine, and relatively little effect of deoxyuridine at the same concentrations. The meaning of these results is clear: the whole complex of morphogenetic effects observed as the result of amethopterin is due to the defect in DNA synthesis resulting from a short supply of thymidine. The failure of deoxyuridine to supply the want identifies the reaction with that studied by Friedkin and Roberts.

A brief comment on the implications of these experiments for the differentiation problem is in order here. The distinctive effect of amethopterin under these nutritional conditions is the appearance of extra bristles, chiefly on the dorsal thorax, signified in the table as polychaete. Bristle formation in *Drosophila* involves the cooperation of a group of cells, several forming the socket; and one, the trichogen, the chief bristle secretor, becomes greatly enlarged with polytene chromosomes. It follows that the differentiation from the hypodermal cells common to all the thorax, into the presumptive trichogen, is a reaction dependent on the thymidine supply, hence either on the rate of DNA synthesis with respect to other cellular events, or on the type of DNA (high thymidine?) in the hypodermal cells. The single step in the morphogenetic process is a limiting reaction in the network; its importance lies in its use as a clue through the labyrinth. Indeed, it should be stated that the effects of amethopterin depend greatly on the basal diet; for example, no extra bristles appear when amethopterin is added to a basal diet of whole casein, with the appropriate vitamin supply, even though the rate of development as a whole is much the same as that on yeast. The specificity of effect, in this case as in so many others, denotes a complicated set of conditions to be satisfied.

Now we may examine the effects on variegation. In these experiments, six different rearrangements have been tested, involving heterochromatic regions of X, Y, 2 and 4. I shall use for the present discussion a rearrangement kindly furnished us by Dr. E. B. Lewis; in this, due to a transposition to the heterochromatic region of 2R, the Stubble mutant shows a variegated pattern, of Stubble and wild type bristles. This is a convenient phenotype for quantitation; the number of Stubble and of wild type bristles at each bristle locus on the fly can easily be counted. We can therefore (amethopterin having no influence on the shape of the bristles) determine the effect of this antimetabolite on variegation in a tissue whose differentiation is specifically affected by it.

Under the influence of amethopterin and the other folic acid analogues tested, the total number of bristles on one side of the fly may increase from the normal 21 to 50 or 60. Comparisons of variegation must therefore be made on the basis of the proportion of the total number which have been changed from Stubble to wild type. In the Tables 15 and 16, the mean percentage of wild type bristles per fly is presented as a measure of the extent of variegation. In this way the complications due to the increase of bristle number and the change in the pattern consequent on this, are avoided. These patterns are a problem in themselves; the analysis of the data in this regard is not yet complete.

From Table 15, it is clear that the mean percentage of wild type bristles per fly on the amethopterin-yeast diet is significantly higher than the control. When thymidine is added to the amethopterin diet, the percentage of wild type bristles is like the control. Thymidine by itself has no effect on the extent of Stubble variegation, measured in this way. It appears, therefore, that this variegation involves a DNA synthesis in which

the amount of thymidine is a limiting factor. Can any of the other factors be identified at present?

A critical datum in the analysis of DNA structure is the ratio of the purine and pyrimidine components to each other. It is, therefore, of interest to determine whether adenine deoxyriboside, the purine companion of thymidine according to DNA structure, has any effect of interest in this system. Such experiments are presented in Table 16. Instead of reversing the amethopterin effect, adenine deoxyriboside accentuates it. I should add that this accentuation is also apparent in the severity of the morphological abnormalities. It would appear that both in variegation and morphogenesis, the process is one in which the relationship of the purine and pyrimidine deoxyribosides may be critical. The inference is evident that the composition of DNA would have importance both for the genetic function and the properties of differentiation in a tissue.

It is clear that more experiments—the permutations of the different factors are obvious enough —are needed, particularly to define the relation-

TABLE 15. REVERSAL OF AMETHOPTERIN
EFFECT ON STUBBLE VARIEGATION

(Mean percentage of wild type bristles per individual)

Treatment Conc. = mg/cc	Genetic Type	
	Sb^v ♀	Sb^v ♂
Control (autoclaved 10% yeast-agar)	24.70 ± 2.06 n = 33	21.88 ± 2.70 n = 16
1.0 Thymidine	26.77 ± 1.91 n = 34	22.06 ± 1.66 n = 17
.001 Amethopterin	36.21 ± 1.76 n = 33	41.43 ± 2.97 n = 28
.005 Amethopterin	48.33 ± 2.11 n = 6	46.67 ± 3.07 n = 6
.001 Amethopterin + 1.0 Thymidine	23.06 ± 1.43 n = 36	25.42 ± 2.29 n = 24
.005 Amethopterin + 1.0 Thymidine	31.67 ± 1.97 n = 24	31.88 ± 2.37 n = 16

TABLE 16. ACCENTUATION OF AMETHOPTERIN
EFFECT ON STUBBLE VARIEGATION

(Mean percentage of wild type bristles per individual)

Treatment Conc. = mg/cc	Genetic Type	
	Sb^v ♀	Sb^v ♂
Control (autoclaved 10% yeast-agar)	24.70 ± 2.06 n = 33	21.88 ± 2.70 n = 16
1.0 Deoxyadenosine	28.60 ± 1.58 n = 39	30.31 ± 2.38 n = 32
.001 Amethopterin	36.21 ± 1.76 n = 33	41.43 ± 2.97 n = 28
.001 Amethopterin + 1.0 Deoxyadenosine	47.86 ± 2.46 n = 28	49.00 ± 2.77 n = 25

ship between the differentiation and the genetic effect in variegation. We may recall that both of these are set off from somatic crossing over by their clear dependence on reactions involving DNA synthesis. Thus we are led back to the hypothesis of variegation I developed some time ago, in which it was related to a then hypothetical normal occurrence of nuclear differentiation during development (Schultz, 1941, 1947, 1952). It is evident, from the nuclear transplantation work (King and Briggs, 1956), and from the present data, that it should now be possible to proceed with an analysis.

The experiments in this section, therefore, show that a genetic phenomenon dependent on the activity of the heterochromatic regions, is dependent on DNA synthesis. It follows that not only in the gametogenesis, but also in the mitotic activities of the imaginal tissues, the heterochromatic regions are involved with nucleic acid metabolism.

Recapitulation and General Discussion

It will be useful now to recapitulate the information presented in the body of this paper. The Y chromosome in *Drosophila melanogaster* has been shown to be active in the metabolism of the nucleic acids during the formation of the egg. Not only does it appear to produce more than its own constitutive fraction of the DNA in the nucleus of the nurse cell; but the RNA of the mature egg cytoplasm changes in base constitution due to its presence; and among the nucleoside precursors the amount of thymidine is raised considerably, although neither the total amount of RNA or nucleoside precursors seems to be altered. When we turn to the effect of the Y in the imaginal tissues, the most striking effect is the suppression of variegation—a phenomenon which is shown by the reversal of the amethopterin effects upon it, to contain a process involving the synthesis of thymidine.

Is the behavior of the Y chromosome to be regarded *sui generis*, or is it likely to establish a pattern of the kind of reactions influenced by the heterochromatic regions as a whole? The analysis of the phenomenon of variegation in *Drosophila*, induced as a position effect of the heterochromatic chromosome regions, lends evidence for the idea that the cytological homology of the heterochromatic regions is paralleled by a similarity of function. Of the variety of antimetabolites tested on a group of rearrangements involving X, 2 and 4 heterochromatin, all those enhancing variegation blocked steps in the *de novo* synthesis of the nucleic acids. And the analysis of the reaction in the case of amethopterin showed not only the dependence on thymidine but also a relation to deoxyadenosine interpretable in terms of an importance of the ratios of the two bases in the constitution of the DNA. In view of the evidence from microorganisms and viruses for the importance of DNA in the

specificity of genetic function, it is tempting to accept these data also—perhaps the first of their kind in an organism with known chromosomes—as going in the same direction.

Lest we overstep the bounds of legitimate enthusiasm, however, it should be noted that only the amethopterin effect is reversed by thymidine; for the extent of variegation in the controls is unaffected by thymidine at the same concentrations. While there is some indication of a significant effect of deoxyadenosine alone, an increase in the extent of variegation over the control (Table 16), it is clear that the data are as yet insufficient to tell what the interrelations really are.

Nevertheless, the accord of the different types of experiment—nucleic acid analysis, antimetabolite effects, genetic interrelations of the Y and the other heterochromatic regions—support the idea that the heterochromatic regions have to do with the system for nucleic acid syntheses in the cell.

It will have been noted that I have said nothing here about the role of the nucleolus in this system. The Y carries a nucleolar organizer; it has often been suggested that the role of the nucleolus is the synthesis of cytoplasmic RNA. We intend to investigate this system in some detail in nurse cell, oocyte and other tissues, and for this reason I shall not discuss it further here.

Similarly, the possible role of the heterochromatic regions in the synthesis of proteins (Caspersson, 1950), by way of their effects on the nucleic acids, is not ripe for discussion in these new contexts.

Two general problems, however, may be touched on here. One is the possible role of heterochromatic regions in nuclear differentiation during development. With the demonstration by Briggs and King that irreversible changes of some kind take place in nuclei during amphibian development, the suggestion I made that the variegation phenomenon is related to the process of embryonic differentiation, deserves new consideration. The experiments presented on the determination of variegation in the malpighian tubules reinforce the view that the genetic variegation occurs during the time when the organ is determined embryologically. The known nuclear differentiation of the heterochromatic regions, and the relation of variegation to DNA synthesis all would seem to fit together as part of the still obscure picture whose outlines are emerging.

The distinctive feature of the heterochromatic regions originally was that at metaphase they contained more "chromatin"—in contemporary terms DNA—than the euchromatic regions, per unit genetic length. If we now consider that they are themselves influential in controlling a general nucleic acid synthesis pattern, it follows that the heterochromatic regions of the chromosomes provide the elements of a feed-back system. For since they themselves are composed of the substance whose synthesis they control, the progress of that synthesis will in turn influence their own replication.

It is tempting to think of these regions as duplications, in the course of evolution, of some unit which had to do with an important step in nucleic acid synthesis. As the differentiation of the duplicate genes occurred during the evolutionary process, according to the type of speculation of which Lewis (1951) furnishes an example for the pseudo-allelic systems, the individual members might take over special steps of the increasingly complex reaction sequence. And the net result could be what we now have in the heterochromatic regions, groups of homologous genes having very little apparent specific effect because of their relation to the de novo synthesis of the building blocks of the nucleic acid which determines the specificities of the cellular enzymatic systems.

REFERENCES

ALEXANDER, N., and GREENBERG, D. M., 1956, Studies on the purification and properties of the serine-forming enzyme system. J. Biol. Chem. 220: 775–785.

ALTORFER, N., 1953, Teneur en acide ribonucléique de différents genotypes chez Drosophila melanogaster. Experientia 9: 463–465.

AUERBACH, C., 1945, The problem of chromosome rearrangement in somatic cells of Drosophila melanogaster. Proc. Roy. Soc. Edin. B. 62: 102–127.

BAUER, H., 1938, Die polypoide Natur der Riesen chromosomen. Naturwiss. 26: 77.

BAYREUTHER, K., 1956, Die Oogenese der Tipuliden. Chromosoma 7: 508–557.

BEERMAN, W., 1956, Nuclear differentiation and functional morphology of chromosomes. Cold Spr. Harb. Symp. Quant. Biol. 21: 217–232.

BREUER, M. E., and PAVAN, C., 1955, Behavior of polytene chromosomes of Rhynchosciara angelae at different stages of development. Chromosoma 7: 371–386.

BROWN, G. B., and ROLL, P. M., 1955, Biosynthesis of nucleic acids. In: The Nucleic Acids, Chargaff, E., and Davidson, J. N., (eds.). New York, Academic Press, Inc., Chap. 25: 341–392.

CALLAN, H. G., 1948, Ribose nucleic acid in the Drosophila egg. Nature, Lond. 161: 440.

CASPERSSON, T., 1950, Cell growth and Cell Function. New York, W. W. Norton & Co.

CASPERSSON, T., and SCHULTZ, J., 1938, Nucleic acid metabolism of the chromosomes in relation to gene reproduction. Nature, Lond. 142: 294–295.

1951, Cytochemical measurements in the study of the gene. In: Genetics in the 20th Century, ed. L. C. Dunn. New York, The Macmillan Co., Chap. 9: 155–173.

CHARGAFF, E., and ZAMENHOF, S., 1948, The isolation of highly polymerized deoxypentose nucleic acid from yeast cells. J. Biol. Chem. 173: 327–335.

CHARGAFF, E., and DAVIDSON, J. N., ed. 1955, The Nucleic Acids, Vols. I and II. New York, Academic Press, Inc.

COHEN, S. S., 1954, Virus-induced metabolic transformations and other studies on unbalanced growth. Chap. VI in: Aspects of Synthesis and Order in Growth. Princeton, New Jersey, Princeton University Press.

COOPER, K. W., 1956, Phenotypic effects of Y chromosome hyperploidy in Drosophila melanogaster, and their relation to variegation. Genetics 41: 242–264.

ELSON, D., and CHARGAFF, E., 1952, On the DNA content of sea-urchin gametes. Experientia 8: 143–149.

FREED, J. J., and SCHULTZ, J., 1956, Effect of the Y chromosome on the DNA content of ovarian nuclei in Drosophila melanogaster females. J. Hist. Cytochem. 4 (in press).

FRIEDKIN, M., and ROBERTS, D., 1956, Conversion of uracil deoxyriboside to thymidine of deoxyribonucleic acid. J. Biol. Chem. 220: 653–660.

HANNAH, A., 1951, Localization and function of heterochromatin in Drosophila melanogaster. Adv. Genetics 4: 87–125.

HARTMAN, S. C., LEVENBERG, B., and BUCHANAN, J. M., 1955, Involvement of ATP, 5-phosphoribosyl pyrophosphate, and L-azaserine in the enzymatic formation of glycinamide ribotide intermediates in inosinic acid biosynthesis. J. Amer. Chem. Soc. 77: 501–503.

HINTON, T., 1955, The genetic basis of a nutritional requirement in Drosophila. Genetics 40: 224–234.

1956, Nucleic acid utilization by Drosophila. Physiol. Zool. 29: 20–26.

HINTON, T., NOYES, D. T., and ELLIS, J., 1951, Amino acids and growth factors in a chemically defined medium for Drosophila. Physiol. Zool. 24: 335–353.

HOFF-JØRGENSEN, E., 1952, A microbiological assay of deoxyribonucleosides and deoxyribonucleic acid. Biochem. J. 50: 400–503.

1954, Deoxyribonucleic acid in some gametes and embryos. In: Recent Developments in Cell Physiology, ed. J. A. Kitching. New York, Academic Press, Inc., pp. 79–90.

HOFF-JØRGENSEN, E., and ZEUTHEN, E., 1952, Evidence of cytoplasmic deoxyribonucleosides in the frog's egg. Nature, Lond. 169: 245.

KING, T. J., and BRIGGS, R., 1956, Serial transplantation of embryonic nuclei. Cold Spr. Harb. Symp. Quant. Biol. 21: 271–290.

LEVENBROOK, L., TRAVAGLINI, E. C., and SCHULTZ, J., 1953, Nucleic acids and free polynucleotide fragments in the egg of Drosophila melanogaster. Anat. Rec. 117: 585.

1955, The effect of the Y chromosome on nucleic acids and polynucleotide fragments in the unfertilized Drosophila melanogaster egg. 3eme Congr. Intern. Biochim. Bruxelles, Resumés: 70.

LEWIS, E. B., 1950, The phenomenon of position effect. Adv. Genetics 3: 73–115.

1951, Pseudo-allelism and gene evolution. Cold Spr. Harb. Symp. Quant. Biol. 16: 159–174.

LINDSLEY, D. L., 1955, Spermatogonial exchange between the X and Y chromosomes of Drosophila melanogaster. Genetics 40: 24–44.

LINDSLEY, D. L., and NOVITSKI, E., 1950, The synthesis of an attached XY chromosome. Drosophila Information Service 24: 84.

LORING, H. S., FAIRLEY, J. L., BORTNER, H. W., and SEAGRAN, H. L., 1952, A spectrophotometric method for the analysis of the purine and pyrimidine components of ribonucleic acid. J. Biol. Chem. 197: 809–821.

MARKHAM, R., and SMITH, J. D., 1952, The structure of ribonucleic acids. Biochem. J. 52: 552.

PAINTER, T. S., 1940, On the synthesis of cleavage chromosomes. Proc. Nat. Acad. Sci. Wash. 26: 95–100.

PAINTER, T. S., and REINDORP, E., 1939, Endomitosis in the nurse cells of the ovary of Drosophila melanogaster. Chromosoma 13: 276–283.

PATTERSON, E. K., LANG, H. M., DACKERMAN, M. E., and SCHULTZ, J., 1954, Chemical determinations of the effect of the X and Y chromosomes of the nucleic acid content of the larval salivary glands of Drosophila melanogaster. Exp. Cell Res. 6: 181–194.

RHOADS, C. P., ed. 1955, Antimetabolites and Cancer. A.A.A.S. Publ. Washington, D. C.

ROEPKE, R. R., LIBBY, R. L., and SMALL, M. H., 1944, Mutation or variation of Escherichia coli with respect to growth requirements. J. Bact. 48: 401–412.

RUDKIN, G. T., and SCHULTZ, J., 1949, A comparison of the tryptophane requirements of mutant and wild type *Drosophila melanogaster*. Proc. 8th Intern. Congr. Genet., Hereditas, (Suppl.): 652.

Schultz, J., 1936, in Morgan, T. H., Bridges, C. B., and and Schultz, J. The constitution of the germinal material in relation to heredity. Yearbook Carneg. Instn. *35:* 289–297.

1941, The evidence of the nucleoprotein nature of the gene. Cold Spr. Harb. Symp. Quant. Biol. *9:* 55–65.

1941, The function of heterochromatin. Proc. 7th Intern. Congr. Genet., J. Genet. (Suppl. Vol.): 257–262.

1947, The nature of heterochromatin. Cold Spr. Harb. Symp. Quant. Biol. *12:* 179–191.

1952, Interrelations between nucleus and cytoplasm: problems at the biological level. Exp. Cell Res. (Suppl.) *2:* 17–43.

1952, The place of cytogenetics in cancer research. Proc. 2nd Natl. Cancer Conf. *2:* 1152–1160.

Schultz, J., and Rudkin, G. T., 1949, Nutritional requirements and the chemical genetics of *Drosophila melanogaster*. Proc. 8th Intern. Congr. Genet., Hereditas (Suppl.): 657.

Schultz, J., and Service, Margaret Mann, 1951, Genetic difference in the requirement for ribosenucleic acid and glycine in *Drosophila melanogaster*. Federation Proc. *10:* 245.

Schultz, J., Rothman, N., and Aronson, M. M., 1955, The growth and morphogenesis of *Drosophila melanogaster* as criteria for screening tests. Cancer Research, (Suppl.) *3:* 86–96.

Spirtes, Morris A., 1951, Demonstration of the presence of Krebs cycle enzymes in *Drosophila melanogaster*. Federation Proc. *10:* 251.

Villee, C. A., and Bissell, H. B., 1948, Nucleic acids as growth factors in *Drosophila*. J. Biol. Chem. *172:* 59–66.

The Function of the Nucleus in the Synthesis of Cytoplasmic Proteins

J. Brachet and H. Chantrenne

Laboratoire de Morphologie animale, Faculté des Sciences, Université libre de Bruxelles

Of all biochemical processes, the synthesis of specific proteins seems to depend most directly upon the nuclear genetic material. The simplest hypothesis to explain such a relation is that the proteins are built under the direct control of DNA. Ingenious mechanisms have been presented to show that this is possible and specific relations between groups of nucleotides and amino acids have been suggested to account for template mechanisms. Moreover—and this is more convincing than any speculation—experimental evidence showing that DNA is directly involved in the synthesis of certain proteins, has been provided. In isolated thymus nuclei, the quantitatively small protein fraction which is strongly bound to DNA takes up labeled amino acids more actively than any other of the nuclear proteins; in this system, destruction of DNA by desoxyribonuclease reduces protein synthesis, and the addition of DNA restores it to some extent (Allfrey, 1954, 1955; Mirsky, 1956). These experiments have been repeated in our laboratory by A. Ficq who studied the incorporation of labelled phenylalanine into isolated thymus nuclei by track autoradiography. Her results (unpub.) are in perfect agreement with those of Allfrey and Mirsky. Gale (1955) has obtained similar results with disrupted staphylococci. It can be concluded that DNA probably plays a direct part in the synthesis of certain proteins, especially of some nuclear proteins.

These observations, however, do not prove that all the proteins of the cell are synthesized under the immediate influence of DNA; other experiments suggest a rather high degree of independence of protein synthesis from the nucleus. For instance, when DNA synthesis is suppressed in a lactobacillus by lack of thymidine, protein synthesis can go on undisturbed (Jeener, 1952). A thymidine-less mutant of *E. coli* still makes adaptive enzymes in a thymidine-free medium in which DNA synthesis is completely stopped (Cohen and Barner, 1955). The nuclear material of microorganisms can be damaged by X-rays to the point that the cells become unable to divide and to make new DNA, without any adverse effect being observed on protein synthesis and even on adaptive enzyme formation (Baron *et al.*, 1953; Gros, 1955). Adaptive enzyme synthesis in protoplasts of *B. megatherium* is insensitive to DNAase which removes up to 50 per cent of the DNA from the preparation (Landman and Spiegelman, 1955). In liver homogenates, incorporation of labelled amino acids occurs in preparations apparently free of nuclear material (Siekevitz, 1952; Keller, 1954). Incorporation of amino acids, and even net protein synthesis, are observed in reticulocytes (Nizet, 1953; Koritz, 1954). All these observations suggest that the relation between protein synthesis and DNA is a rather loose one.

However, a clear answer to the question as to whether the nucleus is the center of all protein synthesis in the cell can only be obtained by the comparison of a nucleus-free cytoplasm to the same cytoplasm provided with its normal nucleus. Many experiments of this type have been performed in our laboratory, in order to study the physiological functions (not only the genetic role) of the nucleus. We will restrict this discussion to those results which have a direct bearing on protein synthesis. We have used two very different organisms for these studies: *Amoeba proteus*, and the green marine alga, *Acetabularia mediterranea*. Both can be cut into nucleated and non-nucleated parts, which will survive for a considerable time.

Let us consider first *Acetabularia*. In his classical work on this organism, Hämmerling (1934) has shown that non-nucleated fragments retain a remarkable capacity for morphogenesis. Since the chloroplasts increase in number in such fragments, one has to assume that an important synthesis of proteins occurs in the absence of the nucleus. That this assumption is correct has been established in this laboratory with biochemical methods. As can be seen from Table 1, the rate of incorporation of radioactive CO_2 into the proteins is not changed immediately after section of the algae; the incorporation is the same in both types of fragments during the first two weeks after sectioning (Brachet and Chantrenne, 1951). In other experiments the rate of incorporation has been compared in the proteins of the chloroplasts and in the other proteins of the alga: The results were that both protein fractions keep incorporating $C^{14}O_2$ for two weeks at the same rate, in both types of fragments (Brachet and Chantrenne, 1952).

Results obtained with labelled glycine are similar, except that the incorporation of glycine is not sensitive to light and that this amino acid is more rapidly incorporated into the microsomes than into the chloroplasts, the reverse being observed for labelled CO_2. The pathways for CO_2 and for glycine incorporation are thus quite different but, with both precursors, the effect of enucleation is the same (Chantrenne, Brachet and Brygier, 1953).

TABLE 1. INCORPORATION OF CO_2 INTO THE PROTEINS
OF *Acetabularia* FRAGMENTS

Days after Sectioning	Nucleated	Non-Nucleated	Ratio
9	197	202	1.02
11	245	250	1.02
16	159	145	0.92
23	220	133	0.61
33	192	131	0.68
38	148	95	0.64
41	166	74	0.45
48	142	60	0.42

The incorporation of a small precursor into a large molecule does not necessarily mean that *net* synthesis takes place; F. Vanderhaeghe (1954) followed the protein content, as a function of time, both in the chloroplasts and in the other cellular fractions in batches of nucleated and non-nucleated fragments. Her experiments showed that *net* protein synthesis takes place in non-nucleated stems as well as in nucleated halves; it is even faster (Fig. 1) in non-nucleated fragments if

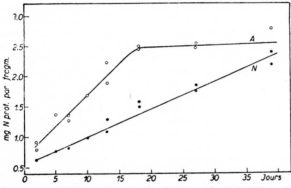

FIGURE 1. Net protein synthesis in nucleated (N) and non-nucleated (A) fragments of *Acetabularia mediterranea*. Time of cutting is taken as 0. The algae were cut just before hat formation, and well illuminated, in order to obtain maximal regeneration.

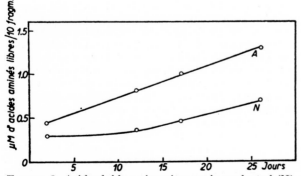

FIGURE 2. Acid soluble amino nitrogen in nucleated (N) and non-nucleated (A) fragments of *Acetabularia mediterranea*. The algae were cut on time 0.

optimal culture conditions are adopted (Brachet, Chantrenne and Vanderhaeghe, 1955). It is thus quite clear that *net* protein synthesis can take place in the absence of the nucleus, and that this is true not only for chloroplastic proteins, but for other cytoplasmic proteins as well.

However, some two weeks after the algae have been cut, the rate of incorporation of CO_2 into the non-nucleated parts drops by about 30 per cent below that of the nucleated halves (Table 1). The results are still clearer when net protein synthesis is followed (Vanderhaeghe, 1954; Brachet *et al.*, 1955); this synthesis stops altogether in non-nucleated parts which have been separated for two weeks (Fig. 1). Incidentally, these experiments show that the turnover of the proteins is very high in these plants, since net synthesis could be responsible for only 30 per cent of the observed incorporation of CO_2 into the proteins.

The picture in *Acetabularia* is thus quite clear: enucleation does not reduce protein synthesis immediately; but the non-nucleated cytoplasm, after a period of two weeks, ceases to synthesize proteins (net synthesis) although their turnover remains at a high value (Brachet *et al.*, 1955).

It can be concluded that the presence of the nucleus is not required for net synthesis of cytoplasmic proteins, and that a complete system for the renewal of the amino acids within the proteins is contained in the cytoplasm. In other words, no part of the mechanism for the synthesis of cytoplasmic proteins is exclusively contained in the nucleus, and the latter is not the unique center of the synthesis of cytoplasmic proteins.

We have seen, however, that the nucleus exerts a remote control on the net synthesis of these proteins, since this process comes to a stop two weeks after enucleation (Fig. 1). This observation suggests that some substance, which is required for net protein synthesis in the cytoplasm and is dependent on the nucleus, has been exhausted. It is not necessary to postulate that this substance is very specific; it is conceivable that a very ordinary biochemical constituent, but one which is produced in the nucleus only, is required for net protein synthesis. One might wonder whether precursors of the proteins are produced in the nucleus; the fact is (Fig. 2) that the level of non-protein nitrogen compounds is higher in non-nucleated than in nucleated parts (Brachet *et al.*, 1955). There are good reasons to believe that some of the nucleotide coenzymes (especially DPN) originate in the nucleus: Several enzymes required for this synthesis are localized in the nucleus of liver cells (Hogeboom and Schneider, 1952; Stern *et al.*, 1952) and in the nucleoli of starfish oocytes (Baltus, 1954).

With *Acetabularia*, Hämmerling (1939) has observed in his grafting experiments that a specific agent of nuclear origin disappears after some time from the cytoplasm; during the differentiation of cytoplasm which has been grafted on a nucleated fragment of another species, the degree to which the cytoplasmic characters are retained is related to the amount of cytoplasm present. It looks as if some substance, coming from the nucleus, were being consumed during growth and differentiation. The amount of this morphogenetic substance is greater in the region close to the nucleus than at the tip of the alga (Hämmerling, 1953). Hämmerling's interpretation is that "under the influence of the genes controlling the characters studied, chemical compounds are synthesized within the nucleus and released into the cytoplasm. They direct metabolism in such a way that from protoplasm as a substrate of morphogenesis, eventually a cap of definite shape is formed." It is quite possible that the products of gene action which induce the specific morphogenetic response in Hämmerling's experiments are the same that are required for net protein synthesis to continue. But at present we cannot decide whether the remote control of the nucleus on protein synthesis that we have observed is exerted by some substance produced under the action of genes and which carries specific information to the protein synthesizing mechanism, or by a much more common biochemical compound.

If the nucleus secretes into the cytoplasm morphogenetic substances carrying the information from the genes to the protein synthesizing systems, these morphogenetic substances must be rather complex in nature, and one immediately thinks of proteins, nucleic acids or nucleoproteins. Ribose nucleic acid is probably the best candidate as a cytoplasmic carrier of genetic information since, among all cytoplasmic constituents, it is so much related chemically to DNA, the genetic material. Very interesting studies have recently established that, in tobacco mosaic virus, RNA is the component carrying the information necessary for its own correct copying and, moreover, for the organization of the specific protein normally associated with it (Jeener, 1956; Fraenkel-Conrat, 1956; Gierer and Schramm, 1956). Furthermore, a great number of facts have established that RNA is one of the essential elements of the protein synthesizing system (Brachet, 1954).

A question thus immediately arises: is RNA produced by the nucleus? Experiments on the incorporation of labelled precursors into different RNA fractions have consistently shown that the rate of incorporation of various precursors is higher into the RNA contained in the nucleus, and especially in the nucleolus, than into the cytoplasmic RNA fraction (Marshak, 1948; Marshak and Calvet, 1949; Jeener and Szafarz, 1950; Barnum and Huseby, 1950; Hurlbert and Potter, 1952; Bergstrand et al., 1948; Payne et al., 1952; Smellie et al., 1953). This does not prove, however, that nuclear RNA is the precursor of cytoplasmic RNA. As a matter of fact, recent work by Barnum et al. (1953), by Crosbie et al. (1953) and by Elson and Chargaff (1955) rather suggests that nuclear and cytoplasmic RNA are synthesized independently. Studies on non-nucleated cells were undertaken in this laboratory, with the hope of throwing some light on this matter.

We first attempted, in Acetabularia, to measure the incorporation of C^{14}-labeled orotic acid into the RNA of nucleated and non-nucleated fragments. It was found (Brachet and Szafarz, 1953) that the amount of C^{14} incorporated into the RNA of the nucleated fragments was 40 per cent higher per unit dry weight than into that of the non-nucleated fragments; this situation did not change markedly even 70 days after enucleation. This result means that the system necessary for incorporating orotic acid into RNA is present in the cytoplasm, where it is preserved for a long time in the absence of the nucleus. The observed incorporation is most probably due to a turnover, for it is too high to be due to net synthesis. No conclusions can be drawn from the value obtained for the ratio of the rates of incorporation in the nucleated and non-nucleated fragments, since RNA has not been determined in these experiments. The higher incorporation in the nucleated fragments is probably due in part to a higher RNA content of the nucleated halves (the cytoplasm around the nucleus is strongly basophilic) and in part to a higher turnover of nuclear RNA. As we have seen, this is a common situation and Acetabularia is no exception. Hämmerling and Stich (1956) have actually observed that P^{32} is rapidly taken up—and also rapidly lost—by nucleolar RNA in this alga. Unpublished autoradiograph experiments by F. Vanderhaeghe also show that adenine is very quickly incorporated in the nucleolus of Acetabularia.

It thus became necessary to measure net RNA synthesis. This proved very difficult for technical reasons and could only be done by an isotopic dilution method with labelled adenine (Brachet et al., 1955; Vanderhaeghe and Szafarz, 1955). The results of our RNA determinations on batches of nucleated fragments (Fig. 3) showed that non-nucleated fragments synthesize RNA somewhat more rapidly than their nucleated counterparts during the first few days after separation; afterwards, net RNA synthesis becomes more sluggish in non-nucleated fragments than in nucleated ones, although it continues for several weeks.

The experiments prove that cytoplasmic RNA can be synthesized in the absence of the nucleus and one can thus reject the idea that all cytoplasmic RNA necessarily comes from the nucleus. It is of course possible that part of the RNA synthesized in the nucleus passes into the cytoplasm, but this remains to be proven in the case of Acetabularia.

It can be concluded that, in Acetabularia, the nucleus has no immediate role in cytoplasmic proteins or nucleic acid synthesis, but it has a remote effect on the net synthesis of both these substances.

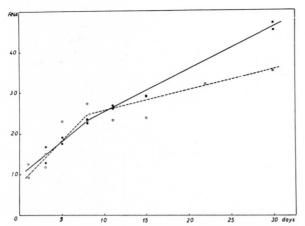

FIGURE 3. Net RNA synthesis in nucleated (●) and non-nucleated (○) fragments of *Acetabularia mediterranea*. Algae cut on time 0. Ordinates: RNA expressed as 10^{-5} μmole of RNA adenine per fragment.
FIGURES 4 AND 5. Change in RNA and enzyme content of non-nucleated as compared to nucleated fragments of *Amoeba proteus*. Ordinates:
$$R = \frac{\text{amount of enzyme (or RNA) per non-nucleated half}}{\text{amount of enzyme (or RNA) per nucleated half}}$$

Let us now examine the results obtained with *Amoeba*.

It is essential to realize first that the amoeba fragments are in completely different physiological conditions than those of *Acetabularia*. When *Amoeba proteus* is cut into two approximately equal parts, the fragment containing the nucleus retains all the morphological characters of a normal amoeba, whereas the non-nucleated piece rounds up very soon after the section; it then loses its ability to draw pseudopodia and to catch prey. Non-nucleated fragments survive for 10 to 15 days, but they are of course starving; therefore one has also to keep under starvation conditions the nucleated fragments or the intact amoebae which serve as controls. In *Acetabularia*, the situation is obviously different, since both fragments are able to live by photosynthesis.

Clearly, starving amoebae cannot be expected to show any net protein synthesis. Mazia and Prescott (1955) have made an interesting study of S^{35} methionine incorporation into the proteins of nucleated and non-nucleated amoebae. Immedi-

ate effects of enucleation were observed: during the first few hours after section already, the non-nucleated parts took up only half as much as the nucleated fragments or as an equal weight of the intact amoebae; furthermore, out of the amount of methionine which had entered the fragments, more than twice as much was incorporated into proteins in the presence of the nucleus as in its absence. Autoradiograph experiments, performed in our laboratory by A. Ficq (1955) and by Skreb (unpub.) using C^{14}-labelled phenylalanine, also showed a lower incorporation in the cytoplasmic proteins of the non-nucleated parts soon after the section; the differences were, however, less than in Mazia and Prescott's experiments. Obviously, the cytoplasm of *Amoeba*, just as that of *Acetabularia*, contains the complete system necessary for the incorporation of amino acids into proteins; but in the amoebae, enucleation very rapidly depresses the turnover of cytoplasmic proteins.

It is a possibility that some of the cytoplasmic proteins, in amoebae, require the participation of the nucleus for their renewal, whereas others are much less dependent on nuclear control. Although this explanation is not the only possible one, as we shall see later, the study of the fate of several enzymes in non-nucleated fragments makes this interpretation rather plausible. Striking differences have indeed been observed (Brachet, 1955) when different enzymes were studied in nucleated and non-nucleated *Amoeba* halves. Let us first consider the total protein content: starved nucleated fragments do not lose more than 15 per cent of their proteins in eleven days, whereas non-nucleated ones lose as much as 50 per cent, a sharp drop occurring around the third day (Table 2). This strong attack of the proteins in the non-nucleated part might very well be an indirect consequence of enucleation, for the non-nucleated cytoplasm becomes unable to use its lipids and glycogen stores after two to three days; it is therefore not surprising that it starts consuming its proteins at that moment. A more significant fact is that all the proteins do not disappear simultaneously or at the same rate (Figs. 4 and 5): protease, enolase and ATPase are just as stable in both types of starving fragments. Amylase also does not change much. Dipeptidase drops rapidly between the first and the third day and stays unchanged afterwards. Esterase and phosphatase show the most striking change, since the bulk of these enzymes disappears from the non-nucleated fragments between the fourth and the twelfth days (Fig. 5). It is a possibility that the different enzymes we studied are bound to distinct cytoplasmic particles; the latter might be more or less dependent on the nucleus for their maintenance or for their formation. We do not know very much about the localization of enzymes in amoeba, but we know at least (Holter and Løvtrup, 1949; Holter and

TABLE 2. PROTEIN IN *Amoeba* FRAGMENTS

Days after Sectioning	Nucleated	Non-Nucleated	Ratio $\frac{\text{Non-N}}{\text{N}}$
1	0.27	0.23	0.89
3	0.29	0.22	0.76
5	0.26	0.14	0.54
7	0.27	0.15	0.56
9	0.23	0.12	0.53
11	0.23	0.12	0.53

The figures are γ of tyrosine per 100 fragments.

Pollock, 1952) that protease and amylase are bound to the mitochondria; these enzymes, as well as ATPase (which incidentally is found in liver mitochondria) and the overall respiration largely escape nuclear control. On the other hand, acid phosphatase and esterase undergo the same changes as RNA (see below) and one may wonder whether they are not, as in liver, contained in the microsomes. This would indicate that the microsomes (or rather the ergastoplasm) disappear rather rapidly in the absence of the nucleus; such an interpretation of the findings is in keeping with the view, expressed by Gay (1955), that the ergastoplasm is formed by the nuclear membrane.

Already, in the first experiments on amoebae (Brachet, 1950), cytochemical observations had shown that the RNA content rapidly drops in a non-nucleated cytoplasm, whereas it keeps nearly constant in nucleated fragments. This drop in the RNA content does not begin before the second or third day after enucleation. RNA determinations have confirmed these results: non-nucleated parts start losing their RNA around the third day and, by the twelfth day, they have lost up to 60 per cent of the original amount (Fig. 4 and Table 3). On the other hand, whole amoebae and nucleated halves retain their RNA content on starving. Similar results were reported by James (1954), except that he observed a drop in the RNA content of intact amoebae as well as in non-nucleated halves. The discrepancy between James' results and ours, in the case of the whole amoebae, is due to differences in growing techniques; under the conditions described by James, the amoebae shrink markedly during starvation and his results can then be confirmed.

It can be concluded that, in amoebae, the nucleus controls the maintenance of cytoplasmic RNA and probably of the ergastoplasm. It certainly would be interesting to know more about the enzymes associated with the microsomes in amoebae.

Does it necessarily follow that cytoplasmic RNA in *Amoeba* is entirely synthesized in the nucleus? Preliminary experiments with labelled adenine (Skreb, unpub.) have shown that although its incorporation into cytoplasmic RNA is reduced in the absence of the nucleus, considerable incorporation nevertheless occurs. Since we know very little about nucleic acid metabolism in amoebae, and since we are certainly dealing with a turnover (since the total amount of RNA is decreasing), no clear conclusions can be drawn from the present results. The very striking experiments by Goldstein and Plaut (1955) on the transplantation of P³²-labelled nuclei in growing amoebae makes it very probable that the RNA produced in the nucleus can pass into the cytoplasm; they do not prove, however, that nuclear RNA is not metabolized, nor that all of the cytoplasmic RNA is of nuclear origin.

Let us now compare the results which have

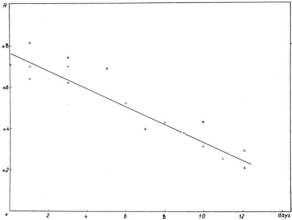

Figure 4: ○: RNA; ▲: phosphatase; +: lipase.

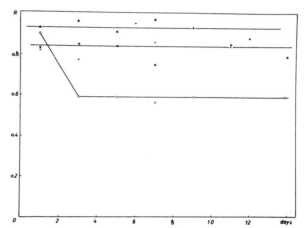

Figure 5: ○: dipeptidase; ▲: protease; +: enolase; ◗: ATPase.

been obtained with *Acetabularia*, *Amoeba* and a few other cells. There is a complete agreement that non-nucleated cytoplasm can still incorporate labelled amino acids into proteins to a considerable extent. This has been proven for *Acetabularia*, *Amoeba*, reticulocytes and for sea urchin (Malkin, 1954) and newt (Tiedemann and Tiedemann, 1954) eggs. *Net* synthesis of proteins also takes place in the absence of the nucleus in *Acetabularia*

TABLE 3. γ RNA PER 200 FRAGMENTS

Days after Sectioning	Nucleated Fragments	Non-Nucleated Fragments	Ratio
0	0.62	0.44	0.71
1	0.63	0.44	0.70
3	0.58	0.36	0.62
6	0.56	0.29	0.52
8	0.54	0.23	0.43
10	0.61	0.19	0.31
12	0.62	0.18	0.29

TABLE 4.

Days after Sectioning	Chloroplasts		Microsomes	
	Nucleated fragments	Non-nucleated fragments	Nucleated fragments	Non-nucleated fragments
28	6.5	2.6	1.7	0.5
34	6.3	3.6	2.3	1.6
41	8.7	4.3	5.1	1.9
48	8.2	3.1	3.6	1.9

and in reticulocytes; in these cases the synthesized proteins are perfectly normal proteins (*e.g.* enzymes), not just substances of proteinaceous nature. The case of *Amoeba* is no exception to these conclusions, since no net protein synthesis can be expected when no food is provided.

There are however striking differences between *Amoeba* and *Acetabularia*. In *Amoeba*, an immediate inhibitory effect on amino acid incorporation is observed after removal of the nucleus, whereas in *Acetabularia* no such effect is noted before two weeks. It has been pointed out (Mazia and Prescott, 1955) that the cytoplasm of *Acetabularia* might be largely independent of the nucleus because the chloroplasts it contains are self-duplicating organelles, and thus share some of the properties of the nucleus. We do not think this is a valid remark for the following reasons: First, the net synthesis of the chloroplastic proteins *does* depend on the nucleus, since it ceases two weeks after enucleation (Table 4); the proteins of the chloroplasts behave in this respect exactly like the non-chloroplastic proteins (Vanderhaeghe, 1954). Besides, we do not know how much of the cytoplasmic proteins of an ordinary animal cell are part of "self-duplicating particles"; in which category shall we place the proteins of mitochondria and microsomes, for instance? Finally, if we are studying the nuclear control of the synthesis of cytoplasmic proteins, it is essentially because we want to know more about the mechanism of the genetic control of metabolism. *Acetabularia* is precisely one of the (not so numerous) cases where it has actually been shown, by the brilliant experiments of Hämmerling, that the genetic determinants of morphogenesis are ultimately contained in the nucleus.

In *Amoeba*, the turnover of the total cytoplasmic proteins is reduced by about 50 per cent immediately after enucleation, and this might indeed mean that certain cytoplasmic proteins undergo turnover within the nucleus. However, it should be kept in mind that another very conspicuous change occurs immediately after the cytoplasm is deprived of the nucleus: Protoplasmic movement is brought to a standstill. The absorption of methionine into the cell is also reduced (Mazia and Prescott, 1955), a fact which suggests that important changes in the properties of the

cell membrane occur as a result of enucleation. The locomotion does not stop because of lack of ATP, since the non-nucleated fragments contain somewhat more ATP than the nucleated ones (Brachet, 1952). Other deep metabolic changes follow enucleation. For instance the cytoplasmic fragments are not able to keep their ATP level in anaerobiosis as well as the nucleated parts do (Brachet, 1954). It looks as if, in *Amoeba*, the nucleus directly controlled the glycolytic system; cytoplasm without a nucleus apparently depends on aerobic metabolism exclusively. Provision of energy is not the only function of the glycolytic system, it is also the source of many metabolites used in various biochemical processes. Under these circumstances one realizes that the immediate drop of protein turnover to about 50 per cent of normal after enucleation does not prove that the nucleus plays a direct part in the turnover of some of the cytoplasmic proteins. The immediate effect might result from the deep metabolic changes which follow enucleation rather than from a direct participation of the nucleus in the synthesis of cytoplasmic proteins.

We shall finally consider the degradation of the proteins in the non-nucleated cytoplasm. As we have pointed out above, the proteins begin to break down when the cytoplasm becomes unable to use its carbohydrate reserves. It is a common phenomenon that starving cells use their proteins when no other food is available. It is also a common observation that they use their different proteins at different rates. Nevertheless the fact that some cytoplasmic particles might be more directly connected with the nucleus and under more strict a control than others should be considered as a good possibility. The further exploration of this matter will require a better knowledge of the distribution of the enzymes in the cytoplasm of the amoebae.

Nearly all the observations concerning the effect of enucleation on protein synthesis are paralleled by very similar results concerning RNA synthesis. This remarkable similarity is certainly in keeping with the now generally accepted idea (Brachet, 1941; Caspersson, 1941) that RNA is one of the essential parts of the protein synthesis mechanism. About all that has been said for the influence of the nucleus on protein synthesis could be repeated for RNA formation. There is evidence that in *Amoeba* part of the cytoplasmic RNA might be synthesized in the nucleus; our experiments with *Acetabularia* show however that the nucleus is not the only center of RNA synthesis and that such a synthesis can occur in isolated cytoplasm.

It remains however that the nucleus is an important center of protein and RNA synthesis. In fact the incorporation of labelled adenine into the RNA of the nucleus is more rapid than that into the cytoplasmic RNA. With starfish oocytes A. Ficq has observed, using an autoradiograph technique, that the incorporation of RNA precursors is 100 times more rapid in the nucleoli than in the same volume of cytoplasm. For the incorporation of phenylalanine, a ratio of ten was observed; the proteins of the nucleoli reached their maximum radioactivity after three hours, whereas cytoplasmic proteins continued to incorporate linearly for several hours thereafter. Even in the nuclear sap, the uptake of adenine and phenylalanine was respectively three and two times greater than in the cytoplasm. Similar results have been obtained for amphibian oocytes. The incorporation of $C^{14}O_2$ into frog or pleurodele embryos, from the two blastomere stage to the neurula, is also greater in the nuclei than in the cytoplasm; the same results were obtained using labelled adenine or phenylalanine, up to the gastrula stage (after this stage these substances are no longer taken up by the embryos).

In mammalian tissues, however, the situation is different. When labelled phenylalanine is injected into a mouse, no preferential incorporation into the nuclei is observed for pancreas, intestine, spleen, kidney, uterus, lung or heart; in the liver, adenine is incorporated six times faster into the nucleus than into the cytoplasm, and a ratio of four is observed for phenylalanine.

Considering all the data available at present, it would seem that RNA as well as protein can be formed concurrently and independently in the nucleus and in the cytoplasm; either part of the cell contains the complete system necessary for their synthesis, but the rate of protein synthesis can be greater in the nucleus or in the cytoplasm, according to the cell type.

We may now go back to the main problem of nuclear control of protein synthesis, and to the question as to how the genetic information is transmitted to the systems making the cytoplasmic proteins. The idea that RNA is the carrier of this information from the nucleus to the cytoplasm is compatible with the results reported above, although they do not lead new support to this hypothesis. But the simple idea that DNA organizes RNA which in turn organizes proteins should be discarded, or at least qualified. The relations are certainly more indirect. There might be a certain similarity between the function of nuclear RNA and that of the RNA of a virus, which causes the host cell to make correct copies of the RNA and of a specific protein.

Other possibilities should also be kept in mind. Proteins synthesized in the nucleus might be the carriers of genetic information; studies on bacteriophage make it probable that, at a certain stage of bacteriophage production, the genetic information is carried by a substance in which phosphorus atoms do not play an important part (Stent, 1955; Burton, 1955).

REFERENCES

ALLFREY, V. G., 1954, Amino acids incorporation by isolated thymus nuclei. I. The role of desoxyribonucleic acid in protein synthesis. Proc. Nat. Acad. Sci. Wash. *40*: 881–885.

ALLFREY, V. G., MIRSKY, A. E., and OSAWA, S., 1955, Protein synthesis in isolated cell nuclei. Nature, Lond. *176*: 1042–1049.

ALLFREY, V. G., MIRSKY, A. E., and STERN, H., 1955, The chemistry of the cell nucleus. Adv. Enzymol. *16*: 411–500.

BALTUS, E., 1954, Observations sur le rôle biochimique du nucléole. Biochim. biophys. Acta *15*: 263–267.

BARNUM, C. P., and HUSEBY, R. A., 1950, The intracellular heterogeneity of pentose nucleic acid as evidenced by the incorporation of radiophosphorus. Arch. Biochem. *29*: 7–26.

BARNUM, C. P., HUSEBY, R. A., and VERMUND, H., 1953, A time study of the incorporation of radiophosphorus into the nucleic acids and other compounds of a transplanted mouse mammary carcinoma. Cancer Res. *13*: 880–889.

BARON, L. S., SPIEGELMAN, S., and QUASTLER, H. J., 1953, Enzyme formation in non-viable cells. J. Gen. Physiol. *36*: 631–641.

BERGSTRAND, A., ELIASSON, N. A., NORBERG, B., REICHARD, P., and UBISCH, H., 1948, Experiments with N^{15} on purines from nuclei and cytoplasm of normal and regenerating liver. Cold Spring Harb. Symp. Quant. Biol. *13*: 22–25.

BRACHET, J., 1941, La localisation des acides pentosenucléiques dans les tissus animaux et les oeufs d'amphibiens en voie de développement. Arch. Biol. *53*: 207–257.

1950, Une étude cytochimique des fragments nucléés et énucléés d'amibes. Experientia *6*: 294–295.

1952, Le rôle des acides nucléiques dans la vie de la cellule et de l'embryon. Paris, Masson.

1952, Le rôle du noyau cellulaire dans les oxydations et les phosphorylations. Biochim. biophys. Acta *9*: 221–222.

1954, Nuclear control of enzymatic activities. Colston Papers *7*: 91–102.

1954, Influence of the nucleus on anaerobic breakdown of adenosinetriphosphate. Nature, Lond. *173*: 725.

1954, The biological role of pentose nucleic acids. In: The Nucleic Acids, Davidson and Chargaff, ed. New York, Acad. Press.

1955, Recherches sur les interactions biochimiques entre le noyau et le cytoplasme chez les organismes unicellulaires. I. *Amoeba proteus*. Biochim. biophys. Acta *18*: 247–268.

BRACHET, J., and CHANTRENNE, H., 1951, Protein synthesis in nucleated and non-nucleated halves of *Acetabularia* studied with carbon-14 dioxide. Nature, Lond. *168*: 950.

1952, Incorporation de $C^{14}O_2$ dans les protéines des chloroplastes et des microsomes de fragments nucléés et anucléés d'*Acetabularia mediterranea*. Arch. intern Physiol. *60*: 547–549.

BRACHET, J., CHANTRENNE, H., and VANDERHAEGHE, F., 1955, Recherches sur les interactions biochimiques entre le noyau et le cytoplasme chez les organismes unicellulaires. II. *Acetabularia mediterranea*. Biochim. biophys. Acta *18*: 544–563.

BURTON, K., 1955, Protein and nucleic acid synthesis in bacteriophage multiplication. Commun. 8–12 to the 3rd intern. Congress Biochem. Brussels.

CASPERSSON, T., 1941, Studien über den Eiweiszumsatz der Zelle. Naturwissenschaften *29*: 33–43.

CHANTRENNE, H., BRACHET, J., and BRYGIER, J., 1953, Quelques données nouvelles sur le rôle du noyau cellulaire dans le métabolisme des protéines chez *Acetabularia mediterranea*. Arch. intern. Physiol. *61*: 419–420.

COHEN, S. S., and BARNER, H., 1955, Enzymatic adaptation in a thymine requiring strain. J. Bacteriol. *69*: 59–66.

CROSBIE, G. W., SMELLIE, R. M. S., and DAVIDSON, J. N., 1953, Phosphorus compounds in the cell. 5. The composition of the cytoplasmic and ribonucleic acids of the liver cells. Biochem. J. *54:* 287–292.

ELSON, D., TRENT, L. W., and CHARGAFF, E., 1955, The nucleotide composition of pentose nucleic acids in different cellular fractions. Biochim. biophys. Acta *17:* 362–366.

FICQ, A., 1955, Etude autoradiographique du métabolisme de l'oocyte d'*Asterias rubens* au cours de la croissance. Arch. Biol. *66:* 509–524.

    1955, Incorporation de phénylalanine-2-14C dans les fragments nucléés et anucléés d'amibes. Arch. intern. Physiol. *64:* 129–130.

FRAENKEL-CONRAT, H., 1956, The role of the nucleic acid in the reconstitution of active tobacco mosaic virus. J. amer. Chem. Soc. *78:* 882–883.

GALE, E. F., 1956, Incorporation of amino acids by disrupted staphylococci. Proc. 3rd Intern. Congress Biochem. Brussels: 345–349.

GALE, E. F., and FOLKES, J. P., 1955, Promotion of incorporation of amino acids by specific di- and trinucleotides. Nature, Lond. *175:* 592–593.

GAY, H., 1955, Nucleo-cytoplasmic relations in salivary gland cells of *Drosophila*. Proc. nat. Acad. Sci. Wash. *41:* 370–375.

GIERER, A., and SCHRAMM, G., 1956, Die Infektionität der Nukleinsäure aus Tabakmosaikvirus. Z. Naturforsch. *11b:* 138–142.

GOLDSTEIN, L., and PLAUT, W., 1955, Direct evidence of nuclear synthesis of cytoplasmic ribonucleic acid. Proc. nat. Acad. Sci. Wash. *41:* 874–880.

GROS-DOULCET, F., GROS, F., and SPIEGELMAN, S., 1955, Enzyme synthesis and DNA metabolism. Proc. 3rd intern. Congress Biochem., Brussels.

HÄMMERLING, J., 1934, Über Formbildende Substanzen bei *Acetabularia mediterranea*, ihre Räumliche und Zeitliche Verteilung und ihre Herkunft. Roux Archiv ges. Physiol. *131:* 1–31.

    1953, Nucleocytoplasmic relationships in the development of *Acetabularia*. Intern. Rev. Cytology *2:* 475–498.

HÄMMERLING, J., and STICH, H., 1956, Einbau und Ausbau von ^{32}P im Nukleolus, nebst Bemerkungen über intra und extranukleare Proteinsyntheses. Z. Naturforsch. *11b:* 158–161.

HOGEBOOM, G. H., and SCHNEIDER, W. G., 1952, Cytochemical studies. VI. The synthesis of diphosphopyridine nucleotide by liver cell nuclei. J. biol. Chem. *197:* 611–620.

HURLBERT, R. B., and POTTER, V. R., 1952, A survey of the metabolism of orotic acid in the rat. J. biol. Chem. *195:* 257–270.

JAMES, T. W., 1954, The role of the nucleus in the maintenance of pentosenucleic acid in amoeba. Biochim. biophys. Acta *15:* 367–371.

JEENER, H., and JEENER, R., 1952, Cytological study of *Thermobacterium acidophilus* R 26 cultured in absence of deoxyribonucleotides or uracil. Exp. Cell Res. *4:* 675–680.

JEENER, R., 1956, Le rôle de l'acide ribonucléique dans la multiplication des virus. Proc. 3rd intern. Congress Biochem., Brussels: 343–344.

    1956, RNA and Virus Multiplication. Adv. Enzymol. *17* (in press).

JEENER, R., and SZAFARZ, D., 1950, Relations between the rate of renewal and the intracellular localization of ribonucleic acid. Arch. Biochem. *26:* 54–67.

KELLER, E. B., ZAMECNIK, P. C., and LOFTFIELD, R. B., 1954, The role of microsomes in the incorporation of amino acids into proteins. J. Histochem. Cytochem. *2:* 378–386.

KORITZ, S. B., and CHANTRENNE, H., 1954, The relationship of ribonucleic acid to the *in vitro* incorporation of radioactive glycine into the proteins of reticulocytes. Biochim. biophys. Acta *13:* 209–215.

MALKIN, H. M., 1954, Synthesis of RNA purines and proteins in enucleated and nucleated sea urchin eggs. J. Cell. Comp. Physiol. *44:* 105–112.

MARSHAK, A., 1948, Evidence for a nuclear precursor of ribo- and desoxyribonucleic acid. J. Cell. Comp. Physiol. *32:* 381–406.

MARSHAK, A., and CALVET, F., 1949, Specific activity of P32 in cell constituents. J. Cell. Comp. Physiol. *34:* 451–455.

MAZIA, D., and PRESCOTT, D. M., 1955, The role of the nucleus in protein synthesis in *Amoeba*. Biochim. Biophys. Acta *17:* 23–34.

MIRSKY, A. E., 1956, Some biochemical aspects of the cell nucleus. Proc. 3rd Intern. Congress Biochem., Brussels: 349–353.

NIZET, A., and LAMBERT, S., 1953, Synthèse de l'hémoglobine *in vitro* à partir de DL-3-phénylalanine-2-C14 et de glycine-2-C14. Rôle des formes isomériques de la phénylalanine. Bull. Soc. Chim. Biol. *35:* 771–780.

PAYNE, A. H., KELLY, L. S., BEACH, G., and JONES, H. B., 1952, Effect of neoplasia on turnover of nucleic acids studied with formiate-C14 and glycine-2-C14. Cancer Res. *12:* 426–428.

SIEKEVITZ, P., 1952, Uptake of radioactive alanine *in vitro* into the proteins of rat liver fractions. J. Biol. Chem. *195:* 549–565.

SMELLIE, R. M. S., McINDOE, W. M., and DAVIDSON, J. N., 1953, The incorporation of N15, S35 and C14 into nucleic acids and proteins of rat liver. Biochim. biophys. Acta *11:* 559–565.

STENT, G., 1955, Decay of incorporated P32 during reproduction of bacteriophage T2. J Gen. Physiol. *38:* 853–865.

STERN, H., ALLFREY, V. G., MIRSKY, A. E., and SAETREN, H., 1952, Some enzymes of isolated nuclei. J. Gen. Physiol. *35:* 559–578.

TIEDEMANN, H., and TIEDEMANN, H., 1954, Einbau von CO_2 in gefurchte und ungefurchte Eihälften und in verschiedene Entwicklungsstadien von Triton. Naturwissenschaften *41:* 535.

VANDERHAEGHE, F., 1954, Les effets de l'énucléation sur la synthèse des protéines chez *Acetabularia mediterranea*. Biochim. Biophys. Acta *15:* 281–287.

VANDERHAEGE, F., and SZAFARZ, D., 1955, Enucléation et synthèse d'acide ribonucléique chez *Acetabularia mediterranea*. Arch. intern. Physiol. *63:* 267–268.

DISCUSSION

PLAINE: One objection which might be raised with respect to Dr. Chantrenne's *Amoeba* experiments is his consideration of the sameness of the nucleated and non-nucleated halves of cytoplasm. It is quite likely that these two cytoplasms are not identical as regards specific localizations or chemical gradients. In addition, the juxtanuclear cytoplasm is probably quite different from the remainder, if *this* indeed is more or less homogeneous. It would appear, therefore, that there are two variables in these experiments: First, a nucleus in contrast to no nucleus; and second, juxtanuclear cytoplasm in contrast to other cytoplasm; and even other cytoplasmic differences may exist. There seems to be a way of surmounting this problem. If, instead of cutting *Amoeba* in half, a sister *Amoeba* were used, then one could be enucleated and the other could serve as a control. While some cytoplasmic disturbance may result from the enucleation process, this would not be as serious as cutting the cytoplasm in half. I would believe, or at least hope, that the final results would not be different from those reported by Dr. Chantrenne, although there may be a time difference. Only a few such experiments need be done to substantiate Dr. Chantrenne's results, unless of course the results are quite different. As a final point, I wonder what the effect would be of transplanting a nucleus into an enucleated cell after protein synthesis had stopped; would synthesis begin again, and, if so, how much of a time lag would occur? If protein synthesis does occur, what would be the effect of putting a nuclease into such a cell and then removing it again before synthesis had actually started?

CHANTRENNE: It is true that in many types of cells the cytoplasm close to the nucleus differs from that in the outer regions of the cell. In *Amoeba*, however, the cytoplasm looks very uniform; in sections, no differences can be observed between the juxtanuclear cytoplasm and the rest of the cytoplasm; RNA distribution, for instance, as measured by ultraviolet absorption or as observed after staining with pyronine, is quite uniform throughout the cytoplasm. I do not think that enucleation or nuclear transplantation would completely escape the criticism raised by Dr. Plaine, for I doubt that the nucleus could be removed or transferred without removing or transferring some surrounding cytoplasm at the same time.

I agree however that such experiments would be worth trying and I am sure that interesting observations could be made on the operated cells by means of cytochemical and autoradiograph techniques.

The Ontogeny of Divergent Metabolic Patterns in Cells of Identical Genotype[1]

Clement L. Markert

University of Michigan, Ann Arbor, Michigan

The evidence for genetic changes in microorganisms is generally expressed in the properties or behavior of the entire organism. In metazoans, on the other hand, the effects of gene changes are commonly observed in only a restricted number of their cell types; the vast majority of their cells provide no obvious evidence that their cellular genotype is in any way different from that present in cells of alternative genotypes. Yet our understanding of mitosis leads directly to the conclusion that the somatic cells of a metazoan are endowed initially at cell division with the same basic chromosomal equipment—with identical arrays of genes. How then are we to account for the fact that during embryogeny metazoans develop numerous distinctive cell types with persistent characteristics that are transmitted from one generation of cells to the next? The answer to this question obviously concerns the functioning of the genetic mechanism of cells as well as the mechanisms of cellular differentiation. In the solution of these problems of cell differentiation the disciplines of genetics and embryology inevitably meet and lose their individual identities.

It should be noted that many types of differentiated or semi-differentiated cells will undergo extensive multiplication without losing their distinctive properties and, as King and Briggs (1956) have clearly pointed out, the same is true for the nuclei of embryonic amphibian cells. Thus differentiated characteristics are passed from one generation of cells to the next—that is, the characteristics are inherited. Even though this type of inheritance may not directly concern the genes, some type of genetic mechanism must, by definition, be involved. The genetic mechanism responsible for this type of cell inheritance has been found to lie both in the nucleus and in the cytoplasm of various types of cells. The work of Briggs and King (1952) and of King and Briggs (1955, 1956) with transplanted amphibian nuclei clearly implicates the nucleus in the hereditary transmission of differentiated cell characters. Likewise Sonneborn (see reviews 1947, 1953) has fixed responsibility on the nuclei of the protozoan *Paramecium* for transmitting differentiated mating type characteristics, and Nanney (1956a, 1956b) has shown that the nucleus of the protozoan *Tetrahymena* is also involved in the transmission of mating type characteristics arising during the differentiation of this protozoan. However, the nucleus of *Paramecium* holds no monopoly of the genetic mechanisms. The cytoplasm has been shown to maintain and pass on certain specificities arising during the life of this ciliate (Sonneborn, 1950; Beale, 1954).

The work of Beerman (1956) and of Pavan and Breuer (1955) and Breuer and Pavan (1955) on the correlation between the changing morphology of specific chromosomal bands and the state of differentiation of the tissues of certain larval insects supports the conclusion that the nucleus and its chromosomes are importantly involved in the development and activity of differentiated cell characters and possibly also in their hereditary transmission during larval development.

Differentiated cell characters may be classified as morphological, physiological, or as developmental capacities, but basically all of these characteristics stem from and depend upon successive patterns of metabolic activity in the cell. Thus the problem of cell differentiation involves primarily a study of the acquisition and transmission of characteristic patterns of metabolic activity by differentiating cells. At the outset we may identify two aspects of this problem. First, the gene complement of a cell obviously places limits on the metabolic capacity of the cell. Mammalian cells carrying the two recessive genes for albinism cannot synthesize melanin, nor can any of the cells of a chicken synthesize valine or other essential amino acids, nor apparently can human cells carrying the genes for phenylketonuria make tyrosine from phenylalanine. Second, from among the numerous and diverse metabolic potentialities of cells only certain ones are brought to full realization. Those metabolic systems that do develop are prompted to do so by the tissue environment in which the cell develops. Thus cell differentiation is a function of intrinsic gene makeup in interaction with a changing cellular environment. Since differentiating cells by virtue of their metabolic activity contribute to their own environment, a dynamic imbalance is created between the cell and its environment that pushes the cell along its historical path of differentiation. Like other complex historical phenomena, cell differentiation appears to be essentially irreversible, although this conclusion is disputed by some investigators. Until recently the very complexity of the problem plus inadequacies of technique prevented any satisfactory assessment of the changing metabolic

[1] Supported by a grant from the Michigan Memorial Phoenix Project No. 56.

patterns of differentiating cells. Now, however, advances in the techniques of tissue culture, chromatography, and autoradiography, and the general availability of C^{14} labeled compounds make it possible to glimpse at least a part of the metabolic activity of cells at successive stages in their differentiation and thus to make a start at describing differentiation in biochemical terms (Markert, 1955). Furthermore, it is possible to identify the pattern of chemical contributions that the cell makes to its environment and thus to the differentiating influences that act upon itself as well as upon other cells.

Materials and Methods

The central problem of this investigation has been to measure as comprehensively as possible the kinds and relative amounts of substances produced by cells at successive stages in their development. From an examination of these cell products valid inferences may be drawn concerning both the changing metabolic machinery of the cell and the changing chemical environment of the cell.

In the simplest type of measurement, groups of cells were dissected from developing chick embryos and cultivated *in vitro* in the presence of glucose uniformly labeled with C^{14}. After a period of time sufficient to permit the synthesis of adequate quantities of substances from the glucose, the cells were separated from the culture medium and mechanically (repeated freezing and thawing) or chemically (HCl or trypsin hydrolysis) fractionated. The cell constituents were then separated chromatographically on paper and an autoradiogram made of the chromatogram. The culture medium was likewise chromatographed and an autoradiogram prepared. The substances separated on such chromatograms may be identified by a variety of techniques including colorimetric, spectrophotometric, or chromatographic measurements. By reference to the autoradiograms those substances made from the radioactive glucose may be identified and the relative amount of each radioactive substance calculated from measurements of its radioactivity. Thus a pattern of synthetic activity may be identified and this pattern compared with that found in other types of cells. In analyzing the pattern of metabolic activity for any cell type, it is necessary to consider the radioactive metabolites found both within the cells and in the surrounding medium. The simple metabolites retained within cells are indicative of cell composition but provide only a partial picture of cellular activity. Most of some kinds of metabolites are released into the surrounding medium.

It is important to note that a number of practical problems have been encountered in this investigation and the fact that they have not been entirely solved places restrictions on any interpretations of the data.

First, it has been assumed that the metabolic behavior of an isolated group of cells in tissue culture will be substantially like that of the cells at the time of removal from the embryo. This assumption can be only approximately true. How greatly the metabolic activity of cells in tissue culture diverges from that in the embryo is not known. The opportunity for change in culture may be reduced by restricting the duration of culture to the minimum consistent with adequate synthesis. Furthermore, changes occurring during culture may be recognized through measurements made at successive intervals on replicate cultures. Of course, such measurements cannot reveal metabolic changes induced in the cells as an immediate consequence of transplanting the cells from the embryo to a culture medium.

Second, it must be realized that the explanted tissues are commonly composed of more than one kind of cell. Therefore the metabolic patterns observed represent the joint activity of diverse cell types. Frequently, however, by means of careful dissection and trypsin digestion it is possible to obtain tissues that are predominantly, and possibly exclusively, of one cell type. Any minority cell components of such tissues probably make negligible contributions to the total metabolic pattern and thus they can be disregarded at least in so far as their direct contributions are concerned.

Third, the specific conditions existing in the tissue culture may significantly affect the metabolic activity of the tissue. Possibly important are such factors as the chemical composition of the culture medium, the ratio of tissue mass to the volume of culture medium, the physical properties of the medium (solid or liquid), the physical arrangement and mass of the tissue in the culture—whether disposed as a thin sheet of cells or as a rounded mass; all these and other unrecognized culture conditions may significantly affect the metabolic activity of cells. The effects of these variables restrict valid comparisons between different types of cells to those cultured under identical conditions. The effects of different conditions of culture on metabolic activity can, of course, be examined directly by culturing identical tissue explants under a variety of conditions and noting any differences in their metabolic behavior.

Fourth, measurements of metabolites within cells or in culture media can reveal only partial pictures of metabolic activity. In these cultures the quantity of a metabolite present at any given time is the resultant of the two opposed processes of synthesis and degradation (or conversion to other products). Either increased synthesis or decreased conversion of a metabolite would increase the measured yield. Likewise, the apparent absence of a metabolite may be due to an increased rate of conversion to another product rather than to a decreased synthesis of the metabolite. Obviously the relative importance of these degradative and synthetic processes varies greatly in determin-

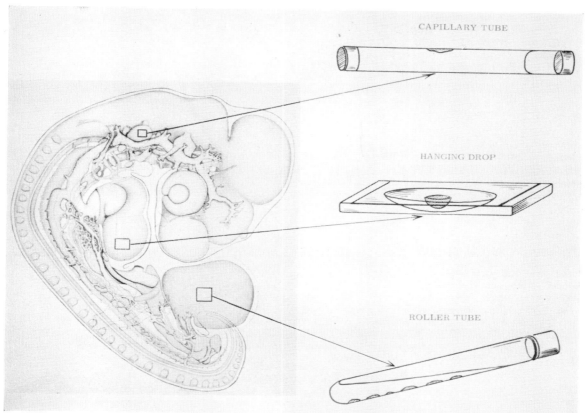

FIGURE 1. This figure illustrates the three types of tissue cultures used. Roller tubes were used for the largest masses of tissue, hanging drop cultures for smaller explants, and capillary tubes for the smallest tissue fragments. (The drawing of the chick embryo was taken from *The Embryology of the Chick* by B. M. Patten, published by Blakiston Division, McGraw Hill Book Co.)

ing the measured quantities of different metabolites. For simplicity of presentation in this report the term "synthesis" is used loosely in the sense of "net synthesis" and is recognized and measured by the products of a synthetic reaction that are present at any given time.

In the experiments reported here the explanted tissues were cultured in roller tubes in a chemically defined complex medium (Eagle, 1955) or in a conventional hanging drop preparation in which the medium was embryo extract and chick plasma (Fig. 1). The roller tubes contained about one million cells attached in clumps directly to the glass. In the typical hanging drop preparation a clump of several thousand cells was embedded in the clot next to a glass coverslip which was sealed to a depression slide. When very small pieces of tissue (the smallest containing about 100 cells) were to be cultured the tissue was first drawn into a capillary tube which was then embedded in a hanging drop of plasma and embryo extract. The capillary tube effectively reduced the immediately available volume of medium and considerably enhanced the viability of the tissue.

Radioactive glucose was added to all these cultures in amounts ranging from five to ten microcuries. The total glucose concentration was about one mg/ml of medium. The explants were typically maintained in culture for seven days at which time the cells from roller tubes or the cells plus the medium from hanging drop preparations were hydrolyzed in 6 N HCl under 15 lbs pressure at 120°C for 6 hours or, alternatively, frozen and then digested in 3 per cent trypsin (Difco 1:250) for 12 to 18 hours at 37°C. These hydrolysates were then chromatographed and an autoradiogram taken of the chromatogram (Fig. 2). The medium from the roller tube cultures was desalted before being chromatographed. In the chromatographs discussed in this report the irrigating solvents were phenol and 2,6-lutidine (*cf.* Block *et al.*, 1955, for procedures). Thus, amino acids were the principal substances resolved by this procedure. Autoradiography using no-screen X-ray film generally required about 10 days for adequate exposure.

RESULTS

Since cellular differentiation involves a progressive specialization of diverging cell lines, one might reasonably expect to find that the most highly differentiated cell types would be most sharply distinguished from one another by distinctive patterns of metabolic activity. Accordingly, a variety of tissues from a 12-day chick embryo were explanted to roller tubes in one ml of chemically defined medium (Eagle, 1955) containing ten microcuries of glucose uniformly labeled with C^{14}. After seven days' growth the skin, liver, spleen, kidney, heart and the pigmented layer of the retina were analyzed for their synthetic abilities under these culture conditions. An examination of the autoradiograms (examples shown in Fig. 3) made of the products of glucose metabolism that were retained within the cells revealed some differences and many similarities among these tissues. All of these tissues synthesized at least six non-essential (in terms of nutrition) amino acids—aspartate, glutamate, cysteine, serine, alanine, and proline—from glucose. However, they did not retain these amino acids in the same relative amounts.

These differences in amino acid incorporation do not adequately elucidate the metabolic differences among these tissues. It is necessary to analyze the culture media in order to reveal the striking metabolic differences which distinguish these tissues. Autoradiograms of the chromatographed media from liver, heart, kidney, and skin are reproduced in Figure 4. It is evident that heart tissue, for example, synthesizes more

alanine and proline than it does other amino acids. The liver synthesizes relatively less proline, but produces augmented amounts of glutamate, serine, and cysteine as contrasted with heart tissue. The skin synthesizes very little alanine or proline, but does produce relatively large amounts of glutamate and serine. The kidney synthesizes relatively large amounts of all six of these amino acids (the abundance of amino acids on this chromatogram prevented adequate resolution). Measurements of the radioactivity in the chromatographically separated constituents of the medium confirm the conclusions reached from an examination of the autoradiograms.

It is apparent that the pattern of synthetic activity even for these simple substances is characteristically different for each tissue. Perhaps more significant for cell differentiation are the qualitative gains or losses in synthetic activity. If we examine the radioactive constituents of the cells of the spleen and pigmented retina (Fig. 3) distinctly new substances, so far found in no other tissue, can be located to the left of alanine in the autoradiogram of splenic constituents and to the right-center in the autoradiogram of pigmented retina constituents. Both of these spots represent apparently new syntheses arising during ontogeny. Unfortunately neither substance has

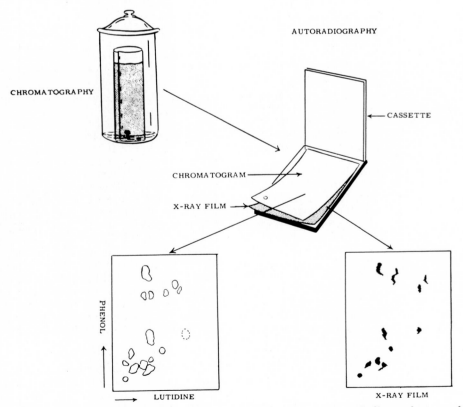

FIGURE 2. Procedure used in analyzing the tissue or the culture medium for metabolic products made from C^{14} labeled glucose. See text for details.

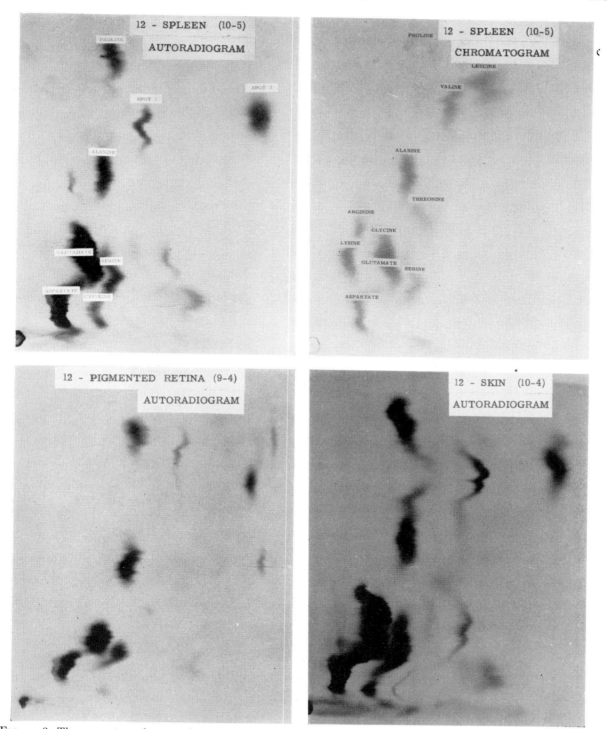

FIGURE 3. The upper two photographs show an autoradiogram on the left taken of the chromatogram on the right. The two lower photographs show autoradiograms of the metabolic products of glucose metabolism found in the pigmented retina and in the skin. Note particularly the distinctive radioactive product of splenic metabolism located to the left of alanine and also the unique product (possibly tyrosine) made by the retina and located to the right-center of the retina autoradiogram. All tissues were from a 12-day embryo.

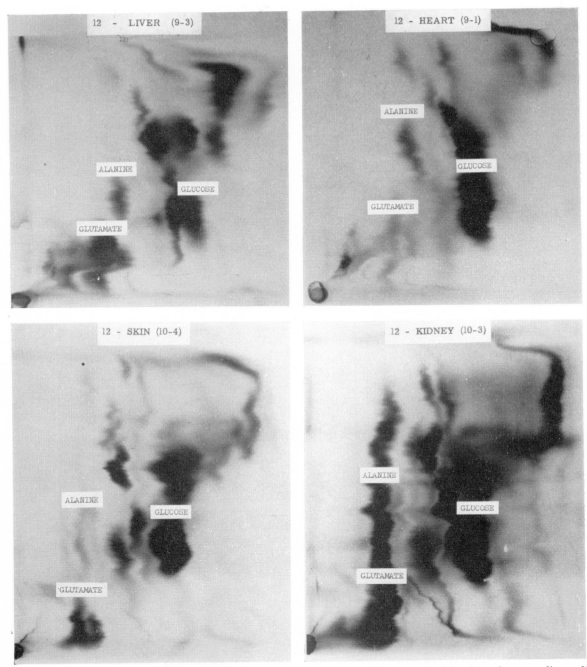

FIGURE 4. Autoradiograms of the chromatographically separated constituents found in the culture medium after growth of the indicated tissues taken from a 12-day chick embryo. The tissues were allowed to metabolize for one week in the presence of radioglucose. The spots representing glucose, alanine, and glutamate have been labeled to facilitate comparison of the autoradiograms. See text for discussion.

been definitely identified, but the radioactive substance from the pigmented retina may be tyrosine as judged by chromatographic behavior. Although the chick requires tyrosine (or phenyl-alanine) as part of its diet, it may be that the pigmented retina can nevertheless synthesize some tyrosine in connection with the synthesis of melanin. Possibly only the side chain of the tyrosine molecule contains radioactive carbon; if so, an exchange reaction would account for the observed radioactivity without involving a complete synthesis of the tyrosine molecule.

These autoradiograms show that differentiated tissues may be characterized by their patterns of metabolic activity. These patterns exhibit distinguishing variations in relative synthetic activity for common metabolic products, and in a few examples qualitatively new synthetic activities may be discerned. An additional type of metabolic change involves the loss of a previously possessed activity. This type of change was first noted in studies of heart tissue. When heart ventricle tissue from a 12-day chick is explanted to a roller tube culture in such a fashion that the tissue floats freely in the medium, then growth is suppressed although the tissue continues to contract and to metabolize glucose. Such heart tissue does not synthesize appreciable quantities of serine although other amino acids are synthesized in more nearly usual quantities. However, if the ventricular tissue is affixed to the glass and growth of tissue (largely fibroblasts) out over the glass surface occurs, then serine is synthesized. Moreover, the mesodermal anlage of the heart taken from a 24-hour chick likewise synthesizes serine as do heart fibroblasts from a 12-day chick growing in the absence of muscle tissue. A plausible interpretation of these observations is that cells destined to become cardiac muscle abandon the synthesis of serine during the course of their differentiation and come to rely upon other cells such as heart fibroblasts for the supply of this amino acid. Whether or not this loss is irrevocable has not yet been determined.

The chemically-defined culture medium (Eagle, 1955) contains many organic compounds including essential amino acids. The presence of these substances might specifically affect the metabolic activity of cultured cells. To test this possibility liver tissue from a 12-day chick was explanted to three roller tube cultures. The first contained Eagle's synthetic medium; the second contained only balanced salt solution (Earle, 1943); and the third contained a plasma-embryo extract clot. Subsequent analysis of the cells from these three tubes showed them to contain the same radioactive compounds in essentially the same relative proportions. Thus the metabolic activity of these cells remains unchanged, at least for a short time, in culture media of vastly different compositions. That a similar indifference to the medium would be exhibited by all types of cells is very doubtful. It is worth noting that microorganisms, in contrast to these tissue cultures, are usually very responsive to variations in the composition of the culture media (cf. Roberts et al., 1955). The fact that many types of chick cells are relatively unresponsive to gross changes in the culture medium should not obscure the fact that the fine chemical structure of the cell environment within tissue explants is of primary importance in directing metabolic changes inside the constituent cells. This fact is evident when a comparison is made between the metabolic patterns of intact tissue fragments and those of trypsin-dissociated cells from the same tissue plated out in roller tubes.

The *process* of biochemical differentiation can be studied by ascertaining the pattern of syntheses in embryonic cells at successive stages in their development. Such studies were made on a variety of tissues explanted to hanging drop preparations. After a period of metabolic activity the entire culture (medium plus cells) was digested with trypsin, chromatographed, and autoradiographed. Such autoradiograms revealed the presence of radioactive compounds not seen on the previously discussed autoradiograms because trypsin digestion leaves intact many compounds which are destroyed by HCl hydrolysis. These autoradiograms clearly show changing metabolic patterns during cell differentiation. Figure 5 illustrates the changes that occurred in corresponding areas of the ectoderm as the chick developed from the 16-somite to the 28-somite stage. Equivalent spots are indicated by identical letters; most of the substances revealed on these autoradiograms have not yet been identified chemically. Perhaps the most conspicuous change occurring in the ectoderm during the approximately twelve hours of development from the 16 to the 28-somite stage is the reduction in the synthesis of substance D. Changes in the relative synthesis of substances A, B, and C (as well as other substances) are also evident. Although the quality of the autoradiogram makes interpretation uncertain; it appears that substance A is not synthesized in the 16-somite ectoderm, but is synthesized, albeit in relatively small amounts, by the 28-somite ectoderm. The synthesis of substance D is generally characteristic of a wide variety of tissues in the early chick embryo, but with increasing development this synthetic activity is lost. This is particularly evident in the sequence of autoradiograms shown in Figure 6. The optic cup from a 28-somite chick still synthesizes substance D although in smaller amounts than the precursor ectodermal tissue. By five days of development the retina synthesizes only small amounts of substance D, and at 16 days of development no trace of this synthetic activity is left in the cells of the retina. As the retina develops from the optic cup there is also a conspicuous shift in the relative synthesis of substances A, B, and C. Figure 7 illustrates the patterns of metabolism found in the optic lobe of the brain in 8-day and 16-day chick embryos. It is obvious that the pattern of synthesis for substances A, B, and C changes greatly. In fact, the synthesis of substance A appears to have stopped entirely in the older optic lobe while the synthesis of substance C has been greatly enhanced.

DISCUSSION

From these data it is apparent that conspicuous differences in metabolic activity exist among the differentiating tissues of the chick embryo. Al-

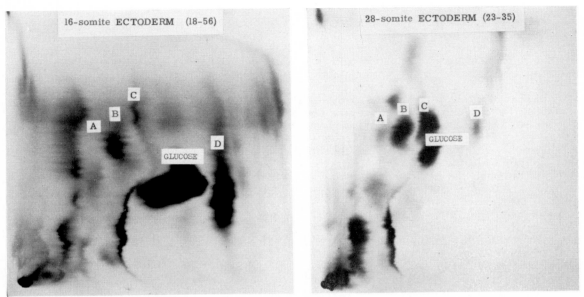

FIGURE 5. Autoradiograms showing the products made from radioglucose by corresponding areas of the ectoderm in 16-somite and in 28-somite chick embryos. Note the shift in the pattern of synthetic activity with increasing age.

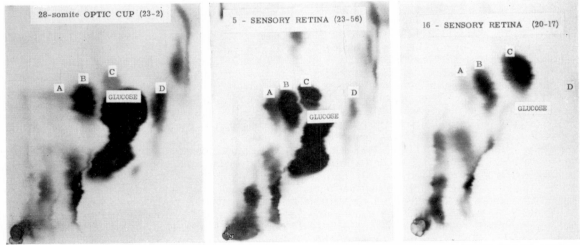

FIGURE 6. Autoradiograms showing the gradual changes in the pattern of metabolic activity as the cells of the eye cup develop into the sensory retina of the 5-day and of the 16-day chick embryo. The glucose in the culture of the 16-day sensory retina was completely metabolized. See text for discussion.

though these tissues were not always pure cell types, many having admixtures of some connective tissue, nevertheless the net effect of their metabolic activity was to produce distinctive and characteristic relative quantities of several simple compounds. When pure cell types are studied the differences among them should be even more marked.

It is of course to be expected that the differentiation of cells should be reflected in their biochemistry as well as in their morphology That biochemical differentiation should involve changes in the synthesis of such simple substances as amino

acids should not obscure the fact that even more important differences among cells are to be found in the synthesis of complex molecules such as enzymes. The synthesis of these complex molecules can also doubtless be studied by a combination of isotopic labeling and a modification of the procedures found useful in this study of smaller molecules.

However, it is unlikely that analysis of cells themselves can tell us much about the mechanisms of differentiation. The differentiating mechanisms are surely to be found in the relationship of cells to their environment. And since cell metabolism

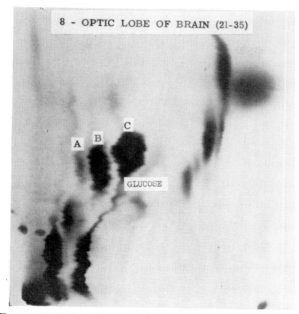
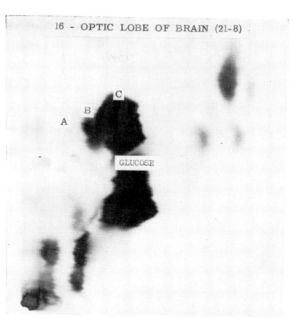

FIGURE 7. Autoradiograms showing the products of radioglucose metabolism in the optic lobe of the brain from 8-day and from 16-day chick embryos. Note the loss in the synthesis of substance A.

is the principal source of the constituents of the cellular environment attention may profitably be focused on the changing metabolic contributions that cells make to their environment. Cells probably alter their synthetic activities in response to environmental stimuli through a wide variety of mechanisms localized in various parts of the cell including the chromosomes. Although the chromosomes are primarily involved in the storage and transmission of information from one generation of cells to the next, these same chromosomes must be dependent upon instructions from the environment in order to make use of this information in cell differentiation.

CONCLUSIONS

1. The synthetic activities of cells in culture are relatively independent of the gross chemical composition of the medium but are more dependent upon the arrangement of the cells into organized tissues.

2. Although the cellular constituents made from C^{14} labeled glucose are similar in distinctly different tissues the proportions of these substances released into the medium are greatly different for different kinds of cells.

3. Unique, specific synthetic activities characterize certain tissues such as the pigmented layer of the retina at relatively advanced stages of development.

4. The acquisition of distinctive metabolic patterns by cells during the course of differentiation involves three types of change:
   a. qualitative losses in synthetic activity;
   b. qualitative gains in synthetic activity;
   c. shifts in relative synthetic activity.

ACKNOWLEDGEMENTS

The author is grateful for the skillful assistance of Laura J. Losin throughout the course of this investigation. Valuable assistance was also rendered by Dale H. Johnson and Frances F. Wooledge.

REFERENCES

BEALE, G. H., 1954, The genetics of *Paramecium aurelia*. Cambridge, Cambridge Univ. Press.

BEERMAN, W., 1956, Nuclear differentiation and functional morphology of chromosomes. Cold Spr. Harb. Symp. Quant. Biol. *21:* 217–232.

BLOCK, R. J., DURRUM, E. L., and ZWEIG, G., 1955, A manual of paper chromatography and paper electrophoresis. New York, Academic Press Inc.

BREUER, M. E., and PAVAN, C., 1955, Behavior of polytene chromosomes of *Rhynchosciara angelae* at different stages of larval development. Chromosoma *7:* 371–386.

BRIGGS, R., and KING, T. J., 1952, Transplantation of living nuclei from blastula cells into enucleated frogs' eggs. Proc. Nat. Acad. Sci. Wash. *38:* 455–463.

EAGLE, H., 1955, Nutrition needs of mammalian cells in tissue culture. Science *122:* 501–504.

EARLE, W. R., 1943, Production of malignancy *in vitro*. IV. The mouse fibroblast cultures and changes seen in the living cells. J. Nat. Cancer Inst. *4:* 165–212.

KING, T. J., and BRIGGS, R., 1955, Changes in the nuclei of differentiating gastrula cells as demonstrated by nuclear transplantation. Proc. Nat. Acad. Sci. Wash. *41:* 321–325.

1956, Serial transplantation of embryonic nuclei. Cold Spr. Harb. Symp. Quant. Biol. *21:* 271–290.

MARKERT, C. L., 1955, Substrate utilization in cell differentiation. Ann. N. Y. Acad. Sci. *60:* 1003–1014.

NANNEY, D. L., 1956, Caryonidal inheritance and nuclear differentiation. Amer. Nat. 90: 291–307.

1956, The role of the cytoplasm in heredity. McCollum-Pratt Symposium on The Chemical Basis of Heredity, ed. by W. D. McElroy and H. B. Glass 90: 291–307.

PAVAN, C., and BREUER, M. E., 1955, Differences in

nucleic acids content of the loci in polytene chromosomes of *Rhynchosciara angelae* according to tissues and larval stages. Symp. Cell Secretion (1955): 90–99.

ROBERTS, R. B., ABELSON, P. H., COWIE, D. B., BOLTON, E. T., and BRITTEN, R. J., 1955, Studies of Biosynthesis in *Escherichia coli*. Carnegie Inst. of Wash. Publ. 607.

SONNEBORN, T. M., 1947, Recent advances in the genetics of *Paramecium* and *Euplotes*. Adv. Genetics *1*: 263–358.

1950, The cytoplasm in heredity. Heredity *4:* 11–36.

1953, Patterns of nucleocytoplasmic integration in *Paramecium*. Proc. 9th Intern. Congress Genetics. Caryologia, suppl. 1954: 307–325.

DISCUSSION

RUDKIN: I would like to ask Dr. Markert whether or not he found evidence that the disappearance and appearance of a compound in a tissue was accompanied by appearance and disappearance of the same compound in the medium. It seems to me that both analyses are pertinent to the determination of the loss or gain of a synthetic capability during development.

MARKERT: So far no obvious correlation has been discerned between the quantity of a metabolite retained within the cells and the quantity released into the medium. However, several tissues at early embryonic stages of development retained certain synthesized substances almost entirely within the cells; at later stages of development some of these substances were also released in relatively large amounts into the medium. This release of metabolites into the medium presumably reflects an enhanced synthesis and possibly an increased permeability of the substances. Although all the radioactive metabolites found in the medium were synthesized by the cells of the culture, it is interesting to note that in several instances the quantity of the metabolite retained within the cells was too small to be detected by the analytical methods used.

ENGLESBERG: Would it be possible to use this system to investigate the breaks in the essential amino acid requirements of the developing tissue? If the entire pathway in the synthesis of a particular amino acid has not been lost as is the case with regard to the natural amino acid requirements of *Pasteurella pestis*, as we have shown, it might be possible to identify the breaks in the biosynthetic pathways by the identification of accumulated intermediates employing radioactive glucose as you have been doing. In fact, the unknown spots in the chromatograms you last spoke of might possibly be such compounds. Also by the addition of radioactive intermediates involved in the synthesis of the amino acids it might be possible to demonstrate the synthesis of the particular amino acid or its precursors.

MARKERT: Your suggestions are good ones, and I hope to investigate the nature of the loss of synthetic activity by these developing embryonic cells. As in the case of mutant cells, there may be a loss of only one step in a long sequence of reactions leading to the final product. However, since cell differentiation is a natural process, molded and modified during the long course of evolution, I should not expect to find intermediates in a synthetic chain accumulating in differentiating cells unless these intermediates were essential in performing some alternative metabolic activity. Nevertheless, the attractive possibility exists for determining whether the cessation of a given synthesis represents an interruption at one point in a chain or a diminution of activity throughout the chain. Perhaps a decision between these alternatives can be reached during the coming year.

Genetic Mechanism in Limb Development[1]

Edgar Zwilling

Storrs Agricultural Experiment Station, Storrs, Connecticut

With no intention of emphasizing field or subject chauvinism I should like to point out that the heading "developmental level" is an unfortunate one for the current session. Obviously, developmental phenomena involve many or all of the other levels which have been discussed previously. If designation of a "level" is needed then it can be said that the phenomena with which I shall deal occur at the level of tissue interaction.

It would be very nice if I could present a story of limb development in terms of integrated enzyme-substrate systems or specific protein syntheses. Unfortunately we have not yet achieved even part of this ultimate goal. Many hypotheses relate early developmental phenomena at the chemical or cellular level to final form and structure. None of these, to my knowledge, has received critical substantiation. We are so uncertain of the relationship between biochemical and biophysical events and morphogenesis that a good deal of our work, including the present material, can still be done with profit at a simple and unsophisticated level.

We can, I believe, accept as a truism the statement that all aspects of limb development are somehow controlled by some kind of genetic mechanism. Most indications of genetic involvement come from instances of atypical limb development. The anomalies are very diverse. There are distortions of the basic distal pattern (polydactyly, syndactyly, hypodactyly, etc.). There are deficiencies in which more or less of a limb is missing (amelia, ectromelias, etc.). Some of these may result from early failures of development while others are the consequence of some form of regression in a fairly well developed limb. There are instances in which the basic defect is anomalous histogenesis. Sometimes the derangement seems to occur early, at the time of formation of a tissue. In other cases the anomaly is expressed somewhat later. There is little doubt, in either event, that the visible effects are manifestations of prior disturbances.

My own contribution to our understanding of limb development is based on a technique. It is possible to remove limb buds from three day chick embryos and to effect an interchange between the ectoderm and mesoderm of two of them. The composite limb bud can then be grafted to a host embryo and may develop reasonably well. The ectodermal component of the graft is obtained

with trypsin digestion while the mesodermal element is prepared by treating the limb bud with a chelating compound (Zwilling, 1955).

The ectodermal covering of a limb bud in most vertebrates is low columnar ectoderm except for a raised crest or ridge along the free edge. This ridge consists of high columnar (or pseudostratified) ectoderm. (Limb buds of amphibian embryos, with which most experiments have been performed, do not have such an apical ridge of ectoderm. Instead this layer forms a thickened cap over the distal end of a limb bud.) Saunders (1948) first demonstrated, in chick embryos, that distal limb development ceased when the apical ridge was removed. Almost all of the limb was lacking when the ridge was removed from an early limb bud and was less deficient when an older bud was treated in this way. This observation was supported by some of our own made upon a "wingless" mutation of chickens. In this mutant the homozygous recessives were characterized by complete absence of the wings. We found (Zwilling, 1949) that the apical ectodermal ridge was present in all wing buds early on the third day but that it regressed during the third day in homozygous recessives. On the fourth day there was no trace of an ectodermal ridge. This sort of evidence indicated that the apical ectodermal ridge was quite important for limb development. The interchange procedure was devised in order that we might extend our knowledge of the role of this structure in normal development as well as in the case of selected mutants.

Thus far two mutant conditions have been studied by this approach. Interchanges have been made between polydactylous and wingless limb components and genetically normal ones. The results have enabled us to advance an hypothesis about normal limb development and this hypothesis has been tested with genetically normal material. This, as well as more recent material, will be the subject of today's discussion.

POLYDACTYLY

Limb bud components from two polydactylous mutations were combined with components from genetically normal limb buds of the same age (Zwilling and Hansborough, 1956). One was the Duplicate mutation (Po^d) which results in a marked polydactyly of the wings as well as the feet. Only the wing buds were used. The other was the standard (Po) polydactyly of the feet. Leg buds for these experiments were obtained from Silkie embryos.

A high proportion of grafts which developed

[1] Aided by research grant C-1790(R) from the National Cancer Institute of the National Institutes of Health, U. S. Public Health Service.

from limb buds consisting of polydactylous mesoderm and genetically normal ectoderm was polydactylous (Fig. 1). The basic pattern of duplication in such limbs was the same as seen in control

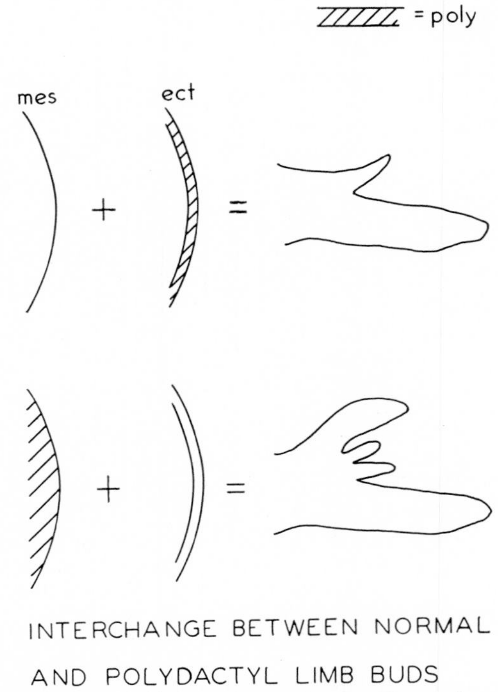

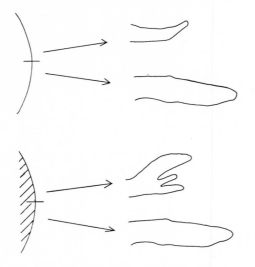

= poly

mes   ect

+   =

+   =

INTERCHANGE BETWEEN NORMAL

AND POLYDACTYL LIMB BUDS

FIGURE 1. Interchange of mesoderm and ectoderm between genetically normal and polydactylous limb buds.
The polydactylous condition developed from the combination of mutant mesoderm and normal ectoderm.

TANTALUM FOIL MARKERS

FIGURE 2. The results of marking polydactylous and
normal limb buds (3 days) with tantalum foil. Even
though dimensionally identical, the pre-axial halves of
the two kinds of buds have different developmental
capacities.

limbs (the unoperated wing of the mesoderm
donor). With one exception (see Zwilling and
Hansborough, 1956, for discussion) the reciprocal
combination developed into normal wings (Fig.
1).

A polydactylous condition is preceded by one
in which the limb pat is enlarged. In the case of
the extreme duplicate wings this is very noticeable by the fourth day of development. The excess outgrowth is associated with a more extensive
apical ectodermal ridge. Experiments in which the
mid-point of duplicate and normal limb buds was
marked (with tantalum foil inserted into an inci-
sion) revealed that this area of excessive limb
growth and more extensive apical ridge develops
from a region which at three days, is dimensionally
identical in both polydactyl and normal limb buds
(Fig. 2).

Since the excess limb area comes from a region
of the three-day limb bud which has the same
dimensions as a normal one, and since the excess
limb area is characterized by a more extensive
ectodermal ridge and since the latter will develop
in genetically normal ectoderm which is in contact
with polydactylous mesoderm it follows that the
ectoderm is influenced by some factor in the
mutant mesoderm. The sequence must be:

(1)   factor in mutant mesoderm
                           ↓
(2)   more extensive apical ectodermal ridge
                           ↓
(3)   excessive distal outgrowth of limb

Hansborough (unpub.) has demonstrated that
step 3 will not occur without step 2. When he
removed the pre-axial one third of the apical ridge
from a three-day limb bud the result was a normal
limb without polydactyly.

WINGLESS

Essentially the same sort of experiment has
been done with wingless embryos (Zwilling,
1956a). Limb buds were removed from early three-
day embryos. At this time the homozygous recessive buds still have an ectodermal ridge. The
operated embryo was kept until the condition of
the control side could be ascertained. When
mesoderm from a mutant was provided with
genetically normal ectoderm there was considerably more outgrowth than in the control. However, within 24 to 36 hours, the genetically normal
ectodermal ridge regressed and eventually disappeared. Distal development ceased. The usual
condition which developed in such grafts was a
mound topped off by a spike (Fig. 3). These have
a marked resemblance to the legs of some homozygous wingless mutants. Ectodermal ridge regression occurs a bit later in affected hind limbs than
in the fore limbs. The reciprocal combination,
normal mesoderm and mutant ectoderm, does no
better than the control wing (Fig. 3).

It is difficult to decide whether the mutant ectoderm has been affected by the mutant mesoderm

so that it cannot recover even in the presence of normal mesoderm or if the mutant genotype has an autonomous effect in the ectoderm. However, the fact that the mutant mesoderm cannot support the genetically normal ectoderm is of importance regardless of the situation in the mutant ectoderm. I have interpreted this observation to mean that the wingless mesoderm can respond to the outgrowth-inducing influence of the genetically normal Saunders' ridge but is deficient in some factor which is required for the maintenance of the latter. (It is equally possible that the mesoderm produces some detrimental condition. The former possibility has been adopted for the sake of simplicity and harmony with the other data.)

HYPOTHESIS OF EARLY LIMB BUD DEVELOPMENT

The data from the experiments with these two mutant conditions indicate a reciprocal dependence between ectoderm and mesoderm and have served as the basis for an hypothesis for limb development (Zwilling, 1956b). This postulates:

1. That distal development of a limb is the result of the outgrowth-inducing activity of the apical ectodermal ridge. The mesoderm responds to this influence.

2. That the apical ectodermal ridge is not an independent structure. It depends on some mesodermal factor for its continued existence. This is called the "apical ectoderm maintenance factor." This factor is not uniformly distributed in the mesoderm.

3. That the two mutants studied have their effect on the maintenance factor. In the case of polydactylous forms there is an atypical distribution of the factor—more is present pre-axially. In the case of wingless limb buds the factor is deficient or entirely absent (Fig. 4).

CHICK-DUCK INTERCHANGES

Results of component interchange between chick and duck limb buds may be pertinent to a discussion of genetic mechanism. This, of course, involves genetic differences of a gross sort. The chief question for which I sought an answer was whether there exists species or generic specificity in outgrowth induction and in the maintenance of Saunders' ridge. Could a duck ectodermal ridge induce outgrowth of chick mesoderm and could the latter maintain the former? If the answer were "yes" then we might, incidentally, obtain information about which component of a duck limb bud is responsible for the formation of the webbing.

The results of these experiments (unpub.) are clear. The ectoderm from either form can induce outgrowth in the mesoderm of the other. The mesoderm of either form, in turn, can maintain the apical ectodermal ridge of the other. Virtually perfect limbs have been obtained with both combinations. When duck leg-bud mesoderm is covered by chick ectoderm a typical duck leg, com-

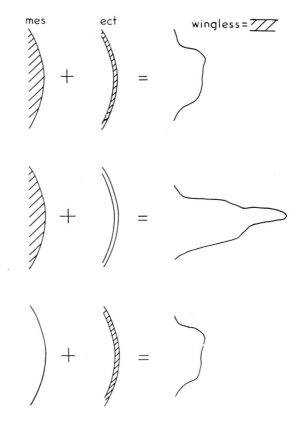

INTERCHANGE BETWEEN NORMAL

AND WINGLESS LIMB BUDS

FIGURE 3. Interchange of components between normal and wingless limb buds. No combination yields a normal limb. The combination of mutant mesoderm and normal ectoderm gave more outgrowth than did controls; but failed to form distal parts.

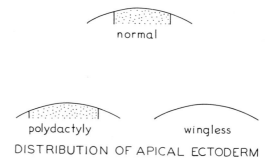

DISTRIBUTION OF APICAL ECTODERM

MAINTENANCE FACTOR

FIGURE 4. (After: Zwilling, 1956b). Diagram of probable distribution of apical ectoderm maintenance factor in normal, polydactylous and wingless limb buds.

plete with webbing, is formed (Fig. 5). Even when the duck mesoderm is cut into pieces (.1–.2 mm in diameter) and placed at random into chick limb bud ectoderm, unmistakable webbing forms between digits. Every case of the reciprocal com-

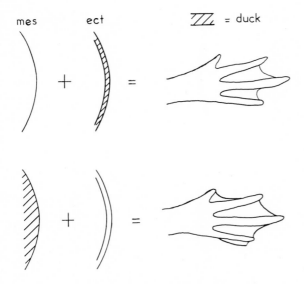

COMPONENT INTERCHANGE

BETWEEN DUCK AND CHICK

FIGURE 5. Results of interchange of components between duck and chick limb buds. Both combinations may yield good limbs. Webbing appears in each case; that from chick mesoderm + duck ectoderm is thinner.

bination which has yielded a recognizable limb has had webbing between some, if not all, of the digits (Fig. 5). The webbing is thinner and less conspicuous than typical duck webbing. But it is present, and sections reveal that it has the same basic structure in both forms. In each case the webbing consists of epidermis and connective tissue. It is the latter which is thinner in the chick mesoderm-duck ectoderm combination.

These results reveal that both duck ectoderm and mesoderm may be involved in the formation of webbing in an all-duck limb. Certainly each may impose its predilection to form webbing upon the opposite component of a chick limb bud. The web is, in reality, an elaboration of the interdigital material which is present during the limb pat stage in most vertebrate limbs. In most cases this tissue leaves little or no indication of its presence when the hand or foot is finally formed. Chicken feet do have a sort of webbing which is restricted to the proximal junction of the digits. It is likely that the duck ectoderm inhibits or delays some regressive process which is normally involved in the elimination of most of the chick's interdigital tissue.

DISAGGREGATION EXPERIMENTS

I should like, finally, to discuss some experiments which I have recently done with genetically normal three-day limb buds. These may have some bearing, by analogy, on our discussion of genetic mechanism.

One of the objects of these experiments was to study the regulative properties of the limb bud mesoderm. Mesoderm from a single limb bud was cut into 25 to 30 pieces, each some .1–.2 mm in diameter. Eight or ten of these pieces were stuffed, at random, into an intact ectodermal jacket (Fig. 6). Even after such treatment the graft from these "limb buds" may form recognizable limbs. The proximal bone elements are quite distorted but the distal structures, though not fully normal, are undoubted hands or feet (unpub.).

The next step was to disaggregate the limb bud mesoderm completely. A cell suspension was made by a modification of Moscona's (1952) tryptic digestion procedure or by treatment with a chelating compound. These cells were either centrifuged into a mass or allowed to reaggregate autonomously. The reaggregated mesoderm was placed into ectodermal jackets and the composites were raised as grafts. Regardless of which disaggregation procedure was employed or the method of reaggregation the results were the same. Within 20 to 24 hours the mesoderm filled the ectoderm and the grafts looked like retarded, but fairly normal, limb buds. Shortly after this the apical ectodermal ridges became thin and thready. In short order there was no evidence of an ectodermal ridge. The best of these "limbs" are long thin spikes which surmount a broad base. The resemblance to our experiments with wingless mutants is striking. These grafts are very much

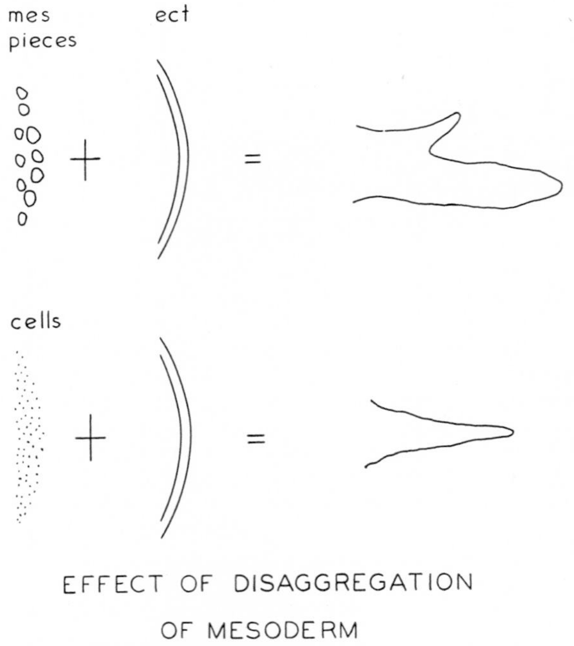

EFFECT OF DISAGGREGATION

OF MESODERM

FIGURE 6. Results of two degrees of fragmentation of limb bud mesoderm. Fragments .1–.2 mm may, when in contact with limb ectoderm, regulate to form a recognizable limb. Compacted cell suspensions from limb bud mesoderm have not done this. The most they have formed (again, in limb ectoderm) are spike-like outgrowths (see Fig. 3).

like the extremely affected legs of homozygous mutants or the "wings" which develop from wingless mesoderm and genetically normal ectoderm. It may interest some to note that this mesoderm is capable of inducing feathers. We frequently find large feather follicles at the site of these grafts, even when they lie in a normally unfeathered area. (Moscona, unpublished, has found that ectoderm of a 4-day limb bud may be disaggregated and will reaggregate to form an epidermis on the surface of limb mesoderm *in vitro*. The apical ridge, however, does not form again.)

Another pertinent experiment was done with non-limb mesoderm. Such mesoderm was taken from the flank, between the two limb buds, deprived of its own ectoderm, placed in a jacket of limb bud ectoderm and grafted to a host embryo. It behaved essentially the same as the completely disaggregated mesoderm. The limb ectoderm filled out, apical ectoderm regressed and outgrowth stopped. None of these grafts has ever formed a spike. They stop as mounds, that is, development does not progress far beyond the equivalent of the three-day stage.

My interpretation of these experiments is as follows: Even after complete disaggregation the limb bud mesoderm retains the capacity to respond to the outgrowth stimulus from the ectodermal ridge. However, it is no longer able to maintain the thickened ridge of ectoderm and the latter regresses and limb development ceases. This is essentially what we have said about the mesoderm of the wingless mutant. Non-limb mesoderm can also respond to the outgrowth stimulus from Saunders' ridge—but it too lacks the capacity to maintain this structure.

DISCUSSION

The contribution which these experiments make to our understanding of genetic mechanism is very modest indeed. About all that we can say is that some factor resident in limb bud mesoderm is affected by the mutants under discussion. Maintenance of the apical ectodermal ridge is dependent on this factor. Whether we have a duplicated limb or none at all depends on whether the mesodermal factor is present over a wider region than normal or is absent.

There is no information about the nature of this "factor." We do not know whether it is an enzyme, a substrate, an RNA molecule or anything else. Dr. L. Loewenthal, in our laboratory, has sought in vain, with a variety of histochemical tests, for a clue to the nature of this factor. Nor do we know anything about the nature of the interaction between the two limb components.

Possibly we have some clues for future investigation and thinking in the experiments which were described last. A significant difference between non-limb mesoderm and that from the limb bud is that the latter has the capacity to maintain an apical ectodermal ridge. Both can

respond to the outgrowth inducing influence of the ridge. Limb bud mesoderm which has been cut to rather small pieces retains, or reacquires the the capacity to support an apical ridge. Our experiments at present indicate that a cell suspension of the same mesoderm, following reaggregation, loses or cannot reacquire the maintenance factor. Even though the reaggregated mesoderm is healthy and can form cartilage (Moscona and Moscona, 1952), it is essentially the same as non-limb mesoderm as far as its apical ectodermal ridge properties are concerned.

Whatever the nature of the maintenance factor (enzyme, substrate, etc.) our present information suggests that its survival, continued existence or continued production seems to be dependent on a supracellular relationship which, under the condition of our experiments, is not restored following complete disaggregation. The clue to this supracellular organization must lie in some essential difference between our small piece (.1 mm) and a cell suspension. Reasoning strictly by analogy (and cognizant of the limitations of such reasoning) there is a possibility that a mutation, such as our "wingless" mutant, may produce its effects via a genetic interference with some similar cell-to-cell relationship. Such things as enzyme or substrate derangement may be secondary. We have, at the present, no idea of the nature of the cell-to-cell relationships which may be responsible for such effects. Their elucidation represents a considerable challenge.

SUMMARY

The results of experimental manipulation of limb bud (3-day) ectoderm and mesoderm have been presented. When mesoderm from polydactylous mutants is combined with genetically normal ectoderm the polydactylous pattern still develops. When mesoderm from a wingless mutant is treated in a similar way there is more distal development than in controls, but the genetically normal apical ectoderm regresses and distal limb structures do not form. These experiments are taken to be evidence for the presence of a factor in normal limb mesoderm upon which continued existence of the ectoderm is dependent. The mutant conditions, according to this interpretation, result from genetic modification of the apical ectoderm maintenance factor.

Neither outgrowth induction nor the apical ectoderm maintenance factor are species specific. Duck ectoderm may be combined with chick mesoderm (or *vice versa*) and still produce good limbs. Both ectoderm and mesoderm of the duck limb seem to be involved in formation of webbing.

Some experiments on disaggregation (partial or complete) of genetically normal mesoderm were discussed. Limb bud mesoderm which has been cut into pieces (.1–.2 mm) may still regulate to form a recognizable limb. Similar mesoderm which has undergone complete disaggregation (*i.e.*, converted to a cell suspension) did not, following reaggregation, form a limb. The apical ectoderm maintenance factor seemed to be eliminated after this treatment. These experiments present the possibility that continued existence or production of the maintenance factor may be dependent on some particular cell-to-cell relationship which is subject to genetic modification.

REFERENCES

Moscona, A., 1952, Cell suspensions from organ rudiments of chick embryos. Exp. Cell Res. *3:* 535–539.

Moscona, A., and Moscona, H., 1952, The dissociation and aggregation of cells from organ rudiments of the early chick embryo. J. Anat. *86:* 287–301.

Saunders, J. W., Jr., 1948, The proximo-distal sequence of origin of the parts of the chick wing and the role of the ectoderm. J. Exp. Zool. *108:* 363–404.

Zwilling, E., 1949, The role of epithelial components in the developmental origin of the "wingless" syndrome of chick embryos. J. Exp. Zool. *111:* 175–188.

1955, Ectoderm-mesoderm relationship in the development of the chick embryo limb bud. J. Exp. Zool. *128:* 423–441.

1956a, Interaction between limb bud ectoderm and mesoderm in the chick embryo. IV. Experiments with a wingless mutant. J. Exp. Zool. *132:* 241–253.

1956b, Reciprocal dependence of ectoderm and mesoderm during chick embryo limb development. Amer. Nat. *90:* 257–265.

Zwilling, E., and Hansborough, L. A., 1956, Interaction between limb bud ectoderm and mesoderm in the chick embryo. III. Experiments with polydactylous limbs. J. Exp. Zool. *132:* 219–239.

DISCUSSION

BALINSKY: I should like to congratulate Dr. Zwilling on the most interesting results of his investigations. I was very gratified to note that some of Dr. Zwilling's experiments bear out the results of my own work. Over 20 years ago I studied the relationship between the epidermis and the mesoderm of the limb rudiment in *Triton*. In a stage comparable to that used by Dr. Zwilling, I removed the epithelium of the forelimb rudiment and replaced it with the epithelium from the head in some cases, and with the presumptive gill epithelium in other cases. The limb rudiments covered by head epithelium developed normally, thus showing (contrary to Filatow's opinion) that the mesoderm can impose its pattern of development on the epidermis. The gill epidermis on the other hand did not conform to the influence of the limb mesoderm, but caused outgrowths of a mixed and atypical nature to be formed. This is similar to the case in Dr. Zwilling's work where epidermis of the wingless mutant could not react adequately to the influence of the normal limb mesoderm and prevented normal cooperation between limb mesoderm and epidermis to be established. Both in the

newt and in the chick lack of cooperation between epidermis and mesoderm makes normal development impossible.

Another parallel between Dr. Zwilling's experiments and my own concerns more directly the genotypical basis of morphogenetic processes. It is usually believed that embryonic tissues can only be induced to form such structures as may occur in the development of the species to which the tissues belong. The development of interdigital membranes on legs in which chick epidermis was grafted on duck limb mesoderm in Dr. Zwilling's experiments contradicts this common belief. I can match this result with some recent work I have done on the development of gills in anuran tadpoles of different species. My experiments consisted of grafting ectoderm heteroplastically between species differing in the number of pairs of external gills. Tadpoles of *Bufo regularis* have two pairs of external gills, those of *Bufo carens* have three pairs of external gills. If epidermis of *B. carens* is grafted to the gill region of *B. regularis*, only two pairs of external gills develop. Conversely, if epidermis of *B. regularis* is grafted to the gill region of *B. carens* three pairs of gills develop. Epidermis having normally only two pairs of gills can thus produce a gill of a third pair. In another combination, the embryos used were *Pyxicephalus delalandii*, a species having two pairs of gills, and *Pyxicephalus adspersus*, the tadpoles of which have only one pair of external gills. Epidermis of *P. adspersus*, grafted to *P. delalandii* produces two pairs of gills, as is normal for the host, but does not occur in the donor. Grafting of *P. delalandii* epidermis to a *P. adspersus* host, however, leads to the development of a small but distinct second gill, in addition to the first gill characteristic of the host species. This rudimentary second gill may be compared to the subnormal interdigital membrane developed by duck epidermis grafted to a chick mesodermal limb rudiment in Dr. Zwilling's experiments.

ZWILLING: There is one very important difference between amphibian and chick embryo limb development which I did not discuss. Dr. Balinsky's statement about development of limb mesoderm which was covered by head ectoderm cannot be repeated for the chick. At the three-day stage non-limb ectoderm, from various parts of the embryo's body, is incapable of inducing limb outgrowth. Evidently such ectoderm cannot form an apical ectodermal ridge. Ectoderm from younger embryos (5–16 somites) has also been placed on limb bud mesoderm. This did not give limb outgrowth either even though the ectoderm of the presumptive limb area was included in some cases.

Genetic Mechanisms in Tissue Transplantation in the Mouse

Gustavo Hoecker

Instituto de Biologia "Juan Noe," Universidad de Chile, Santiago, Chile

I will speak about a very broad field in which rapid developments are being made and concerning which an enormous amount of literature has accumulated in the last few years. The monumental book of Leo Loeb on the biological basis of individuality synthesized much of what was written up to 1945. Since then, several good reviews on the genetic and immunologic aspects of transplantation have appeared (Little, 1950; Snell, 1952; Hauschka, 1952), the emphasis of these being on tumor transplantation in mammals with which the most intensive work has been done during the last 20 years.

The center of interest is now shifting from tumors to the transplantation of normal tissues and organs. No matter how much has been written, the basic fact remains that the fate of a transplant is largely dependent on the genetic relation between host and graft. The terms autotransplant, isotransplant, homotransplant and heterotransplant designate the closeness of the genetic relationship between host and graft. This statement is fully valid when transplants are made in homoeotherm animals, the mechanisms of recognition of cell and tissue individuality being less and less precise as we go down the evolutionary scale, with the notable exception perhaps of the discrimination of gametes against gametes of different species and genera during fertilization.

Probably the most extensive experimental studies on mammalian tissue individuality using transplantation techniques have been made in one species, the mouse, to which I will confine my talk. Most of what I have to say refers to transplantation of tumors because this material illustrates some of the relations between genes and tissue individuality in a simpler way than normal tissues. However, most investigators in this field will agree that the basic mechanisms work the same way in both cases. In genetic studies in mice, many transplanted tumors behave as if operationally they required fewer genes than normal tissues under the same genetic conditions in order to establish a permanent relation with their host. Not infrequently, success of a tumor transplant appears to depend on a single genetic difference. Such a case is but rarely met when normal tissues are used as grafts unless co-isogenic resistant and susceptible strains are used as donor and recipient. This has been the reason for the use of tumors instead of normal tissues in analyzing mechanisms of graft rejection (Mitchison, 1953).

The mendelian nature of resistance or susceptibility to tissue transplantation demonstrated by Little and his followers is already history (Little, 1950; Snell, 1952). In short, susceptibility to tissue transplants in mice results when both the host and the graft have the same set of certain dominant genes, the situation thus closely approximating complementary effects of genes. The number of loci involved is high, 14 being a conservative estimate of the number of loci determining susceptibility or resistance to tumor transplants according to Snell (1948). These are major genes which are able to achieve the rejection of tumor grafts. The number affecting some normal tissues may be somewhat greater, tumors apparently being more resistant to the injurious action of the host defenses than normal tissues (Hauschka, 1954).

For the loci involved in transplantation, the general descriptive name "histocompatibility" (symbols H and h) has been proposed by Snell. Genes at these loci are concerned with tissue compatibility in the mouse (Snell, 1948). Linkage of some H genes to certain of those that determine coat color (Little and Strong, 1924; Bittner, 1933); tail defects (Gorer, Lyman and Snell, 1948); sex-linkage to the X chromosome (Strong, 1929; 1955) and a probable case of Y-linked genes have been discovered (Eichwald and Silmser, 1955; Hauschka, 1955; Snell, 1956). Analysis of three H-loci made by Snell *et al.* (1953–1954 and personal communication) have revealed allelic series in all three, 12 alleles being identified at present at one of them, the H-2 locus (Snell, Smith and Gabrielson, 1953; Allen, 1955). Thus, tissue compatibility in transplantation depends on multiple genes.

DIFFERENCES IN THE EFFECTS OF H-GENES ON TRANSPLANTATION

The different genes and gene combinations of the H-loci do not all have the same importance for tissue compatibility. A definite range from "strong" to "weak" reactions are affected by the different H-loci, the potency of some of these loci probably exhibiting a threshold effect according to genetic background or unpredictable environmental conditions (Little, 1950; Hauschka, 1952; Snell, 1956). This is well illustrated in Table 1 (from Hoecker *et al.*, 1954 and Hoeker, Pizarro and Rubinstein, unpub.): one and the same transplanted tumor line ("A," originated in C58 mice) was transplanted into several different inbred strains: wide differences in the percentage of successful takes and in the speed of the processes of graft resistance were the result.

TABLE 1. RESULTS OF TRANSPLANTING THE "A" LINE OF LEUKEMIA FROM ITS STRAIN OF ORIGIN, C58, INTO SEVERAL FOREIGN STRAINS

Survival of "A" leukemic cells tested by transplanting them back into their strain of origin C58.

Host Strain	No. Dead Mice Total No. Inoculated	Per Cent Dead	H-2 Allele	Days of Survival of "A" Cells in Foreign Hosts
C58	3.000/3000	100	$H\text{-}2^k$	—
AK	179/187	96	$H\text{-}2^k$	<36*
C3H	21/24	88	$H\text{-}2^k$	<10*
Rk	10/28	36	$H\text{-}2^k$	>10
C57BL.10	0/8	0	$H\text{-}2^b$	>9
C57BL.6	0/16	0	$H\text{-}2^d$	>9
DBA/1	0/8	0	$H\text{-}2^q$	>9
A/Sn	0/8	0	$H\text{-}2^a$	>9
BALB/c	0/8	0	$H\text{-}2^d$	>9

Data from Hoecker, Pizarro, Brncic and Gasic, 1955, Cancer Res. *15:* 95; and Hoecker, Pizarro and Rubenstein, unpublished.

* Data from leukemic mice which lived more than the "normal" mean survival time.

The above mentioned experiments give results in which individual effects of genes cannot be distinguished. A more accurate estimate comes from the identification of some of the *H*-loci and the development of co-isogenic strains, both made by Snell at the Roscoe B. Jackson Laboratory. Under these highly controlled conditions, skin grafts between members of co-isogenic pairs differing at the "strong" *H-2* locus, survived about eight days; at the *H-3* locus, 25 and 31 days for reciprocal grafts. Other evidence already at hand indicated *H-1* as of intermediate effect (Counce, unpub. quoted by Snell, 1956). The combined action of some of these loci seem to be more effective, tumor cells being unable to grow when transplanted back to their strain of origin after only seven days in the foreign strain (*cf.* Hoecker *et al.*, 1954 and unpub.).

On the other extreme of the spectra of effects of *H*-genes are some minor genetic differences which fall short in their ability to promote a rejection of the graft but whose effects can be shown, however, by "cosmetic" alterations of skin homografts, not shown by auto and isografts (Billingham, Brent and Medawar, 1955). I will refer later to the possible meaning of this differential action of the different *H*-loci.

VARIATIONS IN TRANSPLANTED TUMORS

A point of interest pertaining to gene action in transplantation is the variability in *H*-gene requirements observed to happen during serial transfers of tumors within their strains of origin. Transplanted tumors very often undergo morphological, physiological and probably genetical changes that seem to be the result of changes in the cellular composition of the transplanted tumors. Physiological changes are, with few exceptions, in the direction of increased rate of growth up to a certain limit, increased number of metastases and increased ability to kill hosts of genotypes previously shown to be resistant. As a result, there is an apparent *decrease* in the number of *H*-genes required for the successful transplant into hybrid mice, or in other words, the tumors suffer an apparent genetic simplification. (Review in Snell, 1952 and Hauschka and Schultz, 1954.) Extreme examples of this "genetic simplification" are the so-called non-specific tumors which can grow across normally "strong" H-barriers (Hauschka, Transpl. Bull., 1954). Concomitant with some of these changed properties, a shift in the predominant cell types and changes in some cell structures have been observed (Mac Dowell, 1947). Most conspicuous amongst these are those occurring in chromosome number, thoroughly analyzed by Hauschka *et al.*, (Hauschka and Levan, 1952; Levan and Hauschka, 1953). Here a correlation between the loss of gene-determined cell individuality and chromosomal make-up has been uncovered: Specific tumor cells populations are predominantly diploid. Tumors with decreased specificity exhibit a mosaic condition of tumor-cell populations, with presence of variable proportions of hyperploid and other chromosomal variants (Hauschka, 1953).

The apparent decrease in *H*-gene requirements are sometimes abrupt, a tumor may change from a seven or five *H*-gene requirement to a two or even one gene requirement from one transfer to another (Strong, 1926). Recent experiments by Amos *et al.* (1955) are indicative that they may be spurious and the result of the special properties of transplanted tumors. I will discuss this topic later on, after considering the nature of gene action in transplantation.

THE NATURE OF GENE ACTION IN TISSUE TRANSPLANTATION

The mendelian nature of tissue compatibility in mice makes it possible to expect several possible modes of gene action in transplantation. For instance, the outcome of a graft of a tissue requiring for its continued growth some hormonal or enzymatic system in a host not possessing that system could be imagined to determine its "resistance" by that particular host. If the presence of these requirements is itself genetically determined, a segregation into susceptible and resistant groups would be expected among test hybrids of strains lacking and having those growth factors (Hauschka and Schultz, 1954). Except for the analysis of some induced non-autonomons hormone-dependent tumors this chapter of transplantation is unexplored and practically nothing is known of its genetic nature.

At present it would be generally agreed that antigenic differences between host and graft are the main cause of incompatibility both of normal and tumor tissue transplants (Amos *et al.*, 1955; Hauschka, 1952). In the words of Medawar (1948) ". . . the phenomenon of the breaking down of skin grafts has shown that it conforms in broad outline with a reaction of actively acquired immunity." More specifically a skin homograft builds up a systemic reaction against itself at a rate which varies with the antigenic relation between donor and recipient and with the quantity of foreign tissue that is grafted (Gibson and Medawar, 1943). As long ago as 1919 a relation between blood group antigens and tissue compatibility in transplants was suggested in man. However, these early attempts to transplant skin between men otherwise compatible for ABO met with failure (Shawan, 1919; Dyke, 1922). We owe to Gorer the first specific demonstration of the relation of gene-determined cell-antigens and tissue compatibility (1937).

Gorer used two inbred strains—A (albino) and C57BL (black), their F_2 and BC hybrids and tumors originating in the A strain. Black mice invariably resisted A tumors. These resistant mice developed in their blood agglutinins against A strain red cells. These antibodies could be absorbed by A tumors and A normal tissues which, therefore, shared a common antigen called antigen II. F_2 and BC mice from crosses between these two strains tested both for susceptibility to the A tumors and presence of antigen II revealed that all mice lacking antigen II were resistant to A tumors. Some mice carrying antigen II were also resistant because of a second segregating *H* gene. This classical experiment thus established a definite relation between cell antigens and tissue compatibility. Later, Gorer, Lyman and Snell (1948) established the close linkage of antigen II with Fused (a gene in the 9th linkage group), the gene determining antigen II being called *H-2*. A series of 12 alleles at this locus has been identified at present (Snell, Smith and Gabrielson, 1953); Allen, 1955; and personal communication by Snell).

As the *H-2* "locus" has been most extensively studied and shows better than any other the interactions among genes, gene products and gene determined mechanisms in transplantation, I will discuss it more fully.

THE COMPLEX NATURE OF *H-2*

An indication that antigen II was really complex came from the discovery by Snell (1951) that all compounds of $H-2^d$ and $H-2^k$ alleles would grow A strain tumor 15091a. The *H-2* allele of the A strain was therefore called $H-2^{dk}$. As will be clear from the following, all alleles at this locus display some sort of antigenic complexity. For this reason, Gorer proposed to change $H-2^{dk}$ to $H-2^a$.

The serology of *H-2* antigens has been worked out just recently thanks to the development by Gorer *et al.* (1954) of suitable methods of agglutination of mouse red cells further studies are

TABLE 2. THE KNOWN ANTIGENIC STRUCTURE OF *H-2* COMBINATIONS*

H-2 "Alleles"	H-2 Phenotype	"Private" Antigens	Antigens Common to Several Alleles
$H-2^a$	CDEFKH	—	CDEFKH
$H-2^b$	BEF	B	EF
$H-2^d$	CDE^{d}FH	E^d	CDFH
$H-2^f$	GHI	I	GH
$H-2^k$	CEHK	—	CEHK
$H-2^p$	CEP	P	CE
$H-2^q$	CEFQ	Q	CEF
$H-2^s$	CEFGS	S	CEFG

* Combined data from Hoecker, Counce and Smith, 1954; Amos, Gorer and Mikulska, 1955; and Pizarro and Hoecker, unpublished. Only those antigens for which serological evidence exist are shown.

currently in progress. The analysis have revealed a highly complex antigenic situation similar to that of the Rh system in man or the complex antigens of the B system in cattle (Stormont, 1955). The different *H-2* alleles have been found to determine combinations of three, four, five or six antigens at once and these figures seem not to be definitive, the real antigenic complexity probably being much greater. The existence of new antigens is suspected from the rejection of tumors in certain *H-2* combinations of host and graft in coisogenic strains which according to the antigens already known should have been accepted.

A summary of *H-2* alleles and their antigenic composition is given in Table 2 (from Hoecker, Counce and Smith, 1954; Amos, Gorer and Mikulska, 1955; and Pizarro and Hoecker, unpub.) Only those alleles that have been examined serologically are included. These can be identified either by characteristic ("private") antigens (B-E^d-I-P-Q-S) or by characteristic combinations of antigens (CEKH-CDEKH, etc.). Alleles are stated by orthodox symbols ($H-2^a$, etc.). Phenotypes are indicated by the prefix *H-2* followed by the antigens already known each one indicated by a capital letter. A list of inbred strains and the *H-2* alleles that they carry has been given by Snell *et al.* (1953).

All strains which have been classified as having identical *H-2* alleles on the basis of transplantation tests have been shown to have the same antigens present. Each of these antigenic factors behaves as a discrete serological entity. Though the red cells of most strains respond with fair uniformity against the same antibodies, there are exceptions. For instance, strains A and A.SW, and C58 show a consistently stronger response for some of the antigens that they have in common with other strains. The reverse is true for DBA/1 and STOLI. Whether these differences in agglutination titer are the result of a quantitative phenomenon, or else, cross-reactions between similar but not identical antigens, is not possible to tell at present. These differences could also be the result of some kind of interaction between antigens on the one hand or between genes on the other. An indication that this kind of phenomenon may operate sometimes is given by the lowered titers for anti-C when this antigen is combined with antigen D (Amos *et al.*, 1955). The same situation apparently applies to antigen F which according to the same authors is more potent when combined with B than with D. The former group of strains would seem to have a greater quantity of some antigens as they absorb more antibodies per volume of tissues than do other strains under the same conditions.

All antigens already mentioned are present in all normal tissues studied so far but significant quantitative differences between tissues can be shown to exist by absorption experiments. The greatest absorbing capacity is exhibited by lymphoid tissues, mammary gland and tumor tissues, the least by striated muscle and red blood cells (Amos, Gorer and Mikulska, 1955; and Hoecker, Pizarro and Gorer, unpub.). The red cells of some strains present a curious situation: One of the antigens may be absent from them, or nearly so. This is clearly seen in the erythrocytes of C57BL mice whose E component is practically lacking. Apparently this antigen depends on nuclear elements for its continued presence because young red cells induced to appear in circulation by repeated bleeding exhibit some response to antigen E (Amos *et al.*, 1955a).

The antigenic composition of non-specific tumors, that is, those which can transgress the histocompatibility barriers deserves further com-

ment. These tumors are an extreme case of the phenomenon of "genetic simplification" already mentioned. To explain their behavior in transplantation, an "antigenic simplification" has been postulated by Gorer (1938). A cytologic basis for explaining these puzzling situations was given by the observations of Hauschka and Levan on the chromosomal composition of some of these genetically and immunologically indifferent tumors. In these transplanted tumors the loss of tissue specificity was shown by these authors to be correlated with distinct chromosomal aberrations. Heteroploidy, polyploidy and probably deletions of chromosome segments concerned with antigen determination and impaired function of antigenic synthesis resulting from chromosomal imbalance would account for the loss of specificity observed by these investigators (Hauschka, 1954). Without consideration of the mechanisms involved, these cells would not elicit in their foreign host the reactions normally caused by the antigenic differences.

The experiments shown in Table 3 are a test of this hypothesis using an extremely favorable material (Hoecker and Hauschka, in press, Tr. Bull.). Two ascites tumor lines, the lymphomas A-1 and A-2, originated in the same inbred strain A show the following characteristic: A-2 has a narrow chromosome number distribution very near diploid and behaves in transplantation as a strictly specific tumor that grows only in $H\text{-}2^a$ mice. The A-1 tumor is composed mostly of hyperploid cells with a chromosome modal number near tetraploid and was shown to be able to grow

TABLE 3. TYPICAL RESULTS OF A COMPARISON OF THE ABSORBING CAPACITIES FOR H-2 ANTIBODIES OF THE TWO TRANSPLANTED TUMORS A-1 AND A-2, BOTH ORIGINATED IN A STRAIN MICE*

A-2 is diploid and strictly specific. A-1 is near-tetraploid and less specific

Controls		32	64	128	256	512	1024	2048	4096
Anti C-D antiserum									
Unabsorbed	r r	c	ac	+++	+++	++	+±	+±	+
Absorbed A-1	− −	++	++	++±	++	+	±	−	−
Absorbed A-2	r r	tr	tr	tr	r	−	−	−	−
Anti D-K antiserum									
Unabsorbed	− −	c	c	ac	+++	+++	++	++	+±
Absorbed A-1	r r	++±	++	+±	+±	+	tr	−	−
Absorbed A-2	− r	tr	−	−	−	−	−	−	−
Anti-E antiserum									
Unabsorbed	− −	+++	ac	+++	+++	++	++	+±	+
Absorbed A-1	− −	ac	ac	+++	++±	++	+±	+	±
Absorbed A-2	− −	−	−	−	−	−	−	−	−

* From Hoecker and Hauschka (Tr. Bull., in press).

All agglutinations were done with A strain RBC. Titers = reciprocal of antibody dilution. c = complete agglutination; ac = almost complete; crosses stand for varying degrees of clumping of the agglutinated RBC; tr = traces of agglutination; r = slight rouleaux formation.

in the foreign strains DBA/2 and BALB/c. A-2 does not grow in C3H mice. Taking into account the all-important locus H-2 and the antigens determined thereby, strain A mice have gene H-2^a and antigenic factors CDEFKH. Strains DBA/2 and BALB/c mice both have the H-2^d allele and antigenic factors CDE^{d}FH; C3H has antigens CEKH. A comparison of the transplantation behavior of these two tumors indicated that A-1 had generally lowered production or a loss of antigenic factors E and K. Typical results of absorption tests done with these two tumors shown in Table 3, indicates that there is a significant difference in the absorbing capacity between A-1 and A-2 tumors with all three antisera tested. This is most notable with respect to anti-E antibodies in which case the specific near-diploid tumor A-2 absorbed all antibodies present in the serum whereas the tetraploid A-1 absorbed practically nothing. On the other hand, in spite of the difference in absorbing ability for the anti-D antibodies, it would seem that both tumors have this antigen present in their cells though the quantity of D is greatly reduced in the tetraploid. These results have been confirmed and greatly extended by Dr. Bernard Amos at Dr. Hauschka's laboratory (Amos, 1956).

The serological results fit almost exactly the behavior of these two tumors in transplantation and are in accord with Gorer's assumption of an antigenic simplification and Hauschka's hypothesis of non-specificity. The meaning of this puzzling phenomenon is a different question. Recent experiments on the relation between genetic behavior and antigenic structure of a transplanted tumor by Amos, Gorer and Mikulska (1955b) indicate that the genetic simplification observed in tumor transplantation may, in some cases, be spurious and due to the fact that tumors may grow and kill their host in spite of antigenic differences. Though the loss of H-2 antigens observed in tetraploid tumors could simply follow from changes in cell surface as a result of increased volume so that the antigens are no longer exposed where they can cause absorption it may also be true that a true loss of antigens occurred in this instance (Hauschka et al., 1956). A similar situation was found by Lewis (1952) in Oenothera where diploid pollen grains heterogenic for self-sterility alleles are able to overcome the self-sterility barriers. This case is not completely comparable because homogenic diploid pollens produce their full quota of antigen-like substances and consequently are not able to cross the genetic self-sterility barriers.

The Problem of an Oppositional Relationship between Antigens

The association of several antigens into a unit which segregates as a single gene has been described in man and other species. An important theoretical question is the genetic nature of these antigenic complexes: Are they the product of one gene or of closely linked genes? The second alternative as applied for example to the Rh system in man implies a one to one relation between gene and antigen (Wiener and Wexler, 1956: Stormont, 1955; Race and Sanger, 1952). Under the single gene hypothesis gene action, as applied to antigen production, is visualized as determining one block of agglutinogen, within which unit molecule two or more antigenically active patches (antigenic factors) would determine the observed antigenic complexity (cf. Wiener and Wexler).

This controversy is further complicated by the well-known fact that antibodies are not absolute in their specificities, a spectrum of antibodies with varying degrees of cross-reactivity and specificity being the normal response to the immunizing procedures. Thus the validity of transferring directly the serological evidences into a genetical relation in all cases has been strongly questioned (cf. Stormont, 1955; and Wiener and Wexler, 1956). In spite of these criticisms, the question can be asked in the following terms: is there any evidence to show that a gene can determine more than one antigenic specificity? Or the inverse proposition, can a serological specificity arise from the action of more than one gene?

A consideration of some rare H-2 mutants and the experiments of Fox et al. on the antigens determined by the vermillon and lozenge pseudoalleles bear on these questions. In this connection the observations on Drosophila suggest that more than one antigen may be associated with a single gene though this is only one out of several possibilities and one which will be extremely difficult to prove (Barish and Fox, 1956; Chovnik and Fox, 1953). As for the H-2 locus, Borges, Kvedar and Foerster (1955) have recorded five mutations in this locus, all of them being a change to the H-2^d allele. Twice the change has involved H-2^q and twice H-2^b and according to Borges et al., the H-2 locus might mutate more frequently than has been suspected. A serological analysis of three strains of mice derived from the mutants has revealed the surprising fact that in each case at least three antigens had changed at once (Hoecker, Counce and Smith, 1954); for instance, mutations from H-2^b to H-2^d have resulted in change from antigens BEF to CDE^{d}FH. As our knowledge of the antigenic make-up of the mutant and original strains widens, it is possible that more antigenic factors may have been involved in these changes. The evidence on the inverse proposition, namely, gene interaction in antigen production has been proved in several cases, some in Drosophila as well as in other species, the most recent example being the "hybrid antigen" discovered by Cohen in rabbits (1956).

The Compound Nature of H-2

According to Hoecker, Counce and Smith (loc. cit.) all these observations would, if taken together, support the allelic nature of complex blood-group inheritance. These authors tested a small sample of BC hybrids and demonstrated these antigens to be tightly linked, no cross-overs having been observed in some 100 mice, though results have been published on only 30.

A new light into this problem has been thrown by the discovery by Amos *et al.* (*loc. cit.*) and by Allen (1955), of phenotypic recombination between the H-2 antigenic components. These have been further confirmed by Dr. Gorer, the crossover value being approximately one per cent (personal communication). Three of the four authenticated cross-overs have separated antigen D from C and K and one has occurred between B and E. No test have yet been made on the rest of the associated antigens. In passing we should note that two new loci have been distinguished as a result of cross-overs. Thus, the *H-2* belongs in the already increasing list of compound loci with similar functions.

Crossing-over makes it necessary to submit to closer scrutiny the mutations already recorded at the *H-2* and points toward a greater antigenic complexity of this locus and to the need of a revision of present nomenclature. On the other hand the total mutational variability plus crossing over makes this chromosome segment a most attractive one for studies of polymorphism in nature.

The mutations observed by Borges *et al.* appeared, all of them, in strains of mice already inbred a great number of generations, their genetic uniformity being shown by the uniform susceptibility to transplants of tissues originating in the same isogenic strain. This would rule out crossing-over between heterozygotes to account for the mutants. The question now arises whether one or two or more genes may have mutated simultaneously since two of the gene-determined antigens involved in the change, C and E, bear no allelic relationship. If one surveys various inbred strains, we know that C and E may occur separately or together. Moreover, Gorer and Allen have shown that not only these two antigens are separable by crossing over but that other gene-determined antigens may also show recombination. Therefore, we can ask whether these loci within the *H-2* region are not mutationally independent, or else, whether the gene products are not independent. It seems to me that the apparent lack of interaction observed by Dr. Gorer in his crossover mice speaks against the second hypothesis: crossing over at D did not interfere with the serological specificities of C and K. Another explanation would involve a differential action of these loci on a common substrate, whose change would entail a multiple change of serological specificities. In any case the problem is left open.

If any one of these assumptions is right the question still remains of the allelic relations between antigenic factors. This is a much debated problem in Rh and other systems in humans (*cf.* Wiener and Wexler, and Stormont) and in spite of crossing over we are faced with difficulties. Some of the antigenic factors bear an oppositional relationship because they are characteristic of certain "alleles." Amos and Gorer and Mikulska (*loc. cit.*) assume that probably genes determining B, D, Q, P and I are homoallelic and that E and E^d are determined by a second pair of homoalleles. The relation of C, K and G and H is not clear and the information is not sufficient to ascribe to them any particular sequence. These authors "feel it preferable to try to fit the known *H-2* antigens into an orderly system than to record them as a jumble of unrelated and illegible symbols." This is a position entirely opposed to that of Stormont and of Wiener and implies, in addition to a one-to-one relation between genes and antigens, a linear order. A corollary of it is the postulation of allelic fators to C, G and K and presumably any other new antigens to be discovered in the same way as has been done by the British blood-group researchers in Rh and MNS systems. Whether some of the H-2 antigens are dependent on the presence of others for their expression as is the case for the K antigenic factor at the B locus in cattle or whether some *H-2* gene products are only haptenic or are immunologically inactive we do not know at present. This possibility is suggested for some of the vermillon pseudoalleles in *Drosophila* (*cf.* Barish and Fox) and would be a handicap to any test on allelism between blood group antigens. Therefore, I will leave this delicate problem untouched in the present context.

CONCLUDING REMARKS

It is clear from the preceding survey that the main factor in tissue compatibility as seen in transplantation experiments in mice, and by extension to other mammals, is the antigenic composition of cells, one of the best examples to date being perhaps that of the H-2 antigens. The rejection of a transplant is therefore an especially complex antigen-antibody reaction. This term is used *sensu lato*. The validity of this statement is firmly supported by several lines of evidence, all of them pointing to the need of an active antibody producing system as a *sine qua non* condition for the anti-graft reaction to take place (see reviews by Hauschka, 1952; and C. B. Favour, 1955).

The strong reactions against homotransplants elicited by some *H* loci as compared to the relative mildness of other loci seem to be related to the already unsettled problem of a possible physiological function of cell antigens (Boyd, 1947) and this, in turn, to their probable role in the well-known polymorphism exhibited by some blood-groups and types in man and other species. If this turns out to be the case we may anticipate the H-2 and perhaps related antigens in other species to mediate important cell functions. Gene clusters may evolve because certain key processes are best carried out when the initiating materials themselves are spatially closely integrated. (Pontecorvo, 1952). In this connection the use of the co-isogenic resistant and susceptible strains developed by Snell provide an almost unique biological material for this type of inquiry.

A final comment I would like to make concerns the graded range of genetical situations and interpretations found in the literature on complex antigens which stretches from apparently single genes as exemplified by the B system in cattle (Stormont, *loc. cit*) through complete linkage in the Rh system through a variable amount of separability by crossing-over. In this respect it seems to me that the extreme views about the genetic nature in these cases may be due more to methodological approach rather than to the biological realities involved in which case both theories may eventually come to a reconciliation.

REFERENCES

ALLEN, S. L., 1955, Linkage relations of the genes histocompatibility-2 and fused tail, brachyury and kinky tail in the mouse, as determined by tumor transplantation. Genetics *40:* 627–650.

AMOS, D. B., 1956, Serological differences between comparable diploid and tetraploid lines of three mouse ascites tumors. Ann. N. Y. Acad. Sci. *63:* 706–710.

AMOS, B., GORER, P. A., and MILKUSKA, Z. B., 1955a, An analysis of an antigenic system in the mouse (the H-2 system). Proc. Roy. Soc. B *144:* 369–379.

—— 1955b, The antigenic structure and genetic behaviour of a transplanted leukosis. Brit. J. Cancer 9- 209–215.

BARISH, N., and FOX, A. S., 1956, Immunogenetic studies of pseudo-allelism in *Drosophila melanogaster*. II. Antigenic effects of the vermillion pseudo-alleles. Genetics *41:* 45–57.

BILLINGHAM, R. E., BRENT, L., MEDAWAR, P. B., and SPARROW, E. M., 1954, Quantitative studies on tissue transplantation immunity. I. The survival times of skin homografts exchanged between members of different inbred strains of mice. Proc. Roy. Soc., B, *143:* 43–58.

BITTNER, J. J., 1934, Linkage in transplantable tumors. J. Genet. *29:* 17–27.

BORGES, P. R. F., KVEDAR, B. J., and FOERSTER, G. E., 1954, The development of an isogenic subline of mice (C57BL/6-H-2^d). Resistant to transplantable neoplasms indigenous to strain C57BL. J. Nat. Cancer Inst. *15:* 341–346.

BRILES, W. E., McGIBON, W. H., and IRWIN, M. R., 1950, On multiple alleles affecting cellular antigens in the chicken. Genetics *35:* 633–652.

CHOVNICK, A., and FOX, A. S., 1953, Studies of pseudoallelism in *Drosophila melanogaster*. I. Antigenic effects of the Lozenge pseudoalleles. Proc. Nat. Acad. Sci., Wash. *39:* 1035–1043.

COHEN, C., 1956, Occurrence of three red blood cell antigens in rabbits as the result of interaction of two genes. Science *123:* 935–936.

DYKE, S. C., 1922, Blood grouping and its clinical applications. Lancet *1:* 581.

EICHWALD, E. J., and SILMSER, C. R., 1955, Communication. Transpl. Bull. *2:* 148.

GORER, P. A., 1937, The genetic and antigenic basis of tumor transplantation. J. Path. Bact *44:* 691–697.

GORER, P. A., LYMAN, S., and SNELL, G. D., 1948, Studies on the genetic and antigenic basis of tumor transplantation. Linkage between a histocompatibility gene and "fused" in mice. Proc. Roy. Soc., London *135:* 499–505.

GORER, P. A., and MILKUSKA, Z. B., 1954, The antibody response to tumor inoculation. Improved methods of antibody detection. Cancer Res. *14:* 651–655.

HAUSCHKA, T., 1952, Immunologic aspects of cancer. A review. Cancer Res. *12:* 615–653.

—— 1953, Cell population studies on mouse ascites tumors. Trans, N. Y. Acad. Sci. *16:* 64–73.

—— 1955, Probable Y-linkage of a histocompatibility gene. Tr. Bull. *2:* 154–155.

HAUSCHKA, T., and LEVAN, A., 1953, Inverse relationship between chromosome ploidy and host-specificity of sixteen transplantable tumors. Exp. Cell. Res. *4:* 457–467.

HAUSCHKA, T. S., and SCHULTZ, J., 1954, Cytologic aspects of immunogenetic specificity. Transpl. Bull. *1:* 203–206.

HAUSCHKA, T. S., KVEDAR, B. J., GRINNELL, S. T., and AMOS, B. D., 1956, Immuno selection of polyploids from predominantly diploid cell populations. Ann. N. Y. Acad. Sc. *63:* 683–705.

HOECKER, G., COUNCE, A. J., and SMITH, P. M., 1954, The antigens determined by the *H-2* locus: a rhesus-like system in the mouse. Proc. Nat. Acad. Sci. Wash, *40:* 1040–1052.

HOECKER, G., PIZARRO, O., BRNCIC, D., and GASIC, G., 1955, Variation of virulence of transplantable leukemias of mice on successive transfers into genetically unrelated hosts. Cancer Res. *15:* 9–14.

LEVAN, A., and HAUSCHKA, T., 1952, Chromosome number of three mouse ascites tumors. Hereditas Lund. *38:* 251–255.

LEWIS, D., 1952, Serological reactions of pollen incompatibility substances. Proc. Roy. Soc. B *140:* 127–135.

LITTLE, C. C., 1950, The genetics of cancer. In: Genetics in the 20th Century, L. C. Dunn, Ed., New York, Macmillan.

LITTLE, C. C., and STRONG, L. C., 1954, Genetics studies on the transplantation of two adenocarcinomata. J. Exp. Zool. *41:* 93–114.

LOEB, L., 1945, The Biological Basis of Individuality. Springfield, Illinois, Charles C Thomas.

MacDOWELL, E. C., 1946, Variation in leukemic cells of mice. Cold Spr. Harb. Symp. Quant. Biol. *11:* 156–174.

MEDAWAR, P. B., Test by tissue culture methods on the nature of immunity to transplanted skin. Quart. J. Micr. Sci. *89:* 239–252.

RACE, R. R., and SANGER, R., 1954, Blood Groups in Man. Oxford, Blackwell.

SHAWAN, H. K., 1919, Principles of blood grouping applied to skin grafting. Amer. J. M. Sci. *157:* 503.

SNELL, G. D., 1956, A comment on Eichwald and Silmser communication. Transpl. Bull. *3:* 29–31.

—— 1951, A fifth allele at the histocompatibility-2 locus of the mouse as determined by tumor transplantation. J. Nat. Cancer Inst. *11:* 1299–1305.

—— 1948, Methods for the study of histocompatibility genes. J. Genet. *49:* 87–108.

—— 1952, Transplantable tumors. Chapter 14 in: Physiopathology of Cancer, Homburger and Fischman, Eds.

SNELL, G. D., SMITH, P. M., and GABRIELSON, F., 1953, Analysis of the histocompatibility-2 locus in the mouse. J. Nat. Cancer Inst. *14:* 457–480.

STORMONT, C., 1955, Linked genes, pseudoalleles and blood groups. Amer. Nat. *89:* 105–116.

STRONG, L. C., 1929, Transplantation studies on tumors arising spontaneously in heterozygous individuals. J. Cancer Res. *13:* 103–115.

WIENER, A. S., and WEXLER, I. B., 1956, The interpretation of blood groups reactions, with special reference to the serology and genetics of the Rh-Hr types. In: Novant' anni delle leggi mendeliane. L. Gedda, Ed. Rome, Instituto Gregario Mendel.

DISCUSSION

S. L. ALLEN: The difficulties of distinguishing a high mutation rate from a very low crossover rate are gargantuan in an organism such as the mouse. I was wondering if it would be possible to use some sort of functional relationship in order to characterize the loci within the *H-2* region. Perhaps you could apply the very delicate test of graft survival—tumor, or even the more refined test of skin transplant survival— which you have used in distinguishing the order of "strength" of the *H-2* and *H-3* loci, to co-isogenic lines differing within the *H-2* region. Perhaps you might be able to group the antigenic components into functionally separate units. Thus, one might be able to determine linearity along the chromosome, if one is so interested.

Hoecker: I would like to indicate that we may very probably find at the *H-2* locus a situation similar to that observed in man, that is, that a difference in only one antigenic factor within the complex is enough to provoke an incompatibility reaction. Evidence of this type for the E antigenic factor has been found by Dr. Avrion Mitchison in transplantation experiments in the mouse. If each antigen within the *H-2* complex behaves in this same way it will be a difficult task to separate them into functionally separate units.

Patterns of Biochemical and Developmental Pleiotropy

Ernst Hadorn[1]

Zoologisch-vergleichend anatomisches Institut der Universität Zürich

We usually classify mutations according to their most conspicuous effects. Thus lethal factors may be characterized by their final "patterns of damage" which eventually cause the death of the carriers. In the case of eye color genes we initially observe only the directly visible pigments. As a rule, however, these easily recognizable features are preceded and accompanied by an additional set of characters (phenes) which become apparent only by the use of special methods. The totality of all phenes, in which a mutant deviates from a normal or standard genotype, constitutes the "pleiotropic pattern of manifestation" of the respective gene or factor. Such a pleiotropy of genic action conditions biochemical and physiological, as well as morphological phenes (Hadorn, 1954). It is the aim of this report to describe and to analyze some new findings on different manifold patterns of pleiotropy. Earlier results have recently been reviewed (Hadorn, 1955a).

1. Abnormal Protein Metabolism in Mutants of *Drosophila*

a. Lethal-meander (*lme* 2-71 to 73) is a Mendelian factor which causes a standstill of growth and development at the beginning of the third larval instar (Fig. 1). The *lme* genotypes never enter upon metamorphosis but die after a period of time as rather small larvae. On the morphological level the *lme* mutant is characterized by a very disproportionate pattern of growth. By starving genetically normal larvae, my collaborator, Schmid (1949), could produce phenocopies of the *lme* type, the morphology of which corresponded completely with the mutant. It was therefore concluded that the *lme* factor might interfere in some way with the nutrition of the larvae. From some further experiments we were then able to assume that in particular a block in the protein metabolism would be responsible for the cessation of growth and development (*cf.* Hadorn, 1955a). We first examined with paper chromatography the free amino acids and peptides in body extracts of *lme* individuals (Chen and Hadorn, 1955). The chromatographic patterns of Figure 1 demonstrate the differences between the inventory of substances present in *lme* and in normal larvae at corresponding stages. Most characteristic of *lme* is an extreme impoverishment of amino acids, peptides and amides. First of all, most of the essential metabolites such as

[1] Our experiments were supported by grants from the Georges and Antoine Claraz-Schenkung. I am much indebted to my collaborator P.-D. Dr. P. S. Chen.

valine, leucine, histidine, arginine and lysine are completely absent. Of the others, such as threonine, only traces are present. In contrast to these losses we find, however, a very strong glycine spot (7 in Fig. 1). Apparently this simple metabolite is specifically accumulated in the lethal genotype.

We have now to ask how this special kind of disturbed and reduced protein metabolism is brought about. Four different possibilities should be considered: 1) Lethal larvae do not feed any more; 2) the lethals indeed take in food, but they are unable to digest the proteins; 3) feeding, as well as digestion, proceeds normally, but the resorption of amino acids is blocked in *lme*; 4) the *lme* factor interferes neither with feeding nor with digestion or resorption, but inhibits the synthesis of body proteins from the resorbed amino acids.

Experiments performed in order to decide between these possibilities gave the following results (Chen and Hadorn, 1955): We found in stages in which the lethal crisis was already in full progress, that the intestines of *lme* larvae were still filled with food. It was further found that feeding of sucrose to starved normal and *lme* larvae led, in both genotypes, to the same degree of increase of some amino acids, such as α-alanine in the hemolymph. It is well known that carbohydrates can be used as sources for the synthesis of certain nonessential amino acids. From these results we conclude that the intake of food is not hampered in *lme*, and we see further that in our lethals, the sugar is digested and its fractions resorbed and metabolized.

Feeding with proteins (pure caseine) led to a completely different result. Whereas, 12 hours after the meal, the hemolymph of starved normal larvae is literally overflowing with free amino acids, we found no traces of additional amino acids in the hemolymph of those *lme* larvae which were likewise fed with caseine (Fig. 2).

The question is now whether the inefficacy of caseine feeding is due to non-digestion of the protein, or to non-resorption of the amino acids. We put starved larvae of both genotypes on a medium which contained besides kaoline, the amino acids valine and leucine. After a few hours both metabolites are found in the same increased amount in the hemolymph of *lme* as in the normal controls. Thus *lme* is able to resorb amino acids from the gut.

Whether or not resorbed amino acids can be used by *lme* larvae for the synthesis of body proteins must still be shown by further experiments.

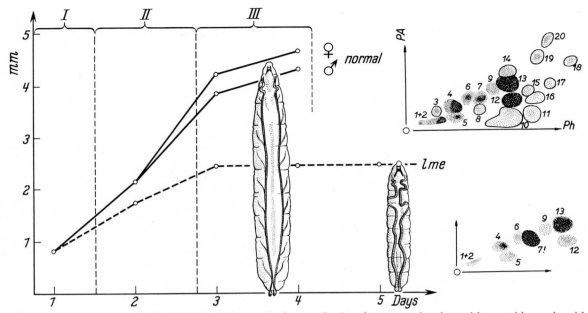

FIGURE 1. Growth curves of normal and lethal meander larvae (*lme*) and content of amino acids, peptides and amides in body extracts of the two genotypes, as revealed in two-dimensional paper chromatograms. Above, the normal; below, the *lme* pattern. The solvents used were n-propanol-ammonia (PA) and phenol (Ph). 1 + 2, 5, 8: peptides, 3: aspartic acid, 4: glutamic acid, 6: serine, 7: glycine, 9: threonine, 10: lysine, 11: arginine, 12: glutamine, 13 and 15: α- and β-alanine, 14: tyrosine, 16: histidine, 17: γ-amino butyric acid, 18: proline, 19: valine, 20: leucine and isoleucine. The substances missing in *lme*, but present in normals are encircled. Note the accumulation of glycine (7!) in *lme*. (After results from Schmid, 1949; Hadorn, 1955; Chen and Hadorn, 1955.)

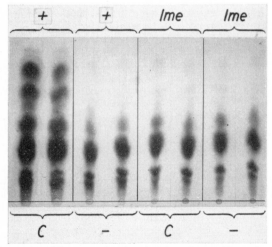

FIGURE 2. Photograph of a developed one-dimensional chromatogram treated with ninhydrin. At each starting spot the hemolymph of 5 larvae was released. Normal larvae, + ; lethals, *lme*. C, after feeding with caseine; —, without feeding. (From Chen and Hadorn, 1955.)

We know, however, that valine and leucine when injected directly into the hemolymph, disappear from this medium at the same rate in *lme* as in the normal controls.

All experiments so far reviewed make it most probable that lethality in *lme* results from an inability of this genotype to digest proteins. This interpretation can be corroborated by a further

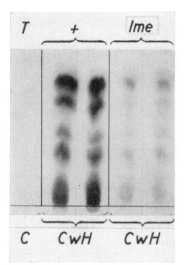

FIGURE 3. Proteolytic activity of homogenates (H) from intestines of normal larvae (+) and *lme* larvae. The photograph shows the free amino acids and peptides. C, the caseine substrate; C w H, caseine with the respective homogenates. (From Chen and Hadorn, 1955.)

experimental test. We homogenized intestines from normal and *lme* larvae and demonstrated their respective enzymatic activities *in vitro*. Figure 3 shows the result. The control solution of pure caseine contained no free amino acids. Much caseine was digested into free amino acids when a homogenate from normal intestine was added to the protein. In contrast to this strong effect, we see only slight traces of free amino acids in the chromatograms made with a solution taken from cultured test tubes which contained, besides casein, the *lme* homogenate. We do not know whether these spots result from digested caseine or from the homogenized *lme* tissues. In any case we can now conclude that a much reduced activity of the proteolytic enzymes in gut tissue is, at least to a decisive extent, responsible for the pleiotropic disturbances of the protein metabolism found in the *lme* mutant. It might however be that the *lme* factor affects in an independent way still other physiological processes which are primarily essential for growth and metamorphosis. This reservation must be made because the above mentioned starvation phenocopies, though morphologically identical with the mutant, do indeed differ in some biochemical phenes from the *lme* genotype (Chen and Hadorn, 1955; Hadorn, 1955a).

b. *Lethal-translucida* (*ltr* 3-20.7 ± 0.8) is a mutant of *Drosophila melanogaster* in which there accumulates, during the second half of larval life, a tremendous amount of hemolymph (Fig. 4). Nevertheless these bloated larvae are able to pupate and to reach a certain degree of partial metamorphosis (Hadorn, 1949; Sobels and Nijenhuis, 1953). Several later investigations (*cf.* Hadorn, 1954, 1955a) revealed some of the biochemical and physiological traits which might be at the base of the ensuing developmental and morphological pattern of damage. The total amount of free amino acids and peptides has been determined per individual (Hadorn and Stumm-Zollinger, 1953). We see from the columns of Figure 4A that this group of substances hardly changes in normal larvae from 84 hours until metamorphosis. This is remarkable since there is much growth during this period. We found, however, the concentration of amino acids and peptides in the hemolymph to be steadily decreasing before metamorphosis (Fig. 4A, curve). The free metabolites which are available in the

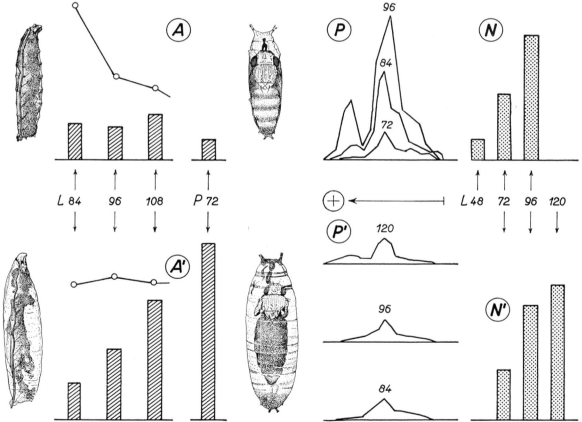

FIGURE 4. The biochemical and developmental traits of normal larvae (L) and pupae (P), above, as compared with corresponding stages of the mutant lethal translucida (*ltr*), below. The figures (48–120) refer to the age in hours after egg laying for larvae and after puparium formation for pupae; 25°C. A and A': differences in amino acids and peptides. The columns stand for the total amount of ninhydrine positive substances (mean values per individual, measured from paper chromatograms). The curves indicate the change in the concentration per unit of volume of free amino acids and peptides present in the hemolymph. P and P': the amount of protein per equal volumes of hemolymph present in different larval stages as determined with paper electrophoresis. The two peaks indicate the two main protein fractions. Arrow: direction of flow toward the anode. N and N': the total nitrogen content per individual. (Combined from data and figures of Hadorn and Stumm-Zollinger, 1953; Hadorn, 1955; Chen, 1956.)

hemolymph apparently are used more and more for the synthesis of body proteins. Thus in larvae ready for pupation (108 hours) there is, in relation to the cell substance, much less of free amino acids and peptides present than in earlier stages. In older pupae we find still less of these substances (last column in Fig. 4A). The *ltr* larvae and pupae exhibit a metabolic pattern that corresponds inversely to the events which proceed in normal genotypes (Fig. 4A'). The content of amino acids per individual increases up to a level which surpasses by six to seven times the normal amount; simultaneously the concentration in the hemolymph remains constant during the intensive growth period. The lethal genotype grows indeed, but it seems to grow from the third instar on, mainly at a low level of amino acids and peptides.

In order to test this interpretation it was necessary to determine the protein content of the decisive developmental stages. This was recently done by Chen (1956) with electrophoretic and colorimetric methods. By using a current of 160 volts and 4 milliampères and in a buffer solution of pH 8.6, two main fractions, which migrate towards the anode, could be separated. The respective results for equal volumes of hemolymph are shown in the diagrams of Figure 4, P and P'. We see that in normal larvae both protein fractions increase steadily from 72 hours until 96 hours. For comparison, corresponding determinations were made with hemolymph from the lethals. Since the *ltr* genotypes develop more slowly than the normals, the hemolymph of older stages (84–120 hours) was used. Within this period hardly any increase in proteins was found. We see now that in *ltr* the abnormally high accumulation of amino acids and peptides is correlated with a corresponding lack of protein synthesis in the hemolymph. Does this statement hold true also for the body as a whole? We have not yet determined the total protein content of the larvae. But if *ltr* differs from normals only in that the developmental shift from amino acids and peptides to proteins is blocked, we should find the same content of nitrogen in corresponding stages of both genotypes. This is actually the case. The stippled columns at the right border of Figure 4 (N and N') demonstrate this fact. They are based on a micro-Kjeldahl technic. It is clear that the increase of nitrogen containing compounds reaches, in *ltr* larvae at least, the same level as in normals. This growth process is only slightly delayed in *ltr*.

Though we now know that the *ltr* factor interferes with a normal synthesis of proteins, we are not certain that we have therewith discovered the only and the primary point of attack of our mutant. In any case we have to explain why *ltr* accumulates so much water in its hemolymph. This could be the direct consequence of the unused amino acids which increase the osmotic pressure. But there is an alternative possibility to be considered. If for instance the Malpighian tubes or

the anal organ would not function properly, an abnormal accumulation of water could result. Some regulative mechanism could then retain the available amino acids in the hemolymph, thereby protecting the animal from being destroyed by hypotonia. In this case the pleiotropic anomalies in the protein metabolism would be merely the secondary effects of a primarily disturbed osmoregulation.

Such an alternative interpretation has been discussed tentatively by Hadorn and Stumm-Zollinger (1953) and by Stumm-Zollinger (1954). My collaborator Zwicky (1954) found however no increase in free amino acids in genetically normal larvae of *Drosophila* which had been immersed in distilled water. The osmoregulation is, under these conditions, mainly due to concentration changes of the chlorides. Furthermore, we found even in younger stages, that is, before the extensive accumulation of body fluid becomes apparent, that the lethals are much poorer in proteins than the corresponding normals.

c. Conclusions. The two mutants lethal-meander (*lme*) and lethal-translucida (*ltr*) interfere with the protein metabolism of the larvae, but the main targets of attack are different. Whereas in *lme* the digestion of proteins becomes insufficient, the *ltr* genotype is unable to use the resorbed amino acids for a normal synthesis of proteins. Both factors act as lethals; *lme* prevents the onset and *ltr* the end-phase of metamorphosis. Both mutants exhibit their locus-specific pattern of damage on a biochemical, physiological and morphological level. The inventory of substances is, as far as the amino acids and peptides are concerned, specifically altered. In *lme* most of the essential amino acids are lacking or much reduced, except glycine which reaches an abnormally high concentration (Fig. 1). As to *ltr* we have so far only referred to the tremendous accumulation of the total ninhydrin positive substances. It could be shown (Stumm-Zollinger, 1954) that not all amino acids and peptides take part in this increase. There are mainly the simpler compounds such as glycine, serine, ornithine, lysine, cystine and glutamine which are much accumulated, whereas other substances, such as proline, tyrosine and several peptides are even less concentrated in *ltr* than in normal hemolymph. We do not yet understand the genic and physiological basis of such a complicated pleiotropy. We can only state that mutations at different loci lead to very different biochemical patterns and from here we might extrapolate that the respective normal alleles have each their locus-specific functions too. There is much work ahead of us and many more mutants must be thoroughly studied before we shall understand how developmental processes are governed by the specific functions of genes.

For *lme* and *ltr*, there remains a further enigma as yet unsolved. We do not understand why these mutants only become abnormal and moribund in later stages of life. The former is at first able to digest proteins and the latter synthesizes proteins in earlier larval life. We can only conclude that each developmental step requires its own set of genic actions (phase specificity).

Each pleiotropic pattern is composed of one or more primary characters which are directly and intrinsically caused by the genetic constitution (autophenes), and of a set of characters which are not due to a genic action intrinsic to the character-forming cells (allophenes; *cf.* Hadorn, 1955a). The size and the developmental performance of some primordia within *lme* and *ltr* larvae are to be classified as allophenes. Transplantation experiments (Hadorn, 1949; Schmid, 1949; Sobels, 1950) proved that primordia of eyes and gonads dissected from *lme* or *ltr* larvae become normally differentiated in normal hosts, where they can participate in the normal protein metabolism.

2. THE PLEIOTROPIC ACTION OF EYE COLOR GENES

It has been shown that genes which change the eye colors of *Drosophila* or *Ephestia* affect in a pleiotropic way the amount and the occurrence of different fluorescent substances (Hadorn and Mitchell, 1951; Hadorn and Kühn, 1953). Some of these substances are now identified as pterines (Forrest and Mitchell, 1954a and b, 1955; Hadorn, 1954b; Nawa and Taira, 1954; De Lerma and de Vincentiis, 1955; Viscontini, Schoeller, Loeser, Karrer and Hadorn, 1955; Viscontini, Loeser, Karrer and Hadorn, 1955a and b). In the following sections we will consider a selected group of facts and problems which are of general interest and which deserve still more thorough studies.

a. On the interrelationship of biochemical phenes. In order to study the correlation between substances which are pleiotropically affected by different genes we might first classify a series of mutants of *Drosophila melanogaster* according to the amount of red eye pigments (Hadorn, 1951). Such a grouping is made in Table 1. We find a maximal quantity of pigments in the wild type ($++++$) and different degrees of reduction in the groups 2–6 ($+++$; $++$; $+$). No red pigments are present in lz^{cl} and *se* ($-$). We have now to see how the pterines react to a gene conditioned decrease of the red eye pigments. The isoxanthopterine by no means follows the behavior of the red eye pigments in all of the mutants. A somewhat parallel reduction is only apparent in groups 2, 3 and 6, while in other mutants a normal amount of isoxanthopterine was found even in cases in which only few (4 and 6) or no red eye pigments at all (7 and 8) are formed.

A similar lack of correlation holds true for other pterines. Under the heading "pterines of the HB-group" three compounds are taken together which were measured only as a group on account of their poor separation in one-dimensional chromatograms. These substances are: $HB_1 = $ 2-amino-6-oxy-pterine; $HB_2 = $ a pterine with blue fluorescence, the constitution of which is not yet clear;

TABLE 1. APPROXIMATE AMOUNTS OF RED EYE PIGMENTS AND BODY PTERINES IN DIFFERENT GENOTYPES OF *Drosophila melanogaster*

The number of $+$ signs indicates the relative quantities. $++++ = $ normal amount. $- = $ substance not present.

Group	Genotypes	Red Eye Pigments	Isoxanth-opterine	Pterines of the HB-Group
1	wild type	$++++$	$++++$	$++++$
2	v, st	$+++$	$+++$	$++++$
3	pr, car, ltd	$++$	$++$	$++++$
4	ca, pn^2	$+$	$++++$	$++++$
5	ry^2	$+$	$-$	$++++++$
6	p^p, g^2	$+$	$+$	$++$
7	lz^{cl}	$-$	$++++$	$++$
8	se	$-$	$++++$	$++++++++$

a yellow pterine which becomes highly increased in the sepia mutant, and which has been isolated and analyzed by Forrest and Mitchell (1954a, b). In addition to the three pterines, our HB group may also contain some riboflavine. The HB substances show all possible kinds of relation to the red eye pigments. We find a parallel decrease in group 6 and 7, no reaction to the eye color gene occurs in groups 2–4 and a great exaggeration takes place in some genotypes (5 and 8) which are weak or deficient in the red pigments. Furthermore there is no regular parallelism between the isoxanthopterine and the HB-pterines.

From these results, though of preliminary quantitative precision, we conclude that each mutant influences the inventory of substances in a specific way. Observations made only on single mutants could thus lead to a false interpretation of the causal relationship which might connect the different biochemical traits. It is unwise to put forward a general theory on such a very special basis. One would be prone for instance to assume from the ry^2 (rosy) and the sepia (*se*) cases that there is a very strong overproduction in the HB-substances because only a few or no red pigments are formed. A precursor or transformation hypothesis seems to be justified. But garnet (g^2) and lozenge-clawless (lz^{cl}) are likewise deficient in red pigments; and reduction in the HB-substances is however found here. The genic interactions and the physiological connections on which the observed pleiotropic biochemical patterns are based, apparently are of a rather complex nature and they cannot easily be reconstructed by mere observation of the final results as shown by single mutants.

b. Organ-specific pleiotropic patterns. Hadorn and Mitchell (1951) have shown that the different organs of *Drosophila* each contain a specific set of fluorescent substances. The differences between eyes, testes, ovaries, Malpighian tubes and other organs are partly of a qualitative nature insofar as some substances are restricted to one or a few organs; in addition, large quantitative

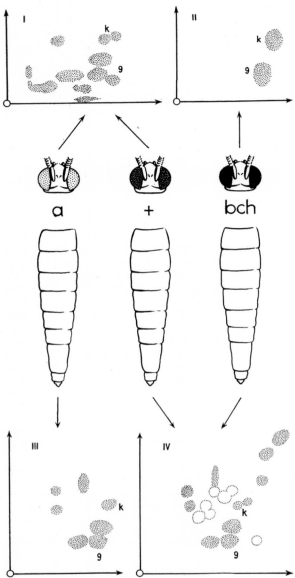

FIGURE 5. Organ specificity of biochemical pleiotropy in three genotypes of *Ephestia kühniella*, *a*, + and *bch*. The diagrams above the heads show the set of fluorescent substances present in eyes as revealed by two-dimensional paper chromatograms (I for *a* and +; II for *bch*). Below we see the inventory of substances present in abdomens (III for *a*; IV for + and *bch*). The letters near two fluorescent spots indicate isoxanthopterine (g) and 2-amino-6-oxy-pterine (k). (After results from Hadorn and Kühn, 1953; Hadorn and Egelhaaf, 1956.)

differences are found. We may now ask how mutations affect these organ-specific distributions, and we wish to know whether or not a gene causes biochemical changes in every organ in the same direction. These questions could be studied on two mutants of the meal moth, *Ephestia kühniella*.

It was first found (Hadorn and Kühn, 1953) that a black eyed mutant "biochemica" (*bch*)

contains, in its eyes, only two fluorescent substances, which were identified by Prof. M. Viscontini (unpub.) as isoxanthopterine and 2-amino-6-oxy-pterine (spots g and k in Fig. 5, II). These pterines are present however in a very high concentration. In contrast to the simple *bch* inventory, the chromatograms of the brown-blackish wild type eyes (+) show a manifold set of different substances (Fig. 5, I). Almost the same compounds are formed in the red eyes of the mutant *a*; yet there are some striking qualitative differences among the substances of + and *a*, which are not shown in Figure 5.

We first thought that *bch* would not be able to synthesize more than the two pterines. To our surprise, however, we found in the abdomen of *bch* a set of substances of quite the same richness and the same quantities as in + abdomen (Fig. 5, IV; Hadorn and Egelhaaf, 1956). On the other hand the *a*-abdomen produces a smaller amount of different fluorescent substances than normal (+) or *bch* abdomens (Fig. 5, III).

Thus the organ-specific substrates which are different in eyes and abdomens determine to a great extent the biochemical pleiotropy of genes like *bch* and *a*. In the eyes the *bch* factor meets a condition which leads to the described restriction in formation and deposition of pterines, whereas the abdominal cell systems allow—in spite of the presence of the *bch* locus—the manifestation of a normal biochemical pattern. For the *a*-gene, the situation is somewhat reversed. It is true that we find a pleiotropic effect on fluorescent substances also in the eyes where no ommochrome pigments are formed. But the difference from the normal genotype is more pronounced in the *a*-abdomen. In this connection it should be mentioned that a main part of the abdominal fluorescent substances become concentrated in all genotypes in the excretion material.

How organ-specific conditions or structures may influence the manifestation of a gene can be seen in the case of the white eyed mutant (*wa*) of *Ephestia* (Hanser, 1948; Kühn, 1956). In the *wa* eyes no protein granules are formed. Since these structures act as the sites where normally the end phase of pigment synthesis is proceeding, the *wa* genotype lacks the visible eye pigment. It is likewise deficient in fluorescent pterines.

From the reported facts it follows that the character forming function of a gene and its pleiotropic manifestation do vary, in an organ-specific way, according to the local biochemical and physiological conditions and structures in different cell systems which build up a body.

c. Developmental changes and excretion. It was first reported that *Drosophila* imagoes of the genotypes white (*w*) and brown (*bw*) do not contain any fluorescent substances (Hadorn and Mitchell, 1951). But this statement holds true only for flies which are older than two days. Further chromatographic investigations brought an unexpected result. In pupae and young flies we found pterine pigments in w and bw individuals also (Hadorn and Kürsteiner, 1955). These substances become accumulated during metamorphosis till they reach a maximum in old pupae. After hatching, that is, during the first two days of imaginal life, the pterines gradually disappear from the bodies of the flies. This rise and fall is shown for isoxanthopterine in the diagram (w) of Figure 7. We measured this compound comparatively in different stages of w and normal pupae and flies. In normal males ($+$) the isoxanthopterine increases steadily and it remains at the peak high level throughout life. The w males too store up isoxanthopterine, but considerably less than the normals. There are still distinct quantities of this substance present in one day old w flies. At the third day of imaginal life, however, practically all isoxanthopterine has vanished, and in still older flies, none of it is left. (Our curve does not reach the zero level on account of some other substance of weak fluorescence which has the same Rf-value as isoxanthopterine.)

What happens in the w genotypes to the isoxanthopterine and to all the other fluorescent substances which likewise disappear? A first approach to an explanation was gained from a chromatographic study of the excretion material which is deposited by the flies after hatching. From w and $+$ animals kept without food, we collected the small "flat cakes" of this meconium and chromatographed it. (Hadorn and Kürsteiner, 1955). The amount of each substance was determined fluorometrically. The columns of Figure 6 show the inventory of substances and the relative quantity of each one. For one chromatogram we used the excretion material from 80 to 100 flies. It is evident that the meconia of w animals are qualitatively richer: the substances 4/5 e and 7 are not found in $+$ chromatograms. Furthermore it is most impressive that some pterines, as 3g, 4/5 a and 4/5 c, are much more abundant in the w than in the $+$ excretions.

How are we to interpret the fact that the w mutant excretes much more pterines than the wild type? Neither red nor brown eye pigments

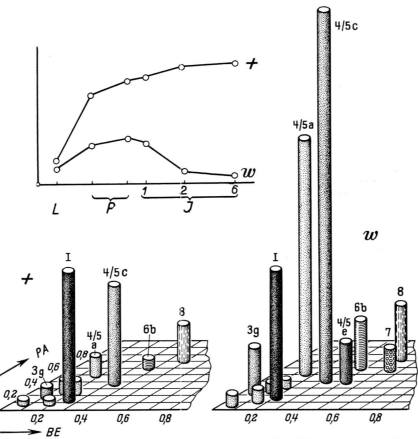

FIGURE 6. Biochemical differences between normal genotypes ($+$) and the white mutant (w) of *Drosophila melanogaster*. The curves represent the mean quantities of isoxanthopterine present in males of different developmental stages: L, larvae before metamorphosis; P, younger and older pupae; J, 1, 2, 6 imagoes one, two and six days after hatching. The diagrams with the columns show the set of fluorescent substances found in corresponding quantities of meconial excrements, for $+$ (left) and w (right). Distribution with Rf-values in two-dimensional chromatograms developed in n-propanol-ammonia (PA) and butanol-acetic acid (BE). The heights of the columns indicate the relative quantities as measured fluorometrically. (After Hadorn, 1954a; Hadorn and Kürsteiner, 1955.)

are formed in *w* pupae. It is possible, but so far unproved, that there exist metabolites which are used in normal genotypes for the synthesis of eye pigments as well as for pterines. In *w* (and *bw*) these substances would not be used, and after having been metabolized to pterines they would be excreted. It could even be that some pterines might be directly engaged in pigment formation. In this case too they would become superfluous. But the situation is by no means simple. We do not understand why normal flies keep a considerable amount of pterines after the formation of eye pigments, whereas *w* flies excrete all of them. This fact may, however, explain why in *w* and + meconia we meet approximately the same amount of isoxanthopterine (J in Fig. 7). The white mutant does initially form less of this compound, but excretes all of it; the normal genotype builds up much more isoxanthopterine, but gives it off only partly.

Not every eye color mutant influences the biochemical pleiotropy of excretion. No difference was, for instance, found between the meconia of + and *se* flies. This is to be expected if the *se* gene would affect only the end phase of pigment metabolism. On the other hand the manifold effect of the *w* factor on the pattern of substances in the meconia might be the consequence of a metabolic block at a more fundamental level, which would influence many biochemical processes directly or indirectly.

For mammals the investigation of biochemical properties of excreted material has led, since the classical work of A. E. Garrod on man, to many a valuable insight into genic function. Our preliminary experiences on insect meconia might show that it will also be worth while to study the inventory of excreted substances in different mutants of *Drosophila* and *Ephestia*.

3. The Mutant Rosy[2]

The new eye color mutant (*ry²*) was isolated from one of our *cn bw* stocks of *Drosophila melanogaster*. Since this genotype showed a set of very interesting and specific features in chromatograms, we investigated it more carefully. A first group of observations and experimental results have been published recently (Hadorn and Schwinck, 1956a, b).

The mutant factor was located (3-51±) and later crossed with many available eye color mutants of the third chromosome. Our gene behaves as an allele of rosy.

a. Pleiotropy of action. The pleiotropic pattern of manifestation of the *ry²* mutant is characterized, among other features, by the following main phenes. The eyes are dark reddish brown; in combination with *cn* they become orange (many of our experiments were carried out with a *cn ry²* stock). The amount of red eye pigments is very much reduced in *ry²* and still more in *cn ry²* (Fig. 7). Most characteristic of the mutant is the complete lack of isoxanthopterine in all developmental stages. This substance is generally present in arthropods and we found it in all of 28 *Drosophila* mutants so far tested. On the other hand there is much more of the HB-pterines present in rosy² than in the wild type. The Malpighian tubes of rosy² show in all stages signs of abnormality, they are shortened, bloated, and contain in their lumen characteristic concrements of a yellow to orange colored excretion material. Rosy² behaves at 25°C as a semilethal. More than half of the homozygotes die either as fully differentiated pupae or as weak imagines shortly after hatching. At a lower temperature (18°C) the viability is considerably improved.

In connection with the topics of our Symposium, only a few of the problems which we came across during the work on rosy² will be discussed.

b. The correlation between red eye pigments and pterines. The reduction of red eye pigments in *ry²* is pleiotropically accompanied by the lack in isoxanthopterine and the exaggeration of HB-pterines. Other mutants with reduced or missing red pigments show a quite different genic action on pterines (Table 1). Thus no general conclusions as to the causal relations between red pigments and pterines should be drawn from the rosy² case. Nevertheless, we can investigate the reaction of the pterines to experimental influences which change the amount of red pigments in *ry²*. First, it was found that the eyes of *cn ry²* individuals become yellow orange at 28°, orange at 22°, and reddish orange at 18°. Thus a lower temperature acts in the direction of an approach to normal as far as the red pigments are concerned. This effect is paralleled, as already mentioned, by a rise in viability. If the excessive HB pterines of *ry²* would also be influenced by a decreasing temperature toward the normal standard, they should become less concentrated at 18° than at 22° or 28°.

We determined fluorometrically the quantities of both the red eye pigments and the HB pterines from many chromatographed individuals which had been bred at different temperatures, between 28° and 18° respectively. The results are summarized in the form of a correlation diagram in Figure 7. It is clear that an increase in the red pigments is paralleled by an increase in HB pterines. Thus the more normal the eye color of *ry²* becomes, the more the amount of HB pterines deviates from the normal standard. A similar paradoxical reaction was also found in *ry²* individuals in which the content of the red pigments was normalized by the action of implanted + Malpighian tubes (*cf.* Fig. 9). These facts have to be considered as a base for an eventual interpretation of the possible gene conditioned biochemical connections between the different substances of the *ry²* pattern. In contrast to the opposite behavior of the two groups of substances in *ry²*, Kühn and Egelhaaf (1955) found for the mutant *a* of *Ephestia* a parallel reaction to injected kynurenine. The eyes become normal with respect to the formation of ommochrome pigment, and the pterines, which are abundant in untreated *a*-genotypes, decrease to a normal level.

c. Nonautonomous formation of red eye pigments. The well known work of G. W. Beadle, B. Ephrussi, E. L. Tatum, C. W. Clancy, A. Kühn, E. Caspari, A. Butenandt and others on the biochemical role of genes in the formation of the brown insect eye pigments was possible, because a few eye color mutants do not behave autonomously. A corresponding analysis of the red eye pigments in *Drosophila* was until now hampered by the fact that all available mutants seemed to behave autonomously. Our ry^2 mutant proved to be a very welcome exception.

Numerous transplantations of larval eye anlagen (imaginal discs) were made by using reciprocally as hosts or donors the ry^2 mutant, and a series of other genotypes. The eye discs metamorphose well within the abdomen. They were dissected from the flies, inspected and each of them individually chromatographed. The amount of red eye pigments could then be determined fluorometrically. One eye of each host was likewise treated, and its pigments measured. By this method we gained information on the quantities of red pigments in eyes, as transplants as well as *in situ*.

Figure 8 summarizes the results of one set of experiments. The length of each column represents the mean quantity of red pigment per eye as calculated from 10 to 16 individuals. From experiments I and II it follows that a transplanted eye anlage, when of the same genetic constitution as the host, never reaches in the abdomen the same amount of eye pigment as an eye *in situ*. Experiment III shows the nonautonomous pigment formation in ry^2 transplants; the ry^2 eyes become, in the abdomen of + hosts, wild type colored and they contain as much red pigment as the + transplants in + hosts. But we observe also in the reciprocal experiment IV an interesting fact. Here, a genetically normally + implant reaches, in a ry^2 host, a scarcely higher pigment level than an implanted ry^2 eye in a ry^2 host (II). On the other hand, we find in experiment IV a higher amount (statistically significant) of pigments in the hosts eye than in experiment II. Thus the + implant can promote to a certain extent pigment formation in ry^2 hosts.

In analogy to the work done on the brown pigments of *Drosophila* we may now tentatively postulate a "ry^+ substance" which would be abundant in normal genotypes but scanty in the ry^2 mutant. Normal hosts would supply this substance to ry^2 implants, therein inducing the wild type eye color. But anlagen of + eyes also seem to be dependent to a certain extent on the supply of ry^+ substances. This follows from the fact that the + implants are not "self sufficient" in ry^2 hosts (Experiment IV). Such a situation reminds one of the "claret effect" on the brown eye pig-

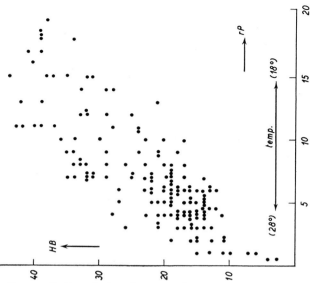

FIGURE 7. Correlations between the amount of red eye pigments (rP) and HB-pterines (HB) in ry^2 eyes of *Drosophila melanogaster*. Each point indicates the fluorometric value of the two groups of substances as determined from chromatographed single individuals. The figure gives furthermore approximate information as to the temperature dependence of the measured substances.

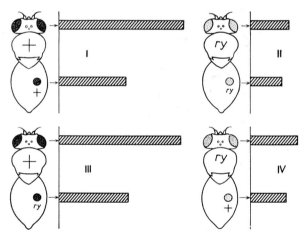

FIGURE 8. Amount of red pigments found *in situ* and in implanted eyes. The genotype of the host is marked on the thorax, that of the implant on the abdomen: +, wild type; ry^2, rosy². The columns represent mean quantities. (After data of Hadorn and Schwinck, 1956b.)

ments (Ephrussi and Chevais, 1938; Clancy, 1942). Though we have as yet no direct proof as to the existence of the ry^+ substance, we may use our interpretation as a provisional working hypothesis.

It could be shown by further transplantations that the ry^+ substance cannot be the red eye pigment itself; genotypes like *ca, ma, p, bw, se* and *w*, which produce only a little or none of the red pigments, are as successful as the red eyed wild

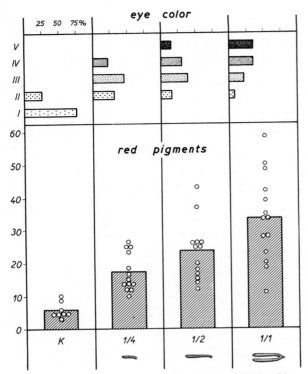

FIGURE 9. Relations between the size of + Malpighian tube implants and the quantity of red eye pigments found in the *cn ry²* hosts. K control without implantation; ¼, ½ and ⅟₁ differently sized implants as shown below. The upper part of the diagram refers to a classification based on mere external inspection of the hosts eye color. I yellow orange, II orange, III deep orange, IV almost red, V full red like wild type. Here the horizontal columns indicate the percentage distribution of cases to the estimated color classes I to V. In the lower part of the figure each circle points to the fluorometrically measured quantity of red pigments as present in chromatographed individual heads. The broad columns stand for the mean of the controls and the three experimental series (ordinate: 0–60).

types in helping the *ry²* implants to reach the normal red eye color. We implanted furthermore several larval organs of + donors into *ry²* hosts in order to find out which of them could supply the *ry⁺* substance. Most effective are Malpighian tubes and fat bodies; evidently less help comes from eyes, as shown in Figure 8, IV. On the other hand no *ry⁺* substance was released from implanted larval testes, ovaries and salivary glands.

By implanting different quantities of cell material of Malphighian tubes from normal donors (+) the results shown in Figure 9 were obtained. In this unselected sample where all cases of the experimental series are plotted, we find a rather great variability, which may be due to differences in successful implantation. It is, however, evident that the amount of red eye pigments in the *cn ry²* hosts increases roughly proportionally to the implanted cell material. With one whole pair of tubes (1/1) we reached, in the best cases, the full color amount of a wild type eye.

d. *Nonautonomous formation or accumulation of*

isoxanthopterine. The *ry²* mutant forms, as already mentioned, no isoxanthopterine. But if we implant Malpighian tubes, fat bodies, eyes or testes from + donors into *ry²* larvae, we find after metamorphosis, in chromatograms of host flies, a distinct isoxanthopterine spot. Ovaries and salivary glands are ineffective. It could be shown that the "nonautonomous" substance is most concentrated in the *ry²* testes. Two interpretations are to be considered: Either the isoxanthopterine is actually formed in the *ry²* organs, or the implanted + organs release complete isoxanthopterine molecules, which are then stored only in the *ry²* organs. So far, no experiments have been made which could decide between these alternative possibilities. However, as a result of some further observations we are inclined to favor the first interpretation, that implanted + fat bodies, which themselves contain only traces of isoxanthopterine, cause the *ry²* testes to contain considerable amounts of this substance.

It will be most interesting to study, in the *ry²* mutant, the relations between the nonautonomous formation of additional red eye pigments and the appearance of isoxanthopterine which is a true "foreign" substance to this genotype.

Summary

1. It is shown how two lethal factors (*lme* and *ltr*) of *Drosophila melanogaster* interfere with the normal protein metabolism. In the lethal meander mutant (*lme*) the proteolitic activity of the intestines becomes insufficient, whereas the lethal translucida mutant (*ltr*) fails in the synthesis of body proteins from the resorbed amino acids. Each genotype is characterized by a pleiotropic and locus-specific pattern of manifestation on the biochemical, physiological and morphological level.

2. From studies of different eye color mutants of *Drosophila* and *Ephestia* the following results are obtained:

a. The gene conditioned interrelation of eye pigments with a series of fluorescent substances (pterines) is of a complex nature and becomes altered by each mutant in a locus-specific way.

b. The deviation caused by a given mutation from the normal or standard inventory of substances varies to a great extent in different cell systems of an organism.

c. Eye color genes can affect, pleiotropically, a set of pterines which are excreted with the pupal meconium.

3. a. The pleiotropic action of a new eye color mutant rosy² (*ry²*) is described and discussed.

b. Rosy² forms only a small amount of red eye pigments and lacks completely the isoxanthopterine, but accumulates abnormally high quantities of other pterines.

c. Eye primordia of *ry²* form a normal amount of red pigment when they are grown as implants in wild type hosts or in other *ry⁺* genotypes. Such a nonautonomous development can also be induced in *ry²* hosts in eyes *in situ*, through different implanted organs of ry^+ constitution. Transplanted + eyes in ry^2 hosts are unable to form the normal red eye color; they reach only the pigment level of the ry^2 genotype.

d. In ry^2 organs a nonautonomous formation or accumulation of isoxanthopterine has been demonstrated experimentally.

e. The ry^2 mutant is considered as suitable for studying the genic and biochemical basis of the formation of red pigments and pterines.

REFERENCES

CHEN, P. S., 1956, Elektrophoretische Bestimmung des Proteingehaltes im Blut normaler und letaler (ltr) Larven von Drosophila melanogaster. Rev. suisse Zool. (in press).

CHEN, P. S., and HADORN, E., 1955, Zur Stoffwechselphysiologie der Mutante letal-meander (lme) von Drosophila melanogaster. Rev. suisse Zool. 62: 338–347.

CLANCY, C. W., 1942, The development of eye colors in Drosophila melanogaster. Further studies on the mutant claret. Genetics 27: 417–440.

EPHRUSSI, B., and CHEVAIS, S., 1938, Développement des couleurs des yeux chez la Drosophile: Relations entre production, utilisation et libération des substances diffusibles. Bull. biol. France et Belg. 72: 48–78.

FORREST, H. S., and MITCHELL, H. K., 1954a, Pteridines from Drosophila. I. Isolation of a yellow pigment. J. Amer. Chem. Soc. 76: 5656–5658.
1954b, Pteridines from Drosophila. II. Structure of the yellow pigment. J. Amer. Chem. Soc. 76: 5658–5662.
1955, Pteridines from Drosophila. III. Isolation and identification of three more pteridines. J. Amer. Chem. Soc. 77: 4865–4869.

HADORN, E., 1949, Zur Entwicklungsphysiologie der Mutante "letaltranslucida" (ltr) von Drosophila melanogaster. Rev. suisse Zool. 56: 271–280.
1951, Chromatographische Trennung und Messung fluoreszierender Stoffe bei Augenfarb-Mutanten von Drosophila melanogaster. Arch. Jul. Klaus-Stiftg. 26: 470–475.
1954a, Approaches to the study of biochemical and developmental effects of mutations. Caryologia, Suppl. to Vol. 6: 326–337.
1954b, Ontogenetische Aenderungen im Gehalt an Isoxanthopterin bei verschiedenen Genotypen von Drosophila malanogaster. Experientia 10: 483–484.
1955, Letalfaktoren in ihrer Bedeutung für Erbpathologie und Genphysiologie der Entwicklung. Stuttgart, Georg Thieme.

HADORN, E., and EGELHAAF, A., 1956, Biochemische Polyphänie und Stoffverteilung im Körper verschiedener Augenfarb-Genotypen von Ephestia kühniella. Z. Naturforsch. 11b: 21–25.

HADORN, E., and KÜHN, A., 1953, Chromatographische und fluorometrische Untersuchungen zur biochemischen Polyphänie von Augenfarb-Genen bei Ephestia kühniella. Z. Naturforsch. 8b: 582–589.

HADORN, E., and KÜRSTEINER, R., 1956, Unterschiede in Exkretstoffen bei verschiedenen Genotypen von Drosophila melanogaster. Arch. Jul. Klaus-Stiftg. 30: 494–498.

HADORN, E., and MITCHELL, H. K., 1951, Properties of mutants of Drosophila melanogaster and changes during development as revealed by paper chromatography. Proc. Nat. Acad. Sci. Wash. 37: 650–665.

HADORN, E., and SCHWINCK, I., 1956a, A mutant of Drosophila without isoxanthopterine which is nonautonomous for the red eye pigments. Nature, Lond. 177: 940–941.
1956b, Fehlen von Isoxanthopterin und Nicht-Auto-

nomie in der Bildung der roten Augenpigmente bei einer Mutante (rosy²) von Drosophila melanogaster. Z. Vererbungslehre 87: 528–553.

HADORN, E., and STUMM-ZOLLINGER, E., 1953, Untersuchungen zur biochemischen Auswirkung der Mutante "letal-translucida" (ltr) von Drosophila melanogaster. Rev. suisse Zool. 60: 506–516.

HANSER, G., 1948, Ueber die Histogenese der Augenpigmentgranula bei verschiedenen Rassen von Ephestia kühniella Z. und Ptychopoda seriata Schrk. Z. Vererbungslehre 82: 74–97.

KÜHN, A., 1956, Versuche zur Entwicklung eines Modells der Genwirkungen. Naturwissenschaften 43: 25–28.

KÜHN, A., and BERG, B., 1955, Zur genetischen Analyse der Mutation biochemica von Ephestia kühniella. Z. Vererbungslehre 87: 25–35.

KÜHN, A., and EGELHAAF, A., 1955, Zur chemischen Polyphänie bei Ephestia kühniella. Naturwissenschaften 42: 634–635.

LERMA, B. DE, and DE VINCENTIIS, M., 1955, Identificazione chimica e valuazione biologica delle sostanze fluorescenti di Drosophila melanogaster Meig. Boll. Zool. 22: 1–15.

NAWA, S., and TAIRA, T., 1954, Pterins found in Silkworm and Drosophila. Proc. Jap. Acad. 30: 632–635.

SCHMID, W., 1949, Analyse der letalen Wirkung des Faktors lme (letal-meander) von Drosophila melanogaster. Z. Vererbungslehre 83: 220–253.

SOBELS, F. H., 1950, Experimentell erzeugte Nachkommenschaft von letalen Ovarien der Mutante letaltranslucida (ltr) von Drosophila melanogaster. Experientia 6: 139.

SOBELS, F. H., and NIJENHUIS, L. E., 1953, An investigation into metamorphosis of the mutant letal-translucida of Drosophila melanogaster. Z. Vererbungslehre 85: 579–592.

STUMM-ZOLLINGER, E., 1954, Vergleichende Analyse der Aminosäuren und Peptide in der Hämolymphe des Wildtyps und der Mutante "letal-translucida" (ltr) von Drosophila melanogaster. Z. Vererbungslehre 86: 126–133.

VISCONTINI, M., SCHOELLER, M., LOESER, E., KARRER, P., and HADORN, E., 1955, Isolierung fluoreszierender Stoffe aus Drosophila melanogaster. Helvet. chim. Acta 38: 397–401.

VISCONTINI, M., LOESER, E., KARRER, P., and HADORN, E., 1955a, Fluoreszierende Stoffe aus Drosophila melanogaster II. Helvet. chim. Acta 38: 1222–1224.
1955b, Fluoreszierende Stoffe aus Drosophila melanogaster III. Helvet. chim. Acta 38: 2034–2035.

ZWICKY, K., 1954, Osmoregulatorische Reaktionen der Larve von Drosophila melanogaster. Z. vergl. Physiol. 36: 367–390.

DISCUSSION

LEWIN: De you know whether the lethal effect of "translucent" results from a specific inhibition of protein synthesis, or from a general impairment of anabolism perhaps connected with energy-transfer mechanisms?

HADORN: No, I do not know.

RIZKI: Biochemica does not differ from the wild type except for the chromatographic character. Is it possible vice to call biochemica wild type rather than vice versa? This question is asked particularly in view of the variability we find in the so-called "wild type" of Drosophila.

HADORN: We do not know whether the bch genotype is present in wild populations of Ephestia. But Prof. Kühn found recently a wild species of moth which exhibits the biochemica pattern in its head. Thus bch could be considered as a possible wild type.

Genetic Mechanisms in the Localized Initiation of Differentiation

Curt Stern

University of California, Berkeley, California

This discussion deals with a limited part of the problem of differentiation. As a whole the problem involves both the initiation and the progression of a sequence of events which lead to the appearance in development of specific structures and functions. Genes partake directly or indirectly in all the reactions which are involved in differentiation. While these reactions are distinguished from those occurring in differentiated cells by their progressive, nonequilibrium nature, by themselves these reactions may be thought of as basically similar to those in cells with more stationary life processes. But a peculiarity of developmental reactions is the fact that they seem to have a beginning. A unique situation arises, at a specific region of the developmental system. This unique situation then leads to further developmental newness. We shall be concerned with the role of genes in the localized initiation of newness.

Two different views of genic activity have been expressed. The one sees in each gene an at all times vitally necessary agent of every cell of the organism. The other thinks of genes in terms of bodies more or less inactive at some times and to be called to action at others. Development particularly is considered as a period in which alternate batteries of genes are mobilized at one stage and retired at another. According to the view of each gene as a necessary cellular agent, absence of a single gene, as in diploid cells homozygous for a deficiency or in haploid cells hemizygous for it, is incompatible with the cell's survival. The evidence in favor of such ever-needed genic action is based on only two groups of phenomena. Demerec (1934, 1936) has shown that hypodermal cells of *Drosophila melanogaster* do not form a viable tissue patch if they have become homozygous for one or the other of a variety of deficiencies. True, some such deficiences are compatible with growth and multiplication but it has been assumed that in these cases substances provided by the surrounding tissues of the not-homozygous-deficient "host" are able to spread into the deficient cells. Similar phenomena were encountered in corn by McClintock (1938). Cells homozygous for chromosomal deficiencies were able to multiply and to form tissue patches in an environment of plant tissue which was not deficient. Here the same possibility remains that survival is based on dependence of the deficient tissue on the normal. If the techniques were available one might predict that a tissue culture medium which is adequate but minimal for genically not deficient cells would not be sufficient for any type of genically deficient cells.

The other indications for ever-needed genic action come from the male gametophytes of a variety of flowering plants. The majority of these haploid stages do not survive and function if they are deficient for any one of a great variety of chromosomal sections. Female gametophytes of the same genotypes are usually viable to a much higher degree than the male gametophytes, a fact well compatible with the former's more intimate contact with the nondeficient sporophyte tissue. There are exceptions to the nonsurvival of genetically deficient pollen grains. With some very short deficiencies in corn Stadler and Roman (1948) obtained transmission through the gametophyte. But even such exceptions do not rule out the basic need for each gene. Gene dependent products are known in some instances to be present in cells after segregation or even elimination of the whole nucleus has removed the gene responsible for them. If *Acetabularia* can live for months without a nucleus in spite of basic dependence on it, male gametophytes of flowering plant may do likewise for a few days.

In the preceding paragraphs exceptions from obvious dependence of cellular existence on every gene have been "explained away" in various ways. There remain some exceptions of higher order. Some genetic deficiences have been described as being compatible not only with survival of individual cell patches but with complete development of viable individuals (*Drosophila, e.g.* Muller, 1935; Demerec and Hoover, 1936; corn, McClintock, 1941, 1944). Here it is necessary to invoke further hypotheses if one wishes to save the basic assumption. One must either postulate that the genes involved in these deficiencies are normally present in non-deficient cells in more than diploid number, perhaps as the result of evolutionary recent duplications, or that the cells are able to adapt themselves to the absence of certain genes by establishing alternate pathways of reactions. While the existence of exceptions to cell-lethality of deficiencies in specific tissues might be thought of as being more compatible with the idea of specific periods of action and inaction of genes in development than of permanently needed activity, the exceptions to the abundantly prevalent non-development of deficient zygotes offer the same difficulty to either alternative.

In reality the two alternatives are compatible with each other. Genes may be integral parts of every cell's metabolism and yet participate in it to very different degrees at different times. Evolutionarily considered the unicellular ancestors of multicellular organisms must have possessed a set of genes necessary for their function. It would seem to have been a more economic way to use these same genes for the differentiation of multicellular animals and plants than to superimpose solely developmentally needed sets of genes on those basically needed. But if the same set of genes serves both the more or less stationary functions as well as the developmental ones then an expansion and contraction of the activities of specific genes in different parts of a developing system is a reasonable assumption. Cytologic evidence for such spatial and timed phenomena in chromosomes has been obtained (Beermann, 1952a, b; Mechelke, 1953; Breuer and Pavan, 1954, 1955) but the minimal degree of genic activity needs more study, if possible by means of the extension of experiments with gene-deficient cells from a variety of developmental stages and sites.

For many years embryologic concepts of differentiation have been concerned with regional differences within eggs and embryos or other differentiating systems. Proofs of the existence of differences in metabolic activity, enzymatic properties and other qualities defined at the molecular or a less precise higher level have been provided. Interactions between the specific properties of different regions and their nuclei were early postulated by Driesch and admitted as probable by later students in general. But it has been difficult to link individual genes to regional singularity in the initiation of differentiation. The majority of genes available to geneticists if concerned at all with differentiation rather seem to modify than to initiate it. Genes for singed bristles as opposed to straight ones determine not the basic event of development of a bristle but only the minor alternatives of its shape. Genes for chondrodystrophy interfere with the development of the skeletal system once it has been formed but not with its origin. Genes for shape of leaves exert their effects on buds which have already been destined to become leaves. But there are other genes which are truly linked to the initiation of differentiation. These are the genes whose effect is absence or duplication of an organ or the genes which result in differentiation of new organs in old places as in homoeosis.

How such genes may exert their effects may be hypothetically indicated for genes responsible for duplications of differentiation as for instance genes for polydactyly in mammals or doubleness of petals in flowering plants. Such duplications usually take place in regions normally characterized by differentiation of the organ involved, and the formation of extra organs may be a consequence of special but relatively trivial gene-induced properties of the cells present in these regions or of the regions themselves. Thus the cells of a genetically polydactylous limb bud may possibly differ from those with a nonpolydactylous genotype by a different rate of multiplication which may exempt them to some degree from a unifying interaction with other parts of the differentiating anlage. Or the cells of a genetically double flower bud may possibly simply be subjected to an abundance of a substance which, in a genotype for single flowers, induces petal differentiation in a single circle.

Similarly genes controlling the presence or absence of an organ at its typical site may produce their decisive effect in a minor way. Thus, for instance, genetic absence of limbs could be due to the inability of an allele to promote one of many reactions necessary in the course of some process involved in the initiation of limb differentiation. Related hypotheses may be elaborated even for the differentiating action of homoeotic mutants but such speculations will be postponed until later.

The words trivial and minor have been used for the role of genes in the initiation of differentiation. These terms are both ill-advised and intentionally chosen. Ill-advised it would be to distinguish some actions of genes as trivial and minor from others as important and major. All genes as agents at the molecular level are equivalent in their actions. What the words trivial and minor intend to stress is the action of individual genes if measured against the complexities of events at the level of differentiation and morphogenesis. An analytic approach to complex problems is by nature bound to end in trivialities.

In this simplified form the problem of genic mechanisms in the localized initiation of differentiation involves two different possibilities. Alternative genes, involved either in the occurrence or nonoccurrence of a specific differentiation at a specific site may either exert their effect by means of establishment or nonestablishment of the regional singularity which must precede the differentiation; or they may do so by responding differentially to the singularity which could then be present in both genotypes, a presence which would be independent of its ultimately becoming visible or not visible in a differentiation. On previous occasions I have called a "prepattern" the regional singularity which logically must be recognized as being present before the time of the actual appearance of or differentiation at a given embryonic site (Stern, 1954a, b). This term simply implies a differentness, in any one of innumerable possible aspects, of the site from other sites in the embryo. A prepattern may be a highly localized singularity or a gradient of one or many properties. Such a singularity or a gradient may or may not result in obvious developmental diversity. Using the term prepattern the action of alternative genes involved in the occurrence or nonoccurrence of differentiation in the typical spatial pattern may be restated as concerning either the origin of differences in the prepattern, or, in the presence of an invariable prepattern, of differences in the response of cells located in the region of the prepattern.

The earliest experiments bearing on the problem of genetically controlled different prepatterns leading to different morphogenetic results versus genetically controlled different responses to a constant prepattern were those of xenoplastic embryonic transplantations in amphibians. When a small piece of undifferentiated tissue of one species was transplanted into the head region of another, the transplant differentiated into organs, such as teeth or balancers, appropriate to the site in its host species but in a fashion specific to the donor species from which it had been removed. This shows that the prepatterns of the head region in host and donor are essentially the same, distinguishing this region from others of the embryos which do not induce teeth or balancers. But the response of the genetically different tissues is specifically variable since host and donor tissues give alternative differentiations.

One may speak here of local action of the genes presumably differentiating the species involved. Such local gene action would be contrasted to indirect gene action as described, for instance, in the abnormal development of homozygous creeper fowl where eye defects are consequences not of the genetic constitution of the eye primordia themselves but of abnormal properties of the mesenchyme (Gayer and Hamburger, 1943; see also Landauer, 1933). But indirect gene action and action in the determination of a prepattern are not the same phenomena. The former solely signifies action at a distance, by such means as nerves, hormones and metabolic influences, the latter is the production of regional differentness, the necessary though not sufficient prerequisite for differentiation.

In *Drosophila* the genetic control of differentiation at specific sites is well demonstrated by the many alleles at the scute (*sc*) locus. The dorsal surface of head and thorax of a wild-type fly is patterned in a highly characteristic way (Fig. 1). At 40 specific sites large bristle-organs occur each of which consists of a few but highly differentiated cells. The specificity of the bristle pattern is attested by the nomenclature which assigns individual names to each bristle organ. Individuals which carry at the scute locus not the sc^+ allele but for instance sc^1, sc^2, or sc^4 often differentiate only 26, 30 or 12 bristles, respectively. This genetic control of differentiation follows patterns specific for each allele. Thus sc^1 and sc^2, while both affecting in like manner 28 of the 40 sites occupied by bristles in the wild type, act differently on 12 sites. At these latter sites sc^1 brings forth differentiation where sc^2 fails or vice versa. These findings were reported many years ago by Dubinin (1929), Serebrovsky (1930) and other workers and their meaning, in terms of developmental hypotheses, discussed by

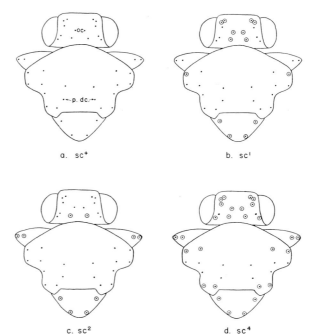

FIGURE 1. (a). Dorsal view of head, pro- and mesothorax of *Drosophila melanogaster* with the positions of the 40 sites of bristles on normal flies. oc = ocellars; p dc = posterior dorsocentrals.
(b), (c) and (d). The same for flies of the genotypes sc^1 and sc^2 and sc^4. Sites surrounded with a circle do not usually differentiate bristles.

Goldschmidt (1931), Sturtevant and Schultz (1931) and Child (1935). No satisfactory interpretation became apparent but the challenging facts remained. We may now restate the problem in terms of the hypotheses that the action of the scute alleles consists in either varying the underlying prepattern of differentness resulting in differentiation of bristle-organs or by leaving unchanged an ever-present prepattern but by endowing the cells with different sensitivities to the morphogenetic stimulus inherent in the prepattern.

A tool for elucidation of the situation, akin to transplantation, is the use of genetic mosaics. If different *sc* alleles cause different prepatterns then in mosaics in which the preponderant part of the relevant body region is made up of tissue of one *sc* genotype and only a very small patch of tissue of another *sc* genotype the prepattern should be that characteristic for the main part. Thus, on a sc^+ wild type prospective head region, with only a very small sc^1 patch of tissue the specific differentness of the sites of the two future ocellar bristles from the surrounding not bristle-differentiating areas should be present essentially as on a completely wild type head region. Therefore, if differentiation of an ocellar bristle depended on presence or absence of the prepattern a patch of sc^1 tissue at the site of the ocellar bristle should respond to the wild type prepattern by developing a typical ocellar bristle, even though on a completely or

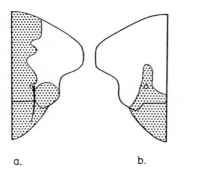

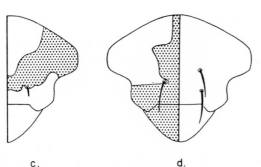

FIGURE 2. (a)–(c): Half-thoraxes of different mosaic individuals of *Drosophila*. Shaded regions *ac*; white regions *ac*⁺; (d): Whole thorax, same key.
(a). Presence of the posterior dorsocentral bristle in *ac*⁺ tissue.
(b). Absence in *ac* tissue.
(c). Presence of a rudimentary bristle in *ac* tissue at the border of the two tissues.
(d). Differentiation in *ac*⁺ tissue of a mosaic individual of a dorsocentral bristle at an unusual site. The right half of the thorax consists of *ac*⁺ tissue only. Here the anterior and posterior dorsocentral bristles are present at their typical sites.

preponderantly *sc*¹ fly no such bristle is formed. On the other hand, if the difference in presence or absence of this bristle on nonmosaic *sc*⁺ and *sc*¹ individuals is based on differential responses of the local cells to the same prepattern then even a small patch of *sc*¹ cells in *sc*⁺ surroundings should fail to form a typical ocellar bristle. Experiments have shown that the latter expectation is fulfilled (21 mosaics; D. Swanson, unpub.). And, complementary evidence, a small patch of *sc*⁺ tissue in overwhelmingly *sc*¹ surroundings responded to the usual prepattern which is apparently present in this *sc*¹ head by differentiating a normal ocellar bristle.

This seems to be a typical case. Sturtevant, in 1932 had first described autonomy of *sc* tissue in mosaics and probably recognized its significance. But no further attention has been paid to this type of local genic action. Its importance is fundamentally different from the frequently studied local gene action which leads not to the initiation but affects only the elaboration of differentiation. The initiation of differentiation of specifically localized organs cannot be a purely locally caused process but is possible only on the basis of a prepattern which itself is the result of interrelation of parts of a developing whole. Therefore, the demonstration of local gene action in the initiation or noninitiation of localized differentiation is evidence of a constant prepattern and a variable genetically controlled response.

Experiments with alleles of the achaete (*ac*) locus in *Drosophila* show the same features. Individuals with the allele *ac*⁺ differentiate all 40 bristles on head and thorax while after substitution of *ac*⁺ by *ac* some bristles including the two posterior dorsocentrals are not formed. In mosaic flies in which the site of a posterior dorsocentral bristle is occupied by *ac*⁺ tissue its differentiation is always initiated regardless of the size and distribution of the *ac* tissue which may form the preponderant part of the relevant rest of the fly (Fig. 2a). Conversely, *ac* tissue at the site of the bristle will in general not differentiate it even when the overwhelming relevant rest of the fly is *ac*⁺ in constitution (Fig. 2b).

Some additional phenomena, however, are apparent. One of these relates to the behavior in the potential bristle region of *ac* tissue, the other to that of *ac*⁺ tissue. While it is true that *ac* tissue usually does not form a posterior dorsocentral bristle even on a mosaic thorax there are exceptions to this rule. Sometimes a bristle does appear though it is not one of normal size. All exceptions have one feature in common, namely close neighborhood to the site of differentiation of *ac*⁺ tissue (Fig. 2c). It is worth stressing that it is close neighborhood unrelated to total extent of the *ac* area which may appear as a small island just covering the bristle site or a large patch whose border happens to pass by it. This suggests a simple spread of *ac*⁺ dependent material into the *ac* tissue patch. This material then nonautonomously endows the *ac* cells with the ability to respond to the prepattern by differentiation of a bristle if only of rudimentary size. It seems to be a case of substitution therapy equivalent to the presumed support in mosaics of gene-deficient cells by nondeficient tissue. In the *sc*¹ mosaics described above the same phenomenon of spread will account for the observation that a small *sc* patch on a *sc*⁺ background does not always fail to differentiate an ocellar bristle but may often form a rudimentary one.

The presumed spreading phenomenon from tissue genetically able to respond to the prepattern into genetically not responsive tissue is one of minor significance. In contrast a property of the genetically responsive tissue in mosaics leads to a clearer definition of the bristle prepattern. It occurred occasionally that the *ac*⁺ tissue did not cover the site of the dorsocentral bristles but only an area close to them. In these instances a dorsocentral bristle became differentiated by the *ac*⁺ cells at a site in which no such bristle would have been formed had the whole individual been of *ac*⁺

constitution (Fig. 2d). This shows that the singularity which marks the prepattern of the posterior dorsocentral bristle affects a region which is larger than apparent in normal differentiation. The unknown property of the prepattern is distributed over a gradient field which has a peak at the site typical for the bristle but which still can evoke response at lower levels. It is necessary to assume a suppressing action on further bristle differentiation in the neighborhood of a bristle in order to explain the absence of bristles at the lower level when, in a whole ac^+ fly, a bristle is formed at the peak. There is, however, much evidence for such suppression in other differentiations.

The examples cited made use of mutant genes whose response to the prepattern was less than that of their normal alleles. There are other situations where the mutant condition seems to have higher sensitivity to a prepattern than the wild type. An interesting example is provided by certain X-chromosomal duplications which result in the appearance of an extra bristle on each side of the thorax. In wild-type flies the site occupied by this bristle is not visibly distinguished from its surroundings. Studies on mosaic individuals can again be interpreted by the assumption of a prepattern which singles out the region of the extra bristle even in wild type flies. However, only duplication containing cells are able to respond to the prepattern by initiation of differentiation of a bristle (Stern, 1956). It is interesting to note that this "interalar" bristle is typically present in other species of flies. Whether *Drosophila melanogaster* lost the ability to respond to the interalar prepattern while its ancestors possessed it or whether the evolutionary sequence was the reverse, the significant fact is that different species have the same prepattern although it is expressed normally in some only.

Lack of an organ is not always the result of complete nondifferentiation but rather of an initiation of differentiation followed by regression. It is possible, though not known, that the absence of bristles in some of the genotypes treated is due to regression or to inhibition of growth. If this is true, the term localized initiation would have to be changed to localized regression or inhibition. No essential alteration in the interpretation would be involved.

A final example throws further light on the interrelation between prepattern and response. It has been shown, again by studies on mosaics, that the possession of the peculiar sex-comb of the male *Drosophila melanogaster* in contrast to the absence of this row of morphologically unique bristles in a restricted zone of the distal part of the first tarsal segment of the foreleg, is due to positive response of male cells to a prepattern present in both sexes (Stern and Hannah, 1950). Triploid intersexes unlike females usually possess sex combs. It seemed worthwhile to make a detailed study of sexcombs on intersexes (Hannah-Alava and Stern, 1957). If male and female forelegs are endowed with the same prepattern one might assume that in this respect intersexes do not differ from them. Since on the other hand the two normal sexes differ so fundamentally in their responsiveness it would appear that intersexes may show a response of intermediate strength. Accordingly, the lengths and widths of the individual teeth were measured in males and in intersexes and compared with each other. Depending on specific genotypes there was considerable variability in mean lengths within each of the two sexual types but no systematic differences between males and intersexes were found. Is then the response of cells with these two different sexual constitutions the same? The answer is both affirmative and negative. The sexcombs of intersexes consist of fewer teeth than those of males and therefore occupy a shorter segment of the tarsus. This is the result of a differential intersexual level of responsiveness. The prepattern of the tarsal segment may be assumed to be represented by a gradient which covers a region of at least the extent of the sexcomb realized in males (Fig. 3). The level of the prepattern decreases towards the ends of the region. Cells of male genotype can respond even to the low-level property of the ends but intersexual cells require a stronger stimulus. As a result differentiation of teeth in intersexes occurs only in the central region of greater strength of the prepattern. Once, however, that differentiation of a tooth has been initiated the developmental reaction of the cells proceeds in typical male fashion, regardless of male or intersexual genotype.

None of the foregoing analyses has yielded an example for genic control of prepatterns instead of the response to their presence. This is not due to an intrinsic property of prepatterns. On a former occasion I have referred to the Himalayan rabbit in which the relatively cool, exposed tips of the body, the feet, snout, ears and tail, respond to the temperature prepattern by formation of melanin while no pigment is deposited in the warmer regions of the body surface. The pattern of pigmentation of the Himalayan is due to its c^hc^h genotype with its differential response. In contrast a CC rabbit, with a threshold of response independent of the temperature gradient of the body surface is wholly pigmented. It would be easily conceivable that genes exist which, by controlling a greater blood supply to the exposed tips of the body, raise their temperature above the minimum needed for a response by c^hc^h. Such genes would thus change the normal prepattern and the postulated wholly unpigmented Himalayan rabbit would developmentally be distinguished from its typical partner not by a changed response but by a new prepattern.

It is likely that homoeotic mutant genes produce their effects by a remodeling of the prepattern. A morphological analysis of the second and third pairs of legs of homoeotic mutants has shown that the whole organization of the first tarsal segment as well as of other parts of these appendages

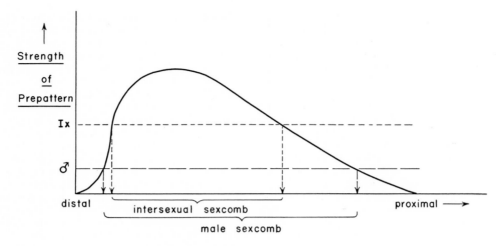

Tarsal Segment

FIGURE 3. Model diagram of the strength of the sex comb prepattern along the proximal-distal axis of the tarsal seg ment and of the thresholds for response to the prepattern of male and intersexual cells.

differs from that in wild type genotypes. Thus, genes for sex combs on the second and third pairs of legs which normally do not differentiate these structures do not simply place sex combs on legs otherwise typical for their location. On the contrary the homoeotic genes "remodel" the first tarsal segment of the second and third legs in such a fashion as to make it in either sex, in many details similar to that of the first legs. It seems reasonable to suppose that in the case of males the appearance of sex combs on these second and third legs is the consequence of a genetically changed prepattern, a prepattern to which male tissue can respond as it always does on the true first legs.

It may be permissible to present a naive model which would fit the assumed change of the prepattern of the middle leg under the influence of a genotype esc for extra sexcombs. In this scheme it is assumed that two different substrates I and II are present in the embryonic anlagen of the first (1) and second (2) leg. In anlage (1) substrate I is in excess of II and in anlage (2) a gradient in the embryo, that is, an early prepattern has changed the proportion toward an excess of II over I. The normal gene esc^+ is assumed to be able to interact with both I and II, the reaction proceeding overwhelmingly in favor of whatever substrate is in excess. Thus, in (1) $esc^+ + I \rightarrow$ derived prepattern of first leg, while in (2) $esc^+ + II \rightarrow$ derived prepattern of second leg. In contrast to esc^+ the allele esc lacks specificity to react substantially with II though it can react with I. As a result the same reaction $esc + I \rightarrow$ derived prepattern of first leg occurs in both the first and the middle leg. No more is intended with this speculation than a hint that processes of the type with which biochemical genetics is so familiar may be the trigger for the localized initiation of specific gene-controlled differentiations.

The localized initiation of differentiations is

thus seen in the interaction of regional differentnesses, prepatterns, with genes competent to respond to them. The different genes react with astonishingly great sensitivity to regional differences. Thus each different scute allele probes in a unique way the variety of prepatterns simultaneously present on head and thorax of *Drosophila*, one allele responding to some of these, another to others, a third to a combination of some of them. The experiments discussed do not force a decision of the questions whether the timed responses of different genes imply increased activities or whether they only signify unchanged activities which become discernible by their morphogenetic effects. But it would appear likely that quantitatively or qualitatively different substrates are actually responsible for tuned peaks and valleys of genic action.

REFERENCES

BEERMANN, WOLFGANG, 1952a, Chromosomenstruktur und Zelldifferenzierung in der Speicheldrüse von *Trichocladius vitripennis*. Zeitschr. f. Naturforschung 7: 237–242.
  1952b, Chromomerenkonstanz und spezifische Modifikationen der Chromosomenstruktur in der Entwicklung und Organdifferenzierung von *Chironomus tentans*. Chromosoma 5: 139–198.
BREUER, M. E., and PAVAN, C., 1954, Salivary chromosome and differentiation. Proc. 9th Intern. Congr. Genetics, Part II: 778.
  1955, Behavior of polytene chromosomes of *Rhynchosciara angelae* at different stages of larval development. Chromosoma 7: 371–386.
CHILD, GEORGE, 1935, Phenogenetic studies on scute-1 of *Drosophila melanogaster*. I. The associations between the bristles and the effects of genetic modifiers and temperature. Genetics 20: 109–126.
DEMEREC, M., 1934, Biological action of small deficiencies of X-chromosome of *Drosophila melanogaster*. Proc. Nat. Acad. Sci. Wash. 20: 354–359.
  1936, Frequency of "cell-lethals" among lethals obtained at random in the X-chromosome of *Drosophila melanogaster*. Proc. Nat. Acad. Sci. Wash. 22: 350–354.

DEMEREC, M., and HOOVER, M. E., 1936, Three related X-chromosome deficiencies in *Drosophila*. J. Hered. *27:* 205–212.

DUBININ, NICOLAI P., 1929, Allelomorphentreppen bei *Drosophila melanogaster*. Biol. Zbl. *49:* 328–339.

GOLDSCHMIDT, RICHARD, 1931, Die entwicklungsphysiologische Erklärung des Falles der sogenannten Treppenallelomorphe des Gens scute von *Drosophila*. Biol. Zbl. *51:* 507–526.

GAYER, KENNETH, and HAMBURGER, V., 1943, The developmental potencies of eye primordia of homozygous Creeper chick embryos tested by orthotopic transplantation. J. Exp. Zool. *93:* 147–183.

HANNAH-ALAVA, A., and STERN, C., 1958, The sexcombs in males and intersexes of *Drosophila melanogaster*. J, Exp. Zool. (in press).

LANDAUER, WALTER, 1944, Transplantation as a tool of developmental genetics. Amer. Nat. *78:* 280–284.

McCLINTOCK, BARBARA, 1938, The production of homozygous deficient tissues with mutant characteristics by means of the aberrant mitotic behavior of ring-shaped chromosomes. Genetics *23:* 315–376.

———— 1941, The association of mutants with homozygous deficiencies in *Zea mays*. Genetics *26:* 542–571.

———— 1944, The relation of homozygous deficiencies to mutations and allelic series in maize. Genetics *29:* 478–502.

MECHELKE, FRIEDRICH, 1953, Reversible Strukturmodifikationen der Speicheldrüsenchromosomen von *Acricotopus lucidus*. Chromosoma *5:* 511–543.

MULLER, H. J., 1935, A viable two-gene deficiency. J. Hered. *26:* 469–478.

SEREBROVSKY, A. S., 1930, Untersuchungen über Treppenallelomorphismus. IV. Transgenation sc. 6. Roux' Arch. f. Entw. mech. Organ. *122:* 88–104.

STADLER, L. J., and ROMAN, H., 1948, The effect of X rays upon mutation of the gene *A* in maize. Genetics *33:* 273–303.

STERN, C., and HANNAH, A., 1950, The sex combs in gynanders of *Drosophila melanogaster*. Portug. Acta. Biol., Series A. R. B. Goldschmidt Vol: 788–812.

STERN, C., 1954a, Two or three bristles. Amer. Scientist *42:* 213–247.

———— 1954b, Genes and developmental patterns. Proc. 9th Intern. Congr. Genetics. Part I: 355–369.

———— 1956, The genetic control of developmental competence and morphogenetic tissue interactions in genetic mosaics. Roux' Arch. f. Entwick, mech. Org. *149:* 1–25.

STURTEVANT, A. H., and SCHULTZ, JACK, 1931, The inadequacy of the sub-gene hypothesis of the nature of the scute allelomorphs of *Drosophila*. Proc. Nat. Acad. Sci. Wash. *17:* 265–270.

STURTEVANT, A. H., 1932, The use of mosaics in the study of the developmental effect of genes. Proc. 6th Intern. Congr. Genetics *1:* 304–307.

DISCUSSION

POULSON: Certain points pertinent to this discussion were mentioned in your introduction. The first is that the majority of genetic changes are lethal to the organism and that lethality may be expressed at the cellular level or at tissue or organ levels. As you have indicated cell lethals probably represent losses of synthetic function not reparable by crossfeeding. Other lethals include a whole array of possibilities ranging from failure of self-differentiation to disturbances of cell and tissue interactions. Among these an important group concerned with female sterility and oögenesis is only beginning to be looked into, in terms of developmental disturbances, by Counce. The importance of lethals for the understanding of normal development has been ably set forth by Hadorn in his recent book, "Letalfaktoren," and need not be further pursued except to point out that no really adequate sample of lethals has yet been fully investigated, even in *Drosophila*, although considerable progress is being made in this direction.

Since most of the conclusions of developmental genetics have been based on comparisons between normals and mutants in which no visible loss of genetic material has been detected it is pretty evident that a genetic prepattern is almost a foregone conclusion where only substitutions in a complete genome are involved. This brings us to the second point in the introduction which I would like to emphasize: with rare exceptions sectional chromosomal losses or deficiencies are lethal when homozygous or hemizygous and, further, a considerable proportion of lethals when carefully analyzed cytologically have proved to be such deficiencies rather than point mutations. This long ago suggested that the function of a given chromosomal region can be most adequately understood only through study of the disturbances produced by its physical loss. It has been my contention that such lethal deficiencies provide highly favorable materials for the genetic analysis of developmental patterns and processes.

Two examples will illustrate what can be done with this approach. Dr. Alice Bull, now at Wellesley College, has studied the effects of deficiencies including the *vestigial* locus in the second chromosome of *D. melanogaster* all of which are zygotic lethals. One of these differs from the others in that its effects are detectable in the early cleavage divisions as a stickiness of the chromosomes giving a high proportion of anaphase-telophase bridges. This persists as long as mitoses continue. Although the major features of early development are completed the nuclei eventually become pycnotic and tissue differentiations generally fail. Thus the absence of a particular chromosome region affects the properties of the whole set of chromosomes, leading eventually to pycnosis, and their abilities for subsequent participation in differentiation. An account of this is in press in the Journal of Experimental Zoology.

The other example is from the Notch deficiencies the developmental effects of which have now been analyzed in rather full detail. The loss of the band 3 C 7, or material within it, from the X-chromosome of *D. melanogaster* leads to a change in the pattern of determination and differentiation in embryos hemizygous for the condition. Large numbers of cells which in normal embryos would become hypoderm and its derivatives, including imaginal discs, head structures and salivary glands become neuroblasts instead. Such Notch deficient embryos are incomplete with regard to hypoderm and the structures mentioned, possess an outsized nervous system, and are incomplete with regard to gut and mesodermal organs although gonads appear to be normal. There is no evidence of cell lethality in these embryos and, monstrous as they are, they continue to live for many hours after normal sibs have hatched. When transplanted into normal hosts these larval tissues are capable of very considerable growth. Thus far no evidence of imaginal discs has been found in the embryos or in transplanted tissues. This is of some interest in view of Demerec's finding that Notches are cell-lethal in patches of imaginal hypoderm. Up to the time that neuroblasts first make their appearance it is not possible to distinguish morphologically between Notch deficient and normal embryos. From that moment the change in pattern of ectodermal differentiation becomes increasingly evident. Most of the characteristic features of the Notch deficient embryos appear to arise as simple mechanical consequences of the changed proportions of potential dermal and neural regions of the blastoderm. What relationship there may be between these disturbances in the hemizygote and the dominant phenotypic effects in heterozygous females to which the term Notch was originally applied remains to be established. However, we have here a remarkably clearcut instance of a localized chromosomal region, or gene, concerned with the pattern of early embryonic determination. How this control is exerted is a most tantalizing problem.

As yet insufficient series of deficiencies have been analyzed to enable us to make any statements about the distribution of such loci concerned with early embryological processes. So far the disturbances produced by loss of particular chromosomal regions have proved to be essentially unique thus substantiating the significance of this approach. While we are far from having solved the problems of development in terms of genetic systems, the paradox which has been posed may conceivably be resolved through this line of attack.

WOLSKY: May I draw attention to the experiments, which I have performed on *Drosophila* pupae, exposing localized portions of them during metamorphosis to the respiration-depressing effect of carbon monoxide-oxygen mixtures (1937, Nature, Lond., *139:* 1069). In these experiments the strongest effects were observed on the development of bristles, which were greatly reduced in size under the influence of carbon monoxide and looked like the reduced bristles which Dr. Stern obtained in achaete territory surrounded by nonachaete tissue. Knowing that carbon monoxide reduces the intensity of metabolic processes by combining with a part of the cytochrome oxidase system, would it be possible to interpret the prepattern, postulated by Dr. Stern, to explain bristle development phenomena in some bristle mutant mosaics, in terms of metabolic gradients in the sense of Child and to assume that the reduction or complete absence of the bristles is due to a flattening or complete disappearance of the metabolic gradient?

MARKERT: Dr. Stern pointed out that melanin formation in the Himalayan rabbit is dependent upon the genotype of the rabbit and upon the temperature of the tissue containing the differentiating pigment cells. In this connection I should like to point out that one of the most useful cells for studying the relationship between cell genotype and cell environment during the course of differentiation is the mouse melanoblast. This cell is available in a wide assortment of genotypes and may be transplanted to a variety of tissue environments in mice of known genotypes. Such transplantation experiments, performed by several investigators, have shown that certain characteristics of differentiated melanocytes are dependent upon the genotype of the melanocyte whereas other characteristics are dependent upon the genotype and state of differentiation of the cells composing the tissue environment. Furthermore, it has been observed that the migrating melanoblasts of mice will differentiate in only a restricted number of mouse tissues, and differentiation in these tissues occurs only when the genotype of the tissue is suitable.

Index to Volume XXI